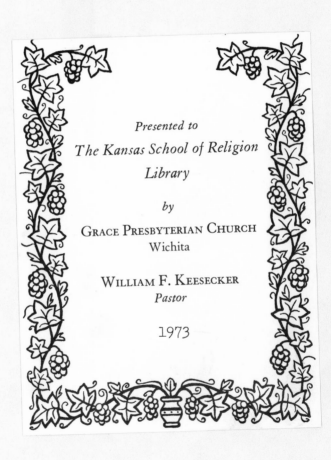

Forty-first issue
Annual

yearbook of american and canadian churches 1973

Constant H. Jacquet, Jr. Editor

Prepared and edited in the Office of Research, Evaluation and Planning of the National Council of the Churches of Christ in the U.S.A., 475 Riverside Drive, New York, NY 10027

Published and distributed by Abingdon Press

Nashville and New York

Printed in the United States of America

Price: $8.95

ISBN 0-687-46627-X

Library of Congress catalog card number: 16-5726.

INTRODUCTION

This 41st edition carries the new title **Yearbook of American and Canadian Churches** and continues a series of volumes issued under various titles dating back to 1916. The **Yearbook of American and Canadian Churches,** as complete for Canada as it is for the U.S., expands what was a unique national compilation into a bi-national one.

The **Yearbook of American and Canadian Churches** does not duplicate, to any significant degree, information found elsewhere in other published directories or statistical compilations, although some duplication is unavoidable. The material the **Yearbook** contains is organized into three major sections: I. A Calendar for Church Use; II. Directories; III. Statistical and Historical Section. The entire volume is indexed in Section IV.

Data for each edition are gathered, for the most part, by means of printed statistical and directory forms mailed to individuals in various ecclesiastical and secular organizations and returned by them. Almost all the information in this edition is current; that is, for the year 1971 or 1972. Non-current information is identified.

Hundreds of people in both the U.S. and Canada, through their generous cooperation with the editor, make each edition of the **Yearbook** possible. To all of them the editor extends his gratitude and thanks. Mrs. Alice Jones, of the Office of Research, Evaluation and Planning, has rendered valuable assistance in the preparation of copy for this edition.

The decision to develop and expand the **Yearbook of American Churches** into a truly bi-national reference work on organized religion called **Yearbook of American and Canadian Churches** was made by a representative group of Canadian churchmen from the widest ecclesiastical spectrum meeting in the offices of the Canadian Council of Churches, in Toronto, on June 24, 1971.

This group created a small committee to carry forward the task of expanding the Canadian section of the **Yearbook** and to work with the editor for as long as was necessary to accomplish this task. The committee appointed consisted of: Dr. T. E. F. Honey, general secretary, The Canadian Council of Churches, Toronto; Mr. Barry Kendall, then a graduate student in library science, University of Western Ontario, London, and now of Sudbury, Ontario; the Rev. David R. Stone, research officer, The United Church of Canada, Toronto; and the Rev. Charles A. Tipp, professor at The Ontario Bible College, Toronto. Miss Ruth Tillman, assistant to the general secretary, The Canadian Council of Churches, was added to the committee in this past year. To these persons the editor owes much for the development of this truly bi-national **Yearbook of American and Canadian Churches.**

Constant H. Jacquet, Jr.
Editor

A GUIDE FOR THE USER OF CHURCH STATISTICS

This guide is placed in a prominent position in each edition of the **Yearbook** to emphasize the fact that church statistics, like those of many other groups, vary greatly in quality and reliability. Therefore, necessary qualifications concerning them must be stated clearly and without reservation.

The **Yearbook of American and Canadian Churches** this year reports data from 223 U.S. religious bodies in Section III, Statistical and Historical Section. Of these, 128 bodies report current data; that is, data for the years 1972 or 1971. Current data, comprising 57 percent of all reports, account for 87 percent of recorded membership.

Of the 223 denominations gathering statistics, some computerize data and have an accurate bank of information on cards or tape. Perhaps the largest group of denominations still gather statistics by conventional hand tabulation methods. Quite a few bodies are still operating on the basis of "educated guesses" in many statistical areas.

In addition to the general observations above, four major qualifications should be made about church statistics:

1) Church statistics are always incomplete, and they pass through many hands, some skilled and some not so skilled, and come up through many channels in church bureaucratic structures.

2) Church statistics are not always comparable. Definitions of membership, and of other important categories, vary from denomination to denomination. Jewish congregations, for example, estimate the number of Jews in their communities. Roman Catholics and some Protestant bodies count all baptized persons, including children, as members. Most Protestant bodies include only "adults," usually 13 years of age and older, as members.

3) Church statistical data reported in the **Yearbook** are not for a single year. Not only do the reporting years differ from denomination to denomination, but some bodies do not report regularly. Therefore, the reports based on data for the year 1970 or earlier are "non-current" reports. Attempts to combine current and non-current data for purposes of interpretation or projection will lead to difficulties.

4) Many of the more important types of statistical data are simply not available for a large group of denominations. Records on church attendance are rarely kept, and there are no socio-economic data generally available. Statistics of participation by members in church activities and programs do not exist.

Statistics form an important part of church life and are necessary for the sound development of planning and program. Therefore, strong efforts should be made in each denomination to upgrade the quality of its church statistics. Interdenominational cooperation leading toward standardization of categories and sharing of techniques hopefully will continue to grow. New ways of adapting data gathered by the U.S. Bureau of the Census to church needs and programs must be discovered and utilized. The use of survey methods to obtain valuable socio-religious information about American religious life should be encouraged and expanded.

CONTENTS

I
A CALENDAR FOR CHURCH USE

1973 - 1974 - 1975 - 1976

The following calendar lists the dates of religious observances in the Protestant, Orthodox, Roman Catholic, and Jewish religious bodies. In addition, certain other special dates frequently recognized by religious bodies are included.

	1973	1974	1975	1976
1st Sunday in Advent	Dec 2	Dec 1	Nov 30	Nov 28
1st Day of Hanukkah	Dec 20	Dec 9	Nov 29	Dec 25
2nd Sunday in Advent	Dec 9	Dec 8	Dec 7	Dec 5
3rd Sunday in Advent	Dec 16	Dec 15	Dec 14	Dec 12
4th Sunday in Advent	Dec 23	Dec 22	Dec 21	Dec 19
(Sunday before Christmas)				
Christmas	Dec 25	Dec 25	Dec 25	Dec 25
Sunday after Christmas	Dec 30	Dec 29	Dec 28	Dec 26
New Year's Eve (Watch Night)	Dec 31	Dec 31	Dec 31	Dec 31
Festival of the Christening	Jan 1	Jan 1	Jan 1	Jan 1
Twelfth Night: Epiphany Eve	Jan 5	Jan 5	Jan 5	Jan 5
Epiphany	Jan 6	Jan 6	Jan 6	Jan 6
1st Sunday after Epiphany	Jan 7	Jan 13	Jan 12	Jan 11
2nd Sunday after Epiphany	Jan 14	Jan 20	Jan 19	Jan 18
(Missionary Day)				
Week of Prayer for Christian Unity	Jan 18 to 25	Jan 18 to 25	Jan 18 to 25	Jan 18 to 25
3rd Sunday after Epiphany	Jan 21	Jan 27	Jan 26	Jan 25
4th Sunday after Epiphany	Jan 28	Feb 3	Feb 2	Feb 1
Presentation of Jesus in the Temple	Feb 2	Feb 2	Feb 2	Feb 2
5th Sunday after Epiphany	Feb 4	Feb 10	Feb 9	Feb 8
6th Sunday after Epiphany	Feb 11	Feb 17	———	Feb 15
Brotherhood Week	Feb 18 to 25	Feb 17 to 24	Feb 16 to 23	Feb 16 to 23
7th Sunday after Epiphany	Feb 18	———	———	Feb 22
8th Sunday after Epiphany	Feb 25	———	———	Feb 29
9th Sunday after Epiphany	Mar 4	———	———	———
The Transfiguration (also Aug. 6)	Mar 4	Feb 24	Feb 9	Feb 29
Ash Wednesday	Mar 7	Feb 27	Feb 12	Mar 3
World Day of Prayer	Mar 2	Mar 1	Mar 7	Mar 5
1st Sunday in Lent	Mar 11	Mar 3	Feb 16	Mar 7
2nd Sunday in Lent	Mar 18	Mar 10	Feb 23	Mar 14
3rd Sunday in Lent	Mar 25	Mar 17	Mar 2	Mar 21
Purim	Mar 18	Mar 8	Feb 25	Mar 16
4th Sunday in Lent	Apr 1	Mar 24	Mar 9	Mar 28
The Annunciation	Mar 25	Mar 25	Mar 25	Mar 25
Passion Sunday	Apr 8	Mar 31	Mar 16	Apr 4
Holy Week	Apr 15 to 21	Apr 7 to 13	Mar 23 to 29	Apr 11 to 17
Palm Sunday	Apr 15	Apr 7	Mar 23	Apr 11
Maundy Thursday	Apr 19	Apr 11	Mar 27	Apr 15
Good Friday	Apr 20	Apr 12	Mar 28	Apr 16
Easter Eve	Apr 21	Apr 13	Mar 29	Apr 17
Easter (Latin)	Apr 22	Apr 14	Mar 30	Apr 18
Easter (Orthodox)	Apr 29	Apr 14	May 4	Apr 25
1st Sunday after Easter	Apr 29	Apr 21	Apr 6	Apr 25
2nd Sunday after Easter	May 6	Apr 28	Apr 13	May 2

1

	1973	1974	1975	1976
1st Day of Passover	Apr 17	Apr 7	Mar 27	Apr 15
3rd Sunday after Easter	May 13	May 5	Apr 20	May 9
4th Sunday after Easter	May 20	May 12	Apr 27	May 16
May Fellowship Day	May 4	May 3	May 2	May 7
Rural Life Sunday	May 27	May 17	May 4	May 23
(Rogation Sunday 5th after Easter)				
National Family Week	May 6	May 5	May 4	May 2
	to 13	to 12	to 11	to 9
Festival of the Christian Home (Mother's Day)	May 13	May 12	May 11	May 9
Ascension Day	May 31	May 23	May 8	May 27
Sunday after Ascension Day	June 3	May 26	May 11	May 30
Shavuot	June 6	May 27	May 16	June 4
	to 7	to 28	to 17	to 5
Whitsunday (Pentecost)	June 10	June 2	May 18	June 6
Trinity Sunday	June 17	June 9	May 25	June 13
2nd Sunday after Pentecost	June 24	June 16	June 1	June 20
Children's Sunday	June 10	June 9	June 8	June 13
3rd Sunday after Pentecost	July 1	June 23	June 8	June 27
4th Sunday after Pentecost	July 8	June 30	June 15	July 4
5th Sunday after Pentecost	July 15	July 7	June 22	July 11
Father's Day	June 17	June 16	June 15	June 20
6th Sunday after Pentecost	July 22	July 14	June 29	July 18
7th Sunday after Pentecost	July 29	July 21	July 6	July 25
8th Sunday after Pentecost	Aug 5	July 28	July 13	Aug 1
9th Sunday after Pentecost	Aug 12	Aug 4	July 20	Aug 8
The Transfiguration	Aug 6	Aug 6	Aug 6	Aug 6
(Also last Sunday in Epiphany)				
10th Sunday after Pentecost	Aug 19	Aug 11	July 27	Aug 15
Festival of Christ the King	Aug 26	Aug 25	Aug 31	Aug 29
11th Sunday after Pentecost	Aug 26	Aug 18	Aug 3	Aug 22
12th Sunday after Pentecost	Sept 2	Aug 25	Aug 10	Aug 29
Labor Sunday	Sept 2	Sept 1	Aug 31	Sept 5
Labor Day	Sept 3	Sept 2	Sept 1	Sept 6
13th Sunday after Pentecost	Sept 9	Sept 1	Aug 17	Sept 5
14th Sunday after Pentecost	Sept 16	Sept 8	Aug 24	Sept 12
15th Sunday after Pentecost	Sept 23	Sept 15	Aug 31	Sept 19
1st Day of Rosh Hashanah	Sept 27	Sept 17	Sept 6	Sept 25
16th Sunday after Pentecost	Sept 30	Sept 22	Sept 7	Sept 26
17th Sunday after Pentecost	Oct 7	Sept 29	Sept 14	Oct 3
Yom Kippur	Oct 6	Sept 26	Sept 15	Oct 4
Sukkot	Oct 11	Oct 1	Sept 20	Oct 9
18th Sunday after Pentecost	Oct 14	Oct 6	Sept 21	Oct 10
19th Sunday after Pentecost	Oct 21	Oct 13	Sept 28	Oct 17
Christian Education Emphases		a week in September		
20th Sunday after Pentecost	Oct 28	Oct 20	Oct 5	Oct 24
Shemini Atzeret	Oct 18	Oct 8	Sept 27	Oct 16
World Communion Sunday	Oct 7	Oct 6	Oct 5	Oct 3
Laity Sunday	Oct 14	Oct 13	Oct 12	Oct 10
Simhat Torah	Oct 19	Oct 9	Sept 28	Oct 17
Thanksgiving Day (Canada)	Oct 8	Oct 14	Oct 13	Oct 11
21st Sunday after Pentecost	Nov 4	Oct 27	Oct 12	Oct 31
World Temperance Day	Nov 4	Nov 3	Nov 2	Nov 7
Reformation Sunday	Oct 28	Oct 27	Oct 26	Oct 31
Reformation Day	Oct 31	Oct 31	Oct 31	Oct 31

	1973	1974	1975	1976
22nd Sunday after Pentecost	Nov 11	Nov 3	Oct 19	Nov 7
All Saints' Day	Nov 1	Nov 1	Nov 1	Nov 1
All Soul's Day	Nov 2	Nov 2	Nov 2	Nov 2
World Community Day	Nov 2	Nov 1	Nov 7	Nov 5
23rd Sunday after Pentecost	Nov 18	Nov 10	Oct 26	Nov 14
24th Sunday after Pentecost	Nov 25	Nov 17	Nov 2	Nov 21
25th Sunday after Pentecost	————	Nov 24	Nov 9	————
26th Sunday after Pentecost	————	————	Nov 16	————
27th Sunday after Pentecost	————	————	Nov 23	————
Stewardship Day	Nov 11	Nov 10	Nov 9	Nov 14
Bible Sunday	Nov 18	Nov 24	Nov 23	Nov 21
Thanksgiving Sunday (U.S.)	Nov 18	Nov 24	Nov 23	Nov 21
Thanksgiving Day (U.S.)	Nov 22	Nov 28	Nov 27	Nov 25

A TABLE OF DATES AHEAD

The following table indicates when Easter and other important festival days occur during the next few years. It also indicates the number of Sundays during Epiphany and after Pentecost for each year of the period. Easter may come as early as March 22 or as late as April 25, thus bringing a wide variation in the number of Sundays included in certain of the Christian seasons.

Year	Sundays in Epiphany	Ash Wednesday	Latin Easter	Orthodox Easter	Whitsunday	Sundays after Pentecost	First Sunday in Advent
1973	9	Mar 7	Apr 22	Apr 29	June 10	24	Dec 2
1974	6	Feb 27	Apr 14	Apr 14	June 2	25	Dec 1
1975	5	Feb 12	Mar 30	May 4	May 18	27	Nov 30
1976	8	Mar 3	Apr 18	Apr 25	June 6	24	Nov 28

II
DIRECTORIES

1. UNITED STATES COOPERATIVE ORGANIZATIONS, NATIONAL

NATIONAL COUNCIL OF THE CHURCHES OF CHRIST IN THE UNITED STATES OF AMERICA

The National Council of the Churches of Christ in the United States of America is a cooperative agency of Christian communions seeking to fulfill the unity and mission to which God calls them. The member communions, responding to the gospel revealed in the Scripture, confess Jesus, the incarnate Son of God, as Savior and Lord. Relying on the transforming power of the Holy Spirit, the Council works to bring churches into a life-giving fellowship and into common witness, study, and action to the glory of God and in service to all creation.

Semi-Annual Meetings of the Governing Board
Pittsburgh, PA, February 27–March 2, 1973
New York, NY, October 11-15, 1973

*Offices at 475 Riverside Dr., New York, NY 10027
except as stated below.
Tel. (212) 870-2200*

GENERAL OFFICERS

President
Rev. W. Sterling Cary.
General Secretary
R. H. Edwin Espy.
Vice-Presidents
Mrs. Victor Baltzell.
Most Rev. Archbishop Torkom Manoogian.
Rev. Eunice Santana Velez.
Treasurer
Carl W. Tiller.
Recording Secretary
Rev. John S. Groenfeldt.
Vice-Presidents for Program
James A. Christison
(Church and Society).
Rev. Andrew White
(Education and Ministry).
Rev. Joel K. Thompson
(Overseas Ministries).
Nelson Price
(Broadcasting and Film).
Rev. Robert V. Moss
(Faith and Order).
Rev. Raymond J. Kearns, Jr.
(Regional and Local Ecumenism).
Rev. Clifford B. Lott
(Stewardship).

ELECTED STAFF
OFFICE OF THE GENERAL SECRETARY

Gen. Sec.,
R. H. Edwin Espy.
Deputy Gen. Sec.,
Rev. David R. Hunter.
Exec. Asst.,
Ann K. Davis.
Assoc. Gen. Sec. for Consortia Relationships,
Neiland J. Douglas, Jr.
Asst. Gen. Sec. for Constituency Services,
Rev. Donald F. Landwer

Asst. Gen. Sec. for Donor Support,
Rev. Raymond B. Knudsen.
Asst Gen. Sec. for the Washington Office,
James A. Hamilton, 110 Maryland Ave., N.E.,
Washington, DC 20002. Tel. (202) 544-2350.

DIVISION OF CHURCH AND SOCIETY

Assoc. Gen. Sec.,
  .
Assoc. Sec.,
Doreen Tilghman.
International Affairs,
Rev. Robert S. Bilheimer.
Rev. Kurtis F. Naylor.
Rev. Gerhard Elston,
Church Center for the United Nations
777 United Nations Plaza, 10th Fl.
New York, NY 10017. Tel. (212) 661-2114.
Education for Development,
Palmera B. Peralta,
Church Center for the United Nations
777 United Nations Plaza, 10th Fl.
New York, NY 10017. Tel. (212) 661-2114.
Criminal Justice,
Rev. Robert C. Chapman.
Social Welfare,
John McDowell.
Civil and Religious Liberty,
Rev. Dean M. Kelley.
Crusade Against Hunger,
Hulbert James.
Church and Culture,
Rev. Roger E. Ortmayer.
The Arts,
Mrs. Rena Hansen.
Corporate Information Center,
Frank P. White.
John W. Brown
Field Relationships,
Rev. William E. Scholes,
Rte. 3, Box 716-A, Golden, CO 80401.
Tel. (303) 277-0895.

Migrant Services,
Mrs. Jean Powers.
Southeastern Field Representative,
Rev. August Vanden Bosche,
3637 N.E. First Ave., Miami, FL 33137.
Tel. (305) 573-4050.
Community Health Ministries,
Rev. John H. Wagner, Jr.,
4952 Sunset Blvd., Hollywood, CA 90027.
Tel. (213) 663-2325.
Delta Ministry,
Dir., Owen H. Brooks, Box 457, Greenville,
MS 38701.
Tel. (601) 334-4587.
Assoc. Dir., Rims K. Barber,
Box 457, Greenville, MS 38701.
Tel. (601) 334-4587.
National Farm Worker Ministry,
Dir., Rev. Wayne C. Hartmire.
Assoc. Dir., David Hernandez.
"Salvation Today" Study,
Rev. David J. Randolph.

DIVISION OF EDUCATION AND MINISTRY

Assoc. Gen. Sec.,
Emily V. Gibbes.
Exec. Asst. for Business Administration,
Howard N. Woodland.
Dir., Geneva Point Center,
Rev. Harry Widman, Star Rte. 62,
Box 469, Center Harbor, NH 03226,
Tel. (603) 253-6767 (summer).

Department of Educational Development

Exec. Dir.,
Rev. Eli F. Wismer.
Staff Assoc. (Special Program and Curriculum),
Barbara P. Poppe (Mrs. Henry B.).
Staff Assoc. (Sexuality and Family Ministries),
Rev. William Genné.
Staff Assoc., (Church and Public Education).
Rev. J. Blaine Fister.
Staff Assoc. (Black Educational Ministries),
————.
Staff Assoc. (Special Education),
Ima Jean Kidd.

Department of Higher Education

Exec. Dir.,
Rev. William N. Lovell.
Assoc. Exec. Dir.,
————.
United Board for College Development,
159 Forrest Ave., N.E., Rm. 514,
Atlanta, GA 30303, Tel. (404) 659-6331.

(The following can be reached at the above address)
Co-Directors,
Edward E. Johnson.
Rev. Charles C. Turner.
Assoc. Dir., Academic Administration Program,
Bernard S. Smith.
Dir., Student Services Institute,
Ozias Pearson.

Assoc. Dir.,
Rudolph V. Green.
Co-Directors, Library Administration and Development Program,
Helen Matthews.
————.

Department of Education for Mission

Exec. Dir.,
Rev. William C. Walzer.
Ed. and Dir., Commission for Children, and Dir. for Promotion,
Dorothy L. Weeks.
Ed. and Dir., Commission for Youth and Adults,
Rev. Ward L. Kaiser.

Department of Ministry

Exec. Dir.,
————.
Assoc. Exec. Dir.,
Burnice L. Fjellman.
Dir. of Ministry Studies,
Rev. Edgar W. Mills, Jr.
Dir. of Emergency Ministry Concerning the War, Rev. Richard L. Killmer.
Field Consultant, Emergency Ministry Concerning the War, Joseph E. Garcia. 2390 N.E. 90th, Seattle, WA 98115. Tel. (206) 523-0321.

DIVISION OF OVERSEAS MINISTRIES

Assoc. Gen. Sec.,
Eugene L. Stockwell.
Assoc. Sec.,
James MacCracken.
Dir. of Interpretation and Promotion,
John J. Mullen.
Assoc. Dir. of Interpretation and Promotion,
Joseph P. Schmelter.
Dir., Overseas Personnel Section,
Rev. John P. Muilenburg.
Dir., Financial Management,
Selma M. Femrite.
Dir., Associated Mission Medical Office
John D. Frame, M.D.

Strategy Technical and Area Program Department

Exec. Dir.,
————.
Mission Dir., Africa Working Group,
Rev. Robert C. S. Powell.
CWS Dir., Africa Working Group,
Jan S. F. van Hoogstraten.
CWS Dir., South Asia Working Group,
Rev. Boyd B. Lowry.
Mission Dir., Latin America Working Group,
Rev. William L. Wipfler.
CWS Dir., Latin America Working Group,
H. Dwight Swartzendruber.
Dir., East Asia Working Group
Rev. Edwin M. Luidens.
Dir., China Program,
Rev. Donald E. MacInnis.
Dir., Middle East and Europe Working Group,
Rev. Livingston H. Lomas.

Dir., Intermedia,
Rev. Vern J. Rossman.
Dir., Print Media,
Marion Van Horne.
Dir., Agricultural Missions,
Rev. J. Benton Rhoades.
Assoc. Dir., Agricultural Missions,
———.
Dir., Nutrition Education and Women's Work,
Mrs. Jessie M. Taylor.
Dir.. Ecumenical Scholarships and Theological
Education,
Rev. Robert C. S. Powell.
Dir., Education Commission,
———.
Dir., Churchmen Overseas,
Rev. John R. Collins.

Church World Service Department

Exec. Dir.,
James MacCracken.
Asst. Exec. Dir.,
Nancy L. Nicalo.
Dir., Material Resources Program,
Melvin B. Myers.
Dir., Immigration and Refugee Program,
Rev. John W. Schauer, Jr.
Dir., Planned Parenthood Program,
Epifania C. Resposo.
National Dir., CROP,
Rev. Albert W. Farmer, Box 968,
Elkhart, IN 46514. Tel. (219) 264-3102.
Assoc. Dir., CROP,
Rev. John Metzler, Jr., Box 968,
Elkhart, IN 46514. Tel. (219) 264-3102.
Dir. of Interpretation, CROP,
Robert Rooker, Box 968, Elkhart, IN 46514.
Tel. (219) 264-3102.

COMMISSION ON BROADCASTING AND FILM

Asst. Gen. Sec. and Exec. Dir.,
Rev. William F. Fore.
Assoc. Exec. Dir. and Dir. of Broadcasting,
Rev. D. Williams McClurken.
Assoc. Dir. of Broadcasting,
Rev. David W. Pomeroy.
Dir. Broadcast News and Public Affairs and
Dir., Ecumedia News Service,
John Warren Day.
Broadcast News Editor,
Lauren I. Stell.
Dir. of Film Operations,
Rev. Herbert F. Lowe.
Dir., Promotion and Distribution,
Lois J. Anderson.

COMMISSION ON FAITH AND ORDER

Asst. Gen. Sec. and Exec. Dir.,
Jorge Lara-Braud.
Assoc. Dir.,
Sr. Ann Patrick Ware.

COMMISSION ON REGIONAL AND LOCAL ECUMENISM

Asst. Gen. Sec. and Exec. Dir.,
Rev. Nathan H. VanderWerf.

Assoc. Exec. Dir.,
Rev. Arleon L. Kelley.
Assoc. Exec. Dir. and Special Asst.
to the Gen. Sec. for Ecumenical Services,
Rev. David J. Bowman, S. J.

COMMISSION ON STEWARDSHIP

Asst. Gen. Sec. and Dir.,
Rev. Nordan C. Murphy.

OFFICE OF RESEARCH, EVALUATION AND PLANNING

Assoc. Gen. Sec. for Program Planning,
Rev. J. Allan Ranck.
Dir. of Research and Information Services,
Rev. Douglas W. Johnson.
Dir. Research Library and Editor, Yearbook
of American and Canadian Churches,
Constant H. Jacquet, Jr.

OFFICE OF ADMINISTRATION AND FINANCE

Assoc. Gen. Sec., for Administration,
Rev. H. Leroy Brininger.

Department of Financial Development

Co-Exec. Dir. (for Donor Support),
Rev. Raymond B. Knudsen.
Co-Exec. Dir. (for Denomination Support),
Rev. Donald F. Landwer.

Department of Financial Management

Exec. Dir. and Asst. Treasurer of NCC,
———.
Assoc. Exec. Dir.,
Anne Krupsky, actg.
Data Processing Manager,
Stanley Haidl.

Department of Personnel

Exec. Dir.,
Helen F. Kindt.
Assoc. Exec. Dir.,
Ellsworth G. Stanton, III.
Employee Benefits Administrator,
Lynn R. Best

Department of Organization and Management

Exec. Dir.,
William F. Haase.

Department of Business Services

Exec. Dir.,
———.

Department of Publication Services

Exec. Dir. and Dir. Art Services,
Roger C. Sadler.

Asst. Exec. Dir.,
Roberta Berenger.
Dir. of Production Services,
Frederick W. Reed.

OFFICE OF COMMUNICATION AND INTERPRETATION

Assoc. Gen. Sec., for Communication,
Rev. L. Maynard Catchings.

Department of Information

Exec. Dir.,
Fletcher Coates.
Asst. Dir.,
Mrs. Dorothy Rensenbrink.

Constituent Bodies of the National Council

(As published by the National Council)

African Methodist Episcopal Church
African Methodist Episcopal Zion Church
American Baptist Churches in the U.S.A.
The Antiochian Orthodox Archdiocese of Toledo, Ohio and Dependencies in North America
The Antiochian Orthodox Christian Archdiocese of New York and All North America
Armenian Church of America, Diocese of the (including Diocese of California)
Christian Church (Disciples of Christ)
Christian Methodist Episcopal Church
Church of the Brethren
The Episcopal Church
Friends United Meeting
General Convention, the Swedenborgian Church
Greek Orthodox Archdiocese of North and South America
Hungarian Reformed Church in America
Lutheran Church in America
Moravian Church in America
National Baptist Convention of America
National Baptist Convention, U.S.A., Inc.
Orthodox Church in America
Philadelphia Yearly Meeting of the Religious Society of Friends
Polish National Catholic Church of America
The Presbyterian Church in the United States
Progressive National Baptist Convention, Inc.
Reformed Church in America
Russian Orthodox Church in the U.S.A., Patriarchal Parishes of the
Serbian Eastern Orthodox Church for the U.S.A. and Canada
Seventh Day Baptist General Conference
Syrian Orthodox Church of Antioch
Ukrainian Orthodox Church in America
United Church of Christ
The United Methodist Church
The United Presbyterian Church in the United States of America

American Bible Society

The American Bible Society was organized in 1816 "to promote the distribution of the Holy Scriptures without doctrinal note or comment and without profit." The Society's program soon expanded from distribution in the United States to worldwide outreach. Presently the ABS cooperates with the United Bible Societies in a global coordination of Scripture translation, production, and distribution.

Through the labors of diligent scholars and the efforts of skilled translators, at least one book of the Bible has been translated and published by various Christian organizations in 1,457 languages and dialects.

The need for Scriptures in different formats has caused the ABS to produce the Scriptures on tapes, records, and cassettes and to provide them in contemporary printed formats: illustrated Selections, paperback and newspaper-style Portions, large-print New Testaments, and a variety of whole Bibles.

Distribution has soared, especially since the publication of the New Testament in Today's English Version. In 1971, Scripture distribution in the U.S. totaled 90,129,921 copies. And overseas, working in more than 150 nations and territories, the United Bible Societies reported a 1971 total circulation of 171,116,543 Scriptures.

Support of the Bible Society's far-flung mission comes from the contributions of concerned Christian individuals, congregations, and denominational appropriations.

Offices:
National Headquarters: 1865 Broadway, New York, NY 10023. Tel. (212) 581-7400.
Eastern Region: 1865 Broadway, New York, NY 10023.
Central Region: 310 N. Michigan Ave., Chicago, IL 60601.
Western and Pacific Region: 1662 Wilshire Blvd., Los Angeles, CA 90017.

OFFICERS

Pres., Edmund F. Wagner.
Vice-Pres., Coleman Burke.
Gen. Sec., Rev. Laton E. Holmgren.
Treas., Charles W. Bass.
Exec. Officers: Alice E. Ball (Women's Activities); Rev. John D. Erickson (Ways and Means/Church Relations); Rev. Warner A. Hutchinson, (Program Division); Rev. James Z. Nettinga (Advance Programs); Rev. Eugene A. Nida (Translations); Russell J. Preston (Production and Supply); John Reimer (Finance); Earl F. Schneider (Finance); Rev. Norman L. Temme (Information); Rev. Arthur P. Whitney (National Distribution).
Consultants: Rev. Gilbert Darlington, Rev. Eric M. North.
Departmental Officers: George Amann (Production and Supply); Rev. J. Milton Bell (Ways and Means); Rev. Robert G. Bratcher (Translations); Nicholas J. Calello (Finance); Eugene Cameron (Finance); Francis W. Carpenter (Overseas Distribution); Rev. Keith R. Crim (Translations); Ruth Culley (Women's Activities); Elizabeth J. Eisenhart (Library); Robert L. Eldredge (Finance); Petra T. Facopoulos (Finance); Mrs. Louise Rose Fink (Ways and Means); John W. Giles

(Finance); Dorothy E. L. Haas (Women's Activities); Rev. Thomas S. Johnson (Ways and Means); Charles Todd Lee (Overseas Distribution); Clifford P. Macdonald (Information); Robert J. Maynes (Finance); Marjorie L. Miller (Church Relations); Rev. Homer B. Ogle (Church Relations); Rev. John W. Osberg (Information); Rev. Dale C. Recker (National Distribution); Weir Spence (Overseas Distribution); Rev. John A. Thompson (Translations); Michael J. Valentine (Finance); Rev. C. Bradley Watkins (Translations); Barney Weissman (Finance); Rev. David J. Williams (National Distribution).

Church Relations Field Secretaries: Rev. L. Venchael Booth, Rev. Thomas T. Holloway, Rev. Walter J. Lake, Rev. William H. Rutgers.

Eastern Region: Regional Exec. Sec., Rev. Fred I. Lessten; Regional Distribution Sec.'s: Rev. Frank Baker, Rev. Chan Young Choi, Rev. J. Melvin Griffin, Rev. Joseph B. Mills, Rev. Ivan H. Nothdurft.

Central Region: Regional Exec. Sec., Rev. Melvin E. Soltau; Regional Distribution Sec.'s: Rev. Gordon Clarke, Rev. E. Edwin Houk, Rev. Theodore R. Van Der Veer.

Western and Pacific Region: Regional Exec. Sec., Rev. Dean S. Collins; Regional Distribution Sec.'s: Rev. Rival Hawkins, Rev. James T. Smith, Rev. Richard E. West; Field Sec., Rev. Mark A. Talney.

Regional Exec. Sec.-designate (Southern Region), Rev. J. Edward Cunningham.

Armed Services Liaison Officer: Rev. Steve P. Gaskins, Jr.

Ways and Means Field Secretaries: Rev. Frederick W. Cropp, Roy I. Madsen, Rev. A. Paul Wright.

Women's Activities Officers: Mrs. John Dorr, Mrs. Paul Moser, Mrs. Andrew E. Newcomer.

PERIODICAL

Bible Society Record (m), 1865 Broadway, New York, NY 10023, Benjamin A. Bankson, Ed.

American Tract Society

The American Tract Society is a nonprofit, nonsectarian, interdenominational organization, instituted in 1825 through the merger of most of the then-existing tract societies. As one of the earliest religious publishing bodies in the United States, ATS has pioneered in the publishing of Christian books, booklets, and leaflets. The volume of distribution has risen to more than 31 million pieces of literature annually.

Office: 660 Kinderkamack Rd., Oradell, NJ 07649. Tel. (201) 261-6900.

OFFICERS
Pres., A. J. Widman.
1st. Vice-Pres., John J. Kubach.
2nd. Vice-Pres., W. Theodore Taylor.
Treas., Edgar L. Bensen.
Asst. Treas., Miss Vera L. Rath.

The Associated Church Press

The Associated Church Press was organized in 1916. Its member publications include all major Protestant and Orthodox groups in the U.S. and Canada. It is a professional religious journalistic group seeking to promote better understanding among editors, raise standards, represent the interests of the religious press to the governments in the U.S. and Canada. It sponsors seminars, conventions, workshops for editors, staff people, business members.

Pres., DeCourcy H. Rayner, 50 Wynford Dr., Don Mills 403, Ontario, Canada
Exec. Sec., Alfred P. Klausler, 343 Dearborn St., Chicago, IL 60604. Tel. (312) 922-5444.
Treas., Ralph M. Delk, 407 S. Dearborn St., Chicago, IL 60605.

The Associated Gospel Churches

Organized in 1939, The Associated Gospel Churches is primarily a service agency for fundamental denominations, colleges, seminaries, and missions. It also provides fellowship for Bible-believing independent churches, various Christian workers, missionaries, chaplains, laymen, and students.

One of the chief functions of AGC is to endorse chaplain applicants from the various denominations it represents, a clientele of over 3,500,000. It is recognized by the U.S. Department of Defense and espouses the cause of national defense.

AGC devotes considerable effort toward gaining proper recognition for fundamental colleges, seminaries, and Bible Institutes. It was one of the founders of The American Association of Christian Schools of Higher Learning.

Associated Gospel Churches believes in the sovereignty of the local church, believes in the doctrines of the historic Christian faith, and practices separation from apostasy.

Office: 1919 Beech St., Pittsburgh, PA 15221. Tel. (412) 241-7656.

OFFICERS
Pres., Dr. W. O. H. Garman.
Vice-Pres., Chaplain (Maj.) Everette J. Thomas.
Sec., Thomas R. Bodnar.
Treas., Howard Niggl.
Natl. Field Sec., Chaplain (Capt.) Ivan E. Speight.
Vice-Chmn., Comm. on Chaplains, Chaplain (Lcdr.) James B. Jones, Jr.

Association of Statisticians of American Religious Bodies

This Association was organized in 1934 and grew out of personal consultations held by representatives from The Yearbook of American Churches, The National (now Official) Catholic Directory, the Jewish Statistical Bureau, and The Methodist (now The United Methodist) Church.

ASARB has a variety of purposes: to bring together those officially and professionally responsible for gathering, compiling and publishing denominational statistics; to provide a forum for the exchange of ideas and sharing of problems in statistical methods and procedure; and to seek such standardization as may be possible in religious statistical data.

OFFICERS

Pres., Paul Picard, The Lutheran Church—Missouri Synod, 210 N. Broadway, St. Louis, MO 63109.

Vice-Pres., B. Edgar Johnson, Church of the Nazarene, 6401 The Paseo, Kansas City, MO 64131; Gary Zimmerman, Reorganized Church of Jesus Christ of Latter Day Saints, The Auditorium, Independence, MO 64051.

Sec.-Treas., Lt. Col. N. P. Simington, The Salvation Army, 120 W. 14th St., New York, NY 10011. Tel. (212) 243-8700.

Christian Holiness Association

The Association is a coordinating agency of those religious bodies that hold the Wesleyan-Arminian theological view. It was organized in 1867.

Central Office: 21 Beachway Dr., Indianapolis, IN 46224. Tel. (317) 241-8281.

105th Annual Convention, Portland, OR, April 26-28, 1973.

OFFICERS

Pres., Bishop Henry Ginden, 8 Hellam Dr., Mechanicsburg, PA 17055.

Exec. Dir., Dr. O. D. Emery, 21 Beachway Dr., Indianapolis, IN 46224.

AFFILIATED ORGANIZATIONS

Brethren in Christ Church
Churches of Christ in Christian Union
Evangelical Church of North America
Evangelical Friends Alliance
Evangelical Methodist Church
Free Methodist Church of North America
Holiness Christian Church of the U.S.A.
The Canadian Holiness Federation
The Church of the Nazarene
The Salvation Army
The Salvation Army in Canada
The Wesleyan Church

COOPERATING ORGANIZATIONS

Methodist Protestant Church
Primitive Methodist Church
The Congregational Methodist Church
The Church of God (Anderson)
The Missionary Church
The Sanctified Church of Christ

A Christian Ministry in the National Parks

The Ministry is an independent movement providing interdenominational religious services in 55 National Parks, Monuments and Recreation Areas. For 20 years it was administered in the National Council of Churches. On January 1, 1972, it became an independent movement representing 22 denominations and 16 separate religious organizations.

Office (Winter): 235 E. 49th St., New York, NY 10017. Tel. (212) 870-2155.

Office (Summer): P. O. Box 32, Kelly, WY 83011. Tel. (307) 733-4762.

OFFICER

Dir., Rev. Warren W. Ost.

PERIODICAL

Opportunities Unlimited (annual), Warren W. Ost, Ed.

Church Women United

Church Women United is an ecumenical lay movement providing Protestant, Orthodox, and Roman Catholic women with programs and channels of involvement in church, civic, and national affairs. CWU has some 2,200 units formally organized in communities located in all 50 states and the District of Columbia.

Office: 475 Riverside Dr., Room 812, New York, NY 10027. Tel. (212) 870-2347.

National Ecumenical Assembly: Oct. 10-13, 1974, Memphis, TN.

Coordinator: Claire Randall.

OFFICERS

Pres., Mrs. Martin L. Harvey, Jr., Jackson, MS

Sec., Mrs. Robert Haworth, New York, NY

Treas., Mrs. Dallas B. Sherman, New York, NY

Vice-Presidents: Mrs. Marcus Aurelius, Des Moines, IA; Mrs. Lee Chupco, Tulsa, OK; Mrs. Raymond B. Davidson, Boonton, NJ; Mrs. Clifton B. Drinkard, Austin, TX; Mrs. John E. Eby, Auburn, WA; Mrs. Carl G. France, Pulaski, VA; Mrs. Eugene McCarthy, Washington, DC; Mrs. James C. Piper, Parsons, KS; Mrs. Robert B. Pratt, Jr., Philadelphia, PA; Mrs. David T. Smith, Tucson, AZ; Mrs. John W. Sonnenday, St. Louis, MO; Mrs. LeRoy V. Walcott, Grand Rapids, MI.

STAFF

Exec. Dir., Margaret Shannon.
Assoc. Exec. Dir., Claire Randall.
Citizen Action, Sr. Mary Luke Tobin, S.L.
Communications, Shireen Subramanya.
Ecu. Rel. and Intl. Communities, Gladys Naylor.
Fin. and Pers. Adm., Betty Stachurski.
Fin. Dev., Hilda Lee Dail.
Legis. Aff. Cons., Deborah Partirdge Wolfe.
Local and State CWU Units, Elizabeth H. Gripe.
Urban Ministries, Katie Booth and Elizabeth Haselden.
WICS Liaison, Dorothe Dow.

PERIODICAL

The Church Woman (m), Ruth Weber, Ed.

Consultation on Church Union

Officially constituted in 1962, the Consultation on Church Union is a venture in reconciliation of nine American communions which has been authorized to explore the formation of a united church truly catholic, truly evangelical, and truly reformed. In 1972 the participating churches were African Methodist Episcopal Church, African Methodist Episcopal Zion Church, Christian Church (Disciples of Christ), Christian Methodist Episcopal Church, The Episcopal Church, The Presbyterian Church in the United States, United Church of Christ, The United Methodist Church.

SECRETARIAT
Address: 228 Alexander St., Princeton, NJ 08540. Tel. (609) 921-7866.
Gen. Sec., Rev. Paul A. Crow, Jr.

GENERAL ORGANIZATION

The *Plenary,* which normally meets annually, is composed of delegations of ten from each of the participating churches. Included also are observer-consultants from over twenty other churches, other union negotiations, and conciliar bodies.

The *Executive Committee* is composed of the officers, the secretariat, and one representative from each of the participating churches.

The *Secretariat* are the full-time executive staff members at the national offices in Princeton.

Various *commissions* and *committees* are periodically set up to fulfill certain assignments (e.g., Plan of Union Commission, Commission on Worship, etc.).

OFFICERS
Chmn., Rev. George G. Beazley, Jr., Council on Christian Unity, 222 S. Downey Ave., Indianapolis, IN 46219.
Vice-Chmn., Rev. Charles S. Spivey, Jr.; Mrs. Ralph Stair, 417 Tenny Ave., Waukesha, WI 53186.
Waukesha, WI 53186.
Sec., Mr. George Mason Miller, 708 Cascade Rd., Mooresville, NC 28115.

REPRESENTATIVES FROM PARTICIPATING CHURCHES
African Methodist Episcopal Church, Bishop Frederick D. Jordan, 5151 Franklin Ave., Hollywood, CA 90027.
African Methodist Episcopal Zion Church, Bishop William J. Walls, 38 Aqueduct Pl., Yonkers, NY 10701.
Christian Church (Disciples of Christ), Rev. William Jackson Jarman, Park Avenue Christian Church, 1010 Park Ave., New York, NY 10028.
Christian Methodist Episcopal Church, Bishop E. P. Murchison, 6322 Elwynne Dr., Cincinnati, OH 45236.
The Episcopal Church, Rt. Rev. Robert F. Gibson, Jr., 110 W. Franklin St., Richmond, VA 23220.
The Presbyterian Church in the United States, Rev. William A. Benfield, Jr., First Presbyterian Church, 16 Broad St., Charleston, WV 25301.
United Church of Christ, Rev. David G. Colwell, 1217 Sixth Ave., Seattle, WA 98101.
The United Methodist Church, Bishop James K. Mathews, 581 Boylston St., Boston, MA 02116. Bishop Paul A. Washburn, 122 W. Franklin Ave., Minneapolis, MN 55404.

PUBLICATIONS
Digest of the Proceedings (annual since 1962).
An Order of Worship for the Proclamation of the Word of God and the Celebration of the Lord's Supper.
Plan of Union for the Church of Christ Uniting.
Report of the National Conference on Program.
"In Common" (occasional newsletter).

Evangelical Press Association

An organization of editors and publishers of Christian periodicals.

OFFICERS
Pres., C. Charles Van Ness, David C. Cook Publishing Co., 850 N. Grove, Elgin. IL 60120.
Vice-Pres., Peter Meeuwsen, The Banner, 2850 Kalamazoo Ave. S.E., Grand Rapids, MI 49508.
Sec., Miss Judy Downs, Collegiate Challenge, Arrowhead Springs, San Bernadino, CA 92404.
Treas., Gary Foster, Moody Monthly, 820 N. La Salle St., Chicago, IL 60610.
Exec. Sec. and Dir. E. P. News, Norman B. Rohrer, P. O. Box 707, La Canada, CA 91001. Tel. (213) 790-2272.

General Commission on Chaplains and Armed Forces Personnel

The Commission is an incorporated civilian agency maintained by 41 affiliated religious bodies. Since 1917 it has been a permanent conference on standards and support for the chaplaincy and the religious programs for armed forces personnel and hospitalized veterans.

Office: 122 Maryland Ave., N.E., Washington, DC 20002.

OFFICERS
Chmn., Harold H. Wilke.
Vice-Chmn., Hugh M. Miller.
Sec., John M. Crowell.
Treas., Paul O. Madsen.
Exec. Sec., A. Ray Appelquist.
Dir. of Publications, Edward I. Swanson.

PERIODICALS
The Chaplain (bi-m), Rev. A. Ray Appelquist, Ed., Rev. Edward I. Swanson, Man. Ed.;
The Link (m), Rev. A. Ray Appelquist, Exec. Ed., Rev. Edward I. Swanson, Ed.

International Christian Youth Exchange

Eleven denominational agencies are members of ICYE, which was formed in 1957 to continue the student exchange program previously administered by the Brethren Service Commission.

The U.S. Committee works in cooperation with national committees in twenty-three other countries and the International Council for ICYE, which has headquarters in Geneva, Switzerland. ICYE sponsors the exchange of young people between nations as a means of international and ecumenical education in order to further commitment to and responsibility for reconciliation, justice, and peace. Exchangees 16-19 years of age spend one year in another country and participate in family, school, church, and community life. Exchanges for for American youth going abroad and for overseas youth coming to the U.S. are sponsored by local churches and/or community groups.
Office: 475 Riverside Dr., Room 1908, New York, 10027. Tel. (212) 666-9445.

OFFICERS
Chmn., Rev. John Gattis.
Exec. Dir., Rev. William A. Perkins; Assoc. Dir., William D. Jones.

11

International Ministerial Federation, Inc.

The Federation, incorporated in 1935, is composed of ministers and churches and has no ecclesiastical authority over members. It is interdenominational, and provides a legal identity for the ministers of nondenominational churches.

GENERAL ORGANIZATION

Annual conventions are announced by notification thereof to the membership.

OFFICERS

Pres., Dr. Sidney Correll, P. O. Box 8000, St. Petersburg, FL 33738.
1st Vice-Pres., Dr. C. E. Britton, 1507 S. Marguerita, Alhambra, CA 91803.
2nd Vice-Pres., Rev. Gerald Boyer, P. O. Box 8000, St. Petersburg, FL 33738.
Exec. Sec., Dr. W. E. Opie, 5290 N. Sherman Ave., Fresno, CA 93710. Tel. (209) 222-9338.

International Society of Christian Endeavor

Christian Endeavor is an international, interracial, and interdenominational youth movement in evangelical Protestant churches. It unites its members for greater Christian growth and service under the motto "For Christ and the Church." The first society was formed by Francis E. Clark in Portland, Maine, February 2, 1881.

The movement spread rapidly and, in 1885, the United Society of Christian Endeavor was organized. In 1927 the name was changed to the International Society of Christian Endeavor, to include Canada and Mexico. The World's Union was organized in 1895. The movement has thousands of societies in local churches, for all age groups. Worldwide there are societies and unions in approximately 75 nations and island groups, with over two million members.

Office: 1221 E. Broad St., Columbus, OH 43216. Tel. (614) 253-8541.
52nd International Convention at Evansville, Indiana, July 2-6, 1973.

OFFICERS

Pres., Dr. LaVerne H. Boss.
Gen. Sec., Rev. Charles W. Barner.
Admin. Sec., Phyllis I. Rike.

PERIODICAL

The Christian Endeavor World (16 times a year), 1221 E. Broad St., Columbus, OH 43216, Phyllis I. Rike, Ed.

Joint Strategy and Action Committee

This is a national ecumenical agency created by several denominational home mission agencies. Through the JSAC system, agencies collaborate with each other about issues, develop strategy options, screen project requests, and work on joint actions. JSAC has a series of national-staff coalitions which work as Strategy/Screening Task Forces, Work Groups or Committees.
National Office: 475 Riverside Dr., Rm. 1700-A, New York, NY 10027. Tel. (212) 870-3105.

OFFICERS

Pres., Rev. Eugene Huff, United Presbyterian Church in the U.S.A.
Vice-Pres., Rev. Paul Sherry, United Church of Christ.
Sec., Rev. John R. Houck, American Lutheran Church.
Coord. Comm. Chmn., Rev. Ernest May, United Methodist Church.
Exec. Dir., Rev. Norman E. Dewire.

MEMBER DENOMINATIONAL AGENCIES

American Baptist Churches
American Lutheran Church
Church of the Brethren
The Episcopal Church
Lutheran Church in America
Lutheran Church—Missouri Synod
Presbyterian Church in the U.S.
Reformed Church in America
United Church of Christ
United Methodist Church
United Presbyterian Church, U.S.A.

COOPERATING DENOMINATIONAL AGENCIES

African Methodist Episcopal Church
Christian Church (Disciples of Christ)
Christian Reformed Church
Cumberland Presbyterian Church
Southern Baptist Convention
United States Catholic Conference
Church Women United

PERIODICAL

Grapevine (10 times a year), Ms. Sheila Collins.

The Lord's Day Alliance of the United States

The Lord's Day Alliance of the U.S. was organized in 1888 as The American Sabbath Union.

It is the catalytic agent for fourteen Christian denominations and four church-related organizations in cultivating the proper recognition and utilization of Sunday as the Lord's Day.

The Alliance produces written and audio-visual materials, furnishes speakers, and counsels with individuals in matters relating to the spiritual benefits of maintaining the Day God made for man.

Office: 159 Forrest Ave., N.E., Suite 408, Atlanta, GA 30303.

OFFICERS

Pres., Rev. Charles A. Platt.
Vice-Pres., Rev. Andrew R. Bird, Jr.
Sec., Joe M. Abbott.
Treas., E. Larry Eidson.
Exec. Dir., Rev. Marion G. Bradwell.
Dir. Info. Services, Archibald Pipe.
Committee Chairmen:
    State and Natl. Affairs, Rev. S. A. Jeanes.
    Communications, Rev. James A. Wesberry.
    Extension, Rev. Melvin M. Forney.
    Finance, Christe E. Parker.

PERIODICAL

Sunday (bi-m), Marion G. Bradwell, Ed.

Lutheran Council in the U.S.A.

The Lutheran Council in the U.S.A. succeeded the National Lutheran Council January 1, 1967, as a cooperative agency of the major U.S. Lutheran church bodies. In addition to The Lutheran Church—Missouri Synod, which had not been a member of the NLC, participating churches are The American Lutheran Church and the Lutheran Church in America. With its authority derived from the participating bodies it serves, the council seeks to effect a threefold objective: (a) further the witness, work, and interests of the Lutheran Church; (b) achieve theological consensus among Lutherans; (c) provide a means of cooperation and coordination of efforts for more effective, efficient service in six major areas: theological studies, education, mission, welfare, public relations, and service to military personnel.

Headquarters: 315 Park Ave. So., New York, NY 10010. Tel. (212) 677-3950.
Other Offices: 2633 16th St., N.W., Washington, DC 20009; 130 N. Wells St., Chicago, IL 60606.

OFFICERS
Pres., Dr. Oswald C. J. Hoffman.
Vice-Pres., Dr. George F. Harkins.
Sec., Mr. Hilbert Schauer.
Treas., Mr. W. Emerson Gentzler.
Gen. Sec., Dr. C. Thomas Spitz, Jr.
Dir. of Business & Finance, Mr. Walter A. Jensen.
Div. of Educational Services, Dr. Donald W. Herb.
Div. of Mission Services, Dr. Harold Haas.
Div. of Public Relations, Mr. Robert E. A. Lee.
Div. of Service to Military Personnel, Dr. William J. Reiss.
Div. of Theological Studies, Dr. Paul D. Opsahl.
Div. of Welfare Services, Dr. Harold Haas.

PERIODICALS
Focus (bi-m), Dr. Robert Van Deusen, Ed.; In Step (m), Div. of Service to Military Personnel; The Lutheran Scouter (q), Mr. Ralph Dinger, Ed.; Interchange (m), Ms. Naomi Frost, Ed.; Volunteer (q), Mr. Harold Hanson, Ed.

National Association of Christian Schools

The National Association of Christian Schools is an affiliate of the National Association of Evangelicals. It is autonomous in its organizational setup.

Headquarters: Box 550, Wheaton, IL 60187. Tel. (312) 653-5595.

OFFICERS
Pres., Joseph T. Bayly.
Exec. Dir., John F. Blanchard Jr.

PERIODICALS
Christian Teacher, Box 550, Wheaton, IL 60187; School Directory, listing 366 private Christian schools.

National Association of Ecumenical Staff

This is the successor organization to the Association of Council Secretaries, which was founded in 1940. The name change was made in 1971.
NAES is an association of professional staff in ecumenical services. It was established to provide creative relationships among them, and to encourage mutual support and personal and professional growth. This is accomplished through training programs, through exchange and discussion of common concerns at conferences, and through the publication of the journal.

Headquarters: Room 850, 475 Riverside Dr., New York, NY 10027. Tel. (212) 870-2157.

Annual Meeting: June 24-30, 1973, Williams Bay, WI

OFFICERS
Pres., Rev. James M. Webb, Rhode Island State Council of Churches, 2 Stimson Ave., Providence, RI 02906
Vice-Pres., Rev. Horace N. Mays, Los Angeles Council of Churches, 1718 North Wilton Place, Los Angeles, CA 90028.
Vice-Pres., Rev. Clifton Kirkpatrick, Houston Metropolitan Ministries, 900 Lovett Blvd., Houston, TX 77006.
Sec., Miss Lenore Mullarney, Commission on Religion in Appalachia, 864 Weisgarber Rd., N.W., Knoxville, TN 37919.
Treas., Rev. Charles H. Straut, Jr., Brooklyn Div. of the Council of Churches of the City of New York, 66 Court St., Brooklyn, NY 11201.

PERIODICAL
National NAES Journal (q), H. Conrad Hoyer, Ed.

The National Association of Evangelicals

The National Association of Evangelicals had its beginning on April 7-9, 1942, when 150 evangelical leaders met in St. Louis, Mo., to launch a movement to bring Christians together in united action.
Since then, NAE has provided a means of "cooperation without compromise" among Bible-believing Christians. This fellowship is based upon a statement of faith that is descriptive of the true evangelical.
The NAE represents 33 complete denominations and has within its membership individual churches from at least 27 other groups, including Bible colleges, Christian schools, seminaries, ministerial fellowships and evangelistic organizations, as well as individual Christians. Actual membership numbers above three million.

GENERAL ORGANIZATION
Headquarters: 350 S. Main Place, P. O. Box 28, Wheaton, IL 60187. Tel. (312) 665-0500.
Office of Public Affairs: 1405 G St., N.W., Washington, DC 20005.

OFFICERS
Pres., Dr. Myron F. Boyd.

UNITED STATES COOPERATIVE ORGANIZATIONS, NATIONAL

Gen. Dir., Dr. Clyde W. Taylor.
Exec. Dir., Dr. Billy A. Melvin.
Sec. of Public Affairs, Dr. Clyde W. Taylor.
Field Directors:
Pacific Region: Dr. Wilmer N. Brown, P. O. Box 19235, Portland, OR 97219.
Southwest Region: Rev. Charles J. Anderson, P. O. Box 2526, Fullerton, CA 92633.
Upper Midwest and West Central Regions: Rev. Donald O. Larson, P.O. Box 35101, Minneapolis, MI 55435.
Midwest and East Central Regions: Rev. Gordon Bacon, Box 670, Glen Ellyn, IL 60137.
Eastern and New England Regions: Rev. Sherwood Becker, Box 475, Allentown, PA 18105.

OTHER ORGANIZATIONS

Chaplaincy Commission; Evangelical Action Commission; Evangelical Churchmen's Commission; Evangelical Home Missions Association; Evangelism and Spiritual Life Commission; Higher Education Commission; Social Concern Commission; Stewardship Commission; Theology Commission; Women's Fellowship Commission; World Relief Commission; Evangelical Foreign Missions Association; National Association of Christian Schools; National Religious Broadcasters; National Sunday School Association.

PERIODICAL

United Evangelical Action (q), 350 S. Main Place, Wheaton, IL 60187, Dr. Billy A. Melvin, Exec. Ed.

MEMBER DENOMINATIONS

Assemblies of God
Baptist General Conference
Brethren in Christ
Christian Church of North America
Christian and Missionary Alliance
Christian Union
Church of God (Cleveland, Tenn.)
Church of the United Brethren in Christ
Churches of Christ in Christian Union
Conservative Congregational Christian Conference
Elim Fellowship
Evangelical Church of North America
Evangelical Congregational Church
Evangelical Free Church of America
Evangelical Friends Alliance
Evangelical Mennonite Brethren Church
Evangelical Mennonite Church
Evangelical Methodist Church
Free Methodist Church
General Conference of the Brethren Church
International Church of the Foursquare Gospel
International Pentecostal Assemblies
Mennonite Brethren Church
Midwest Congregational Christian Fellowship
Missionary Church
Open Bible Standard Churches
Pentecostal Church of Christ
Pentecostal Church of God
Pentecostal Evangelical Church
Pentecostal Holiness Church
Primitive Methodist Church
Reformed Presbyterian Church of North America
Wesleyan Church

LOCAL CHURCHES FROM THE FOLLOWING

Advent Christian Church
American Baptist Churches in the U.S.A.
Berean Fundamental Churches
Bible Churches
Bible Baptist Churches
Christian Churches, Churches of Christ
Christian Reformed Church
Church of the Brethren
Church of the Nazarene
Community Churches
Conservative Baptist Association
Evangelical Covenant Church
Free Baptist Churches
General Association of General Baptists
General Conference Mennonite
Grace Brethren Churches
Independent Churches
Independent Baptist Churches
Independent Presbyterian
National Association of Free Will Baptists
North American Baptist Churches
Presbyterian Church in the U.S.
Reformed Church in America
Southern Baptist Convention
United Baptist Churches
United Methodist Church
United Presbyterian Church in the U.S.A.

National Council of Young Men's Christian Associations

A worldwide organization begun in London, England, in 1844, the first YMCA in the U.S. was established at Boston, Mass., in 1851. The policies of the "Y" are guided by Christian men and women from the fields of commerce, labor, and the professions.

The Young Men's Christian Associations of the United States of America is "in its essential genius, the worldwide fellowship united by a common loyalty to Jesus Christ for the purpose of developing Christian personality and building a Christian society."

Specific goals adopted for the 1973-78 period include elimination of personal and institutional racism; changing the conditions that foster alienation, delinquency, and crime; reducing health problems by strengthening physical and mental health; strengthening family structures by enhancing relationships and improving communication; joining people from other countries in building international understanding and world peace.

There are approximately five and a half million members in 1,834 autonomous Associations. Over 30 percent women, the membership includes men, women, boys and girls of all religious and nonreligious persuasions.
Corporate Name: National Board of Young Men's Christian Associations.

Office: 291 Broadway, New York, NY 10007. Tel. (212) 349-0700.

OFFICERS

Pres., Donald M Payne.
Chmn., Richard C. Kautz.
Exec. Dir., Robert W. Harlan.
Treas., William E. Dietz.

PERIODICAL

YMCA Today, Leonard M. Synder, Ed.

National Interreligious Service Board for Conscientious Objectors

Since 1940 NISBCO has responded to the needs of conscientious objectors to the draft and military service by: providing professional counseling and draft information by mail and phone in our Washington, D.C. office; providing accurate and up-to-date literature on draft and military law and policy for use by local counselors and counselees; aiding COs in the armed forces who seek noncombatant transfer or discharge; maintaining an extensive referral service to local counseling agencies in all areas of the country and to attorneys who can aid those in need of legal counsel; providing alternative service counseling for COs seeking 1-W assignments.

Office: Washington Bldg., Rm. 550, 15th and New York Ave., N.W., Washington, DC 20005. Tel. (202) 393-4868.

OFFICERS

Chmn., William T. Snyder, 21 South 12th St., Akron, PA 17501.
Exec. Dir., Warren W. Hoover.

PERIODICAL

The Reporter for Conscience' Sake (m), Richard Malishchak, Ed.

North American Academy of Ecumenists

Organized in 1967, the Academy is a society of persons engaged in studies relating to the unity of the Christian Church and the dialogue between Christians and other communities of faith.

Headquarters: 5 Horizon Rd., Fort Lee, NJ 07024.

OFFICERS

Pres., Dr. J. Robert Nelson.
Vice-Pres., Rev. Kilian McDonnel, O.S.B.
Sec.-Treas., Dr. William J. Schmidt.
M'ship Sec., Dr. Joseph C. Weber.

PERIODICAL

Journal of Ecumenical Studies (q), Temple University, Philadelphia, PA 19122, Leonard Swidler, Ed. (This periodical is affiliated with the Academy.)

Pentecostal Fellowship of North America

Organized at Des Moines, Iowa, in October, 1948 shortly after the first World Conference of Pentecostal Believers was held in Zurich, Switzerland, in May, 1947, The PFNA has the following objectives: 1) to provide a vehicle of expression and coordination of efforts in matters common to all member bodies including missionary and evangelistic effort; 2) to demonstrate to the world the essential unity of Spirit-baptized believers; 3) to provide services to its constituents to facilitate world evangelism; 4) to encourage the principles of comity for the nurture of the body of Christ, endeavoring to keep the unity of the Spirit until we all come to the unity of the faith.

The PFNA has local chapters in communities where churches of the member groups are located, and fellowship rallies are held. On the national level, representatives of the member bodies are assembled for studies and exchange of views in the fields of home missions, foreign missions, and youth.

EXECUTIVE OFFICERS

Chmn., Robert Taitinger (Gen. Supt., Pentecostal Assemblies of Canada), 10 Overlea Blvd., Toronto 354, Ontario.
1st Vice-Chmn., Dr. Ray H. Hughes (Gen. Overseer, Church of God), Keith at 25th. N.W. Cleveland, TN 37311.
2nd Vice-Chmn., Bishop J. Floyd Williams (Gen. Supt., Pentecostal Holiness Church), Box 292, Franklin Springs, GA 30639.
Sec., Dr. G. Raymond Carlson (Asst. Gen. Supt., Assemblies of God), 1445 Boonville Ave., Springfield, MO 65802.
Treas., Tom Grinder (Chmn., International Pentecostal Assemblies), 924 Berne St., S.E., Atlanta, GA 30316.

PERIODICAL

P.F.N.A. News (q), Keith at 25th, N.W., Cleveland, TN 37311, Dr. Ray H. Hughes, Ed.

MEMBER GROUPS

Anchor Bay Evangelistic Association
Assemblies of God
Carolina Evangelistic Association
Church of God (Cleveland, Tenn.)
Church of God, Mountain Assembly
Congregational Holiness Church
Elim Fellowship
Emmanuel Holiness Church
Free Gospel Church, Inc.
Free Will Baptist (Pentecostal Faith)
International Church of the Foursquare Gospel
International Pentecostal Assemblies
Italian Pentecostal Church of Canada
Open Bible Standard Churches, Inc.
Pentecostal Assemblies of Canada
Pentecostal Assemblies of Newfoundland and Labrador
Pentecostal Church of Christ
Pentecostal Free-Will Baptist
Pentecostal Holiness Church

Religion in American Life, Inc.

Religion in American Life (RIAL) is a cooperative program of 39 major national religious groups (Catholic, Eastern Orthodox, Jewish, Protestant) which enables them to reach the American public through the advertising media. Every year since 1949 RIAL has been one of the major campaigns of The Advertising Council. As such it receives annually over $27 million in free space and time contributed by the media. Its advertising is produced without charge by a volunteer agency (Lieberman-Harrison, Inc.) and its production and administration costs are funded by both the business and the religious community. RIAL's advertising message as defined by its cooperating religious groups stresses the importance of religion in daily life. Local community programs across the country help reinforce the message.

UNITED STATES COOPERATIVE ORGANIZATIONS, NATIONAL

Office: 475 Fifth Ave., New York, NY 10017. Tel. (212) 683-5464.

OFFICERS

Natl. Chmn., William F. May.
Pres., Dr. Theophilus M. Taylor.
Vice-Pres.'s, Bishop Joseph L. Bernadin, Rabbi Henry Siegman, Bishop Silas.
Treas.,_____.
Asst. Treas., Anne Podmol.
Sec., Dr. George F. Harkins.
Asst. Sec., Dr. Marvin C. Wilbur.
Exec. Vice-Pres., Rev. David W. Gockley.
Dir., Program, Jerald Hatfield.
Dir., Fin. Dev., Rev. H. Newton Hudson.

PERIODICAL

The Bulletin, 475 Fifth Ave., New York, NY 10017.

Religion Newswriters Association

Founded in 1949, the RNA is a professional association of religion news editors and reporters on secular daily and weekly newspapers, wire services, and news magazines. It sponsors three annual contests for excellence in religion news coverage in the secular press. Annual meetings precede a major religious convocation.

OFFICERS

Pres., William Fogler, Courier-Express, Buffalo, NY 14240. Tel. (716) 847-8700.
Vice-Pres.: Richard Ostling, Time Magazine, New York, NY 10020; William A. Reed. Jr., Tennessean, Nashville, TN 37203.
Sec., Helen Parmley, News, Dallas, TX 75222.
Treas., William R. MacKaye, Post, Washington, DC 20005.

The Religious Public Relations Council, Inc.

The Religious Public Relations Council, Inc., is an organization whose purposes are to establish, raise and maintain high standards of public relations and communication to the end that religious faith and life may be advanced; and to promote fellowship, counseling and exchange of ideas among its members.

Now an interfaith non-profit professional association, the Council originally was founded as the Religious Publicity Council on November 27, 1929, in Washington, D.C. There were 29 charter members, representing seven denominations, the Federal Council of Churches, and four church-related agencies. In 1967 it opened its membership to qualified people of all Christian communions. In 1970, its membership was opened to all religious faiths.

Today RPRC has over 600 members in 13 chapters, as well as over 50 members-at-large in 38 states and Canada and four nations overseas.

The Council conducts an annual convention, sponsors two awards programs: one for secular journalism and broadcasting; the other, awards of excellence in nine categories for its own members; and each year has a continuing education program at Syracuse University.

Office: 475 Riverside Dr., Rm. 1031, New York, NY 10027. Tel. (212) 870-2014.

Annual Meeting and Interfaith Convention, Indianapolis, IN, April 4-6, 1973.

OFFICERS

Pres., Howard E. Royer, Church of the Brethren General Offices, 1451 Dundee Ave., Elgin, IL 60120.
Vice-Pres., Paula Lee Becker, Southern Publishing Assn. of Seventh-day Adventists, 2119 24th Ave., N., Nashville, TN 37203.
Sec., Lillian Moir, Christian Church (Disciples of Christ), 222 S. Downey Ave., Indianapolis, IN 46219.
Treas., Rev. Edward J. Gorry, The Paulist Fathers, 415 W. 59th St., New York, NY 10019.
Exec. Sec., Marvin C. Wilbur, Asst. Dir., United Presbyterian Foundation, 475 Riverside Dr., Rm. 1031, New York, NY 10027.

PERIODICALS

Counselor (q), 475 Riverside Dr., New York, NY 10027, Dr. Marvin C. Wilbur, Ed.
Mediakit (bi-m), 475 Riverside Dr., New York, NY 10027.

Standing Conference of Canonical Orthodox Bishops in the Americas

This body was established in 1960 to achieve cooperation among the various Eastern Orthodox Churches in the U.S.A. The Conference is "a voluntary association of the Bishops in the Americas established . . . to serve as an agency to centralize and coordinate the mission of the Church. It acts as a clearing house to focus the efforts of the Church on common concerns and to avoid duplication and overlapping of services and agencies. Special departments are devoted to campus work, Christian education, military and other chaplaincies, regional clergy fellowships, and ecumenical relations."

Office: 8005 Ridge Blvd., Brooklyn, NY 11209. Tel. (212) 745-8481.

OFFICERS

Chmn., Most Rev. Archbishop Iakovos.
Sec., Very Rev. W.P.S. Schneirla.
MEMBER CHURCHES
Albanian Orthodox Diocese of America.
American Carpatho-Russian Orthodox Greek Catholic Church.
Antiochian Orthodox Christian Archdiocese of New York and All North America.
Bulgarian Eastern Orthodox Church.
Greek Orthodox Archdiocese of North and South America.
Holy Ukrainian Orthodox Church in Exile.
Orthodox Church in America. (Russian Orthodox Greek Catholic Church).
Romanian Orthodox Church in America.
Serbian Orthodox Church for the U.S.A. and Canada.
Ukrainian Orthodox Church of America.

Young Women's Christian Association of the United States of America

The first YWCA of the U.S.A. group, known as the Ladies' Christian Association, appeared in 1858 in New York City, after the worldwide membership movement began in London, England, 1855. Today, it serves 2.6 million members and program participants.

The National Board unites into an effective continuing organization the autonomous member Associations for furthering the purpose of the National Association, which states:

"The Young Women's Christian Association of the United States of America, a movement rooted in the Christian faith as known in Jesus and nourished by the resources of that faith, seeks to respond to the barrier-breaking love of God in this day.

"The Association draws together into responsible membership women and girls of diverse experiences and faiths, that their lives may be open to new understanding and deeper relationships and that together they may join in the struggle for peace and justice, freedom and dignity for all people."

The National Board also represents Associations of the United States in the World YWCA.

NATIONAL BOARD
Office: 600 Lexington Ave., New York, NY 10022. Tel. (212) 758-4700.

OFFICERS
Pres., Mrs. Robert W. Claytor.

Sec., Mrs. Clarke B. Dowling.
Exec. Dir., Miss Edith M. Lerrigo.

PERIODICAL
The YWCA Magazine (m), Mrs. Ida Sloan Snyder, Exec. Ed.

Youth for Christ, International

Founded in 1945, the current purpose of YFC is to help the teenager understand himself in relation to others and God and to help him develop a physical, mental, social, and spiritual balance in his life that enables him to effectively communicate his faith in Christ to his campus, his friends, and his world.

There is a staff of 800 trained youth leaders directing programs serving 500,000 U.S. teens annually through high school clubs, and 10,000 more through the Lifeline program, aimed at youth in trouble with the law. YFC also works in 39 foreign countries.

GENERAL ORGANIZATION
Headquarters: 360 S. Main Place, Carol Stream, IL 60187. Pres., Dr. Sam Wolgemuth.

PERIODICAL
Campus Life (m), P.O. Box 419, Wheaton, IL 60187. Harold Myra, Ed.

2. CANADIAN COOPERATIVE ORGANIZATIONS, NATIONAL

This directory of Canadian Cooperative Organizations attempts to list major organizations working interdenominationally on a national basis. The editor of the **Yearbook of American and Canadian Churches** would appreciate receiving information on any significant organizations not now included.

The Canadian Council of Churches

The Canadian Council of Churches was organized in 1944. Its basic purpose is to provide the churches with an agency for conference and consultation and for such common planning and common action as they desire to undertake. It encourages ecumenical understanding and action throughout Canada through local councils of churches. It also relates to the World Council of Churches and other agencies serving the worldwide ecumenical movement.

The Council has a Triennial Assembly which is the basic governing body, a General Board which meets semiannually, and an Executive Committee. Program is administered through three commissions—Faith and Order, Canadian Affairs, and World Concerns.

40 St. Clair Ave. E., Toronto, Ontario M4T 1M9 Tel. (416) 921-4152.

OFFICERS AND STAFF
Pres., Rev. Dr. Norman Berner.
Vice-Pres., Rev. Dr. Harriet Christie and Most Rev. E. W. Scott.
Treas., Mr. Fraser Deacon.
Gen. Sec., Rev. Dr. T. E. F. Honey.
Assoc. Secs., Rev. Canon M. P. Wilkinson; Rev. Dr. E. S. Mackay.
Asst. to Gen. Sec., Miss Ruth Tillman.
Sec. for Canadian Girls In Training, Miss Sara Harrison.

AFFILIATED INSTITUTION
Ecumenical Institute of Canada, 11 Madison Ave., Toronto 180, Ontario. Dir., Canon H. L. Puxley; Dean of Studies, Katherine B. Hockin; Staff Ass't., Laity, Rev. James Kirkwood.

MEMBER CHURCHES
The Anglican Church of Canada
The Armenian Church of America—Diocese of Canada.
Baptist Federation of Canada
Christian Church (Disciples of Christ)
Greek Orthodox Archiocese of North and South America—9th District (Canada and Alaska)
Lutheran Church in America—Canada Section
Presbyterian Church in Canada
Reformed Church in America—Classis of Ontario
Religious Society of Friends—Canada Yearly Meeting
Salvation Army—Canada and Bermuda
United Church of Canada

Canadian Bible Society

As early as 1808 the British and Foreign Bible Society was at work in Canada. The Canadian Bible Society Branch at Truro, N.S., has been functioning continually since 1810. In 1904, the various auxiliaries of the British and Foreign Bible Society in Canada joined together to form the Canadian Bible Society.

Presently, the Canadian Bible Society has 19 districts and 3,500 branches. It holds an annual meeting of its Board which consists of two or more representatives of each district plus members appointed by the General Board of the CBS. There is also a meeting of its district secretaries annually.

In 1971, the CBS distributed 2½ million Scriptures in 75 languages in Canada.

Headquarters: Ste. 200, 1835 Yonge St., Toronto 295, Ontario. Tel. (416) 481-1312.

OFFICER
Gen. Sec., Rev. Dr. Kenneth G. McMillan.

Canadian Tract Society

The Canadian Tract Society was organized in 1970 as an independent publisher of gospel leaflets to provide Canadian churches and individual Christians with quality materials in proclaiming the gospel through the printed page. It is affiliated with the American Tract Society, which encouraged its formation and assisted in its founding. The CTS is a nonprofit international service ministry.

Address: Box 203, Port Credit (Toronto) Ontario.

OFFICERS
Pres., Stanley D. Mackey.
1st Vice-Pres., Stephen E. Slocum, Jr.
Sec., William R. McClintock.
Exec. Dir., Robert J. Burns.

Evangelical Fellowship of Canada

The Evangelical Fellowship of Canada was organized in 1964 with Dr. Oswald J. Smith as President and Dr. Harry Faught as Executive Chairman.

Its purposes are three fold: "Fellowship in the gospel" (Phil. 1:5), "the defence and confirmation of the gospel" (Phil. 1:7), and "the furtherance of the gospel" (Phil. 1:12).

The Fellowship believes the Holy Scriptures, as originally given, are infallible and that salvation through the Lord Jesus Christ is by faith apart from works.

In national and regional conventions the Fellowship urges Christians to live exemplary lives and to openly challenge the evils and injustices of society. It encourages cooperation with various agencies in Canada and overseas that are sensitive to man's social and spiritual needs.

Office: 67 Harbord St., Toronto 4, Ontario. Tel. (416) 923-5888

OFFICERS
Pres., Dr. Robert Thompson, M.P.
Vice Pres., Rev. Donald McLeod; Mr. James Cleminger.

Sec., Rev. Charles A. Tipp.
Treas., Mr. John Irwin.
Chmn., Foreign Mission Commission, Rev. Gordon Houser.
Chmn., Publications and Information Commission, Rev. Earl Kulbeck.
Chmn., Christian Education Commission, Rev. Victor Adrian.
Chmn., Social Action Commission, Major David Hammond.

General Commission on Church Union

The Anglican Church of Canada, in October, 1963, requested its Committee on Church Unity, together with the Committee of the United Church of Canada, to prepare a plan of unity which could be submitted to the churches for study and action, if possible by General Synod 1965, and that the plan also be submitted to other communions which would be ready to receive it.

Committees of Ten were set up, which moved in the direction of preparing the principles of union upon which a plan could be based.

In August, 1965, the Anglican Church approved "The Principles of Union," and commended them to the dioceses for their prayerful study and consideration. It also stated that, if and when the United Church of Canada approved "The Principles of Union," the National Executive Council be authorized to appoint Anglican members to the General Commission and to the four Special Commissions which the Principles called for.

When approval was given the following year to "The Principles of Union" by the United Church, a recommendation was made for one or more additional Special Commissions. Agreement was reached by both churches that a fifth Commission on the Church in the World be also established.

In August, 1969, the Christian Church (Disciples of Christ) formally adopted "The Principles of Union."

In 1967, a General Commission and five Special Commissions were established to carry out their responsibilities in accordance with the Principles adopted by the three churches.

The five Special Commissions with their particular concerns and terms of reference were: Constitutional, Legal, Doctrinal, Liturgical, and Church in the World.

In January, 1971, a first draft of a Plan was presented to the three churches as a study document only, and the comments and recommendations from church members are being considered in the revision of the document. It is now expected that the General Commission, meeting in mid-November, 1972, will receive this Plan of Union and authorize its publication and circulation among the churches for study over the next two years. It will then be the responsibility of the three negotiating churches to decide according to their own polity what action they will take regarding the Plan of Union.

Office: 85 St. Clair Ave., E., Rm. 312, Toronto 290, Ontario. Tel. (416) 920-4030.

OFFICERS
Exec. Commissioners, Rev. Canon R. R. Latimer; Rev. Dr. R. B. Craig.

Inter-Varsity Christian Fellowship of Canada

Inter-Varsity Christian Fellowship is a nonprofit, interdenominational Canadian student movement centering on the witness of Jesus Christ to campus communities: universities, high schools, schools of nursing, technical schools, teachers' colleges, and through a Canada-wide Pioneer camping program. IVCF was officially formed in September, 1929, through the enthusiastic efforts of Dr. Howard Guinness, whose arrival from Britain encouraged the few existing but independent prayer and Bible study groups in the student environment. Inter-Varsity's uniqueness lies in its emphases on student responsibility and life together. IVCF calls on Christian young people to become visible in the life of their school, to find fellowship with other Christians by walking together in the light of our Lord Jesus Christ and His Word. It challenges them to allow their lives to become open to the scrutiny of their fellows. It seeks to foster a spirit of honest inquiry which welcomes full investigation of the Faith.

Headquarters: 745 Mount Pleasant Rd., Toronto 298, Ontario. Tel. (416) 487-3431.

OFFICERS
Gen. Dir., Mr. Samuel Escobar.
Sec., R. J. Burns.

The Lord's Day Alliance of Canada

An interdenominational organization devoted to cultivating the proper recognition and utilization of Sunday as the Lord's Day.

The Alliance produces textual and audiovisual materials and furnishes speakers.
Office: Ste. 201, 49 St. Clair Ave., E., Toronto 7, Ontario. Tel. (416) 925-7871.

OFFICER
Gen. Sec., Rev. Gordon A. Walker.

Lutheran Council in Canada

The Lutheran Council in Canada was organized in 1967 and is a cooperative venture of the Evangelical Lutheran Church of Canada, the Lutheran Church in America-Canada Section, and the Lutheran Church-Canada.

The Council has seven divisions: information services, educational services, campus foundation activity, theological studies, Canadian missions, social services, and service to military personnel.

Office: 500-365 Hargrave St., Winnepeg Manitoba R3B 2K3. Tel. (204) 942-0096.

OFFICERS
Gen. Sec., The Rev. Dr. Earl J. Treusch.
Exec. Sec., Social Services, Rev. Clifton L. Monk.
Exec. Sec., Theological Studies, Rev. Norman J. Threinen.
Exec. Sec., Campus Foundation Activity and Educational Services, Rev. Donald H. Voights.
Exec. Sec., Information Services, Walter A. Schultz.

Mennonite Central Committee (Canada)

Mennonite Central Committee (Canada) was organized in 1964 to continue the work which several regional Canadian inter-Mennonite agencies had been doing in relief, service, immigration, and peace. All but a few of the smaller and more conservative Mennonite groups in Canada belong to MCC (Canada).

MCC (Canada) is closely related to the international MCC organization which has its headquarters in Akron, Pennsylvania, and which administers all overseas development and relief projects. MCC (Canada) raised $600,000 in cash for this international ministry in 1971. Additionally, nearly 150 Canadians volunteered for one or more years of service in MCC's program abroad and at home during that same period.

The MCC (Canada) office in Winnipeg administers all voluntary projects located in Canada on behalf of the international MCC office. Whenever it undertakes a project, MCC attempts to relate to the church or churches in the area, regardless of their denominational affiliation. It attempts in this way to support and undergird the local manifestation of the church.

Office: 201-1488 Pembina Hwy., Winnipeg, Manitoba R3T 2C8. Tel. (204) 453-4897.

OFFICER
Exec. Sec., Daniel Zehr.

Student Christian Movement of Canada

The Student Christian Movement of Canada was formed in 1921 from the student arm of the YMCA. It has its roots in the Social Gospel movements of the late nineteenth and early twentieth centuries. Throughout its long and varied history, the SCM in Canada has sought to relate the Christian faith to the living realities of the social and political context of each student generation.

The present priorities are built around the need to form more and stronger critical Christian communities on Canadian campuses within which individuals may develop their social and political analyses and experience spiritual growth.

The Student Christian Movement of Canada is affiliated with the World Student Christian Federation.

Office: 736 Bathurst St., Toronto, Ontario. Tel. (416) 534-1352.

Women's Interchurch Council of Canada

The purpose of this organization is threefold: to assist, promote, and stimulate ecumenical experience through worship, fellowship, and work; to sponsor the observance of the World Day of Prayer and the Fellowship of the Least Coin in Canada; to encourage the establishment of local interchurch councils and committees.

Membership is composed of national women's organizations (or their counterparts) of the churches which confess the Lord Jesus Christ as God and Savior, who are each entitled to appoint up to six representatives to the Council. National Christian organizations invited by the Council may each appoint one member. Ecumenical groups across Canada are located in 6,000 centers.

Office: 77 Charles St., W., Toronto 181, Ontario. Tel. (416) 922-6177.

OFFICERS
Gen. Sec., Mrs. Doreen Place.
Asst. to the Gen. Sec., Mrs. Kathleen Hummeler.

Young Men's Christian Association in Canada

The first YMCA in Canada was established in Montreal, December 9, 1851, the declared purpose being "the improvement of the spiritual and mental condition of young men." Toronto and Halifax followed in 1853. At the centenary (1951) of the Canadian movement, YMCAs were found in all major cities from Halifax to Vancouver, with major programs for intellectual, spiritual, and physical development of Canadian youth.

Originally forming a single movement with the YMCAs in the United States, the Canadian Associations formed their own National Council in 1912. However, the international outreach (assisting in the establishment of YMCA movements in Latin America, Asia, and Africa) was administered jointly with the YMCA in the U.S. through an International Committee until 1970, when an agreement recognized the Canadian YMCA's independent, but coordinate, service abroad.

Headquarters: 2160 Yonge St., Toronto 7, Ontario. Tel. (416) 485-9447.

OFFICERS
Gen. Sec., Rix G. Rogers.
Exec. Sec. for World Service, Gordon S. Ramsay.

Young Women's Christian Association of Canada

The YWCA was founded in Canada in Saint John, New Brunswick, in 1870. Presently there are approximately 60 YWCAs in all provinces and in the Yukon and Northwest Territories, 28 of which are amalgamated with YMCAs. There are approximately 85,000 members.

Office: 571 Jarvis St., Toronto 5, Ontario. Tel. (416) 921-2117.

OFFICERS
Pres., Mrs. Philip Chadsey.
Interim Exec. Dir., Miss Jean Campbell.

3. RELIGIOUS BODIES IN THE UNITED STATES

Introduction

The following is a series of directories of United States religious bodies arranged alphabetically by official name. Individual denominational directories have been corrected by the religious bodies themselves. Those directories which have not been updated for this edition of the **Yearbook** by denominational officials carry the symbol (†) in front of the title of denomination.

Generally speaking, each directory listing follows the following organization: a historical or doctrinal statement; a brief statement of current statistics (data for 1972 or 1971), if any; information on general organization; officers; other organizations; and major periodicals.

More complete statistics will be found in the Statistical and Historical Section of this **Yearbook** in the table on Current and Non-Current Statistics and also in the table entitled "Some Statistics of Church Finances."

A listing of religious bodies by family groups (e.g., Baptists, Lutherans) is found at the end of this directory.

Advent Christian Church

A branch of the original Adventist group, composed of ministers and churches which withdrew from the American Millennial Association between 1854 and 1860, as a result of controversy over the question of immortality. As a corollary to their belief in conditional immortality, the group also held to the utter extinction of the wicked after the judgment. The General Conference was organized in 1860. In 1964 Life and Advent Union merged with this body.

GENERAL ORGANIZATION
General Conference: biennial. (Next meeting, 1974.)
Office: P.O. Box 23152, Charlotte, NC 28212, Rev. J. Howard Shaw, Exec. Sec. Tel. (704) 545-6161
Organizations and periodicals are all at this address unless otherwise noted.

OFFICERS
Pres., Rev. Joe Tom Tate, 138 W. 17th St., Jacksonville, FL 32206.
Sec., Rev. Joyce K. Thomas, 617 Bay Ave., Panama City, FL 32401.
Appalachian Vice-Pres., Rev. Clarence H. Du Bois, Jr., Rt. 1, Box 149, No. Tazewell, VA 24630.
Central Vice-Pres., Rev. Glendon A. Smith, Box 184, Chetek, WI 54728.
Eastern Vice-Pres., Rev. Carlyle B. Roberts, 4 Post Rd., Lenox, MA 01240.
Southern Vice-Pres., F. G. Scurry, Rt. 1, Saluda, SC 29138.
Western Vice-Pres., Rev. F. Earl Crouse, Sumas, WA 98295.

OTHER ORGANIZATIONS
The American Advent Mission Society: Exec. Sec., Rev. Joseph A. Baucom.
The Woman's Home & Foreign Mission Society: Exec. Sec., Mrs. Jean P. Balser.

PERIODICALS
The Advent Christian Witness (m), Rev. Nelson B. Melvin, Ed.
Advent Christian News (bi-w), Rev. Nelson B. Melvin, Ed.
Advent Christian Missions (m), Miss Myrtle L. Putnam, Ed.
Maranatha (q), Rev. Herbert H. Holland, Ed.

African Methodist Episcopal Church

This church began in 1787 in Philadelphia when persons in St. George's Methodist Episcopal Church withdrew as a protest against color segregation. In 1816 the denomination was started, led by Rev. Richard Allen, who had been ordained deacon by Bishop Asbury, and who was ordained elder and elected and consecrated bishop.

GENERAL ORGANIZATION
General Conference: quadrennial. (Next meeting, June 16, 1976.)

OFFICERS
Senior Bishop, Decatur Ward Nichols, 2522 Barhamvilly Rd., Columbia, SC 29204. New York Office: 2295 Seventh Ave., New York, NY 10030. Tel. (212) 926-4259.
Pres. of Bishops' Council, Bishop Harrison J. Bryant.
Sec. of Bishops' Council, H. I. Bearden.
Asst. Sec. of Bishops' Council, Hubert N. Robinson.
Chmn. of the General Board, Bishop H. Thomas Primm.
Sec. of the General Board of the A.M.E. Church, Rev. Russell S. Brown, 8348 S. Vernon Ave., Chicago, IL 60619.
Gen. Sec. of the A.M.E. Church, Rev. Russell S. Brown.
Treas., Joseph McKinney, 1541 14th St., N.W., Washington, DC 20005.
Historian, Dr. Howard D. Gregg, 1716 Varnum St., N.W., Washington, DC 20011.

OTHER ORGANIZATIONS
Board of Missions: Rev. John W. P. Collier, Jr., Hdqtrs: 475 Riverside Dr., New York, NY 10027.
Department of Education: 1461 Northgate Rd., Washington, DC 20012, Sec., Rev. S. L. Greene, Jr.
A.M.E. Sunday School Union: 414 8th Ave., S., Nashville, TN 37203, Sec.-Treas. Henry Belin, Sr.
A.M.E. Urban Ministry & Ecumenical Relations: 5151 Franklin Ave., Hollywood, CA 90027, Head, Bishop F. D. Jordan.
Bureau of Polity: 13855 Superior Rd., Forrest Park Tower, East Cleveland, OH 44118, Head, Bishop Joseph Gomez.
Board of Church Extension: Sec.-Treas., Rev.

AFRICAN METHODIST EPISCOPAL ZION CHURCH

F. C. Cummings, 3526 Dodier, St. Louis, MO 63107.

Division of Christian Education: 414 8th Ave. S., Nashville, TN 37203, Sec., Rev. Andrew White.

Evangelism: Dir., Rev. G. H. J. Thibodeaux, 1150 Portland Ave., Shreveport, LA 71103.

Woman's Missionary Society: 1541 14th St. N. W., Washington, DC 20005, Pres., Miss Mary E. Frizzell. Treas. Mrs. Octavia Dandridge, 905 N. Rodney St., Wilmington, DE 19806.

Pension Department: 414 8th Ave. S., Nashville, TN 37203, Sec.-Treas., Rev. J. M. Granberry.

Religious Literature: 414 8th Ave. S., Nashville, TN 37203, Rev. Therion E. Cobbs, Ed.-in-Chief.

PERIODICALS

Christian Recorder, 414 Eighth Ave. S., Nashville, TN 37203, Rev. B. J. Nolen, Ed.

A.M.E. Review, 468 Lincoln Dr., N.W., Atlanta, GA 30318, W. D. Johnson, Ed.

Voice of Missions (m), 475 Riverside Dr., Rm. 1926, New York, NY 10027, Rev. John W. P. Collier, Jr., Ed.

Woman's Missionary Recorder, 1023 N. 5th St., Birmingham AL 35204, Mrs. Hattie Witt Greene, Ed.

BISHOPS IN THE U.S.A.

First District: E. L. Hickman, 336 Pelham Rd., Philadelphia, PA 19119.

Second District: Henry W. Murph, 1239 Vermont Ave., Washington, DC 20005.

Third District: H. I. Bearden, 11009 Wade Park Ave., Cleveland, OH 44106.

Fourth District: H. Thomas Primm, 2820 Monaco Parkway, Denver, CO 80207.

Fifth District: Harrison J. Bryant, 2804 Sewell St., Kansas City, KS 66104.

Sixth District: R. A. Hildebrand, 171 Ashby St., S.W., Atlanta, GA 30314.

Seventh District: D. Ward Nichols, 2295 7th Ave., New York, NY 10030.

Eighth District: I.H. Bonner, 1937 Peniston St., New Orleans, LA 70115.

Ninth District: V. R. Anderson, 870 W. 6th St., Birmingham, AL 35204.

Tenth District: J. H. Adams, 225 Garrision St., Waco, TX 76704.

Eleventh District: H. N. Robinson, 1658 Kings Rd., Jacksonville, FL 32209.

Twelfth District: S. S. Morris, Jr., 2118 Cross St., Little Rock, AR 72206.

Thirteenth District: W. R. Wilkes, 1002 Kirkwood Ave., Nashville, TN 37203.

Special Assignment: Frederick D. Jordan, Urban and Ecumenical Affairs, 5151 Franklin Ave., Hollywood, CA 90027.

Location (Sick Leave): G. Wayman Blakely, 314 E. Montana St., Philadelphia, PA 19119.

Retired: Joseph Gomez, 11116 Wade Park Ave., Cleveland, OH 44106; O. L. Sherman, 2525 Chester, Little Rock, AR 72206.

African Methodist Episcopal Zion Church

The A.M.E. Zion Church is an independent body, having withdrawn from the John Street Methodist Church of New York City in 1796. The first bishop was James Varick.

GENERAL ORGANIZATION

General Conference: Quadrennial. (Next Meeting, May. 1976.)

OFFICERS

Pres., Board of Bishops, Bishop William M. Smith, 3753 Spring Hill Ave., Mobile, AL 36608.

Sec., Board of Bishops, Bishop Charles H. Foggie, 1200 Windermere Dr., Pittsburgh, PA 15218.

Gen. Sec.-Aud., Rev. R. H. Collins Lee, 1328 You St., N.W., Washington, DC 20009.

Fin. Sec., Richard W. Sherrill P.O. Box 1047, Charlotte, NC 28201.

OTHER AGENCIES

A.M.E. Zion Publishing House: Mr. Lem Long, Jr., Interim Mgr., P.O. Box 508, Charlotte, NC 28201.

Dept. of Foreign Missions: Rev. Harold A. L. Clement, Sec.-Editor, 475 Riverside Dr., Rm. 1910, New York, NY 10027.

Dept. of Home Missions, Pensions, and Relief: Rev. A.P. Morris, Sec.-Treas., P.O. Box 10143, Charlotte, NC 28201.

Dept. of Christian Education: Rev. G. L. Blackwell, Sec., 128 E. 58th St., Chicago, IL 60637.

Dept. of Church School Literature: Rev. Louis J. Baptiste, Ed., P.O. Box 10693, Charlotte, NC 28201.

Dept. of Church Extension: Mr. Lem Long, Jr., Sec.-Treas., P.O. Box 1047, Charlotte, NC 28201.

Dept. of Evangelism: Rev. J. Dallas Jenkins, Sr., Dir., 1328 You St., N.W., Washington, DC 20009.

Dept. of Public Health: Samuel C. Coleman, M.D., Dir., 126 Grove St., Hot Springs National Park, AR 71901.

Dept. of Public Relations: Alexander Barnes, Dir., 407 Columbia St., Durham, NC 27707.

Woman's Home and Foreign Missionary Society: Gen. Pres., Mrs. Willa Mae Rice, 7134 Upland St., Pittsburgh, PA 15208.

1st Vice Pres., Mrs. Mary G. Meeks, 8132 S. Sangamon St., Chicago, IL 60620.

2nd Vice Pres., Mrs. Elizabeth Michael, 724 S. 57th St., Philadelphia, PA 19139.

Exec. Sec., Mrs. Grace L. Holmes, 2526 Linden Ave., Knoxville, TN 37914.

Rec. Sec., Mrs. Ida Francis, 4633 15th Ave., Sacramento, CA 95820.

Treas., Miss Evelyn Harris, 215 W. ,147th St., New York, NY 10039.

Sec. of Young Women, Mrs. Maggie Beard, 1017 Leak St., Rockingham, NC 28379

Supt. of Buds of Promise, Mrs. Willie Heath Bobo, 400 Caulder Ave., Spartanburg, SC 29301.

Sec. of Supplies, Mrs. Josephine Morris, 2722 Bancroft St., Charlotte, NC 28216.

Chmn. Life Members Council, Mrs. Ann Walker, 3427 S. Kemper Rd., Arlington, VA 22206.

Editor, Woman's Column, The Missionary Seer, Mrs. Frealy Garrison, 1702 7th St., Perry, IA 50220.

PERIODICALS

Star of Zion (w), Rev. M. B. Robinson, Editor,

P.O. Box 1047, Charlotte, NC 28201.
Quarterly Review (q), Rev. David H. Bradley, Editor, P.O. Box 146, Bedford, PA 15522.
Missionary Seer. Rev. Harold A. L. Clement, Editor, 475 Riverside Dr., Rm. 1910, New York, NY 10027.
Church School Herald (q), Rev. Louis J. Baptiste, Editor, P.O. Box 10693, Charlotte, NC. 28201.

BISHOPS
First Episcopal Area:
Bishop Herbert Bell Shaw, 520 Red Cross St., Wilmington, NC 28401.
Second Episcopal Area:
Bishop William Milton Smith, 3753 Springhill Ave., Mobile, AL 36608.
Third Episcopal Area:
Bishop William Alexander Hilliard, 690 Chicago Blvd., Detroit, MI 48202.
Fourth Episcopal Area:
Bishop Alfred Gilbert Dunston, Jr., P.O. Box 19788, Philadelphia, PA ,19143.
Fifth Episcopal Area:
Bishop Charles Herbert Foggie, 1200 Windermere Dr., Pittsburgh, PA 15218.
Sixth Episcopal Area:
Bishop James Clinton Hoggard, 6401 Sunset La., Indianapolis, IN 46208.
Seventh Episcopal Area:
Bishop James W. Wactor, 709 Edgehill Rd., Fayetteville, NC 28302.
Eighth Episcopal Area:
Bishop Clinton R. Coleman, 3513 Ellamont Rd., Baltimore, MD 21215.
Ninth Episcopal Area:
Bishop Arthur Marshall, Jr., P.O. Box 41138, Ben Hill Sta., Atlanta, GA 30331.
Tenth Episcopal Area:
Bishop John H. Miller, 4588 W. Klest Blvd., Apt. 1100, Dallas, TX 75211.
Eleventh Episcopal Area:
Bishop George J. Leake, 508 Grandin Rd., Charlotte NC 28208.
Twelfth Episcopal Area:
Bishop Ruben L. Speaks, 305 Brookside Ave., Roosevelt, NY 11575.
Retired:
Bishop William Jacob Walls, 38 Aqueduct Pl., Yonkers. NY 10701.
Bishop Stephen Gill Spottswood, 1931 16th St., N. W., Washington, DC 20009.
Bishop William Andrew Stewart, 2314 20th St., N. W., Washington, DC 20009.
Bishop Charles Ewbank Tucker, 1715 Ormsby Ave., Louisville, KY 40210.
Bishop Joseph Dixon Cauthen, 2843 Princess Ann Rd., Norfolk, VA 23504.
Bishop Felix Sylvester Anderson, 741 S. 44th St., Louisville, KY 40211.

The African Orthodox Church

The African Orthodox Church was instituted in 1921 by Archbishop George Alexander McGuire as a unit of those churches of Christ adhering to the orthodox confession of faith.

GENERAL ORGANIZATION
Headquarters: 122 W. 129 St., New York, NY 10027.

AMANA CHURCH SOCIETY
OFFICERS
Primate Archbishop Metropolitan, Gladstone St. Clair Nurse.
Chancellor, Bishop G. Duncan Hinkson.
Gen. Sec., Ven. Archdeacon O. St. Clement Roett.
Fin. Sec., Rev. Canon Angel Vargas.
Treas., William W. Selkridge.
Historian, Rev. Courtenay C. Elcock.

Albanian Orthodox Archdiocese in America

A member of the autocephalous Orthodox Church in America, ministering to the Albanians in the United States of America.

Churches: 13. Inclusive Membership: 62,000. Sunday or Sabbath Schools: 13. Total Enrollment: 1,375. Ordained clergy: 23.

OFFICERS
Primate, Rt. Rev. Bishop Stephen V. Lasko, 523 E. Broadway, South Boston, MA 02127. Tel. (617) 268-1275; Archdiocesan Chancery, Tel. (617) 268-0267.
Sec., Rev. Arthur El. E. Liolin, 336 Billings Rd., Wollaston, MA 02170. Tel. (617) 479-4158.
Lay Chmn., Anthony Athanas, 75 Atlantic Ave., Swampscott, MA 01907.

PERIODICAL
The Vineyard (Vreshta), (q), Metropolitan Fan S. Noli Library, 529 East Broadway, South Boston, MA 02127.

Albanian Orthodox Diocese of America

This Diocese was organized in 1950 as a canonical body administering to the Albanian Faithful. It is under the ecclesiastical jurisdiction of the Ecumenical Patriarchate of Constantinople (Istanbul).
Churches: 10. Inclusive Membership: 5,100. Sunday or Sabbath Schools: 2. Total Enrollment: 108. Ordained clergy: 4.

GENERAL ORGANIZATION
Headquarters: 54 Burroughs St., Jamaica Plain, MA 02130. Tel. (617) 524-0477.

OFFICER
Diocese Council: Pres., His Grace Bishop Mark (Lipa).

PERIODICAL
The True Light (m), P.O. Box 18162, Sta. A, Boston, MA 02118.

Amana Church Society

Begun as the Community of True Inspiration in Hessen, Germany, in 1714. The group emigrated to America because of persecution in 1844, settling near Buffalo, N.Y., at Ebenezer. The Society then moved to Amana, Iowa, in 1854. The group is located in seven villages and is the only inspirationist movement of its kind in the world. Membership is placed at

23

AMERICAN BAPTIST ASSOCIATION

1,500, living in communal society until 1932 and now reorganized. The Elders conduct church services.

GENERAL ORGANIZATION
Board of Trustees

OFFICERS
Pres., Charles L. Selzer, Homestead, IA 52236.
Vice-Pres., Peter Stuck, Amana, IA 52203.
Sec., _____.
Treas., William F. Noe, Amana, IA 52203.

American Baptist Association

A fellowship of regular and independent missionary Baptist churches distributed throughout the United States, with their greatest strength in the South. Their national fellowship was formed in 1905.

Churches: 3,321. Inclusive Membership: 869,000. Sunday or Sabbath Schools: 3,336. Total Enrollment: 450,000. Ordained clergy: 3,368.

GENERAL ORGANIZATION
American Baptist Association Headquarters: 4605 N. State Line Ave., Texarkana, TX 75501. Tel. (214) 772-2783.

OFFICERS
Pres., Dr. L. Chester Guinn, 3524 Locust, Texarkana, AR 75501.
Vice-Pres., Dr. R. T. Perritt, Box 287, Marlow, OK 73055; Dr. James A. Kirkland, P.O. Box 262, Overton, TX 75684; Dr. Albert Garner, P.O. Box 3505, Lakeland, FL 33802.
Parliamentarian, Dr. C. N. Glover, Sheridan AR 72150.
Bus. Mgr., Publications, Dr. J. B. Powers, Box 1828, Texarkana, AR 75501.
Dir. Public Relations, Dr. I. K. Cross, P.O. Box 901, Texarkana, TX 75501.
Editor-in-Chief Publications, O. H. Griffith, Box 502, Texarkana, TX 75501.
Missionary-Treasurer, Dr. A. L. Patterson, Box 1050, Texarkana, TX 75501.

PERIODICALS
Missionary Baptist Searchlight (s-m), Box 663, Little Rock, AR 72203.
Baptist Monitor (s-m), Box 591, Henderson, TX 75652.
The Missionary (m), Box 5116, Nashville, TN 37206.
The Baptist Anchor (s-m), Box 1641, Lakeland, FL 33802.
The Missionary Baptist News, Box 123, Minden, LA 71055.
Baptist Sentinel, Box 848, Bellflower, CA 90706.
The Soul Winner, Box 8026, Shreveport, LA 71108.
The Baptist World, Box 425 Mabelvale, AR 72103.
The Baptist Review, Box 287, Marlow, OK 23055.
Illinois Missionary Baptist, 2101 Washington. Rd., Washington, IL 61571.
Missionary Baptist Herald, 2041 Wyda Way, Sacramento, CA 95825.

American Baptist Churches in the U.S.A.

Formerly known as the Northern Baptist Convention, this body of Baptist churches changed the name to American Baptist Convention at the annual meeting in Boston, May 24, 1950. The motion to change the name includes this statement, "affirming as we adopt the name American Baptist Convention that we hold the name in trust for all Christians of like faith and mind who desire to bear witness to the historic Baptist convictions in a framework of cooperative Protestantism." Although national missionary organizational developments began in 1814 with the establishment of the American Baptist Foreign Mission Society, the Convention was not formed until 1907. A new name, effective January 1, 1973, is American Baptist Churches in the U.S.A.

Churches: 6,035. Inclusive Membership: 1,562,-636. Sunday or Sabbath Schools: N.R. Total Enrollment: N.R. Ordained Clergy: 8,222.

GENERAL ORGANIZATION
American Baptist Convention: biennial.

OFFICERS
Pres., Rev. Gene E. Bartlett.
1st Vice-Pres., Mrs. C. R. W. Frost.
2nd Vice-Pres., Rev. Oscar Rodriguez.
National Offices: Valley Forge, PA 19481. Offices for some financial and technical services of the Convention and its national agencies are located at 475 Riverside Drive (17th Floor), New York, NY 10027.
Gen. Sec., Rev. Robert C. Campbell, Valley Forge, PA 19481.
  The General Secretary is the administrative officer of the Convention and serves as the coordinator. The Office of the General Secretary serves as a clearing house for all matters pertaining to denominational policy, and all correspondence should be addressed to the General Secretary.
Assoc. Gen. Secs.: James Christison, Rev. Walter B. Hoard, Rev. Chester J. Jump, Jr., Rev. W. Hubert Porter, Rev. Harold W. Richardson, Rev. Dean R. Wright.
Budget Adviser, Rev. Newton E. Woodbury, Valley Forge, PA 19481.
Treas., Milton W. Bennett, 3455 Chapel Court, Toledo, OH 43615.

GENERAL STAFF DIVISIONS
World Mission Support, Valley Forge, PA 194-81; Exec. Dir., Rev. Ralph R. Rott; Assoc. Exec. Dir., Rev. Joseph O. Bass; Assoc. Dir., Rev. Joseph D. Burnett; Assoc. Dir., Rev. Raymond Weigum; Dir. Field Activities, Rev. Haakon Knudsen; Dir. American Baptist Films, Edmund C. Shaw.
Program Planning, Valley Forge, PA 19481: Acting Exec. Dir., Rev. Frank E. Johnston.
Communication, Valley Forge, PA 19481: Exec. Dir., Rev. R. D. Goodwin; Ed. of the American Baptist Magazine and Input, Rev. Norman R. DePuy; American Baptist News Service, Rev. Frank A. Sharp; Home Missions Media Dir., Rev. Victor Tupitza; Asst. H. M. Media Dir., Carol Jean Stifler; Electronic Media, Rev. William K. Waterston.
Management and Organization, Valley Forge,

PA 19481; Assoc. Exec. Dir., Donald W. Brown.

Archives and History (American Baptist Historical Society), 1106 S. Goodman St., Rochester, NY 14620; Curator, Rev. E. C. Starr, Rochester, NY 14620; Pres., Rev. Joseph R. Sweeny, 819 Massachusetts Ave.. Arlington, MA 02174; Vice-Pres., Rev. Eldon G. Ernst, 2606 Dwight Way, Berkeley CA 94704; Sec., Rev. Melvin Phillips, First Baptist Church, 358 E. Fifth St., Jamestown, NY 14701.

Men's Work (American Baptist Men), Valley Forge, PA 19481: Exec. Dir.. W. Burton Andrews; Pres., Henry G. Nylander, 5669 Amy Dr., Oakland, CA 94618; Treas., Rathuel L. McCollum, 16512 Invermere Ave., Cleveland, OH 44128.

Women's Work (American Baptist Women,) Valley Forge, PA 19481: Exec. Dir., Miss Violet E. Rudd; Pres., Mrs. James H. Burns, 424-A Whitehall Rd., Alameda, CA 94501; Treas., Mrs. Nicholas Titus, 30 Blackman Pl., Bridgeport, CT 06604.

Cooperative Christianity, Valley Forge, PA 19-481: Exec. Dir., Rev. Robert G. Torbet.

Committee on World Relief, Valley Forge, PA 19481: Sec., Rev. W. Hubert Porter.

Christian Social Concern, Valley Forge, PA 19481: Exec. Dir., Rev. Elizabeth Miller; Department of International Affairs, 777 United Nations Plaza, New York, NY 10017; Department of Governmental Relations, 110 Maryland Ave., N.E., Washington, DC 20002.

OTHER ORGANIZATIONS

American Baptist Foreign Mission Society: Office, Valley Forge, PA 19481: Pres., Mrs. John Sparrowk, 1 Camanche Pkwy., No., Rt. 1, Box 218, Ione, CA 95640; Vice-Pres., Rev. Modesto Lopez, 1713 W. Montrose Ave., Chicago, IL 60613; Rec. Sec. Rev. Lloyd G. James; Treas., William E. Jarvis; Gen. Sec., Rev. Chester J. Jump, Jr.; Gen. Adm. Assoc., Rev. Barry L. Hopkins; Admin. Asst. (Budget), Rev. Lloyd G. James, Admin. Asst., Rev. Dean R. Kirkwood; *Overseas Division* Sec., Rev. James L. Sprigg; Regional Representatives: Zaire, Europe, Nigeria, Rev. Roland G. Metzger; East Asia (Japan, Okinawa, Philippines, Malaysia-Singapore, Indonesia), Rev. Russell E. Brown; South Asia (Bengal-Orissa-Bihar, Burma, North East India. South India), Rev. R. W. Beaver; Thailand, Hong Kong, Vietnam, Rev. R. G. Johnson; Overseas Program Assoc., Mrs. Marcus Paw; Assoc. Sec., Miss Lillian M. Robertson; Missionary Personnel Sec., Rev. R. G. Beers: *Public Relations Division*, Sec. Rev. Richard Cummings; Adm. Assoc., Rev. Clayton F. Smith; Assoc. Secretaries: Rev. Robert F. DeLano, Rev. Mrs. F. W. (Helen) Powers; *Business and Finance Division:* Treas. and Business Mgr., W. E. Jarvis; Assoc. Sec. and Assoc. Treas., Walter C. Konrath; Assoc. Sec. (Chief Accountant), Austin Windle; Assoc. Sec., (Overseas Property), Rev. Lloyd G. James.

The American Baptist Home Mission Society and Woman's American Baptist Home Mission Society: Office, Valley Forge, PA 19481: Pres., Rev. Jeanie K. Sherman, Timber Lake, SD 57656; Vice-Pres. (Eastern), Mrs. Leo

R. Murphy, Syracuse, NY 13210; (Central), Ashley T. McCarter, Worthington, OH 430-85; (Western), Rev. Samuel McKinney, Seattle, WA 98122; Exec. Sec., James A. Christison; Rec. Sec., Rev. Paul O. Madsen; Assoc. Exec. Secs., Rev. Paul O. Madsen; Rev. Jitsuo Morikawa; Deputy Exec. Secs., Rev. Atha J. Baugh and Rev. Lincoln B. Wadsworth; Treas., Horace W. Gale; Sec., Parish Development, Rev. Harvey A. Everett; Sec., Missions, Rev. Wilbur Larson; Sec., Chaplaincy Services, Rev. Charles F. Wills; Acting Sec., Social Action, Rev. Atha J. Baugh; Western Rep., Paul L. Sturges, Redlands, CA 92373; Treas., Separate Corporations, Alois L. Rutz.

American Baptist Extension Corporation: Office, Valley Forge, PA 19481: Pres., Rev. Wesley Dixon.

American Baptist Management Corporation: Office, Valley Forge, PA 19481: Pres., Rev. Ray L. Schroder.

American Baptist Personnel Services: Office, Valley Forge, PA 19481: Dir., Rev. Richard L. Waltz.

American Baptist Service Corporation: Office, Valley Forge, PA 19481: Pres., Rev. H. John Vanderbeck.

American Baptist Homes and Hospitals Association: Office, Valley Forge, PA 19481: Pres., Rev. Harold Davis, Phoenix, AR; Sec.-Treas., Rev. Ray L. Schroder, Valley Forge, PA 19481.

Committee on Chaplains: Office, Valley Forge, PA 19481: Cor. Sec., Rev. Charles Wills.

American Baptist Board of Education and Publication, including Judson Press and Judson Book Stores: Office, Valley Forge, PA 19481: Pres., Mrs. Henry H. Mitchell, Rochester, NY 14620; Vice-Pres., J. Lee Westrate, Arlington, VA 22213; Rec. Sec., W. Z. McLear, Philadelphia, PA 19100; Exec. Sec., Rev. Harold W. Richardson; Treas., Paul Moore; Heads of Divisions: Educational Ministries, Rev. Grant W. Hanson; Publishing & Business, Peter A. Jensh; Christian Higher Education, Rev. Robert Evan Davis.

The American Baptist Assembly (national conference center), Green Lake, WI 54941: Pres., Arthur L. Brandon, Lewisburg, PA 17837 Exec. Sec., Rev. Harold W. Richardson; Resident Dir., Rev. J. E. Dollar; Operations Director, Gerard J. Van Leeuwen; Accounting Director, L. B. Standifer; Housing Director, Frances Lamb; Program Director, Rev. William R. Nelson; Personnel Director, Rev. Patrick Murphy, Green Lake, WI 54941; Treas., Robert L. Johnson, Detroit, MI 48103.

The Ministers and Missionaries Benefit Board: Office, 475 Riverside Dr. (17th Fl.), New York, NY 10027: Pres., Dr. John W. Reed; Vice-Pres., Colonel Oliver J. Troster; Actuaries, Huggins & Company, 1401 Walnut St., Philadelphia, PA 19102; Exec. Dir., Rev. Dean R. Wright; Treas., Malcolm R. Cary; Rec. Sec. and Mortgage Officer, Frank L. Taylor; Assoc. Dir., Rev. William T. McKee; Assoc. Dir., Southern Region, Rev. J. Martin England; Regional Dir., East, Rev. Richard Arnesman; Regional Dir., West, Rev. Terry L. Burch.

AMERICAN BAPTIST CHURCHES IN THE U.S.A.

Ministers Council: Pres., Rev. Robert E. Shaw, 75th & Roe, Prairie Village, KS 66208; Vice-Pres. (New England), Ms. Phyllis L. Benner, Box 396, North Stratford, NH 03590; (Mid-Atlantic), Rev. William E. Deichler, 124 Main St., Brockport, NY 14420; (Great Lakes), Rev. John Carver, 7th and Broadway, Quincy, IL 62301; (Central), Rev. Richard C. Buckler, Box 231, Clarks Grove, MN 56016; (Western), Rev. William H. Goddard, 75 N. Marengo Ave., Pasadena, CA 91101; Treas., Rev. Gordon Kurtz, 51 S. Third St., Lewisburg, PA 17837; Exec. Dir., Rev. Charles N. Forsberg, Valley Forge, PA 19481; Sec., O. Dean Nelson, 161 E. Freeway Dr., E. Orange, NJ 07018.

REGIONAL/STATE CONVENTIONS

Connecticut—Rev. Orlando L. Tibbetts, 100 Bloomfield Ave., Hartford 06105.

Delaware—(see Pennsylvania).

District of Columbia—Rev. James A. Langley, 1628 16th St., N.W., Washington 20009.

Great Rivers Region—Rev. Albert J. Gernenz, P.O. Box 3786, Springfield, IL 62705.

Indiana—Rev. Dallas J. West, 1350 N. Delaware St., Indianapolis 46202.

Kansas—Rev. William K. Cober, 1001 Gage Blvd., Topeka 66604.

Maine—Rev. Elmer N. Bentley, 107 Winthrop St., Augusta 04330.

Massachusetts—Rev. Ellis J. Holt, 88 Tremont St., Room 500, Boston 02108.

Michigan—Rev. Arthur L. Farrell, P.O. Box 126, Lansing 48901.

Mid-American—Rev. Harry E. Coulter, 2913 Ingersoll Ave., Des Moines, IA 50312.

Nebraska—Rev. Allan R. Knight, 6403 Maple St., Omaha 68104.

New Hampshire—Rev. Raymond F. Smith, P. O. Box 796, Concord 03301.

New Jersey—Rev. Joseph H. Heartberg, 161 Freeway Dr. East, East Orange 07018.

New York—Rev. Harrison E. Williams, 3049 East Genesee St., Syracuse 13224.

North Dakota—(see South Dakota).

Northwest—Rev. E. Wayne Roberts, 1415 N.E. 45th St., Seattle, WA 98105.

Ohio—Rev. Joseph I. Chapman, P.O. Box 386, Granville 43023.

Oregon—Rev. Glenn E. Camper, 0245 S.W. Bancroft St., Portland 97201.

Pacific Southwest—Rev. A. George Downing, 816 S. Figueroa St., Los Angeles, CA 90017.

Pennsylvania—Rev. R. Eugene Crow, Valley Forge 19481.

Puerto Rico—Rev. Luis Fidel Mercado, Apartado 1283, Hato Rey, 00919.

Rhode Island—Rev. W. Eugene Motter, 2 Stimson Ave., Providence 02906.

Rocky Mountains—Rev. James Havens, 1344 Pennsylvania St., Denver, CO 80203.

South Dakota—Rev. Ralph T. Cobb, 1524 South Summit Ave., Sioux Falls 57105.

South—Rev. E.B. Hicks, Ste. 936, Citizens Trust Bldg., 75 Piedmont Ave., N.E., Atlanta, GA 30303.

Vermont—Rev. Otto Nallinger, 19 Orchard Terr., Burlington 05401.

West—Rev. Robert Rasmussen, P.O. Box 23204, Oakland, CA 94623.

West Virginia—P.O. Box 1019, Parkersburg 26101.

Wisconsin—Rev. Chris E. Lawson, 15330 West Watertown Plank Rd., Elm Grove 53122.

CITY SOCIETY OFFICES

Chicago—Rev. Russell S. Orr (interim), 19 South LaSalle St. 60603.

Cleveland—Rev. M. Parker Burroughs, 2246 Euclid Ave. 44115.

Indianapolis—Rev. Ralph Beaty, 1350 N. Delaware St. 46202.

Los Angeles—Rev. Arnold S. Boal, 427 W. Fifth St., Ste. 500, 90013.

Rochester—Rev. Hugh Q. Morton, 175 Genesee St. 14611.

New York—Rev. Angus Hull, 297 Park Ave., S. 10010.

Niagara Frontier—Rev. Edward L. Gunther, 1272 Delaware Ave., Buffalo 14209.

Philadelphia—Rev. William L. Johnston, 33 S. 17th St. 19103.

Pittsburgh—Rev. Carlton B. Goodwin, 507 Investment Bldg., 239 Fourth Ave. 15222.

PERIODICALS

American Baptist (m), Valley Forge, PA 194-81. Rev. Norman R. De Puy, Ed.

The Baptist Leader (m), Valley Forge, PA 19481. Miss Vincie Alessi, Ed.

The Secret Place (q), Valley Forge, PA. 19481. Miss Vincie Alessi and Herschell H. Richmond, Eds.

Foundations (q), Rochester, NY 14620. Rev. John Skoglund, Ed.

The American Carpatho-Russian Orthodox Greek Catholic Church

The American Carpatho-Russian Orthodox Greek Catholic Church is a self-governing diocese that is in communion with the Ecumenical Patriarchate of Constantinople. The late Patriarch Benjamin I, in an official Patriarchal Document listed as No. 1379 and dated September 19, 1938, canonized the Diocese in the name of the Orthodox Church of Christ.

Churches: 70. Inclusive Membership: 108,000. Sunday or Sabbath Schools: 56. Total Enrollment: 5,098. Ordained clergy 67.

GENERAL ORGANIZATION

Sobor: quadrennial (Next Sobor, 1974).

Headquarters: Johnstown, PA 15906. Tel. (814) 536-4207.

OFFICERS

Bishop: His Eminence, The Most Rev. Metropolitan Orestes P. Chornock, 2302 Nichols Ave., Stratford, CT 06497.

Coadjutor Bishop: His Excellency, The Most Rev. John R. Martin, 312 Garfield St., Johnstown, PA 15906.

Vicar General: Rt. Rev. Mitred Peter E. Molchany, 903 Ann St., Homestead, PA 15120.

Chancellor: Very Rev. Msgr. John Yurcisin, 249 Butler Ave., Johnstown, PA 15906.

Treas.: Very Rev. Michael Slovesko, 810 Somerset Ave., Windber, PA 15963.

PERIODICAL

Cerkovny Vistnik—Church Messenger (bi-w), 145 Broad St., Perth Amboy, NJ 15963. Very Rev. Msgr. Stephen Sedor, Ed.

The American Catholic Church, Archdiocese of New York

This body derives its orders from the Syrian Church of Antioch, commonly called the Jacobite Apostolic Church. Its doctrines are, with few exceptions, those held by the Old Catholic Church in Europe.

Churches: 16. Inclusive Membership: 3,435. Sunday or Sabbath Schools: 16. Total Enrollment: 450. Ordained clergy: N.R.

OFFICERS
Primate, Most Rev. James Francis Augustine Lashley, 457 W. 144th St., New York, NY 10031. Bishop Sidney Ferguson, 116 W. 133rd St., New York, NY 10030.

The American Catholic Church (Syro-Antiochian)

This body derives its orders from the Syrian Patriarch of Antioch, commonly called the Jacobite Apostolic Church. Organized in 1915, it is Catholic in worship and discipline and uses Roman Catholic liturgy in the administration of the seven Sacraments. The church is a self-governed American body, however.

Churches: 5. Inclusive Membership: 1,090. Sunday or Sabbath Schools: 1. Total Enrollment: 37. Ordained Clergy: 9.

GENERAL ORGANIZATION
Synod, meeting: biennially, first Sunday in September.
Headquarters: St. Peter's Cathedral, 1811 N.W. 4th Court, Miami, FL 33136.

OFFICERS
Pres., The Most Rev. Archbishop Herbert F. Wilkie, St. Mary Magdalene Catholic Church, 189 Lenox Ave., New York, NY 10027.
Vice-Pres. and Chancellor, Most Rev. Joseph M. Nevilloyd, Sacred Heart of Jesus Church, 15A Hull St., Brooklyn, NY 11233.
Sec. Gen., Most Rev. F. A. C. Dalrymple, St. Francis Oratory, 163 Grafton St., Brooklyn, NY 11212.
Treas., Rev. Ronald St. John Wood, 700 E. New York Ave., Brooklyn, NY 11203.

American Evangelical Christian Churches

Founded in 1944, the A.E.C.C. functions as a denominational body with interdoctrinal views incorporating into its ecclesiastical position both the Calvinistic and Arminian doctrines. Its churches operate under the name of Community Churches, American Bible Churches, and Evangelical Christian Churches.

Headquarters: 192 N. Clark St., Chicago, IL 60601.

OFFICERS
Mod., Dr. G. W. Hyatt, 192 N. Clark St., Chicago, IL 60601.
Sec., Dr. Ben Morgan, 64 South St., Southport, IN 46227.

THE AMERICAN LUTHERAN CHURCH

The American Lutheran Church

This body was organized during a constituting convention at Minneapolis, Minn., April 22-24, 1960. It combined the following three church bodies: American Lutheran Church (ALC), The Evangelical Lutheran Church (ELC), and United Evangelical Lutheran Church (UELC).

The union brought together, for the first time this century, major Lutheran church bodies of different national heritage—German (ALC), Norwegian (ELC), Danish (UELC). National offices of the new church were established beginning January 1, 1961, at Minneapolis. Former headquarters of ALC at Columbus, Ohio, and UELC at Blair, Neb., were discontinued.

On February 1, 1963, the Lutheran Free Church (LFC) merged with The American Lutheran Church.

Churches: 4,823. Inclusive Membership: 2,521,-930. Sunday or Sabbath Schools: 4,556. Total Enrollment: 731,219. Ordained clergy: 6,169.

GENERAL ORGANIZATION
Convention: biennial. (Next meeting, 1974).
National Offices: 422 S. 5th St., Minneapolis, MN 55415. Tel. (612) 338-3821.

OFFICERS
Pres., _____
Vice-Pres., Rev. David W. Preus.
Sec., Arnold R. Mickelson.
Treas., N. Burdette Nelson.

OTHER ORGANIZATIONS
Board of Trustees: Chmn., Elmer Abrahamson; Exec. Sec., Rev. George S. Schultz.
Board of American Missions: Chmn., Rev. James R. Long; Exec. Dir., Rev. John R. Houck.
Board of World Missions: Acting Chmn., Rev. Lawrence M. Gudmestad; Exec. Dir., Rev. Morris A. Sorenson, Jr.
Board of Theological Education: Chmn., Rev. Albert R. Schmidt; Exec. Dir., Dr. Walter F. Wietzke.
Board of College Education: Chmn., Charles R. Bruning; Exec. Dir., Norman D. Fintel.
Board of Parish Education: Chmn., Dr. John E. Quam; Exec. Dir., Rev. C. Richard Evenson.
Board of Youth Activity: Chmn., Rev. Reginald H. Holle; Exec. Dir., Raymond G. Johnson.
Board of Publication: Chmn., Rev. William D. Streng; Exec. Dir., Albert E. Anderson.
Board of Social Service: Chmn., Rev. Paul G. Sonnack; Exec. Dir., Rev. Paul Boe.
Board of Pensions: Chmn., Mr. Herbert C. Hansen; Exec. Dir., Rev. George H. Berkheimer.
Commission on Evangelism: Chmn., Rev. L. J. Satre; Exec. Dir., Rev. Jack Hustad.
Commission on Church and Society: Chmn., Rev. Benjamin A. Gjenvick; Exec. Dir., Carl F. Reuss.
Commission on Worship: Chmn., Rev. Alf Romstad; Exec. Dir., Rev. M. A. Egge.
Commission on Public Communication: Chmn., Rev. A. C. Schumacher; Exec. Dir., Rev. Lester F. Heins.
Board of American Lutheran Church Women:

AMERICAN RESCUE WORKERS

Pres., Mrs. Margaret Bauman; Exec. Dir., Miss Arna Mjaa.
Board of American Lutheran Church Men: Pres., Mr. Virgil Anderson; Exec. Dir., W. Herbert Kent.
Board of the Luther League: Pres., Tim Nelsen; Exec. Dir., Raymond G. Johnson.

PERIODICAL
(Published at 426 S. 5th St., Minneapolis, MN 55415.)
The Lutheran Standard (bi-m), Rev. George H. Muedeking, Editor.

American Rescue Workers

A movement formed in 1896 as an evangelistic home-missionary and non-sectarian church, military in form of organization.
Churches: 46. Inclusive Membership: 5,410. Sunday or Sabbath Schools: 36. Total Enrollment: 9,226. Ordained clergy: 53.

GENERAL ORGANIZATION
Council: annual.
Headquarters: 2827 Frankford Ave., Philadelphia, PA 19134.
Commander-In-Chief, Sara Jane Ives; Pres., Natl. Board of Managers: Brig.-General Helen Gossett; Vice-Pres., Brig.-General Charles E. Dolbow (Chief-of-Staff); Natl. Sec., S. J. Ives.

PERIODICAL
The Rescue Herald (m), 2827 Frankford Ave., Philadelphia, PA 19134, Adjutant Charles Dederick, Ed.

The Anglican Orthodox Church

This body was founded on November 16, 1963, in Statesville, North Carolina, by the Most Rev. James P. Dees who is the Presiding Bishop. The church holds to 39 Articles of Religion, the 1928 Prayerbook, the King James Version of the Bible, and basic Anglican traditions and church government.

Churches: 38. Inclusive Membership: 2,500. Sunday or Sabbath Schools: 35. Total Enrollment: N.R. Ordained clergy: 19.

GENERAL ORGANIZATION
General Convention: biennial. Next meeting, 1974.

OFFICER
Presiding Bishop, The Most Rev. James Parker Dees, 323 E. Walnut St., Statesville, NC 28677. Tel. (704) 873-8365.

Antiochian Orthodox Archdiocese of Toledo, Ohio and Dependencies in N.A.

This body is a constituent part of the Eastern Orthodox Church, and functions by virtue of a Praxis issued by the Patriarch of Antioch and a charter granted by the State of Ohio. The Archdiocese was established in 1936, when the first Archbishop of Toledo was consecrated.

Churches: 16. Inclusive Membership: 30,000. Sunday or Sabbath Schools: 12. Total Enrollment: N.R. Ordained Clergy: 26.

GENERAL ORGANIZATION
Conference: annual
Headquarters: 532 Bush St., Toledo, OH 43604.

OFFICERS
Metropolitan Michael Shaheen, Archbishop, 532 Bush St., Toledo, OH; Vicar Gen. of the Archdiocese, Very Rev. Raphael Husson, 223 Goshorn, Charleston, WV; Chancellor for U.S., Very Rev. John Estephan, 1413 Alexander, S.E., Grand Rapids, MI 49506.

PERIODICAL
Archdiocesan Messenger (m), Very Rev. John Estephan, Ed.

The Antiochian Orthodox Christian Archdiocese of New York and All North America

(formerly Syrian Antiochian Orthodox Archdiocese of New York & N. A.)

This body is a member of the Orthodox Church which is under the jurisdiction of the Patriarch of Antioch. It is a member of the Standing Conference of Canonical Orthodox Bishops in America. The Western Rite Vicariate was established in 1961.

GENERAL ORGANIZATION
General Convention: annual.
Headquarters: 358 Mountain Rd., Englewood, NJ 07631. Tel. (201) 871-1355.

OFFICERS
Metropolitan Archbishop, Metropolitan Philip (Saliba); Administrator of Western Rite, Very Rev. W. S. Schneirla.

Apostolic Christian Church (Nazarean)

This body was formed in America by an immigration from various European nations, from a movement begun by Rev. S. H. Froehlich, a Swiss pastor, whose followers are still found in Switzerland and Central Europe.

Churches: 43. Inclusive Membership: 4,000. Sunday or Sabbath Schools: 39. Total Enrollment: 1,575. Ordained clergy: N.R.

OFFICERS
Apostolic Christian Church Foundation, P.O. Box 5233, Akron, OH 44313, Gen. Sec., Fred J. Tiffan, P.O. Box 5233, Akron, OH 44313. Tel. (216) 644-6587.

Apostolic Christian Churches of America

A body founded about 1847 by Benedict Weyeneth. It is a holiness body with a very informal organization in the U.S.
Churches: 77. Inclusive Membership: 9,160. Sunday or Sabbath Schools: 77. Total Enrollment: 8,950. Ordained clergy: 273.

CORRESPONDENT

Elder, Roy L. Sauder, 3528 N. Linden Lane, Peoria, IL 61604. Tel. (309) 685-0113.

The Apostolic Faith

This body organized in 1907 in Portland, Oregon, is a trinitarian fundamental evangelistic organization. It is Presbyterian in form of government and embraces original Wesleyan teaching of holiness and the Baptism of the Holy Ghost.

Churches: 44. Inclusive Membership: 4,020. Sunday or Sabbath Schools: 44. Total Enrollment: 6,380. Ordained clergy: 75.

GENERAL ORGANIZATION

Convention: annual (July).
Headquarters: Northwest Sixth and Burnside, Portland, OR 97209. Tel. (503)222-9761.

OFFICER

Gen. Overseer, Rev. Loyce C. Carver; 2 N.W. Sixth Ave., Portland, OR 97209.

PERIODICAL

The Light of Hope (bi-m), 2 N.W. Sixth Ave., Portland, OR 97209. Rev. Loyce C. Carver, Ed.

Apostolic Lutheran Church of America

A Finnish body, organized in 1872, under the name of Solomon Korteniemi Lutheran Society. In 1929 the body was incorporated as the Finnish Apostolic Lutheran Church of America. In 1962 the name was changed as above.

GENERAL ORGANIZATION

Meets annually in June.

OFFICERS

Pres., Rev. Andrew Mickelsen, Star Route, Houghton, MI 49931.
Sec., James Johnson, R. 2, Box 99, L'Anse, MI. 49946.
Treas., Fred Tormala, U.S. 41, Chassell, MI 49916.
Statistician, Edwin Reini, Rt. 2, Box 87, Ironwood, MI 49938.

PERIODICAL

Christian Monthly (m), Apostolic Lutheran Book Concern, Rt. 1, Box 150, New York Mills, MN 56567, Helmi Kivisto, Ed., 1001 W. Old Hwy. 61, Proctor, MN 55810.

Apostolic Overcoming Holy Church of God

A Negro body incorporated in Alabama in 1919. It is evangelistic in purpose and emphasizes sanctification, holiness, and divine healing.

OFFICERS

Bishop W. T. Phillips, 2212 Tonlours Dr., Mobile, AL 36617.
Bishop Jasper Roby, 514 10th Ave., W., Birmingham, AL 35204.
Bishop C. R. Harris, 741 E. Bowen Ave., Chicago, IL 60653.

Bishop G. W. Ayers, 1822 Shasta St., Richmond, CA 94804.
Bishop L. M. Bell, 2000 Pio Nono Ave., Macon, GA 31206.
Bishop R. F. Sheriff, 6126 S. Carpenter St., Chicago, IL 60621.
Bishop E. D. Moore, 1540 E. 70th St., Cleveland, OH 44103.
Bishop Gabriel Crutcher, 526 E. Bethune St., Detroit, MI 48202.
Bishop M. L. Lilly, 1633 Castleberry Way, Birmingham, AL 35204.
Bishop F. Lamar, 292 Marion St., Brooklyn, NY 11233.
Sec., Mrs. Juanita R. Arrington, 514 10th Ave., W., Birmingham, AL 35204.
Asst. Sec., Mrs. Sadie R. Lancaster, 1321 Adams St., Mobile, AL 36603.

Armenian Apostolic Church of America

Widespread movement of the Armenian people over the centuries caused the development of two seats of religious jurisdiction of the Armenian Apostolic Church in the World: the See of Etchmiadzin, now in Soviet Armenia, and the See of Cilicia, in Lebanon.

In America, the Armenian Church functioned under the jurisdiction of the Etchmiadzin See from 1887 to 1933, when a division occurred within the American diocese over the condition of the church in Soviet Armenia. One group chose to remain independent until 1957, when the Holy See of Cilicia agreed to accept them under its jurisdiction.

Despite the existence of two dioceses in North America, the Armenian Church has always functioned as one church in dogma and liturgy.

Churches: 29. Inclusive Membership: 125,000. Sunday or Sabbath Schools: 29. Total Enrollment: 2,550. Ordained clergy: 34.

GENERAL ORGANIZATION

National Representative Assembly: annual.
Headquarters: 777 United Nations Plaza, New York, NY 10017. Tel. (212) 682-6850.

OFFICERS

Prelate, Archbishop Hrant Khatchadourian.
Vicar-General, The Very Rev. Yervant Apelian.
Vicar in California, Very Rev. Sumbat Lapajian, Holy Cross Armenian Apostolic Church, 420 E. 20th St., Los Angeles, CA 90011.

PERIODICAL

Cilicia (q), Ed. Bd.: The Very Rev. Yervant Apelian; Archak Sahakian, Ed.

Armenian Church of North America, Diocese of the (Including Diocese of California)

The ancient Church of Armenia was established permanently in North America in 1889, when Armenian immigrants built the first Armenian church in the new world in Worcester, Mass. In 1898, with the establishment of the Diocese of North America, the western hemi-

ASSEMBLIES OF GOD

sphere passed into the jurisdiction of the Holy See in Etchmiadzin, Armenia.

In 1927, as a result of the growth of the communities in California, the churches and parishes there were formed into a separate Western diocese.

Churches: 62. Inclusive Membership: 300,000. Sunday or Sabbath Schools: 90. Total Enrollment: 8,000 Ordained clergy: 71.

GENERAL ORGANIZATION

Eastern Diocese of the Armenian Church of North America (excluding California)
Diocesan Assembly: Annual.
Diocesan offices: 630 Second Ave., New York, NY 10016. Tel. (212) 686-0710.

OFFICERS

Primate, Most Rev. Archbishop Torkom Manoogian, 630 Second Ave., New York, NY 10016.
Chmn., Diocesan Council, Mr. Crosby M. Goshgarian, 64 Mooreland Rd., Melrose, MA 02176.
Sec., Diocesan Council, Very Rev. Zaven Arzoomanian, 6642 N. 4th St., Philadelphia, PA 19126.
Canon Sacrist, St. Vartan Cathedral, Rev. Mampre Kouzouian, 630 Second Ave., New York, NY 10016.

Western Diocese
Diocesan Assembly: Annual.
Diocesan offices: 821 S. Crenshaw Blvd., Los Angeles, CA 90005. Tel. (213) 939-4443.

OFFICERS

Primate, Rt. Rev. Bishop Vatche Hovsepian, 821 S. Crenshaw Blvd., Los Angeles, CA 90005.
Chmn., Diocesan Council, Very Rev. Dirayr Dervishian, 700 S. La Verne Ave., Los Angeles, CA 90022.
Sec., Diocesan Council, Rev. Shahe Semerjian, 17231 Sherman Way, Van Nuys, CA 92406.

PERIODICALS FOR BOTH DIOCESES

The Armenian Church (m), 630 Second Ave., New York, NY 10016.
Hayastanyaitz Yegeghetzy (m) in Armenian, 630 Second Ave., New York, NY 10016.

Assemblies of God

A Pentecostal, evangelical, missionary denomination which grew out of the spiritual revivals of the early 1900's. The organization is composed of self-governing churches which constitute 47 districts and seven foreign language branches. Churches are located in every state of the U.S. and 82 countries of the world. The founding meeting was in Hot Springs, Arkansas, April 2-12, 1914.

Churches: 8,799. Inclusive Membership: 1,078,-332. Sunday or Sabbath Schools: 9,200. Total Enrollment: 1,078,332. Ordained clergy: 12,-037.

GENERAL ORGANIZATION

General Council: biennial. (Miami Beach, Florida, Aug. 16-21, 1973).
International Headquarters: 1445 Boonville Ave., Springfield, MO 65802. Tel. (417) 862-2781.

EXECUTIVE PRESBYTERY

The 13-member Executive Presbytery includes the following:
Resident Executive Presbyters (All of Springfield, Missouri), Gen. Supt.: Thomas F. Zimmerman; Asst. Supt. G. Raymond Carlson.
Gen. Sec.: Bartlett Peterson.
Gen. Treas.: Martin B. Netzel.
Exec. Dir., Foreign Missions: J. Philip Hogan.
Non-Resident Executive Presbyters: Great Lakes: Richard W. Dorth, P.O. Box 323, Carlinville, IL 62626; Gulf: James E. Hamill, P.O. Box 11434, Memphis, TN 38111; North Central: Roy Wead, 1013 James Ave., N., Jamestown, ND, 48301; Northeast: Joseph R. Flower, Colvin Sta., P.O. Box 1, Syracuse, NY 13205; Northwest: N. D. Davidson, P.O. Box 9038, Salem, OR 97305; South Central: Paul Lowenberg, 1009 S. Broadway, Wichita, KS 67211; Southeast: Edgar Bethany, 582 Lakeshore Dr., N.E., Atlanta, GA 30307; Southwest: Dwight H. McLaughlin, 44817 N.E. Fifth St., Lancaster, CA 93534.

INTERNATIONAL HEADQUARTERS

All departmental offices are at Assemblies of God International Headquarters, 1445 Boonville Ave., Springfield, MO 65802.
Division of Christian Education, Natl. Dir., Hardy W. Steinberg.
Church School Literature Dept.: Ed., Ralph W. Harris; Sunday School Quarterly Materials Ed., _____; Sunday School Papers Ed., Dorothy Morris.
Department of Education: Sec., Hardy W. Steinberg; Berean School of the Bible (Correspondence) Registrar, Virginia Kern.
Division of Church Ministries: Natl. Dir., G. Raymond Carlson.
Men's Dept.: Sec., Glen Bonds; Action Crusades Coord., Wildon Colbaugh; Light-for-the-Lost Sec., Ellis Damiani; Royal Rangers Cdr., Johnnie Barnes; Royal Rangers Coord., Donald Franklin.
Music Dept.: Sec., L. B. Larsen.
Sunday School Department: Sec., William E. Kirschke; Field Reps., Mel J. DeVries and Paul Fenton; Sunday School Publications Ed., Harris Jansen; Boys and Girls Missionary Crusade Coord., Helen Rye; Child Evangelism Supt., Jerry Stroup; Natl. Standard Supt., Edith Denton; Workers Training Coord., Samuel Henning; Prom. and Field Services Coord., Glenroy Shedd.
Women's Missionary Council Dept.: Sec., Goldia Anderson; Reps., Ann Ahlf and Angeline Tucker; Missionettes Coord., Charlotte Schumitsch.
Youth Dept. (Christ's Ambassadors): Sec., Norman Correll; Publications Coord., Gayle D. Erwin; Hisway Ed., Glen Ellard; Prom. Dir., H. H. DeMent; Servicemen's Rep., Donald Schorsch; Speed-the-Light Rep., Brenton Osgood; Speed-the-Light Coord., Verne B. MacKinney.
Division of Communications: Natl. Dir., Thomas F. Zimmerman.

Advance Magazine: Ed., Gwen Jones.
Public Relations Dept.: Sec., Warren F. Mc-Pherson; Asst., Elva J. Hoover; A-V Coord., Melvin Snyder.
Radio and Television Dept.: Sec., Leland Shultz; Publ. Dir., Edward S. Caldwell; Field Rep., Jack E. Risner; Revivaltime Choir Dir., Cyril McLellan; Revivaltime Prog. Dir., C. T. Beem; Revivaltime Speaker, C. M. Ward.
The Pentecostal Evangel Magazine: Ed., Robert C. Cunningham; Man. Ed., Richard G. Champion; Circulation Mgr., Arlyn R. Pember.
Division of Finance: Gen. Treas., M. B. Netzel.
Church Loan Dept.: Loan Officer, Raymond Hudson.
Department of Benevolences: Sec., Stanley V. Michael; Prom. Ed., Glen Renick.
Finance Dept.: Admin. Asst., Samuel Ohler; Acct. Supt., Frank Smith; Cashier, Ralph Dunham.
Stewardship Dept.: Sec., Donald Shelton.
Division of Foreign Missions: Exec. Dir., J. Philip Hogan; Sec., Robert T. M. Glasson.
Foreign Field Secs.: Africa, Morris Williams; Latin America, Melvin Hodges; Far East, Wesley Hurst; Eurasia, Charles Greenaway; Home Sec., David Womack; Publications Ed., David Irwin; Missionary Personnel Sec., D. R. Guynes; Spanish Lit. Dept., Ed., Loren Triplett; Intl. Correspondence Inst. Pres., George M. Flattery; Fin. Supt., Joe Kilpatrick.
Division of Home Missions: Natl. Dir., T. E. Gannon.
Deaf and Blind Ministries Coord., Eldon Post; Prison Ministries Coord., Paul Markstrom; Prom. Ed., Ruth Lyon.
Division of Publications (Gospel Publishing House): Actg. Natl. Dir., William Eastlake.
Marketing and Distribution: Mgr., William Eastlake; Adv. Mgr., Thomas F. Sanders; Customers Service Mgr., Arlyn R. Pember; Sales Mgr., David Johnston; Warehousing and Shipping Mgr., Don Goss.
Production: Mgr. R. G. Bowman; Design and Preparation Foreman, Elton Phelps; Printing and Finishing Foreman, Merrell Cooper; Production Control Foreman, Harry Cole; Quality Control Foreman, Marvin Knott.
General Services: Administrator, Joseph R. Green.
Data Processing: Mgr., Carl Hall; Fund and Order Coding: Supervisor, Mary Dutton; Purchasing: Agent, Dick Eisenhour; Maintenance: Chief Engineer, Melvin Sachs.
Other Organizations:
Commission on Chaplains: Chmn., T. E. Gannon; Sec., Herman Rohde; Treas., M. B. Netzel; Curriculum Coord., _____; Food Services: Mgr., Dick Merrifield; Ministers Benefit Assn: Chmn, T. E. Gannon; Sec., Herman Rohde; Treas., M. B. Netzel; Personnel: Mgr., Ray Roepke; Spiritual Life Evangelism: Coord., Charles W. Denton; Mobilization and Placement Serv. Rep., John Ohlin; Paraclete Mag. Ed., Hardy W. Steinberg.

PERIODICALS
All Assemblies of God periodicals are produced by the Gospel Publishing House, 1445 Boonville Ave., Springfield, MO 65802.

Advance, (m), Gwen Jones, Ed.
Campus Ambassador (bi-m), David Gable, Ed.
Caring, (q), Glen Renick, Ed.
God's Word for Today, (q), Tom Sanders, Ed.
Good News Crusades, (bi-m), David Irwin, Ed.
High Adventure, (q), Johnnie Barnes, Ed.
Hisway (m), Glen Ellard, Ed.
Mission America, (bi-m), Ruth Lyon, Ed.
Missionettes Memos, (q), Charlotte Schumitsch, Ed.
Paraclete, (q), Hardy W. Steinberg, Ed.
The Pentecostal Evangel, (w), Robert C. Cunningham, Ed.
Slant, (q), Ann Ahlf, Ed.
Sunday School Counselor, (m), Harris Jansen, Ed.
Superintendent's Planner, (q), Harris Jansen, Ed.
Youth Alive, (m), Gayle D. Erwin, Ed.

Associate Reformed Presbyterian Church (General Synod)

A Synod (changed in 1935 to General Synod) of the former Associate Reformed Presbyterian Church (merged in 1858 with remaining Associate Church into the United Presbyterian Church of North America).

Churches: 147. Inclusive Membership: 28,443. Sunday or Sabbath Schools: 141. Total Enrollment: 17,109. Ordained clergy: 144.

GENERAL ORGANIZATION
General Synod: Meets annually (June).

OFFICERS
Mod., Mr. Charles H. Carlisle, Box 185, Due West, SC 29639.
Principal Clk., Rev. C. Ronald Beard, 1200 S. Beltline Blvd., Columbia, SC 29205. Tel. (803) 787-6370.
Reading Clk., Rev. P. L. Sherrill, 125 W. 11th St., Charlotte, NC 28202.

PERIODICAL
Associate Reformed Presbyterian (w), Due West, SC 29639, Rev. E. Gettys, Ed.

Bahá'í Faith

Baháís are followers of Bahá'u'lláh (1817-1892), whose religion upholds the basic principles of progressive revelation, religious unity, and a new world order.
The Bahá'í administrative order consists of local communities, each with local assemblies, elective national assemblies, and a spiritual and administrative world center at Haifa, Israel, 113 national assemblies.
Within continental United States there are 945 local assemblies, and members in 4,800 cities and towns.

GENERAL ORGANIZATION
National Spiritual Assembly, Headquarters: 536 Sheridan Rd., Wilmette, IL 60091. Tel. (312) 256-4400.

OFFICERS
Chmn., Dr. Firuz Kazemzadeh; Sec., Glenford

31

Mitchell; Public Information Officer, Salvatore A. Pelle, 112 Linden Ave., Wilmette, IL 60091.

Baptist General Conference

This body has operated as a Conference since 1879; its first church was organized in 1852. It has a ministry through 688 churches and six boards of operation.

Churches: 681. Inclusive Membership: 108,474. Sunday or Sabbath Schools: 681. Total Enrollment: 119,192. Ordained clergy: 1,032.

GENERAL ORGANIZATION

General Conference: annual (June). Headquarters: 1233 Central St., Evanston, IL 60201. Tel. (312) 328-8500.

OFFICERS

Gen. Sec., Rev. Warren R. Magnuson, 1233 Central St., Evanston, IL 60201.

OTHER ORGANIZATIONS

Board of Trustees: Exec. Sec., Rev. Warren R. Magnuson.
Board of Home Missions: Sec., Rev. Gordon H. Anderson.
Board of Foreign Missions: Sec., Rev. Franklin O. Nelson.
Board of Publication: Sec., Rev. Oriel L. Hansen.
Board of Christian Education: Sec., Rev. Lawrence Swanson.
Board of Regents: Sec., Dr. Carl H. Lindquist.
Vancouver Bible Institute: 15100 66 A Ave., Surrey 824, British Columbia, Canada.

PERIODICAL

The Standard (bi-w), 1233 Central St., Evanston, IL 60201, Dr. Donald Anderson, Ed.

Baptist Missionary Association of America

A group of regular Baptist churches organized in associational capacity in May, 1950, in Little Rock, Ark. as North American Baptist Association. Name changed in 1969 to Baptist Missionary Association of America. There are several state and numerous local associations of cooperating churches. In theology these churches are evangelical, missionary, fundamental, and in the main premillennial.

Churches: 1,404. Inclusive Membership: 193,439. Sunday or Sabbath Schools: 1,408. Total Enrollment: 107,406. Ordained clergy: 1,800.

GENERAL ORGANIZATION

The Association meets annually (in April). Next meeting: Memorial Auditorium, Sacramento, CA, April 23-26, 1973.

PRESIDING OFFICERS

Pres., Lynn Stephens, 527 Tate St., Camden, AR 71701.
Vice-Pres., Rev. Harold Leytham, Rt. 2, Box 315, Theodore, AL 36582 and C. D. Walker, 2240 Homeway Cr., Dallas, TX 75228.
Rec. Secretaries: Rev. Ralph Cottrell, P.O. Box 2866, Texarkana, AR 75501; Rev. O. D. Christian, Rt. 1, Box 326, Garland, TX 75040; and Rev. Austin Steadman, 1801 Highland Dr., Carrollton, TX 75006.

OTHER ORGANIZATIONS

Baptist Missionary Association Brotherhood: Pres., Rev. James Ray Raines, Rt. 1, Gurdon, AR 71742; Vice-Pres., Bob Hand, 300 Beachwood, Little Rock, AR 72205; Sec., Phillip Wilson, 4953 Marion Ave., Memphis, TN 38117; Treas., Tim Reddin, Conway, AR 72032; Music Dir., Danny Bullock, Rt. 6, Sem. Apt. E-1, Jacksonville, TX 75766; Project Dir., Charles Sullivan, 2545 Williams, Camden, AR 71701; Dir. of Boys, Curtis W. Coleman, P.O. Box 241, McNeill, AR 71752.
National Women's Missionary Auxiliary: Pres., Mrs. Jackie Corbitt, 1308 Krivanek, Bryan, TX 77801; First Vice-Pres., Mrs. Marvin Hudler, 7805 DeWitt, Houston, TX 77028; Second Vice-Pres., Mrs. Tom Richey, Rt. 2, Jasper, TX 75951; Reporter, Mrs. F. R. Ratliff, 800 Shackleford Rd., Little Rock, AR 72205; Rec. Secs.; Mrs. Charles Walker, 7415 Dahlia, Little Rock, AR 72209; Mrs. John Duggar, 67 Kingspark Rd., Little Rock, AR 72207; Youth Dir., Mrs. H. W. Darst, 1169 Whispering Wind, Arnold, MO 63010; Sunbeam Promoter, Mrs. Alfred Jarvis, 215 Loop Ln., Lufkin, TX 75901; GMA and YLA Promoter, Mrs. Charles Sumrall, Rt. 3, Laurel, MS 39440; Corr. Sec., Mrs. Ady J. Smith, 112 6th N. E., Springhill, LA 71075.
Baptist Missionary Association of America Assembly and Encampment: Pres., Rev. Grady Higgs, P.O. Box 3043, Lufkin, TX 75901; First Vice-Pres., James Speer, 24 Melinda Dr., Little Rock, AR 72209; Second Vice-Pres., Johnny McMahan; Third Vice-Pres., Rev. Paul Guantt, Rt. 1, Box 214, Gulfport, MS 39501; Sec., Mrs. Leland Callaway, Box 1171, SSC Magnolia, AR 71753; Supt. of Fed., R. B. Hoshaw, P.O. Box 56, Caldwell, AR 72322; Mgr., Rev. Eugene Gauntt, Gary, TX 75643.
Armed Forces Chaplaincy Committee: Exec. Dir., William Charles Pruitt, Jr., P.O. Box 912, Jacksonville, TX 75766.

PERIODICALS

The Advancer (m), 712 Main St., Little Rock, AR 72201, Charles O. Strong, Ed.
The Gleaner (m), 716 Main St., Little Rock, AR 72201, Craig Branham, Ed.
Baptist Progress (w), P.O. Box 4205, Dallas, TX 75208, Dale Leggett, Ed.
Baptist Trumpet (w), P.O. Box 9502, Little Rock, AR 72209, David Tidwell, Ed.
Louisiana Baptist Builder (bi-w), Rt. 2, Box 280, Franklinton, LA 70438, Leroy Mayfield, Ed.
Mississippi Baptist (bi-w), 4432 Hwy. 15, N., Laurel, MS 39440, G. H. Gordon, Ed.
Missouri Missionary Baptist (bi-w), P.O. Box 1095, Poplar Bluff, MO 63901, M. M. Henson, Ed.

Beachy Amish Mennonite Churches

This group originates mostly from the Old Order Amish Mennonite Church.

Two congregations had been formed as early as 1927, but the others have all been organized since 1938.

Worship is held in meeting houses. Nearly all have Sunday schools, most congregations have prayer meetings, and many have Christian day schools. They sponsor evangelical missions at home and abroad, and a monthly magazine, Calvary Messenger, as an evangelical and doctrinal witness.

Churches: 62. Inclusive Membership: 4,069. Sunday or Sabbath Schools: None. Total Enrollment: None. Ordained clergy: 163.

INFORMATION

Ervin N. Hershberger, R. D. 1, Meyersdale, PA 15552. Tel. (814) 662-6227.

Berean Fundamental Church

Founded, 1934, in Denver, Colorado, this body emphasizes conservative Protestant doctrines.

Churches: 50. Inclusive Membership: 2,419. Sunday or Sabbath Schools: 50. Total Enrollment: 4,466. Ordained clergy: 49.

GENERAL ORGANIZATION

Headquarters: North Platte, NB 69101. Tel. (308) 532-7448.
Church Council meets semi-annually.

OFFICERS

Pres., Rev. Carl Goltz, Box 863, Scottsbluff, NB 69361.
Vice-Pres., Rev. Ivan E. Olsen, Box 549, North Platte, NB 69101.
Sec., Rev. Kenneth D. Blood, 613 Circle Dr., Ft. Morgan, CO 80701.

PERIODICAL

Berean Digest (m), Box 549, No. Platte, NB 69101, Rev. Ivan E. Olsen, Ed.

Bethel Ministerial Association, Inc.

Originally the Evangelistic Ministerial Alliance, founded in Evansville, Indiana, May 1934, later became Bethel Baptist Assembly, then incorporated under the laws of the State of Indiana, March 16, 1960.

Churches: 25. Inclusive Membership: 4,000. Sunday or Sabbath Schools: 25. Total Enrollment: 5,500. Ordained clergy: 90.

GENERAL ORGANIZATION

General Conference: quarterly.
Headquarters: 4350 Lincoln Ave., Evansville, IN 47715. Tel. (812) 422-0431.

OFFICERS

Chmn., W. Bruce Badger, 511 W. Cedar, LeRoy, IL 61752.
Vice-Chmn., Donald C. Etnier, Box 546, Decatur, IL 62522.
Sec.-Treas., Don G. Matthews, 7055 S. Manker, Indianapolis, IN 46227.

PERIODICAL

". . . Words With Power" (q), 4350 Lincoln Ave., Evansville, IN 47715, Max E. Campbell, Ed.

Bible Protestant Church

The Bible Protestant Church is the continuing Eastern Conference of the Methodist Protestant Church. Name changed to Bible Protestant Church at 30th Annual Session held at Westville, N. J., September 26-30, 1940. Original date of incorporation and granting of charter, September 1914; present body still operating under same certificate of incorporation with corporate name changed.

Headquarters: 110 Virginia Ave., Audubon, NJ 08106.

OFFICERS

Pres., Rev. Raymond N. Rowand, 112 S. Main St., Glassboro, NJ 08028.
Vice-Pres., Rev. Robert E. Meisky, 2300 Scroggins Rd., Alexandria, VA 22302.
Exec. Sec., Rev. B. Robert Biscoe, 110 Virginia Ave., Audubon, NJ 08106.
Sec., Rev. William J. Roberts, 239 Courtland Ave., Glenbrook, CT 06906.
Asst. Sec., Rev. William Raymond, 4510 N. Genesee Rd., Flint, MI 48506.
Treas., Rev. Jesse L. Anderson, 4423 Cloverlawn Dr., Flint, MI 48506.
Conference Historian, Rev. F. Leon Taggart, RD#1, Box 64 A, Port Jervis, NY 12771.

PERIODICAL

Bible Protestant Messenger (m), Rev. B. Robert Biscoe, 110 Virginia Ave., Audubon, NJ 08106, Ed.

Bible Way Church of Our Lord Jesus Christ World Wide, Inc.

This body was organized in 1957 in the Pentecostal tradition for the purpose of accelerating evangelistic and foreign missionary commitment and to effect a greater degree of collective leadership than was found in the body in which they had previously participated.

The doctrine is the same as that of the Church of Our Lord Jesus Christ of the Apostolic Faith, Inc. of which some of the churches and clergy were formerly members.

GENERAL ORGANIZATION

Headquarters: 1130 New Jersey Ave., N.W., Washington, DC 20001.

OFFICERS

Presiding Bishop, Smallwood E. Williams, 4720 16th St., N.W., Washington, DC 20011.
Gen. Sec., Rev. Lawrence G. Campbell, 136 Princess Dr., Danville, VA 24541.
Board of Missionaries, Mrs. Sylvia Rose.
Board of Women's Council, Mrs. Lillian Ford.
Board of Foreign Missions, Mrs. Dorothy Pugh.
Board of Education, Rev. Wallace W. Williams.
Board of Publication, Mr. Joseph Hall.
Board of Evangelism, Rev. Alfred Kee.

BRETHREN CHURCH (Ashland, Ohio)

Board of Youth Congress, Elder Huie Rogers.
Board of Youth Department, Elder Bernard Battles.
Board of Sunday Schools, Elder Jesse Davenport.
Sec. to the Presiding Bishop, Mrs. Ozora E. Salmon.

PERIODICALS
The Bible Way News Voice (bi-m), Washington, DC
The Youth Herald (bi-m), Washington, DC

Brethren Church (Ashland, Ohio)

The historical background is the same as that of the Church of the Brethren, until 1882, when the division from that body occurred. A second major division occurred in 1939, resulting in the formation of the National Fellowship of Brethren Churches (Winona Lake, Indiana).

Churches: 119. Inclusive Membership: 16,357. Sunday or Sabbath Schools: 119. Total Enrollment: 12,377. Ordained clergy: 130.

GENERAL ORGANIZATION
General Conference: annual (August).
Headquarters: 524 College Ave., Ashland, OH 44805. Tel. (419) 325-1824.
Exec. Sec. of the Central Council: Smith F. Rose, 641 Sandusky St., Ashland, OH 44805.

OFFICERS
Mod., Donald Rowser, 100 S. Church St., New Lebanon, OH 45345.
Mod. Elect., Henry Bates, 124 Strickler Ave., Waynesboro, PA 17268.
Sec., G. Bright Hanna, Twelve Mile, IN 46988.
Treas., Dale Long, 327 S. Milton St., Smithville, OH 44677.
Statistician, James Black, Box 376, Milledgeville, IL 61051.

BOARDS
The Brethren Publishing Company, 524 College Ave., Ashland, OH 44805.
The Missionary Board, 530 College Ave., Ashland, OH 44805.
Gen. Sec., M. Virgil Ingraham; Assoc. Sec., John Rowsey.
The Benevolent Board, Exec. Sec., Dorman Ronk.
The Board of Christian Education, Dir., Frederick Burkey.

Brethren Churches, National Fellowship of

A division occurred in the Church of the Brethren in 1882 on the question of the legislative authority of the annual meeting. It resulted in the establishment of this body under a legal charter requiring congregational government. Churches: 226. Inclusive Membership: 33,392. Sunday or Sabbath Schools: 226. Total Enrollment: 40,326. Ordained clergy: 418.

GENERAL ORGANIZATION
The National Fellowship of Brethren Churches, National Conference, annual (August).

OFFICERS
Mod., Rev. Robert B. Collitt, 833 Spruce St., Hagerstown, MD 21740.
Vice-Mod., Rev. S. Wayne Beaver, Box 588, Winona Lake IN 46590.
Sec., Clyde K. Landrum, 1108 Chestnut Ave., Winona Lake, IN 46590. Tel. (219) 267-7005.
Asst. Sec., Rev. Jerry Young, Box 566, Lititz, PA 17543.
Treas., Rev. Dean Risser, RR 1, Locust Dr., Coraopolis, PA 15108.
Statistician, Dr. Harold H. Etling, P.O. Box 718, Winona Lake, IN 46590.

OTHER BOARDS
Foreign Missionary Society: Pres., Dr. John C. Whitcomb, RR 8, Wooster Rd., Warsaw, IN 46580; Treas., Homer A. Kent, Sr., 301—6th St., Winona Lake, IN 46590.
Home Missions Council: Pres., Richard P. DeArmey, RR 3, Box 121, Osceola, IN 46561; Treas., Chester McCall, 1529 E. 60th St., Long Beach, CA 90805.
Women's Missionary Council: Pres., Mrs. Richard Placeway, 540 Randall Rd., Elyria, OH 44035; Sec.-Treas., Miss Joyce Ashman, 602 Chestnut Ave., Winona Lake, IN 46590.
Brethren Missionary Herald Company: Pres., Rev. Ralph J. Colburn, 3490 LaJara, Long Beach, CA; 90805; Treas., Dr. E. William Male, RR 3, Warsaw, IN.
Sisterhood of Mary and Martha: Pres., Miss Judy Ashman, 205-13th St., Winona Lake, IN 46590; Treas., Miss Rose Leistner, Grace College, Winona Lake, IN 46590.
National Fellowship of Grace Brethren Men: Pres., Mr. Lyle Marvin, Jr.; Treas., Mr. William Hart, 6675 Worthington-Galena Rd., Worthington, OH 43085.
Christian Education Dept.: Pres., Rev. G. Forrest Jackson, 172 Burgess Ave., Dayton, OH 45415; Office Manager, Miss Bobette Osborn, Box 365, Winona Lake, IN 46590.
Board of Evangelism: Pres., Rev. Robert D. Collitt, 833 Spruce St., Hagerstown, MD 21740; Treas., Mr. Joseph Dombek, Winona Lake, IN 46590.
Grace Schools: Pres., Rev. Kenneth B. Ashman, 3375 Lakeview Dr., Wooster, OH 44691; Pres. of the Corporation, Dr. Herman A. Hoyt, Box 785, Winona Lake, IN 46590.

PERIODICAL
The Brethren Missionary Herald (bi-w), Winona Lake, IN 46590. Rev. Charles W. Turner; Ed.

Brethren in Christ Church
(Formerly known as River Brethren)

The Brethren in Christ Church was founded in Lancaster County, Pa. in about the year 1778 and was an outgrowth of the religious awakening which occurred in that area during the latter part of the eighteenth century. This group became known as "River Brethren" because of their original location near the Susquehanna River. The name "Brethren in Christ" was officially adopted in 1863. In theology they are evangelical, Arminian, Holiness, and premillennial.

Churches: 151. Inclusive Membership: 9,550. Sunday or Sabbath Schools: 155. Total Enrollment: 17,729. Ordained clergy: 235.

GENERAL ORGANIZATION

General Conference: annual.

OFFICERS

Mod., Bishop Henry A. Ginder, 8 Hellam Drive, Mechanicsburg, PA 17055.
Gen. Conf. Sec., Rev. Owen H. Alderfer, 26 Leawood Ave., Ashland, OH 44805.

OTHER ORGANIZATIONS

Board of Administration: Chmn., Bishop Henry A. Ginder, 8 Hellam Dr., Mechanicsburg, PA 17055; Sec., Owen H. Alderfer, 26 Leawood Ave., Ashland, OH 44805; Treas., J. E. Zercher, Napanee, IN 46550.
Board of Christian Education: Chmn., Robert H. Smith, M.R. 1, Souderton, PA 18964; Sec., John A. Byers, M.R. 1, Souderton, PA 18964; Treas., J. Ralph Wenger, 61 W. Long Meadow Rd., Hagerstown, MD 21710.
E. V. Publishing House: Evangel Press, Erwin W. Thomas, Nappanee, IN 46550.
Ministerial Credentials Bd.: Chmn., Rev. A. M. Long, Grantham, PA 17027; Sec., Marion J. Heisey, Bloomfield, NM 87413.
Schools and Colleges: Chmn., John E. Zercher, R.R. 1, Nappanee, IN 46550; Sec., Wayne H. Schiedel, R. 2, Petersburg, Ontario, Canada.
Board for Missions: Chmn., David E. Climenhaga, 529 W. Penn Ave., Cleona, PA 17042; Sec., K. B. Hoover, Grantham, PA 17027; Treas., Mark S. Hess, 24 Carlton Rd., Hershey, PA 17033; Exec. Sec., J. Wilmer Heisey, Missions Office, 48½ S. Market St., Box 149, Elizabethtown, PA 17022.
Board of Benevolence: Chmn., Simon Lehman, Jr., Mechanicsburg, PA 17055; Sec., Millard Herr, 10304 E. 19th St., Cucamonga, CA 91730; Treas., Musser Martin, Grantham, PA 17027.

PERIODICAL

Evangelical Vistor (bi-w), Nappanee, IN 46550, J. N. Hostetter, Ed.

Buddhist Churches of America

Founded in 1899, organized in 1914 as the Buddhist Mission of North America, this body was incorporated in 1942 under the present name and represents the Jodo Shinshu Sect of Buddhism in this country. It is a school of Buddhism which believes in salvation by faith in the Wisdom and Compassion of Amida Buddha.

GENERAL ORGANIZATION

Conference: annual (February).
Headquarters: 1710 Octavia St., San Francisco, CA 94109.

OFFICERS

Bishop, Rt. Rev. Kenryu T.; Exec. Sec., Rev. K. Fujinaga.
Director, Buddhist Education: Rev. Hogen Fujimoto.

Director, Sunday School Dept.: Rev. Ensei Nekoda.

OTHER ORGANIZATIONS

Western Adult Buddhist League: Pres., Tom Masuda.
National Young Buddhist Association: Pres., Ken Nakano.
National Buddhist Women's Association: Pres., ——.

Bulgarian Eastern Orthodox Church (Diocese of N. & S. America and Australia)

Bulgarian immigration to the United States and Canada started around the turn of the century, and the first Bulgarian Orthodox church was built in 1907 in Madison, Illinois. In 1938, the Holy Synod of the Bulgarian E. O. Church established the diocese here as an Episcopate, and Bishop Andrey was sent as diocesan Bishop. In 1947, the diocese was officially incorporated in New York State and Bishop Andrey became the first elected Metropolitan.

By a decision of the Holy Synod in 1972, the Bulgarian Eastern Orthodox Church was divided into the New York and Akron Dioceses.

Churches: 13. Inclusive Membership: 86,000. Sunday or Sabbath Schools: N.R. Total Enrollment: N.R. Ordained clergy: 11.

OFFICERS

New York Diocese, Bishop Znepolsky, temporary Administrator, 2430 Titan Dr., Akron, OH 44321.
Akron Diocese, Bishop Znepolsky, Administrator, 2430 Titan Dr., Akron, OH 44321.

Christ Catholic Church (Diocese of Boston)

The church is a catholic communion established in 1968 to minister to the growing number of people seeking an experiential relationship with God, and who desire to make a total commitment of their lives to him. The church is catholic in faith and tradition and its orders are recognized as valid by catholics of every tradition.

Churches: 4. Inclusive Membership: 441. Sunday or Sabbath Schools: 2. Total Enrollment: 75. Ordained clergy: 5.

GENERAL ORGANIZATION

Conference: annual. Next meeting, January, 1974.

OFFICERS

Presiding Bishop, The Most Reverend Karl Pruter, P.O. Box 528, Zuni, NM 87327. Tel. (505) 782-4989.

PERIODICAL

Old Catholic Missive, The (m), P.O. Box 528, Zuni, NM 87327.

CHRIST CATHOLIC EXARCHATE

Christ Catholic Exarchate of Americas and Eastern Hemisphere

Incorporated in New Jersey. This is an autonomous body now a member of the Holy Synod of Orthodox Catholic Churches in America serving communities of the Eastern and Western Rite in the vernacular languages.

GENERAL ORGANIZATION
Trustees meet annually.

OFFICERS
Most. Rev. Peter A. Zurawetzky, 946 Leesville Ave., Rahway, NJ 07065.
Sec. of the Holy Synod, The Most Rev. Bjorn Marcussen, Den Gammel Katolske Kirkes Sekretariat, Postbox 347, 1503 Kobenhavn V, Denmark.

Christadelphians

A body organized in 1844, opposed to war, interested in primitive Christianity, believing in the setting up of the Kingdom of God in Palestine on the personal return of Christ to the earth, and in spiritual rebirth through immersion.

NO GENERAL ORGANIZATION

OFFICER
Sec.-Treas., Edwin A. Zilmer, 2126 W. 9th St., Waterloo, IA 50702.

The Christian and Missionary Alliance

An evangelical, evangelistic, and missionary movement, organized by Rev. A. B. Simpson, in New York, in 1887. It stresses "the deeper Christian life and consecration to the Lord's service."

Churches: 1,129. Inclusive Membership: 127,353. Sunday or Sabbath Schools: 1,085. Total Enrollment: 141,924. Ordained clergy: 1,227.

GENERAL ORGANIZATION
Council: annual.
Headquarters: 260 W. 44th St., New York, NY 10036.

OFFICERS
Pres., Nathan Bailey.
Vice-Pres., J. A. Bandy.
Sec., R. W. Battles.
Treas., B. S. King.
Home Sec., L. W. Pippert.
Educ. Sec., J. F. Shepherd.
Foreign Sec., L. L. King.

PERIODICAL
Alliance Witness, 260 W. 44th St., New York, NY 10036, H. R. Cowles, Ed.

Christian Catholic Church

Founded in Chicago by Rev. John Alexander Dowie, February 22, 1896. In 1899, the site of the present city of Zion was purchased, and in 1900 the city was opened.

GENERAL ORGANIZATION
Convocation: annual (end of September).
Headquarters: Dowie Memorial Dr., Zion, IL 60099.

OFFICER
Gen. Overseer, Carl Q. Lee.

PERIODICAL
Leaves of Healing (q), Dowie Memorial Dr., Zion, IL 60099, Carl Q, Lee, Ed.-in-Chief.

Christian Church (Disciples of Christ)

Started on the American frontier at the beginning of the 19th century as a movement to unify Christians, this body drew its major inspiration from Thomas and Alexander Campbell in western Pennsylvania and Barton W. Stone in Kentucky. Developing separately for a quarter of a century, the "Disciples," under Alexander Campbell and the "Christians," led by Stone, merged in Lexington, Kentucky, in 1832.

Churches: 4,868. Inclusive Membership: 1,386,374. Sunday or Sabbath Schools: 4,868. Total Enrollment: 623,012. Ordained clergy: 6,886.

GENERAL ORGANIZATION
General Assembly, biennial.
General Office: 222 S. Downey Ave., Box 1986, Indianapolis, IN 46206. Tel. (317) 353-1491.

OFFICERS
Gen. Minister and Pres., Rev. A. Dale Fiers.
Mod., Rev. Walter D. Bingham, 3900 W. Broadway, Louisville, KY 40211.
1st Vice-Mod., Mrs. H. G. Wilkes, North Hollywood, CA.
2nd Vice-Mod., Owen D. Hungerford, Columbus, IN.

GENERAL OFFICE STAFF
Deputy Gen. Minister and Pres., Rev. Howard E. Dentler and Rev. T. J. Liggett; Assts. to Gen. Minister and Pres., Rev. George Earle Owen, Rev. W. K. Fox and Kathleen B. Austin; Exec. Dir., Office of Communication (public relations), Robert L. Friedly; Exec. Dir., Office of Commission on Brotherhood Finance, Walter R. Griffin; Secretary for Administration, Gertrude Dimke.

ADMINISTRATIVE UNITS
Board of Church Extension: 110 S. Downey Ave., Indianapolis, IN 46219. Tel. (317) 356-6333. Pres., Rev. Rolland H. Sheafor.
Board of Higher Education: Box 1986 Indianapolis, IN 46206 Tel. (317) 353-1491. Pres., Rev. William L. Miller, Jr.
Christian Board of Publication (Bethany Press): Box 179, Beaumont and Pine Blvd., St. Louis, MO 63166. Tel. (314) 371-6900. Pres., Orville W. Wake.
Christian Church Foundation: 222 S. Downey Ave., Box 1986 Indianapolis, IN 46206 Tel. (317) 353-1491. Pres., Rev. James R. Reed.
Christmount Christian Assembly: Box 68, Black Mountain, NC 28711. Tel. (704) 669-8977. Pres., Rev. Gaines M. Cook.

Council on Christian Unity: 222 S. Downey Ave., Box 1986, Indianapolis, IN 46206 Tel. (317) 353-1491. Pres., Rev. George G. Beazley.

Disciples of Christ Historical Society. 1101 19th Ave. S., Nashville, TN 37212. Tel. (615) 291-1771. Pres., Hugh E. Williams.

Disciples Peace Fellowship: 222 S. Downey Ave., Box 1986 Indianapolis, IN 46206. Tel. (317) 353-1491. Pres., Rev. J. Proctor Riggans.

European Evangelistic Society: Box 268, Aurora, IL 60507. Pres., Rev. Dean E. Walker.

National Benevolent Association: 115 N. Jefferson Ave., St. Louis, MO 63103. Tel. (314) 652-7070. Pres., Rev. William T. Gibble.

National City Christian Church Corporation: Thomas Circle, Washington, DC 20005. Tel. (202) 232-0323. Pres., John T. Acree, Jr.

National Evangelistic Association: 222 S. Downey Ave., Box 1986, Indianapolis, IN 46206. Tel. (317) 353-1491. Pres., Rev. T. Garrott Benjamin.

Pension Fund: 700 Test Bldg., Indianapolis, IN 46204. Tel. (317) 634-4504. Pres., Rev. William M. Smith.

Unified Promotion: 222 S. Downey Ave., Box 1986 Indianapolis, IN 46206. Tel. (317) 353-1491. Exec. Sec., Rev. Spencer P. Austin.

United Christian Missionary Society: 222 S. Downey Ave., Box 1986, Indianapolis, IN 46206. Tel. (317) 353-1491. Pres., Rev. Thomas J. Liggett; Vice-Pres., Mrs. Kathleen Bailey Austin.

Division of Homeland Ministries (UCMS); Exec. Chmn., Rev. Kenneth A. Kuntz.

Division of Overseas Ministries (UCMS): Exec. Chmn., Rev. Robert A. Thomas.

REGIONAL ORGANIZATIONS

Christian Churches of Alabama: Rev. J. T. Beale, Area Minister, 1336 Montgomery Hwy. S., Box 20037, Birmingham 35216. Tel. (205) 871-9271.

Christian Church in Arizona: Mrs. Mabel M. Figgs, Adm. Sec., 18 E. Roanoke, Phoenix 85004. Tel. (602) 265-0531.

Arkansas Christian Churches: Rev. James W. Rainwater, Exec. Minister, 1719 Broadway, Box 3711, Little Rock 72203. Tel. (501) 372-3141.

Christian Church of Northern California-Nevada: Karl Irvin, Jr., Regional Minister, 1177 San Pablo Ave., Berkeley 94706. Tel. (415) 526-6834.

Christian Churches of Southern California & Nevada: Rev. Charles A. Malotte, Exec. Pastor, 3126 Los Feliz Blvd., Los Angeles 90039. Tel. (213) 665-5126.

Christian Church—Capital Area: Rev. J. J. Van Boskirk, Exec. Sec., 8901 Connecticut Ave., Chevy Chase, MD 20015. Tel. (301) 654-7794.

All-Canada Committee, Christian Church (Disciples of Christ), Kenneth S. Wills, Gen. Sec., 695A St. Clair Ave. W., Toronto 10, Ontario, Canada. Tel. (416) 653-3957.

Central Rocky Mountain Region: Rev. Walter J. Lantz, Exec. Minister, 2599 S. Lincoln, Denver, CO 80210. Tel. (303) 744-6194.

Florida Christian Churches: Rev. John C. Updegraff, Exec. Minister, 401 S.E., 19th Ave., Ocala 32670. Tel. (904) 622-8729.

Christian Churches of Georgia: Rev. E. Lyle Harvey, Regional Minister, 2370 Vineville Ave., Macon 31204. Tel. (912) 743-8649.

Disciples of Christ in Hawaii: C. MacDuff, Bd. Chrm., 1516 Kewalo St., Honolulu 96822.

Christian Church of South Idaho: Rev. Jasper C. Havens, Area Minister, 215 "B" Ave., Box 2188, Boise 83701. Tel. (208) 345-4440.

Illinois Disciples of Christ: Rev. Jack V. Reeve, Gen. Sec., 1011 N. Main St., Bloomington 61701 Tel. (309) 828-6293.

Christian Church (Disciples of Christ) in Indiana: Rev. Gilford E. Olmsted, Gen. Sec., 1100 W. 42nd St., Indianapolis 46208. Tel. (317) 926-6051.

Iowa Society of Christian Churches: Rev. Clinton D. Wolf, Exec. Minister, 3300 University, Box 1024, Des Moines 50311. Tel. (515) 255-3168.

Kansas Christian Churches: State Minister, 1010 Gage St., Topeka 66604. Tel. (913) 232-7281.

Christian Church in Kentucky (Disciples of Christ): Rev. James A. Moak, Gen. Minister, 190 Market St., Box 1418, Lexington 40501. Tel. (606) 254-2732.

Louisiana Assn. of Christian Churches: Rev. W. S. Parish, Jr., Exec. Sec., 316 Eola Dr., Alexandria 71301. Tel. (318) 443-0304.

Michigan Assn. of Christian Churches: Rev. Eric White, Exec. Minister, 2820 Covington Ct., Box 2232, Lansing 48911. Tel. (517) 372-3220.

Christian Churches of Minnesota & N. Dakota: Rev. G. Arland Johnson, Exec. Sec., 122 W. Franklin Ave., Minneapolis 55404. Tel. (612) 332-0963.

Mississippi Christian Churches:. Rev. William E. McKnight, Exec. Sec., 1619 N. West St., Jackson 39202. Tel. (601) 352-6774.

Christian Church (Disciples of Christ) in Missouri: Rev. Lester B. Rickman, Gen. Sec., Hwy. 54 S., Box 1087, Jefferson City 65101. Tel. (314) 636-8149.

Christian Churches of Montana: Rev. D. Franklin Kohl, Area Minister, 1715 First Ave., N., Great Falls 59401. Tel. (406) 452-7404.

Nebraska Fellowship of Christian Churches: Robert M. Hall, Exec. Minister, 1268 S. 20th St., Lincoln 68502. Tel. (402) 432-0359.

Christian Churches of New Mexico: Rev. Herbert Miller, Exec. Minister, 500 E. Bender Blvd., Hobbs 88240. Tel. (505) 392-5600.

Christian Church (Disciples of Christ) in North Carolina: Rev. Charles E. Dietze, Exec. Minister, 509 W. Lee St., Box 521, Wilson 27893. Tel. (919) 243-4047.

Northeastern Assn. of Christian Churches: Rev. Arthur J. Stanley, Area Minister, 1010 Park Ave., New York, NY 10028. Tel. (212) 288-3246.

Ohio Society of Christian Churches. Rev. Herald B. Monroe, Gen. Sec., 17119 Madison Ave., Cleveland 44107. Tel. (216) 221-8600.

Oklahoma Assn. of Christian Churches: Rev. Eulis H. Hill, Exec. Minister, 301 N.W. 36th St., Oklahoma City 73118. Tel. (405) 528-3577.

Christian Church (Disciples of Christ) in Oregon: Rev. Russell Hensley, State Minister, 0245 S.W. Bancroft St., Portland 97201. Tel.

(503) 226-7648.

Christian Church (Disciples of Christ) in Pennsylvania: Rev. Dwight French, Gen. Minister, 727 Penn Ave., Pittsburgh 15221. Tel. (412) 371-5422.

Christian Churches of South Carolina: Rev. David T. Brooks, Exec. Minister, 1B Daniel St., Box 3636, Charleston 29407. Tel. (803) 556-2971.

South Dakota Christian Missionary Society: Rev. G. Arland Johnson, Exec. Minister, 122 W. Franklin St., Minneapolis, MN 55404. Tel. (612) 332-0963.

Tennessee Assn. of Christian Churches: Rev. Allen S. Estill, Exec. Sec., 3700 Richland Ave., Nashville, TN 37205. Tel. (615) 269-3409.

Christian Church (Disciples of Christ) in Texas: Rev. Kenneth L. Teegarden, Exec. Minister, 2909 Lubbock Ave., Fort Worth 76109. Tel. (817) 926-4687.

Christian Church of Utah: Rev. Jasper C. Havens, Area Minister, 215 "B" Ave., Box 2188, Boise, ID 83705. Tel. (208) 345-4440.

Virginia Convention of Christian Churches: Rev. O. Eugene Moore, Exec. Sec., 2200 Monument Ave., Richmond 23220. Tel. (703) 353-5561.

Northwest Regional Christian Church (Disciples of Christ), L. E. Pitman, Regional Exec., 720 14th East St., Seattle, WA 98102. Tel. (206) 632-3537.

Christian Church (Disciples of Christ) in West Virginia: Rev. Charles E. Crank Jr., Exec. Minister, 702 10th Ave., Huntington 25701. Tel. (304) 529-7742.

PERIODICALS

World Call (monthly), 222 S. Downey Ave., Indianapolis, IN 46219, Rev. James L. Merrell, Ed.

The Christian (weekly), Box 179, St. Louis, MO 63166, Rev. Howard E. Short, Ed.

Catalyst (youth), Box 179, St. Louis, MO 63166, Jerry O'Malley, Ed.

Hearthstone (family), Box 179, St. Louis, MO 63166, Albert R. Graves, Ed.

Secret Place (devotional), Box 179, St. Louis, MO 63166, Vincie Alessi, Hershell H. Richmond, Harry G. Taylor, Eds.

Vanguard (church planning), 222 S. Downey Ave., Indianapolis, IN 46219. Rev. Kenneth A. Kuntz, Ed.-in-Chief.

Christian Church of North America, General Council

Incorporated 1948 in Pittsburgh, Pa.; earlier the body was known as Italian Christian Churches. Unorganized. The first General Council was conducted in 1927 in the city of Niagara Falls, New York.

Churches: 110. Inclusive Membership: 8,500. Sunday or Sabbath Schools: N.R. Total Enrollment: 7,000. Ordained clergy: 136.

GENERAL ORGANIZATION

General Council: meets annually (September). Headquarters: 719 East State St., Sharon, PA 16146.

OFFICERS

Board of General Overseers.

Gen. Overseer, Rev. Frank P. Fortunato, 4337 Bleigh Ave., Philadelphia, PA 19136.

Asst. Gen. Overseers: Rev. Carmine Saginario, 1154 White Plains Rd., New York, NY 10473; Rev. Joseph DeMola, 324 Stanley Ave., Staten Island, NY 10301; Rev. Guy Bongiovanni, P. O. Box 801, Sharon, PA 16146; Rev. Joseph Fiorentino, 440 Lexington Street, Woburn, MA 01801.

Gen. Sec.-Treas., Rev. Joseph A. Moscheo, P. O. Box 831, Ellwood City, PA 16117.

Evangelism Dept.: Dir., Rev. John Del Turco, 608 28th St., Niagara Falls, NY 14301.

Foreign and Home Missions Dept.: Dir., Rev. Guy Bongiovanni, P. O. Box 801, Sharon, PA 16146.

Institutions, Benevolences & Fellowships Dept.: Rev. Philip J. Bellisario, Sr., 1019 E. Tejunga Ave., Burbank, CA. 91501.

Youth Dept.: Dir., Rev. Alfred Palma, 705 Hamilton St., Syracuse, NY 13204.

Publications Dept.: Rev. Louis A. DeCaro, 1800 21st Ave., Beaver Falls. PA 15010.

PERIODICALS

Il Faro (m), P. O. Box 66, Herkimer, NY 13350. Rev. Guido Scalzi, Ed.

Vista (m) P. O. Box 117, Beaver Falls, PA 15010, Rev. Louis A. DeCaro, Ed.

Christian Churches and Churches of Christ

This fellowship, whose churches were always strictly congregational in polity, has its origin in the American movement to "restore the New Testament church in doctrine, ordinances and life" initiated by Thomas and Alexander Campbell, Walter Scott and Barton W. Stone in the early years of the nineteenth century.

Churches: 5,901. Inclusive Membership: 1,036,-288. Sunday or Sabbath Schools: 6,012. Total Enrollment: 1,243,445. Ordained clergy: 7,314.

NO GENERAL ORGANIZATION

CONVENTIONS

North American Christian Convention (founded 1927), 3533 Epley Rd., Cincinnati, OH 45239.

National Missionary Convention (founded 1947), Box 177, Kempton, IN 46049.

PERIODICALS

Christian Standard (w), 8121 Hamilton Ave., Cincinnati, OH 45231, Edwin V. Hayden, Ed.

Restoration Herald (m), 5664 Cheviot Rd., Cincinnati, OH 45239. James W. Greenwood, Ed.

Directory of the Ministry (a), 1525 Cherry Rd., Springfield, IL 62704. Ralph D. McLean, Ed.

Horizons (m), Box 177, Kempton, IN 46049. Harrold McFarland, Ed.

The Christian Congregation, Inc.

Original incorporation, March 10, 1887; revised incorporation, October 29, 1898. The New Commandment, John 13:34-35, is the bond of fellowship in creative ethical activism. This denomination provides ministerial affiliation for independent clergymen.

Churches: 263. Inclusive Membership: 51,310. Sunday or Sabbath Schools: 252. Total Enrollment: 33,355. Ordained clergy: 267.

OFFICER
Gen. Supt., Rev. Ora Wilbert Eads, 708 South Bragg St., Monroe, NC 28110.

Christian Methodist Episcopal Church

In 1870 the General Conference of the M.E. Church, South, approved the request of its colored membership for the formation of their conferences into a separate ecclesiastical body, which became the Colored Methodist Episcopal Church.

At its General Conference in Memphis, Tenn., May 1954, it was overwhelmingly voted to change the name of the Colored Methodist Episcopal Church to the Christian Methodist Episcopal Church. This became the official name on January 3, 1956.

GENERAL ORGANIZATION
General Conference: quadrennial. (Next meeting, 1974).

OFFICER
Sec., Rev. N. Charles Thomas, 664 Vance Ave., Memphis, TN 38126.

OTHER ORGANIZATIONS
Board of Missions: Chmn., Bishop Joseph A. Johnson, Jr., 109 Holcomb Dr., Shreveport, LA 71103. Gen. Sec., Rev. Isaiah Scipio, 911 Lafayette E., 1301 Orleans St., Detroit, MI 48207.
Board of Christian Education: Chm., Bishop B. Julian Smith, 564 E. Frank Ave., Memphis, TN 38106; Gen. Sec., Rev. C. D. Coleman, 1474 Humber St., Memphis, TN 38106.
Publishing Board: Chm., Henry C. Bunton, 6524 16th St. N.W., Washington, DC 20012; Publishing Agent, Rev. M. C. Pettigrew, Box 6447, Memphis, TN 38106.
Board of Finance: Chm., Bishop J. Claude Allen, 755 W. 26th Ave., Gary, IN 46407; Gen. Sec., O. T. Peeples, Box 6276, Memphis, TN 38106.
Board of Pension: Chm., Bishop W. H. Amos, 2111 LaSalle Gardens S., Detroit, MI 48206; Gen. Sec., Rev. D. S. Cunningham, 531 S. Parkway, E., Memphis, TN 38106.
Board of Evangelism: Chm., Bishop P. R. Shy, 2780 Collier Dr. N.W., Atlanta, GA 30318; Gen. Sec., Rev. N. L. Linsey, 164-B Rocky Ford Rd., N.E., Atlanta, GA 30317.
Board of Lay Activities: Chm., Bishop Norris S. Curry, 2330 Sutter St., Dallas, TX 75216; Gen. Sec., W. E. Solomon, Box 4012, Columbia, SC 29204.
Woman's Missionary Council: Pres., Mrs. Pauline Grant, 723 E. Upsal St., Philadelphia, PA 19119; Patron Bishop, Bishop Elisha P. Murchison.

PERIODICALS
Christian Index (w), Box 6138, Memphis, TN 31806, John M. Exum, Ed.
Eastern Index (bi-m), P.O. Box 1575, Greenville, SC 29602, Rev. Alex Chambers, Ed.

CHRISTIAN REFORMED CHURCH

Missionary Messenger, 730 Marechaneil St., St., Memphis, TN 38114. Mrs. Mattie I. Suttles, Ed.
Western Index, 1455-75 Golden Gate Ave., San Francisco, CA 94115, Rev. W. Louis Smith, Ed.

BISHOPS
B. W. Doyle, Retired Bishop, 1982 Madison La., Gary, IN 46407.
B. Julian Smith, Senior Bishop, 564 E. Frank Ave., Memphis, TN 38106.
J. Claude Allen, 755 W. 26th Ave., Gary, IN 46407.
E. P. Murchison 6322 Elwynne Dr., Cincinnati, OH 45326.
P.R. Shy, 2780 Collier Dr. N.W., Atlanta, GA 30318.
N. S. Curry, 2330 Sutter St., Dallas, TX 75216.
W. H. Amos, 2111 La Salle Gardens, So., Detroit, MI 48206.
H. C. Bunton, 6524 16th St., N.W. Washington, DC 20012.
J. A. Johnson, Jr., 109 Holcomb Dr., Shreveport, LA 71103.
Chester A. Kirkendoll, 308 10th Ave., Birmingham, AL 35204.

Christian Nation Church U.S.A.

Organized in 1895, at Marion, Ohio, as a group of "equality evangelists," who later formed the Christian Nation Church, semi-congregational in government; emphasizes evangelism. Reincorporated as Christian Nation Church U.S.A., 1961.

Churches: 16. Inclusive Membership: 2,000. Sunday or Sabbath Schools: 11. Total Enrollment: 2,000. Ordained clergy: 29.

GENERAL ORGANIZATION
Congress: annual.

OFFICERS
Gen. Overseer, Rev. Harvey Monjar, Box 142, South Lebanon, OH 45065.
Asst. Overseer, Rev. Dwight E. Harris, Box 525 Hinton, WV 25951.
Gen. Sec., Walter F. Clark, 345 Cedar Dr., Loveland, OH 45140.

Christian Reformed Church

The Christian Reformed Church represents the historic faith of Protestantism. Founded in the United States in 1857, it asserts its belief in the Bible as the inspired Word of God, and is creedally united in the Belgic Confession (1561), the Heidelberg Catechism (1563), and the Canons of Dort (1618-19).

Churches: 718. Inclusive Membership: 286,094. Sunday or Sabbath Schools: 601. Total Enrollment: 69,240. Ordained clergy: 999.

GENERAL ORGANIZATION
Synod: annual (June).

OFFICERS
Stat. Clk., Rev. William P. Brink, Office Address: 2850 Kalamazoo Ave. S.E., Grand Rapids, MI 49508. Tel. (616) 241-1691.

CHRISTIAN UNION

Synodical Treas., Lester Ippel, 1331 Franklin St. S.E., Grand Rapids, MI 49506.

OTHER ORGANIZATIONS
Board of Foreign Missions: Sec., Rev. H. Evenhouse, 2850 Kalamazoo Ave. S.E., Grand Rapids, MI 49508.
Board of Home Missions: Sec., Rev. M. Baarman, 2850 Kalamazoo Ave. S.E., Grand Rapids, MI 49508.
Minister of Evangelism: Rev. Wesley Smedes, 2850 Kalamazoo Ave. S.E., Grand Rapids, MI 49508.
Board of Ministers' Pension Fund: Treas., J. W. Stoepker, 3636 Stilesgate Ct. S.E., Grand Rapids, MI 49508.
Board of Publications: Mgr., Peter Meeuwsen, 2850 Kalamazoo Ave. S.E., Grand Rapids, MI 49508.
Editor for Committee on Education: Rev. Andrew Kuyvenhoven, 2850 Kalamazoo Ave. S. E., Grand Rapids, MI 49508.

PERIODICALS
The Banner (w), 2850 Kalamazoo Ave. S.E., Grand Rapids, MI 49508, Dr. Lester Dekoster, Ed.
De Wachter (w), 2850 Kalamazoo Ave. S.E., Grand Rapids, MI 49508, Rev. W. Haverkamp, Ed.

Christian Union

Organized in 1864 in Columbus, Ohio. It stresses the oneness of the Church with Christ as its only head. The Bible is the only rule of faith and practice and good fruits the only condition of fellowship. Each local church governs itself.

GENERAL ORGANIZATION
General Council: triennial. (Next meeting, 1974.)
Headquarters: P.O. Box 38, Excelsior Springs, MO 64024.

OFFICERS
Pres., Rev. Lawrence Rhoads, Box 31, Otway, OH 45657.
Vice-Pres., Rev. Wilbur Holman, 17500 Hidden Valley Rd., Independence, MO 64057.
Sec., Rev. Robert Chroninger, 5411 Buenos Aires Blvd., Westerville, OH 43081.
Treas., Rev. Harold McElwee, Rt. 1, Elizabethtown, IN 47232.

PERIODICAL
Christian Union Witness (m), P.O. Box 38, Excelsior Springs, MO 64024, Rev. Joseph F. Cunningham, Ed.

†Christian Unity Baptist Association

Organized in 1934 from the Macedonia Baptist Association, believes in Trinity, divine inspiration of the Bible, regeneration, universal atonement, and endurance to the end to be saved.

GENERAL ORGANIZATION
Meets annually.

OFFICERS
Mod., Elder D. O. Miller, Mountain City, TN 37683.
Clk.-Treas., Elder Carl Hart, Husk, NC 28639.

†Christ's Sanctified Holy Church

GENERAL ORGANIZATION
Conference meets annually in September.
Headquarters: S. Cutting Ave. and East Spencer St., Jennings, LA 70546. Tel. (318) 824-3437.

OFFICERS
Pres., Elder J. B. Rigmaiden, 2818 Chapman St., Oakland, CA 94601.
Vice-Pres., Elder I. Franfrico, 4816 Shreveport St., Houston, TX 77028.
Dist. Treas., Deacon Marcus Frowler, Rayne, LA 70578.
Exec. Sec., Rev. Mary A. Paul, Box 555, 714 Orange St., Jennings, LA 70546.

Church of Christ

Organized April 6, 1830, at Fayette, New York, by Joseph Smith and five others; in 1831 Independence, Missouri, was designated as headquarters.

Churches: 32. Inclusive Membership: 2,400. Sunday or Sabbath Schools: N.R. Total Enrollment: N.R. Ordained clergy: 188.

GENERAL ORGANIZATION
General Conference: annual.
Headquarters: Temple Lot, Independence, Missouri.

OFFICERS
Sec. of the Council of Twelve, Apostle Archie F. Bell, 802 So. McCoy, Independence, MO 64050. Tel. (816) 833-3995.
Gen. Bus. Mgr., Bishop C. LeRoy Wheaton, Jr., P.O. Box 472, Independence, MO 64051.
General Recorder, Roland L. Sarratt, 4305 So. Main, Independence, MO 64055.

PERIODICAL
Zion's Advocate, P.O. Box 472, Independence, MO 64051, Harvey E. Seibel, 1502 South Logan, Independence, MO 64055.

† Church of Christ (Holiness) U.S.A.

This body was organized by Bishop C. P. Jones as a holiness group in 1896. The mission of this body is to seek, through proclamation of the gospel, the conversion of sinners, the sanctification of believers, and the perfecting in love, or holiness, of all humanity.

GENERAL ORGANIZATION
National Convention: annual (August).
Headquarters: 329 E. Monument St., Jackson, MS 39202. Tel. (601) 352-5978.

OFFICERS
Senior Bishop and Pres., Bishop M. R. Conic, Victoria Ave., Los Angeles, CA 90043.

Vice-Pres., Bishop O. W. McInnis, 8321 Calumet Ave., Chicago, IL 60619.
Corr. Sec., Elder A. J. Perkins, 360 East Boston Blvd., Detroit, MI 48202.
Rec. Sec., Elder L. P. Camper, 3652 Westchester Dr., Jackson, MS 39213.

PERIODICAL
Truth (m), 552 E. 44th St., Chicago, IL 60658. Bro. Rayford Lee, Ed.

Church of Christ, Scientist

A church founded by Mary Baker Eddy in 1879 to reinstate the healing power of primitive Christianity. Christian Science theology describes divine healing as scientifically based on underlying spiritual reality and law. The denomination is represented by The Mother Church, The First Church of Christ, Scientist, in Boston, Massachusetts, and its more than 3,200 branches throughout the world.

GENERAL ORGANIZATION
Board of Directors, Headquarters: Christian Science Church Center, Boston, MA 02115.

OFFICERS
Bd. of Dirs., Arthur P. Wuth, Mrs. Lenore D. Hanks, David E. Sleeper, DeWitt John, Otto Bertschi.
Pres., George Nay.
Treas., Roy Garrett Watson.
Clk., Charles Henry Gabriel.
First Reader, William Milford Correll
Second Reader, Mrs. Virginia Nichols Chancey.

OTHER ORGANIZATIONS
Board of Education: Teaches a class of 30 pupils once in 3 years for the purpose of providing authorized teachers of Christian Science.
Board of Lectureship: Made up of 25 to 30 members, delivers free lectures.
Committee on Publication: Corrects in a Christian manner impositions on the public in regard to Christian Science and injustices to Christian Scientists.
Trustees Under the Will of Mary Baker Eddy: Owns and publishes Mrs. Eddy's writings.
Publishing Society: Publishes or sells the authorized literature of Christian Science.

PERIODICALS
The Christian Science Monitor (d), Boston, MA
The Christian Science Journal (m), Boston, MA
Christian Science Sentinel (w), Boston, MA
Christian Science Quarterly (q), Boston, MA
The Herald of Christian Science (q), in French, German, Danish, Dutch, Greek, Indonesian, Italian, Japanese, Norwegian, Portuguese, Spanish, Swedish, and Braille.

Church of Daniel's Band

A body Methodistic in form and evangelistic in spirit, organized in Michigan in 1893.

GENERAL ORGANIZATION
Conference: annual.

OFFICERS
Pres., Rev. Wesley Hoggard, R.F.D. 2, Midland, MI 48640.

Vice-Pres., Rev. Arthur Meniger, R 1, Beaverton, MI 48612.
Sec.-Treas., Rev. Marie Berry, R.F.D. 2, Midland, MI 48640.

The Church of God

Inaugurated by Bishop A. J. Tomlinson, who served as General Overseer, 1903 to 1943, and from which many groups of the Pentecostal and Holiness Movement stemmed. Bishop Homer A. Tomlinson served as General Overseer, 1943 to 1968. Episcopal in administration, evangelical in doctrines of justification by faith, sanctification as a second work of grace, and of the baptism of the Holy Ghost, speaking with other tongues, miracles of healing.

Churches: 2,025. Inclusive Membership: 75,890. Sunday or Sabbath Schools: 2,025. Total Enrollment: 96,500. Total Ordained clergy: 2,737.

GENERAL ORGANIZATION
General Assembly: annual, c/o Box 568, Jerusalem, Israel.
National Assembly, U.S.A.: annual, Cape Girardeau, MO.
National Headquarters: U.S.A., 2504 Arrow Wood Dr., S.E., Huntsville, AL 35803. Tel. (205) 881-9629.

OFFICERS
Gen. Overseer and Bishop, Voy M. Bullen; Gen. Sec., and Treas., Betty Bullen.
Church of God Publishing House, 2504 Arrow Wood Dr., S.E., Huntsville, AL 35803. Bus. Mgr., Johnny W. Bruton.

CHURCH AUXILIARIES
Address: 2504 Arrow Wood Dr., S.E., Huntsville, AL 35803.
Assembly Band Movement: Gen. Sec., Bishop James F. Ray.
Women's Missionary Band: Gen. Sec., Mary Alice Bell.
Theocratic Bands: Gen. Sec., Rev. Ted Carr.
Victory Leader's Band, Youth: Gen. Sec., Gene Tolbert.
Sunday Schools: Pres., Ollie Stevens.
National Sunday School Superintendent: Ted Carr.
Administration for Highway and Hedge Campaign: Earnest Hoover.

PERIODICALS
The Church of God (s-m), 2504 Arrow Wood Dr., S.E., Huntsville, AL 35803.
Forward With Christ (m), 144 Fifth Ave., New York, NY 10011. Christopher Economou, Ed.
The Church of God Quarterly (q), 2504 Arrow Wood Dr., S.E., Huntsville, AL 35803. Ollie Stevens, Ed.

Church of God General Conference (Oregon, Ill.)

A number of churches holding premillennial Adventist views organized Churches of God in Christ Jesus in 1888. In 1921, a permanent Conference was organized with the name Church of God of the Abrahamic Faith. The corporate

CHURCH OF GOD (Anderson, Ind.)

name is Church of God General Conference, Oregon, Illinois.

Churches: 127. Inclusive Membership: 7,200. Sunday or Sabbath Schools: N.R. Total Enrollment: 8,400. Ordained clergy: 112.

GENERAL ORGANIZATION
General Conference: annual (August).
Headquarters: Oregon, IL 61061. Tel. (815) 732-2761.

OFFICERS
Chmn., Harold Doan, 12421 Rose Ave., Los Angeles, CA 90066.
Vice-Chmn., Charles Knapp, 100 Colrain, Grand Rapids, MI 49508.
Sec., C. Jesse Pestle, Columbia Station, OH 44028.
Treas., Wayne Laning, Rt. 2, Box 118, Mt. Sterling, IL 62353.
Exec. Sec., S. O. Ross, Box 100, Oregon, IL. 61061.

OTHER ORGANIZATIONS
Berean Youth Department, Oregon, IL
General Sunday School Department, Oregon, IL
Evangelism and Missions Board, Oregon, IL 61061; Supt. and Chmn., S. O. Ross; Sec., Mrs. Mardy Lawrence, 32 E. Marshall, Phoenix, AZ 85012.

PERIODICALS
The Restitution Herald (m), Box 100, Oregon, IL, C. E. Randall, Ed.
Church of God Progress Journal (m), Box 100, Oregon, IL 61061, C. E. Randall, Ed.
Challenge Magazine (bi-m), Box 100, Oregon, IL 61061, Kent H. Ross, Ed.

Church of God (Anderson, Ind.)

This body is one of the largest of the groups which have taken the name "Church of God." Its headquarters are at Anderson, Ind. It originated about 1880 and emphasizes Christian unity.

Churches: 2,271. Inclusive Membership: 152,787. Sunday or Sabbath Schools: 2,000. Total Enrollment: 238,692. Ordained clergy: 3,352.

GENERAL ORGANIZATION
General Assembly: annual. Chmn., Arlo F. Newell, 825 Riverview Blvd., St. Louis, MO 63147.

EXECUTIVE COUNCIL
Box 2420, Anderson, IN 46011. Tel. (317) 642-0256. Exec. Sec., W. E. Reed.
Dir. of World Service, Paul A. Tanner.
Dir. of Church Service, Roscoe Snowden.

OTHER ORGANIZATIONS
Board of Christian Education: Exec. Sec.-Treas., Donald A. Courtney, Box 2458, Anderson, IN 46011.
Board of Church Extension and Home Missions: Exec. Sec.-Treas., Marvin J. Hartman, Box 2069, Anderson, IN 46011.
Foreign Missionary Board: Exec. Sec.-Treas., Lester A. Crose, Box 2498, Anderson, IN 46011.

National Woman's Missionary Society: Exec. Sec.-Treas., Nellie Snowden, Box 2328, Anderson, IN 36011.
Board of Pensions: Exec. Sec.-Treas., E. E. Wolfram, Box 2299, Anderson, IN 46011.
Radio and Television Commission: Dir., R. Eugene Sterner, Box 2007, Anderson, IN 46011.
Warner Press, Inc.: Pres., T. Franklin Miller, Box 2499, Anderson, IN 46011.

PERIODICALS
Vital Christianity (bi-w), Box 2499, Anderson, IN 46011, Harold L. Phillips, Ed.
Church of God Missions (m), Box 2337, Anderson, IN 46011, James H. Treadway, Ed.

Church of God (Cleveland, Tenn.)

America's oldest Pentecostal Church began in 1886 as an outgrowth of the holiness revival under the name Christian Union. Reorganized in 1902 as the Holiness Church and in 1907 the church adopted the name Church of God. Its doctrine is fundamental and Pentecostal; it maintains a centralized form of government and an evangelistic and missionary program.

Churches: 4,095. Inclusive Membership. 287,099. Sunday or Sabbath Schools: 5,266. Total Enrollment: 478,984. Ordained clergy: 7,504.

GENERAL ORGANIZATION
General Assembly: biennial. (Next meeting, 1974.)
General Offices, Keith St. at 25th N.W., Cleveland, TN 37311. Tel. (615) 472-3361.

OFFICERS
Gen. Overseer, Ray H. Hughes.
Asst. Gen. Overseers, Wade H. Horton; Cecil B. Knight and W. C. Byrd.
Gen. Sec.-Treas., G. W. Lane.

OTHER ORGANIZATIONS
World Missions: Gen. Dir., W. E. Johnson.
S. S. and Youth: Gen. Dir., Paul F. Henson.
Publishing House: Publisher, F. W. Goff.
Public Relations: Dir., Hollis L. Green.
Television and Radio Minister: Floyd Timmerman.
Evangelism: Dir., C. Raymond Spain.
Education: Dir., Ray H. Hughes.
Women's Auxiliary: Pres., Mrs. Ray H. Hughes.

PERIODICALS
Church of God Evangel (bi-w), O. W. Polen, Ed.
Lighted Pathway (m), Clyne W. Buxton, Ed.
The Pilot (q), Clyne W. Buxton, Ed.
Campus Call (m), Milton Parsons, Ed.
Sow (q), W. E. Johnson, Ed.
Flame (q), C. Raymond Spain, Ed.
The Willing Worker (m), Mrs. E. C. Darter, Ed.
Christian Challenge Literature (w), Clyne W. Buxton, Ed.

The Church of God of the Mountain Assembly, Inc.

Founded in 1906 by J. H. Parks, S. N. Bryant, Thomas Moses, and Andrew J. Silcox.

42

GENERAL ORGANIZATION

Headquarters and General Offices: Florence Ave., Jellicoe, TN 37762. Tel. (615) 424-8260. General Assembly, annually in August.

OFFICERS

Gen. Overseer, Rev. Ira H. Moses, Box 296, Jellico, TN 37762.
Asst. Gen. Overseer, Rev. C. B. Ellis, Box 248, Goshen, OH 45122.
Gen. Sec./Treas., Rev. J. E. Hatfield, Box 157, Jellicoe, TN 37762.

PERIODICAL

The Gospel Herald (m), Box 157, Jellicoe, TN 37762. Rev. James L. Cox, Sr., Ed.

The Church of God (Seventh Day)

Organization traced from Old and New Testament times. Reorganized at a convention held at Salem, West Virginia, in November 1933. The tithe system is used to pay the ministry.

GENERAL ORGANIZATION

Apostolic Council: meets bi-yearly, in Salem, WV (on the first Sunday in January and the first Sunday in July).
Headquarters: 79 Water St., Salem, WV 26426 (Box 328).

OFFICERS

Apostolic Council, made up of Twelve Apostles.
70 Prophets (Elders).
Seven Financial Stewards.
Overseers of different countries and districts. Eph. 2:20, 4:11.

PERIODICAL

The Advocate of Truth (s-m), The Advocate of Truth Press, Inc., Box 328, Salem, WV 26426. Chris W. Royer, Ed.

The Church of God (Seventh Day), Denver, Colo.

This body observes the seventh day as the Sabbath; believes in the imminent, personal, and visible return of Jesus; and that the earth will be the eternal abode of the righteous.

GENERAL ORGANIZATION

General Conference: biennial. (Next meeting, 1973.)
Headquarters: 330 West 152nd Ave., P. O. Box 2370, Denver, CO 80201. Tel. (303) 452-7973.

OFFICERS

Chmn., Wm. Robert Coulter.
Vice-Chmn., Ray Straub.
Sec.-Treas., David Kauer.

OTHER ORGANIZATIONS

Sabbath School: Chm., Harvey Fischer, 4110 Stillmeadow Way, Sacramento, CA 95821.
Foreign Missions: Chm., Reuben Moldenhauer, 8314 Amboy Ave., Sun Valley, CA 91352.
Home Missions: Chm. and Dir. of Searchlight Correspondence Bible School, R. C. Moldenhauer, Box 33, Harrisburg, OR 97446.
National Women's Association: Pres., Mrs. Darlene Walker, Eureka, SD 57437.
Young People: Chm., Elder Calvin Burrell,

CHURCH OF GOD BY FAITH

1004 Fayetteville Rd., Van Buren, AR 72956.
Ministerial: Chm., Elder E. A. Straub, 322 Concord St., Lodi, CA 95240.
Educational: Chm., Elder Fischer, Rt. 5. Owosso, MI 48867.
Publishing: (Bible Advocate Press, Denver, CO 80201). LeRoy Dais, Mgr.

PERIODICALS

The Bible Advocate (m), Denver, CO 80201, Floyd A. Turner, Ed.
Aim (m), Denver, CO 80201, Mrs. Gail Rincker, Ed.
The Harvest Field Messenger (bi-m), Denver, CO 80201, Floyd A. Turner, Ed.
The Faithful Servant (for ministers only), Box 2370, Denver, CO 80201, S. J. Kauer, Ed.
Women's Association News Digest (WAND) (q), Box 2370, Denver, CO 80201, Mrs. Dorothy Nimchuk, Ed.
Footprints (m), Denver, CO 80201, Gina Tolbert, Ed.

† Church of God and Saints of Christ

Organized in 1896 by William Saunders Crowdy, in Lawrence, Kansas. In the year 1900 the national headquarters was established in Philadelphia. In 1917 Belleville, R.F.D. 1, Portsmouth, VA 23704, became the international headquarters.

GENERAL ORGANIZATION

General Conference: quadrennial. (Next General Conference, 1976.)
National Conference: annual.
All Conferences held at International Headquarters, Belleville, Portsmouth, VA 23704.

OFFICERS

Chief Executive, Bishop Howard Z. Plummer, P.O. Box 187, Portsmouth, VA 23505.
District, Bishop L. S. Plummer, 162 Prairie Ave., Providence, RI 02905.
Chief Aide, Bishop Robert N. Butler, 405 M St. N.W., Washington, DC 20001.
District, Bishop Jehu A. Crowdy, 1031 Cooper St., Camden, NJ 08102.
Gen. Bus. Mgr., Bishop R. N. Butler, R.F.D. 1, Portsmouth, VA 23505.
Gen. Sec., Elder J. W. Robinson, R.F.D. 1, Box 139, Portsmouth, VA 23505.
Asst. Gen. Sec., Elder J. S. Fears, R.F.D. 1, Box 139, Portsmouth, VA 23505.
Statistics: Gen. Sec., Elder Thomas H. Woody, 2015 W. Master St., Philadelphia, PA 19121.

† Church of God by Faith

Founded 1919, in Jacksonville Heights, Florida, by Elder John Bright. This body believes the word of God as interpreted by Jesus Christ to be the only hope of salvation, and Jesus Christ the only mediator for man.

GENERAL ORGANIZATION

General Assembly: meets every August, October, December.
Headquarters: 3220 Haines St., Jacksonville, FL 32206.

OFFICERS

Bishop, Elder Willie W. Matthews, 125 Holman St., Ozark, AL 36360.

43

THE CHURCH OF GOD IN CHRIST

Exec. Sec., Elder James E. McKnight, Rt. 2, Box 377, Gainesville, FL 30501.
Ruling Elders: Daniel H. Lewis, Valdosta, GA; George Robinson, St. Augustine, FL.; C. M. Fogle, Avon Park, FL.

PERIODICAL

The Spiritual Guide (m), 3125 Franklin St., Jacksonville, FL 32206, Aaron Matthews, Jr., Ed.

† The Church of God in Christ

Organized in Arkansas in 1895 by Charles Harrison Mason and incorporated in 1897.

GENERAL ORGANIZATION

National Convocation: annual.
National Headquarters: 938 Mason St., Memphis, TN 38126.

GENERAL BOARD

Presiding Bishop, Bishop J. O. Patterson, 1774 So. Parkway, E., Memphis, TN 38114.
1st Asst. Presiding Bishop, Bishop H. S. Bailey, 3230 Cambridge Rd., Detroit, MI 48221.
2nd Asst. Presiding Bishop, Bishop S. M. Crouch, 8320 Byrd Ave., Inglewood, CA 90305.
Gen. Sec., Bishop D. A. Burton, 552 Lincoln St., Steelton, PA 17113.
Treas., Bishop E. Odom, 2719 Grove St., Kansas City, MO 64109.
Bishop O. T. Jones, Sr., Emeritus, 118 W. Upsal St., Philadelphia, PA 19119.
Bishop O. M. Kelly, 419 Convent Ave., New York, NY 10031.
Bishop Wyoming Wells, 1401 S. Benbow Rd., Greensboro, NC 27406.
Bishop C. E. Bennett, 740 W. 27th Ave., Gary, IN 46407.
Bishop L. H. Ford, 8405 S. Prairie Ave., Chicago, IL 60619.
Bishop J. W. White, 2236 Peniston St., New Orleans, LA 70115.
Bishop J. A. Blake, 2192 Harrison Ave., San Diego, CA 92113.
Bishop F. D. Washington, 1328 President St., Brooklyn, NY 11213.
Bishop J. D. Husband, P. O. Box 184, Atlanta, GA 30301.

OTHER ORGANIZATIONS

Bd. of Bishops, Chmn., Bishop T. D. Iglehart, 325 Terrell Rd., San Antonio, TX 78209.
Bd. of Directors, Chmn., Bishop C. H. Brewer, 260 Roydon Rd., New Haven, CT.
Elders' Council, Chmn., Bishop G. B. Pickens, 4222 S. Wentworth Ave., Chicago, IL 60609.
Bd. of Publications, Chmn., Elder Roy L. H. Wimbush, 328 N. Avenue "B", Crowley, LA 70526.
Women's International Convention President and General and International Supervisor of Women's Department, Dr. Ann L. Bailey, Cambridge Rd., Detroit, MI 48221.
Bd. of Education, Pres., Elder Woodrow W. Hicks, 343 S. 21st St., Maywood, IL 60525.
Board of Home and Foreign Missions, Pres., Bishop Rudolph Martin, Box 733, Seaside, CA 93955.
Bd. of Evangelism, Pres., Bishop L. C. Page,

1716 Victoria Blvd., Los Angeles, CA 90011.
Natl. Youth Congress, Pres., Elder Chandler Owens, 708 High St., Newark, NJ 07102.
Int'l. Sunday School Convention, Pres., Bishop C. W. Williams, 270 Division St., Derby, CT 06418.
Music Convention, Pres., Mrs. Anna Ford, 1431 S. Christiana Ave., Chicago, IL 60623.
Public Relations Commissioner, Elder W. L. Porter, 1235 E. Parkway, So., Memphis, TN 38114.
Ministers' Fellowship, Pres., Elder W. L. Williams, 262 Northland Ave., Buffalo, NY 14208. Security Corps Chmn., Elder W. C. Cook, 26909 Kitch St., Inster, MI 43141.
Church of God in Christ Hospital Fund Bd., Pres., Bishop L. E. Willis, 918 Anna, Norfolk, VA 23502.
Superannuation Commission, Pres., Bishop E. Lenox, 2814 W. Walnut St., Chicago, IL 60612.
Religious Workers' Guild, Elder C. C. Owens, 1835 S. Spaulding St., Chicago, IL 60623.

PERIODICALS

Whole Truth, 930 Mason St., Memphis, TN 38126, Ed., Mrs. Elsie W. Mason.
Sunday School Literature, Publishing House, Church of God in Christ, 930 Mason St., Memphis, TN 38126. Elder Roy L. H. Wimbush, Ed.
Y.P.W.W. Topics, 930 Mason St., Memphis, TN 38126. Elder Charles Blake, Ed.
The Evangelist Speaks, Box 103, Chester, PA 19016. Bishop C. Range, Ed.
Prayer and Bible Band Topics, P. O. Box 352, Jackson, TN 38301, Mrs. Ada F. Jackson, Ed.
Sunshine Band Topics, 648 Pearl St., Benton Harbor, MI 49022. Mrs. Mildred Wells, Ed.
Purity Guide, P. O. Box 1526, Gary, IN 46407, Mrs. Pearl McCullom, Ed.
Bible Band Guide, 1257 Longfellow St., Detroit, MI 48202, Mrs. Selma Locket, Ed.
Church of God in Christ Ministerial Roll, 1970-71, 930 Mason St., Memphis, TN 38126.

The Church of God in Christ, International

Organized in 1969 in Kansas City, Missouri, by fourteen bishops of the Church of God in Christ of Memphis, Tennessee. The doctrine is the same, but the separation came because of disagreement over polity and governmental authority. The Church is Wesleyan in theology (two works of grace) but stresses the experience of full baptism of the Holy Ghost with the initial evidence of speaking with other tongues as the spirit gives utterance.
Churches: 1,041. Inclusive Membership 501,000. Sunday or Sabbath Schools: 984. Total Enrollment: N.R. Ordained Clergy: 1,502.

GENERAL ORGANIZATION

The General Assembly: annual (Next meeting August, 1973, Hartford, CT).
College of Bishops: semi-annual, each January and June.
Headquarters: 1331 Quindare Blvd., Kansas City, KS 66104.

OFFICERS

Office of the Senior Bishop
Bishop Illie L. Jefferson, Senior Bishop, 15 Colonial Dr., Windsor, CT 06095.
Bishop Singleton R. Chambers, Asst. Senior Bishop, 1331 Quintero Blvd., Kansas City, KS 66104.
Bishop J. Arthur Jones, Chmn., The College of Bishops, 1522 Plimpton Ave., Bronx, NY 10452.
Bishop James E. Johnson, Sec., The College of Bishops, 623 Hoag St., Toledo, OH 43607.
Office of the General Secretary
Bishop Wilbur L. Milner, Sr., Gen. Sec., 167 Cleveland Ave., Hartford, CT 06120.
Mrs. Linda Hamlett, Office Mgr., 133 Palm St., Hartford, CT 06112.
Office of the General Treasurer
Gen. Treas., Bishop C. Melchisadec Monk, 774 Putnam Ave., Brooklyn, NY 11221.
Chmn., Bd. of Fin., Bishop R. T. Jones, 947 E. Johnson St., Philadelphia, PA 19138.
General Board of Evangelism
Chmn., Bishop S. R. Chambers, 1331 Quindaro Blvd., Kansas City, KS 66104.
Vice-Chmn., Bishop George Johnson, 1502 W. Maricopa St., Phoenix, AZ 85007.
Sec., Dr. Rupert Holmes, 101 W. 30th St., New York, NY 10001.
General Board of Christian Education
Chmn., Bishop Carl E. Williams, Sr., 170 Adelphi St., Brooklyn, NY 11205.
Sec., Bishop J. Delano Ellis, II, 598-D Thomas Ave., Memphis, TN 38105.
General Board of Home and Foreign Missions
Chmn., Bishop C. Melchisadec Monk, 774 Putnam Ave., Brooklyn, NY 11221.
Sec. of Evangelism, Dr. Georgianna Jones, 947 E. Johnson St., Philadelphia, PA 19138.
General Board of Relations
Chmn., Bishop J. Delano Ellis, II, 598-D Thomas Ave., Memphis, TN 38105.
Sec., Miss Julia M. Arter, 33 Blue Hills Ave., Hartford, CT 06112.
General Board of Publications
Chmn., Bishop Edmond W. Gillespie, 18894 Justine, Detroit, MI 48234.
Sec., Bishop J. Delano Ellis, II, 598-D Thomas Ave., Memphis, TN 38105.
Pub. Agent., Bishop James E. Johnson, 623 Hoag Ave., Toledo, OH 43607.
General Board of Directors
Chmn. Bishop Illie L. Jefferson, 15 Colonial Dr., Windsor, CT 06095.
Vice-Chmn., Bishop S. R. Chambers, 1331 Quindaro, Blvd., Kansas City, KS 66104.
Sec., Bishop W. L. Milner, 167 Cleveland Ave., Hartford, CT 06120.
General Board of Orders and Relations
Chmn., Bishop George Johnson, 1502 W. Maricopa St., Phoenix, AZ 85007.
National Youth Department
Pres., Bishop T. Wesley Swan, 107 Greene St., Springfield, MA 01109.
Sec., Exec. Comm., Elder R. T. Jones, Jr., 7929 Provident Rd., Philadelphia, PA 19150.

BISHOPS AND DIOCESES

(Note: the Dioceses are in parentheses. Bishops are addressed as "The Right Reverend" while the Senior Bishop is addressed as "The Most Reverend.")

Rufus Bullock (Mississippi), Rt. 3, Box 24, Prentiss, MS 39474.
Singleton R. Chambers (Kansas-Missouri), 1331 Quindaro Blvd., Kansas City, KS 66104.
Tony Clemmons (Massachusetts), 70 Berkeley Ave., Waterbury, CT 06704.
J. Delano Ellis, II (Tennessee), 598-D Thomas Ave., Memphis, TN 38105.
Simuel Garner (Arkansas), 1264 Effie Rd., Memphis, TN 38106.
Alvin L. Gaskin (Western Massachusetts), 96 Mapledell St., Springfield, MA 01109.
John Gauson, Jr. (Colorado), 2023 Lafayette St., Denver, CO 80205.
Edmond W. Gillespie (Michigan), 18894 Justine, Detroit, MI 48234.
Illie L. Jefferson (Connecticut), 15 Colonial Dr., Windsor, CT 06095.
C. M. Jenkins (South West), 1719 W. 11th St., San Bernadino, CA 92410.
George Johnson (Arizona), 1502 W. Maricopa St., Phoenix, AZ 85007.
R. T. Jones, Sr. (Pennsylvania), 947 E. Johnson St., Philadelphia, PA 19138.
A. V. Mitchell (Virginia-District of Columbia), 1323-25th St., Newport News, VA 23607.
C. M. Monk (New York), 774 Putnam Ave., Brooklyn, NY 11221.
S. L. Ware (Western New York), 93 South St., Newburgh, NY 12550.
Carl E. Williams, Sr. (Greater New York), 170 Adelphi St., Brooklyn, NY 11205.
Robert Edwards (North-West), 1726 E. 62nd St., Tacoma, WA 98404.
R. L. Mathias (Central States), 40 Gates Ave., Lackawanna, NY 14218.
T. Wesley Swan (Missionary Bishop), 114 Wooster St., Hartford, CT 06120.

PERIODICALS

The Message, 114 Wooster St., Hartford, CT 06120. T. W. Swan, Ed.
The Holiness Call, 598-D Thomas Ave., Memphis, TN 38105. J. Delano Ellis, II, Ed.

Church of God in Christ (Mennonite)

A section of the Mennonite body organized in 1859, in Ohio, for the reestablishment of the order and discipline of the Church.

Churches: 38. Inclusive Membership: 6,204. Sunday or Sabbath Schools: N.R. Total Enrollment: N.R. Ordained clergy: 86.

GENERAL ORGANIZATION
Headquarters: 420 N. Wedel St., Moundridge, KS 67107. Tel. (316) 345-2532.

OFFICER
Conf. Mod., Reuben Koehn, Lahoma, OK 73754.

PERIODICAL
Messenger of Truth (bi-w), Lahoma, OK 737-54. Reuben Koehn, Ed.

The Church of God of Prophecy

Organized, 1903, at Fields of the Wood, near Murphy, North Carolina. The doctrine is fundamental, conservative, and evangelical, stressing

THE CHURCH OF ILLUMINATION

justification by faith, sanctification as a second work of grace, speaking in tongues as the initial evidence of being filled with the Holy Ghost, divine healing, and the second coming of Christ. Churches are established in the 50 states and in 45 countries. The government is central and theocratic.

GENERAL ORGANIZATION
General Assembly: annual.
World Headquarters: Bible Place, Cleveland, TN 37311. Tel. (615) 472-4511.

OFFICERS
Gen. Overseer, M. A. Tomlinson.
Exec. Committee: M. A. Tomlinson, J. R. Kinser, Leonard F. Kendrick.

OTHER ORGANIZATIONS
(All departmental offices located at World Headquarters)
Public Relations: Harry Lee Moore, Dir.
World Missions: Charles G. Hawkins, Sr., Sec.
Victory Leaders (Youth: Darel Talbott, Sec.
Sunday School: Billy Murray, Sec.
Counsel and Followup: Harper Hunter, Jr., Gen. Sec.
Communications: H. L. Moore, Minister.
Women's Missionary Band: Elva Howard, Sec.
White Wing Publishing House and Press: Leonard F. Kendrick, Manager.
Bible Training Institute: Ray C. Wynn, Superintendent.
Church of Prophecy Marker Association: John A. Stubbs, Sec.

PERIODICALS
Published by the White Wing Publishing House and Press, Keith St., Cleveland, TN 37311.
White Wing Messenger (w), R. O. Covey, Asst. Ed.
White Wing Messenger, Spanish (m), R. O. Covey, Asst. Ed.
Happy Harvester (m), Ora Mae Willing, Man. Ed.

The Church of Illumination

Organized in 1908 for the express purpose of establishing congregations at large, offering a spiritual, esoteric, philosophic interpretation of the vital biblical teachings, thereby satisfying the inner spiritual needs of those seeking spiritual truth, yet permitting them to remain in, or return to, their former church membership.

GENERAL ORGANIZATION
The Assemblage: annual.
Headquarters: "Beverly Hall," Clymer Rd., Quakertown, PA 18951.

OFFICER
Dir., Rev. Emerson M. Clymer.

The Church of Jesus Christ (Bickertonites)

Organized 1862 at Green Oak, Pennsylvania, by William Bickerton, who obeyed the Restored Gospel under Sidney Rigdon's following in 1845.

GENERAL ORGANIZATION
General Conference: annual (April).
Headquarters: Sixth & Lincoln Sts., Monongahela, PA 15063. Tel. (412) 258-9923.

OFFICERS
Pres., Gorie Ciaravino, 9591 Dixie, Detroit, MI 48239.
First Counselor, Dominic Thomas, 6010 Barrie, Dearborn, MI 48126.
Second Counselor, Joseph Bittinger, West Leisenring, PA 15489.
Exec. Sec., Nicholas Pietrangelo, 4618 Neff Rd., Detroit, MI 48224.

PERIODICAL
The Gospel News (m), Sixth and Lincoln Sts., Monongahela, PA 15063, Paul Palmieri, Ed.

The Church of Jesus Christ of Latter-day Saints

Organized April 6, 1830, at Fayette, New York, by Joseph Smith. Members consider the Bible, Book of Mormon, Doctrine and Covenants, and the Pearl of Great Price to be the word of God. Their belief is summed up in thirteen Articles of Faith written by Joseph Smith. Membership is worldwide.

Churches: 4,995. Inclusive Membership: 2,133,-072. Sunday or Sabbath Schools: 4,729. Total Enrollment: 2,000,000. Ordained clergy: 17,272.

GENERAL ORGANIZATION
General Conference sessions, April and October, Salt Lake City, Utah.
Headquarters: 47 East South Temple St., Salt Lake City, UT 84111.

OFFICERS
Pres., Harold B. Lee.
1st Presidency: Harold B. Lee, Nathan Eldon Tanner, and Marion G. Romney.
Council of the 12 Apostles: Spencer W. Kimball, Pres., Ezra Taft Benson, Mark E. Petersen, Delbert L. Stapley, LeGrand Richards, Richard L. Evans, Hugh B. Brown, Howard W. Hunter, Gordon B. Hinckley, Thomas S. Monson, Boyd K. Packer, Marvin J. Ashton, and Bruce R. McConkie.
Patriarch to the Church: Eldred G. Smith.
Assistants to the Council of the 12 Apostles: Alma Sonne, ElRay L. Christiansen, Sterling W. Sill, Henry D. Taylor, Alvin R. Dyer, Franklin D. Richards, Theodore M. Burton, Bernard P. Brockbank, James A. Cullimore, Marion D. Hanks, Joseph Anderson, David B. Haight, William H. Bennett, John H. Vandenberg, Robert L. Simpson, C. Leslie Stone, James E. Faust, and L. Tom Perry.
First Council of the Seventy: S. Dilworth Young, Milton R. Hunter, A. Theodore Tuttle, Paul H. Dunn, Hartman Rector, Jr., Loren C. Dunn, and Rey D. Pinegar.
Presiding Bishopric: Victor L. Brown, H. Burke Peterson, and Vaughn J. Featherstone.
Church Historian and Recorder: Leonard J. Arrington.

AUXILIARY ORGANIZATIONS
The Relief Society of the Church of Jesus Church of Latter-day Saints: Gen. Pres.,

Belle Smith Spafford.
Sunday Schools: Gen. Pres., Russell M. Nelson.
Young Men's Mutual Improvement Association: Gen. Pres., W. Jay Eldredge, Jr.
Young Women's Mutual Improvement Association: Gen. Pres., Florence S. Jacobsen.
Primary Association: Gen. Pres., LaVern W. Parmley.
Genealogical Society of The Church of Jesus Christ of Latter-day Saints: Pres., Theodore M. Burton.
Board of Education: Administration, Unified Church School System, Neal A. Maxwell, Commissioner of Education.
Church Welfare Program: Man. Dir., Junior Wright Child.

PERIODICALS

Deseret News (d), Salt Lake City, UT, Gordon B. Hinckley, Pres.
The Ensign of The Church of Jesus Christ of Latter-day Saints (m), Salt Lake City, UT, Jay M. Todd, Man. Ed.
New Era (m), Salt Lake City, UT, Brian K. Kelly, Man. Ed.
Friend (m), Salt Lake City, UT, Lucile C. Reading, Man. Ed.

† Church of Our Lord Jesus Christ of the Apostolic Faith, Inc.

This Church as an organized body was founded by Bishop R. C. Lawson in Columbus, Ohio, and moved to New York City in 1919. It is founded upon the teachings of the Apostles and Prophets, Jesus Christ being its chief cornerstone.

GENERAL ORGANIZATION

National Convocation: annual (August).
Headquarters: 2081 7th Ave., New York, NY 10027. Tel. (212) 866-1700.

OFFICERS

Senior Apostle, Bishop H. Spencer, Apostle, Bishop W. L. Bonner, Apostle, Bishop H. D. Jones, Apostle, Bishop J. P. Steadman.
Chairman Board of Presbyters, Elder Joseph Frazier.
Chairman of Board of Bishops, Bishop Frank Solomon.
Gen. Sec., Elder Arthur Anderson.
Natl. Rec. Sec., Elder T. Woolfolk.
Natl. Corr. Sec., Elder Herman R. Cannady.
Natl. Treas., Bishop T. Richardson.

OTHER ORGANIZATIONS

Woman's Missionary Board: Pres., Mrs. Ruby Dukes, 1107 Virginia Blvd., San Antonio, TX 78203; Rec. Sec. Mrs. Marie Robbins, 15812 Harvard Ave., Cleveland, OH 44128.
National Woman's Council: Chm., Mrs. Alice Ladson, Box 44, Myers, SC 29405.
Young People's Dept.: Pres., James Brown.
Sunday School Dept.: Natl. Supt., Elder John Eddington, 2056 Lawley St., Detroit, MI 48212.
National Youth Congress: Pres. Deacon William Moore.
Religious Education Dept.: Dir., James I. Clark, 25-63 98th St., Elmhurst, NY 11369.
National Board of Education: Chmn., James I.

CHURCH OF THE BRETHREN

Clark, 25-63 98th St., Elmhurst, NY 11369.
Foreign Mission Board: Sec., Mrs. Odessa Wilcox.

PERIODICAL

The Contender for the Faith (m), 112 East 125th St., New York, NY 10035. Bishop John W. Pernell, Richmond, VA, Ed.

The Church of Revelation, Inc.

Founded 1930 at Long Beach, California, by Rev. Janet Stine Wolford, with Christian love as the basis for membership.

Churches: 5. Inclusive Membership: 750. Sunday or Sabbath Schools: None. Total Enrollment: None. Ordained clergy: 38.

GENERAL ORGANIZATION

Board of trustees: annual.
Headquarters: 216 E. 11th St., Hanford, CA 93230.

OFFICERS

Pres., Rev. Winifred Ruth Mikesell, 216 E. 11th St., Hanford, CA 93230.
Vice-Pres., Richard C. Irvine, 4326 Calle Real Sp 113, Santa Barbara, CA 93110.
Sec.-Treas., Muriel Stine, 5644 Downey Ave., Lakewood, CA 90712.

Church of the Brethren

German pietists-anabaptists founded in 1708 under Alexander Mack, Schwarzenau, Germany, entered the colonies in 1719 and settled at Germantown, Pennsylvania. They have no other creed than the New Testament, hold to principles of nonviolence, temperance, and voluntarism, and emphasize religion in life.

Churches: 1,036 Inclusive Membership: 181,183. Sunday or Sabbath Schools: 1,034. Total Enrollment: 82,079. Ordained clergy: 2,011.

GENERAL ORGANIZATION

General Conference: annual (June).
Headquarters: Church of the Brethren General Offices, 1451 Dundee Ave., Elgin, IL 60120. Tel. (312) 742-5100.
Washington Office: 100 Maryland Ave., N.E., Washington, DC 20002.

OFFICERS

Mod., Dean M. Miller, 1 S 071 Luther Ave., Lombard, IL 60148.
Sec., William R. Eberly, 1515 Sunset Dr., North Manchester, IN 46962.
Treas., Robert Greiner, 1451 Dundee Ave., Elgin, Il 60120.

ADMINISTRATIVE STAFF

Gen., Sec., S. Loren Bowman; Assoc. Gen Secs., Earle W. Fike, Jr.; Galen B. Ogden; Joel K. Thompson.
Personnel Office: Hazel Peters, Coordinator.
Treas., Robert Greiner; Asst. Treas., Roy L. Hiteshew; Adm. Asst., Joanne Davis.
General Services: Exec. Sec., Galen B. Ogden; Adm. Asst., Gwendolyn F. Bobb; Div. of Production, Gerald M. Flory. Communication Team: John G. Fike, Richard N. Miller, Kenneth I. Morse, Howard E. Royer. Ste-

wardship Enlistment Team: Stewart B. Kauffman, Ronald D. Petry, Donald L. Stern. Dir. of Marketing, Clyde E. Weaver, Sec. of Pension Board, Galen B. Ogden.

Parish Ministries: Exec. Sec., Earle W. Fike, Jr. Consultant for Educational Development, Shirley J. Heckman; Consultant for Curriculum Development, Hazel M. Kennedy; Consultant for Youth Ministries and Coordinator of Library of Resources, Ralph G. McFadden; Consultant for Personal Evangelism, Matthew M. Meyer; Consultants for Lay Ministry and Congregational Life, Kent E. Naylor and Hubert R. Newcomer; Consultant for Celebration Process and Coordinator for Fund for the Americas in the U.S. Wilfred E. Nolen; Consultant for the Professional Minister and Congregational Life, J. Bentley Peters; Consultant for Congregational Community Involvement, Thomas Wilson.

World Ministries: Exec. Sec., Joel K. Thompson Church Development Consultant, Merle Crouse; Community Development Consultants, Shantilal P. Bhagat, Kenneth E. McDowell; Peace and International Affairs Consultant, H. Lamar Gibble; Washington Representative and Social Justice Consultant, Ralph E. Smeltzer; Ministry to Men Facing the Draft and Dir. Volunteer Services, Charles L. Boyer; Coordinator of Training, Ronald P. Hanft. Annual Conference Manager: Hubert R. Newcomer.

PERIODICAL

Messenger (bi-m), Church of the Brethren General Offices, Elgin, IL 60120. Howard E. Royer, Ed.

Church of the East (Assyrians)

An American group which is a branch of what was for many centuries the major part of the Christian Church, its Patriarch residing in Seleucia-Ctesiphon, Chaldea, Mesopotamia. It spread out from Urhai (Edessa) and Arbil and sent missionaries to Persia, India, China and throughout Asia during the first and succeeding centuries. It is the Aramaic-speaking church.

GENERAL ORGANIZATION

Patriarch: His Holiness Mar Eshai Shimun XXIII, Catholicos Patriarch of the Church of the East and Supreme Head of the Assyrian People in the Republic of Iraq. The Patriarchate, 554 Arballo Drive, San Francisco, CA 94132.

† Church of the Living God

(Motto: Christian Workers for Fellowship)

This organization was formed at Wrightsville, Arkansas, in 1889 by the late Chief William Christian. It emphasizes believers' baptism by immersion, the use of water and unleavened bread, and the washing of saints' feet in the celebration of the Lord's Supper, which is required only once—when one unites with the church. The local organizations are known as "temples."

GENERAL ORGANIZATION

National Assembly: annual, second Tuesday in Oct.

General Assembly: quadrennial.

OFFICERS

Chief Bishop, F. C. Scott, 801 N.E. 17th St., Oklahoma City, OK 73105.
Vice-Chief Bishop, J. B. Mason, Box 156, Andalusia, AL 36420.
Gen. Sec., Overseer Charles E. Porter, 2700 W. 102nd St., Inglewood, CA 90303.
Gen. Treas., Elder Harvey R. Jones, 5033 La-Paz Dr., San Diego, CA 92113.

Church of the Lutheran Brethren of America

Organized in Milwaukee, Wisconsin, in 1900. It accepts as members only those who subscribe to the Lutheran teachings and who profess a personal experience of salvation. Lutheran Brethren churches are nonliturgical, and the pastors do not wear gowns.

Churches: 90. Inclusive Membership: 8,960. Sunday or Sabbath Schools: 90. Total Enrollment: 8,625. Ordained clergy: 114.

GENERAL ORGANIZATION

Convention: annual (June).
Headquarters: Fergus Falls, MN 56537. Tel. (218) 736-5666.

OFFICERS

Pres., Rev. E. H. Strom, 704 Vernon Ave. West, Fergus Falls, MN 56537.
1st Vice-Pres., Rev. Omar Gjerness, Lutheran Brethren Schools, Fergus Falls, MN, 56537.
2nd Vice-Pres., Rev. O. E. Overland, 511 N. 72nd St., Seattle, WA 98103.
Sec., Rev. Robert M. Sletta, 809 20th St. N., Moorhead, MN 56560.
Treas., Rev. Robert Wallin, 611 Alcott Ave. W., Fergus Falls, MN 56537.
Pres., Lutheran Brethren Schools, Rev. C. Lloyd Bjornlie, Lutheran Brethren Schools, Fergus Falls, MN 56537.

PERIODICAL

Faith and Fellowship (semi-m), 1391 N. Grand Oaks Ave., Pasadena, CA 91104, Rev. Robert Overgaard, Ed.

Church of the Nazarene

One of the larger holiness bodies organized in Pilot Point, Texas, in October, 1908. It is in general accord with the early doctrines of Methodism and emphasizes entire sanctification as a second definite work of grace.

Churches: 4,654. Inclusive Membership: 394,-197. Sunday or Sabbath Schools: 4,806. Total Enrollment: 868,911. Ordained clergy: 6,774.

GENERAL ORGANIZATION

General Assembly: quadrennial. (Next meeting, Dallas, Texas, June, 1976.)
International Headquarters: 6401 The Paseo, Kansas City, MO 64131. Tel. (816) 333-7000.

OFFICERS

Gen. Supts.: V. H. Lewis, George Coulter, Edward Lawlor, Eugene L. Stowe, Orville Jenkins, and Charles Strickland.

Gen. Sec., B. Edgar Johnson.
Gen. Treas., Norman O. Miller.

OTHER ORGANIZATIONS

General Board: Sec., B. Edgar Johnson; Treas., Norman O. Miller.
Departments: World Missions: Sec., E. S. Phillips; Home Missions: Sec., Raymond Hurn; Publications: Sec., M. A. (Bud) Lunn; Pensions and Benevolence: Sec., Dean Wessels; Education: Sec., Edward S. Mann; Church Schools: Sec., Kenneth Rice; Evangelism: Sec., John Knight.
General Stewardship Committee: Sec., Earl Wolf.
Nazarene Young People's Society: Pres., Talmadge Johnson.
Nazarene World Missionary Society: Sec., Mary Scott.
Nazarene Servicemen's Commission: Dir., Paul Skiles.
Christian Service Training Commission: Dir., Earl Wolf.
National Trans. Sec., B. Edgar Johnson.
Nazarene Radio League: Dir., H. Dale Mitchell.
Nazarene Information Service: Dir., O. Joe Olson.

PERIODICALS

Herald of Holiness (w), W. T. Purkiser, Ed.
The Other Sheep (m), E. S. Phillips, Ed.
Nazarene Preacher (m), James McGraw, Ed.
Church School Periodicals, A. F. Harper, Exec. Ed.
Church School Builder (m), Erwin G. Benson, Ed.
Conquest (m), Paul Miller, Ed.
All published by the Nazarene Publishing House Box 527, Kansas City, MO 64141.

Churches of Christ

This body is made up of a large group of churches, formerly reported with the Disciples of Christ, but since the Religious Census of 1906 reported separately. They are strictly congregational and have no organization larger than the local congregation.

NO GENERAL ORGANIZATION

PERIODICALS

Gospel Advocate (w), 1006 Elm Hill Road, Nashville, TN 37210. B. C. Goodpasture, Ed.
Firm Foundation (w), 3110 Guadalupe St., Austin, TX 78705. Reuel Lemmons, Ed.
Christian Leader (bi-w), 4507 W. Wilson Ave., Chicago, IL 60630. Elza Huffard, Ed.
20th Century Christian, 1121 W. 79th St., Los Angeles, CA 90044. M. Norvel Young, Ed.
The Christian Chronicle, 650 College Drive, Abilene, TX 79601. Ralph Sweet, Ed.
Gospel Herald (m), Beamsville, Ontario, Canada. Roy D. Merritt, Ed.
North American Christian (m), 60 West St., Keene, NH 03431. James Robert Jarrell, Ed.
Christian Bible Teacher (m), Box 1060, Abilene, TX 79604. Bill Patterson, Ed.
Voice of Freedom (m), Box 150, Nashville, TN 37202. P. D. Wilmeth, Ed.
Mission (m), Box 2822, Abilene, TX 79604. Roy B. Ward, Ed.
Truth (m), Rt. 2, Box 177, Marion, IN 46952.

Churches of Christ in Christian Union

Organized in 1909 at Washington Court House, Ohio, as the Churches of Christ in Christian Union. This body believes in the new birth and the baptism of the Holy Spirit for believers. It is Wesleyan with an evangelistic and missionary emphasis.

Reformed Methodist Church merged in September, 1952, with Churches of Christ in Christian Union.

Churches: 244. Inclusive Membership: 8,741. Sunday or Sabbath Schools: 231. Total Enrollment: 16,623. Ordained clergy: 223.

GENERAL ORGANIZATION

General Council: biennial. (Next meeting 1974).
District Councils: annual.
General Headquarters: 459 East Ohio St. (Mailing address: Box 30), Circleville, OH 43113.

OFFICERS

Gen. Supt., Rev. W. L. Cozad, Box 30, Circleville, OH 43113.
Asst. Gen. Supt., Rev. Donavon Humble, R. 1, Waverly, OH 45690.
Gen. Sec., Rev. Allen Gallimore, 141 Oiler Ave., Oak Hill, WV 25901.
Gen. Treas., Beverly R. Salley, Box 30, Circleville, OH 43113.
Gen. Board of Trustees: Chm., Rev. W. L. Cozad, Box 30, Circleville, OH 43113; Vice-Chm., Rev. Donavan Humble, R. 1, Waverly, OH 45690; Sec., Rev. Jack Norman, 458 Chestnut St., Chillicothe, OH 45601.
District Superintendents (all District Superintendents are also members of the Gen. Bd. of Trustees): North Central Dist., Rev. Joseph Johnson, Box 431, West Jefferson, OH 43162; South Central Dist., Rev. G. L. Blankenship, R.R. 1, Box 163A, Bainbridge, OH 45612; Southeastern Dist., Rev. L. N. Fitts, R. 3, Box 200A, Waverly, OH 45690; Northeastern Dist., Rev. J. L. Watkins, R. 2, Port Crane, NY 13833.

PERIODICALS

Advocate (bi-w), P. Lewis Brevard, Ed.
Missionary Tidings (m), Rev. Dorothy Meadows, Ed.

Churches of God in North America (General Eldership)

This body emerged out of a revival movement among the Germans in Pennsylvania in 1825, under the leadership of John Winebrenner, a German Reformed minister. The Bible is the only rule of faith and practice.

GENERAL ORGANIZATION

General Eldership: meets triennially.
Headquarters: 611 S. 17th St., Harrisburg, PA 17105. Tel. (717) 234-2496.
General Eldership Administrator, Rev. Richard Wilkin, 701 E. Melrose Ave., Findlay, OH 45840. Tel. (419) 423-8386.

OFFICERS

Pres., Rev. Darrell Prichard, 508 E. Walnut St., Nappanee, IN 46550.
Vice-Pres., Dr. K. E. Boldosser, 900 S. Arling-

COMMUNITY CHURCHES

ton Ave., Rm. 200, Harrisburg, PA 17109.
Journalizing Sec., Rev. Harry G. Cadamore, 1210 Carlisle St., Natrona Heights, PA 15065.
Treas.. Mr. James H. Booser, 134 N. Union St., Middletown, PA 17057.
Stat. Clk., Mrs. Ronald Barrick, R.D. 3, Newville, PA 17241.

COMMISSIONS
Evangelism: Chmn., Rev. R. A. Wood, R.F.D. 3, Dillsburg, PA 17019; Sec., Rev. Carroll Mc-Nutt, 817 N. Midway Dr., Auburn, IN 46706.
Christian Education: Chmn., Rev. A. G. Dunn, 211 Market St., Harrisburg, PA 17103; Sec., Dr. K. E. Boldosser, 900 S. Arlington Ave., Rm. 200, Harrisburg, PA 17109.
Stewardship: Chmn. Rev. D. F. Stone, 807 Luther St., Harrisburg, PA 17112; Sec., Rev. W. D. Rodahaver, Box 114, Alverton, PA 15612.
Lay Activities: Chmn., Rev. James Moss, R.F. D. 1, Finksburg, MD 21048; Sec., Mrs. James Booser, 134 North Union St., Middletown, PA 17057.
Publication: Chmn., Rev. C. H. Lacquement, 3415 Belair Rd., Harrisburg, PA 17109; Sec., Rev. K. L. Clouser, 52 Big Spring Ave., Newville, PA 17241.
National Missions: Chmn., Dr. Arthur Eakin, R.F.D. 2, Box 1063 A, Ellwood City, PA 16117; Sec., Rev. Donald Cohick, 26 East Main St., Mechanicsburg, PA 17055.
World Missions: Chmn., Dr. J. E. Lewis, 342 W. Chestnut St., Lancaster, PA 17603; Sec., Mrs. Esther G. Musser, Box 116, Mt. Joy, PA 17552.

PERIODICAL
The Church Advocate (m), P. O. Box 2103, Harrisburg, PA 17105, Rev. John Parthemore, Ed.

Community Churches

See National Council of Community Churches in U.S. Service Agencies directory.

Congregational Christian Churches, National Association of

Organized 1955 in Detroit, Michigan by delegates from Congregational Christian Churches committed to continuing the Congregational way of faith and order in church life. It has no doctrinal requirements. Participation by member churches is voluntary.

Churches: 336. Inclusive Membership: 85,000. Sunday or Sabbath Schools: 326. Total Enrollment: 30,000. Ordained clergy: 391.

GENERAL ORGANIZATION
Annual Meeting. Northfield, MN, 1973.

OFFICERS
Mod., Dr. Erwin A. Britton, 33 E. Forest St., Detroit, MI 48201. Exec. Secs., Dr. John H. Alexander, Rev. George W. Brown, Jr., and Dr. Walter J. Vernon, 176 W. Wisconsin Ave., Milwaukee, WI 53203.

PERIODICAL
The Congregationalist (m), 7330 N. Santa Mon-

ica Blvd., Milwaukee, WI 53217. Rev. Richard P. Buchman, Ed.

Congregational Holiness Church

A body which separated from the Pentecostal Holiness Church in 1921; carries on mission work in Mexico, Honduras, Costa Rica, Cuba and Brazil.

GENERAL ORGANIZATION
General Conference, meets every two years.
General Committee, meets as called. Represents six State divisions.
General Headquarters: Griffin, GA 30223. Tel. (404) 228-1718.

OFFICERS
Gen. Supt., Rev. Terry Crews, Rt. 1, Box 325, Griffin, GA 30223.
Gen. Sec. and Treas., Rev. Cullen Hicks, Rt. 2, Box 104A, Lincolnton, GA 30817. Tel. (404) 359-5030.

PERIODICAL
The Gospel Messenger (m), 701 Davis St., Monroe, GA 30655. Rev. B. L. Cox, Ed.

† Conservative Baptist Association of America

Organized May 17, 1947, at Atlantic City, New Jersey. The Old and New Testaments are regarded as the divinely inspired Word of God and are therefore infallible and of supreme authority. Each local church is independent and autonomous, and free from ecclesiastical or political authority.

GENERAL ORGANIZATION
Meets annually.
Headquarters: Geneva Rd., Box 66, Wheaton, IL 60187. Tel. (312) 653-5350.

OFFICERS
Pres., Dr. John M. Berentschot, 441 Buena Vista, San Mateo, CA 94403.
Rec. Sec., Rev. Horace Taylor, 126 James, Mt. Ephraim, NJ 08059.
Corr. Sec., Rev. Richard P. Camp, 395 Essex St., Hamilton, MA 01982.
Treas., Rev. Robert P. Dugan, 4490 Newland St., Wheat Ridge, CO 80033.
Eastern Vice-Pres., Rev. Carl E. Abrahamsen, Jr., King George Rd., Millington, NJ 07946.
Central Vice-Pres., Rev. Donald Engram, 711 South Fourth St., Pekin, IL 61554.
Western Vice-Pres., Rev. Paul E. Horn, 5635 Cambridge, Montclair, CA 91763.
Gen. Dir., Dr. Russell A. Shive, Box 66, Wheaton, IL 60187. Tel. (312) 653-5350.

OTHER ORGANIZATIONS
Conservative Baptist Foreign Mission Society: Box 5, Wheaton, IL 60187.
Conservative Baptist Home Mission Society: Box 828, Wheaton, IL 60187, Gen. Dir., Dr. Rufus Jones.

PERIODICAL
Conservative Baptist, P.O. Box 999, Wheaton, IL 60187.

Conservative Congregational Christian Conference

The Conference was founded in Chicago, Illinois, in 1948 by a group of Congregational Christian Churches and ministers in order to maintain the historic biblical doctrines and the autonomous polity of the Congregational way. Present membership includes churches from varied denominational backgrounds.

Churches: 120. Inclusive Membership: 19,416. Sunday or Sabbath Schools: 117. Total Enrollment: 14,169. Ordained clergy. 225.

GENERAL ORGANIZATION
General Conference: annual.
Headquarters: Box 171, Hinsdale, IL 60521. Tel. (312) 833-8485.

OFFICERS
Pres., Rev. Wayne J. Hamilton, Box 18, Greenhurst, NY 14742.
1st Vice-Pres., Rev. Robert Vander Zaag, 93 N. Baldwin St., Sierra Madre, CA 91024.
2nd Vice-Pres., Rev. Allen Barry Jones, 1490 Birmingham St., St. Paul, MN 55106.
Missionary-at-large, Rev. Samuel T. Hemberger, 934 Bryan, Elmhurst, IL 60126.
Treas., Roger Christensen, 1555 Lincoln Ave., St. Paul, MN 55105.
Recording Sec., Rev. Raymond Biddle, Rt. 2, Beloit, OH 44609.
Editor, Dr. Graeme C. Smith, Box 101, Vista, CA 92083.
Historian, Rev. Edward Whitman, Box 77, Elnora, NY 12065.

Cumberland Presbyterian Church

An outgrowth of the Great Revival of 1800, the Cumberland Presbytery was organized February 4, 1810, in Dickson County, Tennessee, by three Presbyterian ministers, Revs. Finis Ewing, Samuel King, and Samuel McAdow. A union with the Presbyterian Church, U.S.A., in 1906 was only partially successful and the Cumberland Presbyterian Church continued as a separate denomination.

Churches: 854. Inclusive Membership: 90,368. Sunday or Sabbath Schools: 880. Total Enrollment: 57,726. Ordained clergy. 633.

GENERAL ORGANIZATION
General Assembly: annual (in June).

OFFICERS
Mod., E. T. Shauf, 1410 Golf Club Ln., Clarksville, TN 37040.
Stated Clk., Rev. H. Shaw Scates, Box 4149, Memphis, TN 38104.
Asst. Stated Clk., Rev. T. V. Warnick, 907 E. Main, Murfreesboro, TN 37130.

INSTITUTIONS
Cumberland Presbyterian Center, 1978 Union Ave., Memphis, TN 38104. Mailing Address: Box 4149 (Headquarters for all denominational offices, print shop and bookstore.)

BOARDS
Board of Missions: Pres., Robert M. Shelton, 3102 Sunnylawn Cr., Austin, TX 78723; Exec.

Sec., Rev. Carl Ramsey, Box 4149, Memphis, TN 38104.
Board of Publication and Christian Education: Pres., Davis Gray, 415 Wrather Place, Murfreesboro, TN 37130; Exec. Sec., Rev. Harold Davis, Box 4149, Memphis, TN 38104.
Board of Finance: Pres., Sam B. Miles, 600 Deepwood Dr., Hopkinsville, KY 42240; Exec. Sec., Dr. Eugene Warren, Box 4149, Memphis, TN 38104.

PERIODICALS
The Cumberland Presbyterian (w), Box 4149, Memphis, TN 38104, C. Ray Dobbins, Ed.
The Missionary Messenger (m), Box 4149, Memphis, TN 38104, Rev. Dudley Condron, Ed.
Sunday School Literature (q), Box 4149, Memphis, TN 38104, Rev. James McGuire, Ed.

† Duck River (and Kindred) Associations of Baptists

A group of Baptist associations found in Tennessee, Alabama, Georgia, Kentucky, and Mississippi.

GENERAL ORGANIZATION
Meets yearly, in October.

OFFICERS
Duck River Association: Mod., Elder Clyde Roberts, 123 Collier Ave., Shelbyville, TN 37160; Clk., Rex Shelton, Rt. 3, Shelbyville, TN 37160.
General Association: Mod., Elder W. B. Kerby, Henagar, AL 35978; Clk., Elder James F. Patton, Morrison, TN 37357.

Eastern Orthodox Catholic Church in America

Organized, 1927, in New York.

Churches: 3. Inclusive Membership: 293. Sunday or Sabbath Schools: 1. Total Enrollment: 112. Ordained clergy: 6.

GENERAL ORGANIZATION
Governing Synod meets annually.
Headquarters: 1914 Hwy. 17-92, Fern Park, FL 32730.

OFFICER
Rt. Rev. Gregory R. P. Adair.

PERIODICAL
American Review of Eastern Orthodoxy, 1914 Hwy. 17-92, Fern Park, FL 32730.

Elim Fellowship

The Elim Fellowship, a Pentecostal body, established in 1947, is an outgrowth of the Elim Ministerial Fellowship, which was formed in 1933. By corporate action the official name has been changed from Elim Missionary Assemblies to Elim Fellowship.

Churches: 70. Inclusive Membership: 5,000. Sunday or Sabbath Schools: 70. Total Enrollment: N.R. Ordained clergy: 128.

THE EPISCOPAL CHURCH

GENERAL ORGANIZATION

Annual Representative Assemblies. An Executive Committee meets bi-monthly.

OFFICERS

Gen. Chm., Carlton Spencer, Elim Fellowship, Lima, NY 14485. Tel. (716) 582-1230.
Gen. Vice-Chm., George Veach, 2589 Tilson Rd., Decatur, GA 30032.
Gen. Sec., Winston Nunes, 4 Palomino Crescent Willowdale, Toronto, Ont., Canada.
Gen. Treas., Elden Mudge, 300 S. Tilden St., Pontiac, MI 48053.

PERIODICAL

World Map Digest (bi-m), 900 N. Glenoaks Blvd., Burbank, CA 91502, Donald Crosbie, Ed.

The Episcopal Church

This body entered the colonies with the earliest settlers (Jamestown, Virginia, 1607), as the Church of England. It became autonomous as the Protestant Episcopal Church in the U.S.A. and adopted its present name in 1789. It is an integral part of the Anglican Communion. In 1967 the General Convention adopted "The Episcopal Church" as an alternate name for the Church.

Churches: 7,116. Inclusive Membership: 3,217,-365. Sunday or Sabbath Schools: 6,451. Total Enrollment: 685,596. Ordained clergy: 11,108.

GENERAL ORGANIZATION

General Convention: Triennial. (Next meeting, 1973.)
Headquarters: 815 Second Ave., New York, NY 10017. Tel. (212) 867-8400.

OFFICERS

Presiding Bishop, Rt. Rev. John E. Hines.
Sec. Ho. of Bishops, Rt. Rev. Scott Field Bailey, 520 San Jacinto St., Houston, TX 77002.
Pres. Ho. of Deputies, Rev. John B. Coburn, 865 Madison Ave., New York, NY 10021.
Sec.-Treas., Gen. Conv., Rev. Canon Charles M. Guilbert.

OTHER ORGANIZATIONS

Executive Council: Office, 815 Second Ave., New York, NY 10017.
Pres., Rt. Rev. John E. Hines; Executive Vice-Pres., Rt. Rev. Roger W. Blanchard; Vice-Pres. for Development, Oscar C. Carr, Jr.; Treas., Lindley M. Franklin, Jr.; Sec., Rev. John F. Stevens; Ecumenical Officer, Peter Day.
Jurisdictions: Deputy, Paul A. Tate.
Program: Prog. Officer, Rev. Robert C. Martin, Jr.
General Convention Special Program: Dir., Leon E. Modeste.
Financial Services: Dir., Lindley M. Franklin, Jr.; Asst. Treas., Matthew Costigan.
Communication: Commun. Officer, John C. Goodbody.
Administration: Vice-Pres., Rt. Rev. Roger W.

Blanchard; Admin. Officer, Rev. John F. Stevens.
Office of the Bishop for the Armed Forces; Bishop, Rt. Rev. Clarence E. Hobgood; Administrative Asst., Rev. Cyril Best.
Brotherhood of St. Andrew: Pres., Fred C. Gore; Sec., E. Hudgens, 540 W. King St., York, PA 17404.
Church Army in the U.S.A.: Pres., Rev. H. Boone Porter, 815 Second Ave., New York. NY 10017; Sec., Sister Brooke Bushong, C.A.; Treas., Capt. Howard E. Galley, Jr., C.A.
Church Pension Fund: 800 Second Ave., New York, NY 10017; Chmn., Rt. Rev. William F. Creighton; Pres., Robert Robinson.
Church Historical Society: 606 Rathervue Place, Austin, TX 78705; Pres., Rev. Massey H. Shepherd, Jr.; Sec., Rev. Charles A. Sumners; Archivist, Virginia N. Bellamy.
Forward Movement Publications: 412 Sycamore St., Cincinnati, OH 45202, Ed., Rev. James W. Kennedy.

PERIODICALS

The Episcopalian (m), 1930 Chestnut St., Philadelphia, PA 19103, Henry L. McCorkle, Ed.
The Living Church (w), 407 E. Michigan St., Milwaukee, WI 53202, Rev. Carroll M. Simcox, Ed.
The Witness (w), Tunkhannock, PA 18657, Wm. B. Spofford, Man. Ed.
Historical Magazine (q), Box 2247, Austin, TX 78705, Rev. Lawrence L. Brown, Ed.
The Churchman (m), 1074 23rd Ave., N., St. Petersburg, FL 33704, Edna Ruth Johnson, Acting Ed.
Anglican Theol. Review (q), 600 Haven St., Evanston, IL 60201, Rev. J. C. Hurd, Ed.
Pan-Anglican (occ.), 1335 Asylum Ave., Hartford, CT 06105.

ACTIVE BISHOPS IN THE U.S.A.

(Note: CO, Coadjutor; S, Suffragan)
(Address: Right Reverend)
Headquarters Staff: Presiding Bishop, John E. Hines; Exec. Vice-Pres., Roger W. Blanchard; Suffragan Bishop for the Armed Forces, Clarence E. Hobgood, 815 Second Ave., New York, NY 10017.
Alabama, Furman C. Stough, 521 N. 20th St., Birmingham 35203.
Alaska, William J. Gordon, Box 441, Fairbanks, 99701.
Albany, Allen W. Brown; Charles B. Persel, Jr. (S), 62 S. Swan St., Albany, NY 12210.
Arizona, Joseph M. Harte 110 W. Roosevelt St., Phoenix 85003.
Arkansas, Christoph Keller, 300 W. 17th St., Little Rock 72206.
Atlanta, Bennett J. Sims; Milton L. Wood (S), 2744 Peachtree Rd. N.W., Atlanta, GA 30305.
Bethlehem, Lloyd E. Gressle, 826 Delaware Ave., Bethlehem, PA 18015.
California, C. Kilmer Myers; G. Richard Millard (S), 1055 Taylor St., San Francisco 94108.
Central Florida, William H. Folwell, 324 N. Interlachen Ave., Box 790, Winter Park, 32789.
Central Gulf Coast, George M. Murray, 3809 Old Shell Rd., Mobile AL 36608.
Central N.Y. Ned Cole, Jr., 935 James St., Syracuse 13203.

Central Pennsylvania, Dean T. Stevenson, 215 N. Front St., Harrisburg 17101.

Chicago, James W. Montgomery 65 E. Huron St., Chicago 60611.

Colorado, Edwin B. Thayer, 1313 Clarkson St., Denver, 80210.

Connecticut, J. Warren Hutchens; Morgan Porteus (S), 1335 Asylum Ave., Hartford 06105.

Dallas, A. Donald Davies; Theodore H. McCrea (S), 2220 Main St., Dallas, TX 75201; W. Paul Barnds (S), 2220 Main St., Dallas, TX 75201.

Delaware, William H. Mead, 2020 Tatnall St., Wilmington 19802.

East Carolina, Thomas H. Wright; Hunley A. Elebash (CO), 305 S. 3rd St., Wilmington, NC 28401.

Eastern Oregon, William B. Spofford, Jr., P.O. Box 951, Bend 97701.

Easton, George A. Taylor, Easton, MD 31601.

Eau Claire, Stanley H. Atkins, 510 S. Farwell St., Eau Claire, WI 54701.

Erie, William Crittenden, 329 W. 6th St., Erie, PA 16501.

Florida, Hamilton West, 325 Market St., Jacksonville 32202.

Fond du Lac, Wm. H. Brady, 39 N. Sophia St., Fond du Lac, WI 54935.

Georgia, G. Paul Reeves 611 East Bay St., Savannah 31401.

Hawaii, Edwin L. Hanchett, Queen Emma Square, Honolulu 96813.

Idaho, Hanford L. King, 107 E. Fort St., Boise 83702.

Indianapolis, John P. Craine, 1100 W. 42nd St., Indianapolis 46208.

Iowa, Walter C. Righter, 225 37th St., Des Moines 50312.

Kansas, Edward C. Turner, Bethany Place, Topeka 66600.

Kentucky, C. Gresham Marmion, Jr., David B. Reed (CO), 421 S. 2nd St., Louisville 40202.

Lexington, Addison Hosea, 544 Sayre Ave., Lexington, KY 40508.

Long Island, Jonathan G. Sherman, 36 Cathedral Ave., Garden City, NY 11530; Charles W. Maclean (S), 65 Fourth St., Garden City, NY 11530; Richard B. Martin (S), 157 Montague St., Brooklyn, NY 11201.

Los Angeles, Francis Eric Bloy; Robert C. Rusack (S), 1220 W. 4th St., Los Angeles, CA 90019.

Louisiana, Iveson B. Noland, P.O. Box 50850, New Orleans 70150.

Maine, Frederick B. Wolf, 143 State St., Portland 04101.

Maryland, David Leighton, Sr., 105 W. Monument St., Baltimore 21230.

Massachusetts, John M. Burgess, 1 Joy St., Boston 02143; Morris F. Arnold (S), 1 Joy St., Boston 02143.

Michigan, R. S. M. Emrich; H. Coleman McGehee, Jr. (CO), 4800 Woodward Ave., Detroit 48201.

Milwaukee, Donald H. V. Hallock, 804 E. Juneau Ave., Milwaukee 53202.

Minnesota, Philip F. McNairy, 309 Clifton Ave., Minneapolis 55403.

Mississippi, J. Maury Allin, P.O. Box 953, Jackson 39205.

Missouri, George L. Cadigan, 1210 Locust St., St. Louis 63103.

Montana, Jackson E. Gilliam, 203 Wheat Bldg., Helena 59601.

Nebraska, Robert P. Varley, 1502 W.O.W. Bldg., 2390 W. 7th St., Omaha 68102.

Nevada, Wesley Frensdorff, 2930 W. 7th St., Reno 89503.

New Hampshire, Charles F. Hall, 63 Green St., Concord 03301.

New Jersey, Alfred L. Banyard; Albert W. Van Duzer (S), 808 W. State St., Trenton 08618.

New Mexico and Southwest Texas, Richard M. Trelease, Jr., P.O. Box 2003, Santa Fe., NM 87501.

New York, Paul Moore, Jr. J. Staurt Wetmore (S), 1047 Amsterdam Ave., New York 10025.

Newark, Leland Stark; George E. Rath (CO), 24 Rector St., Newark 07102.

North Carolina, Thomas A. Fraser, Jr.; W. Moultrie Moore, Jr. (S), 201 St. Alban's, Raleigh 27609.

North Dakota, George T. Masuda, 809 8th Ave. So., Fargo 58102.

Northern California, Clarence R. Haden, Jr.; Edward McNair (S), 1322 27th St., Sacramento 95816.

Northern Indiana, William C. R. Sheridan, 117 No. Lafayette Blvd., South Bend 46601.

Northern Michigan, Samuel J. Wylie, 922 Tenth Ave., Menominee 49858.

Northwest Texas, Willis R. Henton, 1520 Bryan St., Amarillo 79102.

Ohio, John H. Burt, 2230 Euclid Ave., Cleveland, 44115.

Oklahoma, Chilton Powell; Frederick W. Putnam, Jr (S), P.O. Box 1098, Oklahoma City 73101.

Olympia, Ivol I. Curtis, 1551 Tenth Ave., East, Seattle, WA 98102.

Oregon, James W. F. Carman; Hal R. Gross (S), 11800 S.W. Military La., Portland 97219.

Panama and the Canal Zone, Lemuel B. Shirley (MB), Box R, Balboa, Canal Zone.

Pennsylvania, Robert L. DeWitt, Jr.; Lyman C. Ogilby (Asst), 202 W. Rittenhouse Sq., Philadelphia 19103.

Pittsburgh, Robert B. Appleyard, 325 Oliver Ave., Pittsburgh 15222.

Puerto Rico, Francisco Reus-Froylan (MB), Box 9002, Santurce, PR 00908.

Quincy, F. William Lickfield, 3900 Hawthorne Pl., Peoria, IL 61614.

Rhode Island, Frederick H. Belden, 275 N. Main St., Providence 02903.

Rochester, Robert R. Spears, Jr., 935 East Ave., Rochester, NY 14607.

San Joaquin, Victor M. Rivera, 4115 E. Dakota Ave., Stockton, CA 93726.

South Carolina, Gray Temple, 138 Wentworth St., Charleston 29401.

South Dakota, Walter H. Jones, 200 W. 18th St., Sioux Falls 57101; Harold S. Jones (S).

Southeast Florida, James L. Duncan, 525 NE 15 St., Miami, 33132.

Southern Ohio, John M Krumm, 412 Sycamore St., Cincinnati 45202.

Southern Virginia, David S. Rose, 618 Stockley Gardens, Norfolk 23507.

Southwest Florida, William L. Hargrave, Box 4043, St. Petersburg, 33731.

Southwestern Virginia, Wm. H. Marmion, P.O. Box 2068, Roanoke 24009.

Spokane, John R. Wyatt, 245 E. 13th Ave., Spokane 99202.

Springfield, Albert A. Chambers, 726 S. 2nd St., Springfield, IL 62704.; Albert W. Hillestad (CO).

Tennessee, John Vander Horst, 692 Poplar Ave., Memphis 38105; William E. Sanders (CO), 908 Knoxville Bank Bldg., Knoxville 37902; William F. Gates, Jr. (S), 692 Poplar Ave., Memphis 38105.

Texas, J. Milton Richardson, 520 San Jacinto St., Houston 77002; F. Percy Goddard (S), 2726 Tanglewood Drive, Tyler 75701; Scott Field Bailey (S), 520 San Jacinto St., Houston 77002.

Upper South Carolina, John A. Pinckney, P.O. Box 1789, Columbia 29202.

Utah, E. Otis Charles, 231 E. First South St., Salt Lake City 84111.

Vermont, Harvey D. Butterfield, Rock Point, Burlington 05401.

Virgin Islands, Edward M. Turner (MB), P.O. Box 1589, St. Thomas, U. S. Virgin Islands.

Virginia, Robert F. Gibson, 110 W. Franklin St., Richmond, 23220; Robert B. Hall (CO), 110 W. Franklin St., Richmond 23220; Philip A. Smith (S), 1000 St. Stephens' Rd., Seminary P.O., Alexandria 22304.

Washington, William F. Creighton; John T. Walker (S), Mt. St. Albans, Washington, DC 20016.

West Missouri, Edward R. Welles, Arthur Vogel (CO), P.O. Box 8578, Kansas City 64114.

West Texas, Harold C. Gosnell; R. Earl Dicus (S), P.O. Box 6885, San Antonio 78209.

West Virginia, Wilburn C. Campbell, 1608A Virginia St. E., Charleston 25311.

Western Kansas, William Davison, 142 S. 8th St., P.O. Box 1383, Salina 67401.

Western Massachusetts, Alexander D. Stewart, 37 Chestnut St., Springfield 01103.

Western Michigan, Charles E. Bennison, 643 W. Crosstown Pkwy., Kalamazoo 49001.

Western New York, Harold B. Robinson, 1114 Delaware Ave., Buffalo 14209.

Western North Carolina, M. George Henry, P.O. Box 368, In-the-Oaks, Black Mountain 28711.

Wyoming, David R. Thornberry, Box 1007, Laramie 82070.

Ethical Culture Movement

A national federation of Ethical Humanist Societies—religious and educational fellowships based on ethics, believing in the worth, dignity, and fine potentialities of the individual, encouraging freedom of thought, committed to the democratic ideal and method, issuing in social action.

Churches: 25. Inclusive Membership: 5,000. Sunday or Sabbath Schools: 20. Total Enrollment: 1,325. Ordained clergy: 37.

AMERICAN ETHICAL UNION
Assembly: annual (April).
Headquarters: 2 West 64th St., New York, NY 10023. Tel. (212) 873-6500.

OFFICERS
Pres., Steven Jacobs.
Vice-Pres., Jack Tourin.
Treas., Walter Neuman.
Sec., Muriel Neufeld.

Administrator, Jean S. Kotkin.
Adm. Asst., Theresa Gould.

ORGANIZATIONS
National Ethical Youth Organization (NEYO), Youth Advisor, Joseph Chuman.
Fraternity of Leaders, Chmn., James F. Hornback.
National Women's Conference, Pres., Mrs. Naomi Shaw.
Encampment for Citizenship, Exec. Dir., Paul Barker.
A.E.U. Conference Center, Chmn., William Phillips.
A.E.U. Race Commission, Chmn., Robert M. Stein.
International Humanist & Ethical Union, Representative, Sidney H. Scheuer.
Joint Washington Office for Social Concern, Dir., Robert E. Jones.

The Evangelical Church of North America

This body was formed in Portland, Oregon in June, 1968. It consists of congregations which declined to enter The United Methodist Church, which resulted from a merger of the Evangelical United Brethren and The Methodist Church. The Evangelical Church of North America incorporated congregations from across the nation including those of the former Holiness Methodist Church. The church is Arminian-Wesleyan in doctrinal orientation.

Churches: 115. Inclusive Membership: 9,451. Sunday or Sabbath Schools: 115. Total Enrollment: 13,418. Ordained clergy: 160.

GENERAL ORGANIZATION
Council of Superintendents which has the power to integrate program and to recommend policy. Such recommendations require the approval of the annual conferences.

OFFICERS
Exec. Sec., Rev. V. A. Ballantyne, 1020 Main St., Milwaukie, OR 97222. Tel. (503) 659-5622.
Chmn., Council of Superintendents, Rev. George K. Millen, 1020 Main St., Milwaukie, OR 97222. Tel. (503) 659-5622.

PERIODICAL
The Evangelical Advocate (m), 128 S. Pine, Albany, OR 97321. Rev. A. D. Enns, Ed.

Evangelical Congregational Church

This denomination had its beginning in the movement known as the Evangelical Association, organized by Jacob Albright in the early nineteenth century. In 1891 a division occurred in the Evangelical Association, which resulted in the organization of the United Evangelical Church in 1894. An attempt to heal this division was made in 1922, but a portion of the United Evangelical Church was not satisfied with the plan of merger and remained apart, taking the above name in 1928. This denomination is Arminian in doctrine, evangelistic in spirit, and Methodistic in church government, with congregational ownership of local church property.

Churches: 160. Inclusive Membership: 29,682. Sunday or Sabbath Schools: 159. Total Enrollment: 28,311. Ordained clergy: 173.

GENERAL ORGANIZATION

General Conference: quadrennial. (Next meeting, 1974).
Headquarters: The Residence of the Bishop, Dr. P. K. Cressman, 1005 Barberry Rd., Wyomissing Park, Reading, PA 19602.

OFFICERS

Presiding Bishop, Dr. P. K. Cressman
Sec., Rev. A. E. Anderson, 602 Marclare St., Dixon, IL 61021.
Asst. Secs: Rev. J. K. Rapp, 125 N. 67th St., Harrisburg, PA 17111 and Rev. F. T. Fink, 242 E. Ralston St., Akron, OH 44301.
Stat. Sec., Rev. C. C. Reeder, 446 E. Broad St., Tamaqua, PA 18252.
Treas., Rev. G. A. Raker, 130 S. Wyomissing Ave., Shillington, PA 17607.
Sec. of Missions: Rev. R. A. Cattermole, Shillington, PA 17607.
Supt, Homes for Aged., Rev. Russell Wise, Myerstown, PA 17067.

OTHER ORGANIZATIONS

Administrative Council: Chmn., Bishop P. K. Cressman; 1st Vice-Chmn., Dr. H. H. Scanlin; 2nd Vice-Chmn., Dr. P. D. Dunn; Sec.-Treas., Rev. R. A. Cattermole.
Board of Church Extension: Pres., Rev. G. A. Raker, Reading, PA; Sec., Rev. C. C. Reeder, Tamaqua, PA.
Board of Missions: Pres., Bishop Emeritus J. A. Smith, Akron, PA.; Sec., E. D. Ehrig, Allentown, PA.
Board of Publication: Pres., Don C. Van Liew, Shillington, PA; Sec., Rev. J. E. Moyer, Emmaus, PA.
Board of Christian Education: Pres., Rev. P. D. Dunn, Akron, OH; Sec., Rev. R. K. Guistwite, Plymouth Meeting, PA.
Board of Pensions: Pres., Bishop Emeritus J. A. Smith, Akron, PA; Sec., Dr. J. D. Yoder, Myerstown, PA.

PERIODICALS

The United Evangelical (bi-w), The New Illustrator (q); Venture Series, S.S. lessons (q); Dr. W. S. Sailer, Myerstown, PA, Ed.; Pub., Church Center Press, Myerstown, PA.

The Evangelical Covenant Church of America

This church has its roots in historical Christianity as it emerged in the Protestant Reformation in the biblical instruction of the Lutheran State Church of Sweden, and in the spiritual awakenings of the nineteenth century. The denomination was organized on February 20, 1885, in Chicago. Prior to 1957 it was named the Evangelical Mission Covenant Church of America.

Churches: 526. Inclusive Membership: 68,428. Sunday or Sabbath Schools: 500. Total Enrollment: 66,194. Ordained clergy: 671.

GENERAL ORGANIZATION

General Conference: annual (June 19-22, 1973,

University of Hartford, W. Hartford CT). Headquarters: 5101 N. Francisco Ave., Chicago, IL 60625.

OFFICERS

Pres., Dr. Milton B. Engebretson, Chicago, IL.
Vice-Pres., Rev. Douglas G. Cedarleaf, Rochester, MN.
Sec., Rev. Clifford W. Bjorklund, Chicago, IL.
Treas., Edgar E. Swanson Jr., Chicago, IL.

ADMINISTRATIVE BOARDS

Board of Christian Education: Chmn., Rev. Ronald F. Lagerstrom; Sec., Mrs. Jarvis O. Barton; Exec. Sec., Christian Education, Rev. David S. Noreen.
Board of Home Mission: Chmn., Willis D. Erickson; Sec., Rev. Wesley C. Swanson; Exec. Sec., Home Mission, Rev. Paul W. Anderson.
Board of the Ministry: Chmn., Rev. J. Robert Hjelm; Sec., Rev. Herbert M. Freedholm; Exec. Sec. of the Ministry, Rev. Earl M. VanDerVeer.
Board of Pensions: Chmn., Marshall C. Dahlstrom; Sec. & Dir. of Pensions, Rev. Earl M. VanDerVeer.
Board of Publication: Chmn., Paul L. Ziemer; Sec., Rev. Darryl L. Larson; Exec. Sec. of Publications, Rev. James R. Hawkinson.
Board of World Mission: Chmn., Rev. Gerald V. Stenberg; Sec., Rev. Elmer B. Pearson; Exec. Sec., World Mission, Rev. Russell A. Cervin.
Board of Benevolence: Chmn., Russell A. Dahlstrom; Sec., Mrs. Henry Stege; Pres. of Covenant Benevolent Institutions, Nils G. Axelson, 5145 N. California Ave., Chicago IL 60625.
Board of Directors of North Park College and Theological Seminary: Pres., Dr. Lloyd H. Ahlem; Chmn., Robert V. Thonander; Sec., Rev. Norbert E. Johnson, 5125 N. Spoulding Ave., Chicago, IL 60625.

PERIODICALS

Covenant Companion (semi-m), Chicago, IL Rev. James R. Hawkinson, Ed.
Covenant Quarterly (q), Chicago, IL., Dr. F. Burton Nelson, Ed.
Covenant Home Altar (q), Chicago, IL., Rev. James R. Hawkinson, Ed.

The Evangelical Free Church of America

Organized in Boone, Iowa, in the 1880's, as the Swedish Evangelical Free Mission; name later changed to above. The Evangelical Free Church Association merged with this group in June, 1950. The merged body is known as the Evangelical Free Church of America.

Churches: 562. Inclusive Membership: 70,490. Sunday or Sabbath Schools: N.R. Total Enrollment: N.R. Ordained clergy: N.R.

GENERAL ORGANIZATION

Conference: annual.
Headquarters: 1515 E. 66 St., Minneapolis, MN 55423. Tel. (612) 866-3343.

OFFICERS

Pres., Dr. Arnold T. Olson, 1515 E. 66 St.,

Minneapolis, MN 55423.
Vice-Pres., Carroll W. High, P.O. Box 275, Richvale, CA 95974.
Sec. of Home Missions, Rev. Herbert E. Kyrk, 1515 E. 66 St., Minneapolis, MN 55423.
Sec. of Overseas Missions, Dr. Lester Westlund, 1515 E. 66 St., Minneapolis, MN 55423.
Vice-Chmn., Rev. Carl W. Linde, 646 Clove Rd., Staten Island, NY 10310.
Gen. Sec., E. James Rodine, 2709 Gerald Ave. N., North St. Paul, MN 55109.
Vice-Sec., Rev. H. Bruce Chapman, 5150 Chicago Ave., Minneapolis, MN 55417.
Treas., Herbert Nordin, 4904 Clinton Ave., Minneapolis, MN 55409.
Fin. Sec., George Hedberg, 3939 N. Hamlin Ave., Chicago, IL 60618.

PERIODICAL
Evangelical Beacon (bi-m), 1515 E. 66 St., Minneapolis, MN 55423. Mel Larson, Ed.

Evangelical Friends Alliance

Formed in 1965 as an organization representing one corporate step of denominational unity, brought about as a result of several movements of spiritual renewal within the Society of Friends. These movements are: 1) the general evangelical renewal within Christianity, 2) the new scholarly recognition of the evangelical nature of seventeenth century Quakerism, and 3) the Association of Evangelical Friends.
The EFA is conservative in theology and makes use of local pastors. Sunday morning worship includes singing, Scripture reading, a period of open worship—usually—and a sermon by the pastor.

Churches: 254. Inclusive Membership: 23,683. Sunday or Sabbath Schools: N.R. Total Enrollment: N.R. Ordained clergy: N.R.

YEARLY MEETINGS
Rocky Mountain YM, Mr. Arthur James Ellis, 2610 E. Bijou St., Colorado Springs, CO 80909.
Kansas YM, Mr. Maurice A. Roberts, 2018 Maple, Wichita, KS 67213.
Northwest YM, Mr. Dorwin E. Smith, Box 190, Newberg, OR 97132.
Evangelical Friends Church, Eastern Region, Mr. Harold B. Winn, Damascus, OH 44408.

Evangelical Lutheran Church in America (Eielsen Synod)

A small Lutheran body, the first Norwegian synod in the U.S., taking its name from its organizer, Elling Eielsen, in 1846.

GENERAL ORGANIZATION
Synod: annual.

OFFICERS
Pres., Rev. Thore Larson, Jackson, MN 56143.
Vice-Pres., Martin Bystol, Lodi, WI 53555.
Treas., Tom Nelson, Centerville, SD 57104.
Sec., Gladys Bystol, Lodi, WI 53555.

Evangelical Lutheran Synod

The Evangelical Lutheran Synod had its beginning among the Norwegian settlers who brought with them their Lutheran heritage and established it in this country. It was organized in 1853. It was reorganized in 1917 by those who desired to adhere to these principles not only in word, but also in deed.
To carry out the above-mentioned objectives, the Synod owns and operates Bethany Lutheran College in Mankato, Minnesota. A Theological Seminary department for the training of pastors is maintained at the same school.
Churches: 89. Inclusive Membership: 16,202. Sunday or Sabbath Schools: 79. Total Enrollment: 4,381. Ordained clergy: 63.

GENERAL ORGANIZATION
Synod: annual (June).

OFFICERS
Pres., Rev. G. M. Orvick, 2670 Milwaukee St., Madison, WI 53704. Tel. (608) 249-3101.
Sec., Rev. Alf Merseth, 106 13th St. So., Northwood, IA 50459.
Treas., Mr. LeRoy W. Meyer, 1038 S. Lewis Ave., Lombard, IL 60148.

OTHER ORGANIZATIONS
Lutheran Synod Book Co.: Office, Bethany Lutheran College, Mankato, MN 56001.

PERIODICAL
Lutheran Sentinel, (bi-m), Lake Mills, IA 50450. Rev. N. Tjernagel, Ed., 626 Landing Rd., N., Rochester, NY 14625.

Evangelical Mennonite Brethren Conference

Formerly known as the Defenseless Mennonite Brethren in Christ of North America, this body emanates from the Russian immigration of Mennonites into the United States in 1873-74.

Churches: 33. Inclusive Membership: 3,753. Sunday or Sabbath Schools: 33. Total Enrollment: 4,854. Ordained clergy: 37.

GENERAL ORGANIZATION
Conference: annual (June or July).
Headquarters: 5800 S. 14th St., Omaha, NB 68107. Tel. (402) 731-4800.

OFFICERS
Executive Committee
Pres., Rev. Frank C. Wiens, Mountain Lake, MN 56159.
Vice-Pres., Rev. W. J. Peters; Winkler, Manitoba Canada.
Sec., Rev. Johnny Reimer, Meade, KS 67864.
Admin. Sec., Wm. Regehr, 5800 S. 14th St., Omaha, NB 68107.
Chmn., Commission on Churches, Rev. J. N. Hiebert, Steinbach, Manitoba, Canada.
Chmn., Commission on Missions, Rev. Pete Peters, Wymark, Saskatchewan, Canada.
Chmn., Commission on Promotion, Rev. Frank G. Thomas, Meade, KS 67864.
Chmn., Commission on Departments, Rev. Pete Unrau, 720 Howe St., Dallas, OR 97338.

PERIODICAL
Gospel Tidings, 5800 S. 14th St., Omaha, NB 68107. William Regehr, Ed.

Evangelical Mennonite Church, Inc.

An independent conference of Mennonites which separated in 1865 from the Amish Mennonite Church over the question of conversion.

GENERAL ORGANIZATION
Conference: annual (August).
Headquarters: 7237 Leo Rd., Fort Wayne, IN 46825.

OFFICERS
Pres., Rev. Andrew Rupp, 7237 Leo Rd., Ft. Wayne, IN 46825.
Chmn., Rev. Charles Zimmerman, 301 Park St., Archbold, OH 43502.
Vice-Chmn., Rev. Charles L. Rupp, Gridley, IL 61744.
Sec., R. David Boyer, 5334 Bluffside Ave., Ft. Wayne, IN 46815.
Treas., Paul Steiner, 1825 Florida Dr., Ft. Wayne, IN 46805.

PERIODICALS
Build (q), Grabill, IN 46741. Andrew M. Rupp, Ed.
Headquarters Communique (m), 7237 Leo Rd., Ft. Wayne, IN 46825. Ric Mathew, Ed.

Evangelical Methodist Church

Organized 1946 at Memphis, Tennessee, largely as a movement of people who opposed modern liberalism and wished for a return to the historic Wesleyan position.

GENERAL ORGANIZATION
General Conference, Annual Conference, District Conference, and Local Church Conference.
Headquarters: 3036 North Meridian, Wichita, KS 67204. Tel. (316) 838-4237.

OFFICERS
General Superintendents: Dr. Ralph A. Vanderwood, Wichita, KS 67204; Rev. Constantino Cardenas (Mexico), Apartado 196, Parral, Chihuahua, Mexico.
Gen. Conf. Sec.-Treas., Rev. Ronald D. Driggers, Wichita, KS 67204.

PERIODICAL
The Voice of Evangelical Methodism (m), 3036 N. Meridian, Wichita, KS 67204. Dr. Ralph A. Vanderwood, Ed.

The Fire Baptized Holiness Church (Wesleyan)

This church came into being about 1890 as the result of definite preaching on the doctrine of holiness in some Methodist churches in southeastern Kansas. It became known as The Southeast Kansas Fire Baptized Holiness Association, which name in 1945 was changed to The Fire Baptized Holiness Church. It is entirely Wesleyan in doctrine, episcopal in church organization, and intensive in evangelistic zeal.

GENERAL ORGANIZATION
Headquarters: 600 Country Club Dr., Independence, KS 67301. Tel. (316) 331-3049.

OFFICERS
Gen. Supt., J. M. Beddow.
Gen. Sec., Rev. Leroy Newport, 1627 E. Independence, Tulsa, OK 74106.
Gen. Treas., Victor White, Route 3, Independence, KS 67301.

PERIODICALS
The Flaming Sword (s-m), 10th St. & Country Club Rd., Independence, KS 67301.
John Three Sixteen (w), 10th St. & Country Club Rd., Independence, KS 67301.

Free Christian Zion Church of Christ

Organized 1905, at Redemption, Arkansas, by a company of Negro ministers associated with various denominations, with polity in general accord with that of Methodist bodies.

GENERAL ORGANIZATION
General Assembly: annual. (November).
Headquarters: Nashville, AR 71852.

Free Methodist Church of North America

This body grew out of a movement in the Genesee Conference of the Methodist Episcopal Church about 1850 toward a more original Methodism. It was organized in 1860.

Churches: 1,264. Inclusive Membership: 65,040. Sunday or Sabbath Schools: 1,264. Total Enrollment: 118,276. Ordained clergy: 1,749.

GENERAL ORGANIZATION
General Conference. (Next meeting, 1974).
Headquarters: Winona Lake, IN 46590. Tel. (219) 267-7161.

OFFICERS
Bishops Myron F. Boyd, W. Dale Cryderman, Paul N. Ellis, Edward C. John.
Gen. Conf. Sec., C. T. Denbo.
Gen. Miss. Sec., C. D. Kirkpatrick.
Gen. Dir. of Christian Education, Robert Crandall.
Gen. Dir. of Evangelistic Outreach, Robert F. Andrews.
Gen. Sec. of Higher Education, Arthur D. Zahniser.
Director-Chaplain, John Wesley Seminary, Clyde E. Van Valin.
Gen. Church Treas., William B. Bruce.
Gen. Sec. of World Ministries Communication, Claude A. Horton.
Publisher, Lloyd H. Knox.

PERIODICALS
Light and Life (bi-w), Editors: Robert M. Fine, Chairman; Frank Van Valin, Donald Demaray, Milo Kaufmann.
Editorial Director of Light and Life Publications, G. Roger Schoenhals.
Missionary Tidings (m), Alice Fensome, Ed.
Youth In Action (m), Julie Hogue, Ed.
All the officers listed above should be contacted at the headquarters address.

Free Will Baptists

This evangelical group of Baptists was organized by Paul Palmer in 1727 at Chowan,

57

North Carolina. Another movement (teaching the same doctrines of free grace, free salvation, and free will) was organized June 30, 1780, in New Durham, New Hampshire, but there was no connection with the southern organization except for a fraternal relationship.

The northern line expanded more rapidly and extended into the West and Southwest. This body merged with the Northern Baptist Convention October 5, 1911, but a remnant of churches reorganized into the Cooperative General Association of Free Will Baptists December 28, 1916, at Pattonsburg, Missouri.

Churches in the southern line were organized into various conferences from the beginning and they finally united into one General Conference in 1921.

Representatives of the Cooperative General Association and the General Conference joined together November 5, 1935 to form the National Association of Free Will Baptists.

Churches: 2,250. Inclusive Membership: 210,000. Sunday or Sabbath Schools: 2,200. Total Enrollment: 181,000. Ordained clergy: 3,374.

GENERAL ORGANIZATION
National Association meets annually (July). National Offices: 1134 Murfreesboro Rd., Nashville, TN 37217. Tel. (615) 244-3470.

OFFICERS
Mod., Dr. Robert E. Picirilli, 3606 West End Ave., Nashville, TN 37205.
Exec. Sec., Rev. Rufus Coffey, 1134 Murfreesboro Rd., Nashville, TN 37217.

DENOMINATIONAL AGENCIES
Board of Foreign Missions: Dir., Rev. Reford Wilson.
Board of Home Missions: Dir., Rev. Homer E. Willis.
Board of Retirement and Insurance: Dir., Rev. Herman Hersey.
Board of Church Training Service: Dir., Malcolm Fry.
Sunday School Board: Dir., Rev. Roger Reeds.
Woman's Auxiliary Convention: Exec. Sec., Mrs. Paul Purcell.

PERIODICALS
Contact (m), 1134 Murfreesboro Rd., Nashville, TN 37217, Eugene Workman, Ed.
Free Will Baptist Gem (m), 830 S. National, Springfield, MO 65804, Rev. Eddie Attis, Ed.
Bible College Bulletin (m), 3606 West End Ave., Nashville, TN 37205, Bert Tippett, Ed.
Free Will Baptist Witness (m), Box 277, East Durham Station, Durham, NC 27703, Rev. Ronald Creech, Ed.
Heartbeat, Foreign Missions Office, 1134 Murfreesboro Rd., Nashville, TN 37217, Don Robirds, Ed.

Friends General Conference

An association of Yearly Meetings organized in 1900 to further the concerns for the advancement of Quakerism and the religious education of Friends.

Churches: 233. Inclusive Membership: 26,671. Sunday or Sabbath Schools: N.R. Total Enrollment: N.R. Ordained clergy: N.R.

GENERAL ORGANIZATION
General Conference: annual (June). Headquarters: 1520 Race St., Philadelphia, PA 19102. Tel. (215) 567-1965.

OFFICERS
Chmn., C. Lloyd Bailey.
Treas., Philip L. Gilbert.
Gen. Sec., Howard Bartram.

PERIODICAL
FGC Quarterly (q), 1520 Race St., Philadelphia, PA 19102, Patricia McBee, Ed.

YEARLY MEETINGS
(Note: * denotes Meetings which are also affiliated with Friends United Meeting.)
Philadelphia YM, Mr. Charles K. Brown, III, 1515 Cherry St., Philadelphia, PA 19102.
Lake Erie YM, Flora S. McKinney, 140 N. Cassingham Rd., Bexley, OH 43209.
*New England YM, Mr. Gordon M. Browne, Jr., Box 586, Cotuit, MA 02635.
*New York YM, Miriam K. Brush, 15 Rutherford Pl., New York, NY 10003.
*Baltimore YM, Mr. John M. Sexton, 17100 Quaker La., Sandy Spring, MD 20806.
*Canadian YM, Mr. Burton S. W. Hill, Box 33, Rockwood, Ontario.
Illinois YM, Mr. Robert L. Wixom, 812 Maplewood Dr., Columbia, MO 65201.
Indiana YM, Mr. Raymond Braddock, R.R. 1, Waynesville, OH 45068.
South Central YM, Mrs. Garnet Guild, 2001 Binz, Houston, TX 77004.
*Southeastern, YM Mr. J. William Greenleaf, 1375 Talbot Ave., Jacksonville, FL 32205.

Friends United Meeting

The Friends United Meeting became the new name in 1965 for that worldwide fellowship of Friends formerly known as the Five Years Meeting of Friends. The latter body was founded in 1902 as a loose federation to coordinate and facilitate a united Quaker witness in missions, peace education, Christian education, and the publication of a bi-weekly magazine.

Since then additional programs in evengelism, stewardship, social concerns, and leadership have been added. Other Yearly Meetings within and beyond the United States have joined, making a total of fifteen member Yearly Meetings representing about half the Friends in the world.

Churches: 512. Inclusive Membership: 68,773. Sunday or Sabbath Schools: 412. Total Enrollment: 36,299. Ordained clergy: 554.

GENERAL ORGANIZATION
Friends United Meeting: triennial (next meeting, 1975).

OFFICERS
Presiding Clk., Thomas R. Bodine, 101 Quaker Hill Dr., Richmond, IN 47374.
Treas., Robert G. Godsey, 308 Earlham Dr., Richmond, IN 47374.
Gen. Sec., Lorton Heusel, 101 Quaker Hill Dr., Richmond, IN 47374.

DEPARTMENTS

(All located at 101 Quaker Hill Dr., Richmond, IN 47374.)

Wider Ministries Commission, Assoc. Gen. Sec., Harold V. Smuck.

Meeting Ministries Commission, Assoc. Gen. Sec., Wayne C. Allman.

General Services Commission, Assoc. Gen. Sec., David O. Stanfield.

Quaker Hill Bookstore (Friends United Press), Mgr. and Ed., Earl J. Prignitz.

PERIODICALS

Quaker Life, 101 Quaker Hill Dr., Richmond, IN 47374, Frederick Wood, Ed.

Friends Missionary Advocate, 2205 N. Canonita Dr., La Habra, CA 90631, Bertha Camphuis, Ed.

YEARLY MEETINGS

(Note: * denotes Meetings which are also affiliated with the Friends General Conference.)

Nebraska YM, Mr. Don Reeves, Central City, NE 68826.

California YM, Mr. Glen Rinard, P. O. Box 1607, Whittier, CA 90603.

*New England YM, Mr. Gordon M. Browne, Jr., Box 586, Cotuit, MA 02635.

*New York YM, Miriam K. Brush, 15 Rutherford Pl., New York, NY 10003.

*Baltimore YM, Mr. John M. Sexton, 17100 Quaker La., Sandy Spring, MD 20860.

Iowa YM, Mr. Bernard L. White, Box 552, Oskaloosa, IA 52577.

Western YM, Mr. Lowell E. Mills, 203 S. East St., Plainfield, IN 46168.

North Carolina YM, Ruth R. Hockett, P.O. Box 8328, Greensboro, NC 27410.

Indiana YM, Mr. Lyman B. Hall, 1403 Briar Rd., Muncie, IN 47304.

Wilmington YM, Mr. Glenn A. Reece, P.O. Box 165, New Vienna, OH 45159.

Cuba YM, St. Maulio Ajo, Apartado 183, Banes, Oriente, Cuba.

*Canadian YM, Mr. Burton S. W. Hill, Box 33, Rockwood, Ontario.

Jamaica YM, Mr. Ernest Nugent, 11 Calendonia Ave., Kingston 5, Jamaica, W.I.

*Southeastern YM, Mr. J. William Greenleaf, 1375 Talbot Ave., Jacksonville, FL 32205.

Fundamental Methodist Church, Inc.

Withdrew from The Methodist Church. Organized August 27, 1942. Located in Springfield, Missouri.

Churches: 14. Inclusive Membership: 722. Sunday or Sabbath Schools: 14. Total Enrollment: 684. Ordained clergy: 16.

GENERAL ORGANIZATION

Conference: annual.

OFFICERS

Supt., Dr. Roy Keith, Aurora, MO 65605.

Asst. Supt., Rev. Loyd Taylor, W. Linn St., Springfield, MO 65802.

Sec.-Treas., E. J. Etheridge, 2652 Horning, Springfield, MO 65802.

General Association of Regular Baptist Churches

Founded in May, 1932, in Chicago, Illinois, by a group of churches which had withdrawn from the Northern Baptist Convention (now the American Baptist Churches in the U.S.A.) because of doctrinal differences. Its Confession of Faith, which it requires all churches to subscribe to, is essentially the old, historic New Hampshire Confession of Faith with a premillennial ending applied to the last article.

Churches: 1,426. Inclusive Membership: 210,-000. Sunday or Sabbath Schools: N.R. Total Enrollment: N.R. Ordained clergy: N.R.

GENERAL ORGANIZATION

Meets annually.

Headquarters: 1800 Oakton Blvd., Des Plaines, IL 60018. Tel. (312) 827-7105.

OFFICERS

Chmn., Dr. James Jeremiah, Cedarville, OH.

Vice-Chmn., Dr. W. Thomas Younger, Ft. Wayne, IN.

Treas., Dr. Merle R. Hull, Des Plaines, IL.

Sec., Dr. Kenneth Elgena, Flint, MI.

National Representative, Dr. Joseph M. Stowell, 1800 Oakton Blvd., Des Plaines, IL 60018.

PERIODICAL

Baptist Bulletin (m), 1800 Oakton Blvd., Des Plaines, IL 60018. Dr. Merle R. Hull, Ed.

General Baptists (General Association of)

An Arminian group of Baptists first organized by John Smyth and Thomas Helwys in England, 1607. Transplanted to the colonies in 1714. Died out along the Seaboard, but revived in the Midwest in 1823 by Rev. Benoni Stinson.

Churches: 854. Inclusive Membership: 65,000. Sunday or Sabbath Schools: 854. Total Enrollment: 80,500. Ordained clergy: 1,115.

GENERAL ORGANIZATION

General Association: annual.

OFFICERS

Mod., Rev Jim Murray, Box 537, Poplar Bluff, MO 63901.

Clerk, Vern Whitten, 1629 Stinson, Evansville, IN 47712.

Exec, Sec., Dr. Kenneth R. Kennedy, Box 537, Poplar Bluff, MO 63901.

OTHER ORGANIZATIONS

General Board: Sec., Vern Whitten, 1629 Stinson, Evansville, IN 47712.

Foreign Mission Board: Exec. Sec., Rev. Don Willingham, Box 537, Poplar Bluff, MO 63901.

Board of Christian Education and Publications: Rev. Cecil Robertson, Sr., 1010 W. Walnut, Springfield, MO 65806.

Home Mission Board Exec. Sec., Rev Leland Duncan, Box 537, Poplar Bluff, MO 63901.

Ministers' Aid Board: Sec., Rev. Glen Spence, Oakland City College, Oakland City, IN 47560.

Women's Mission Board: Exec. Sec., Mrs. Delores Duck, Box 537, Poplar Bluff, MO 63901.

GENERAL CHURCH OF THE NEW JERUSALEM

College Board: Chmn., Rev Elvis Wilson, 1803 Stoddard, Cape Girardeau, MO 63701.

Publishing House, General Baptist Press, Box 790, Poplar Bluff, MO 63901. Rev. Minvil L. Clark, Exec. Dir.

PERIODICALS

General Baptist Messenger (w), Poplar Bluff, MO, Rev. Edwin Runyon, Ed.

The Pastor's Digest, Riley M. Mathias, Ed.

Vanguard Signal, Rev. Ollie Latch, Ed.

General Church of the New Jerusalem

The General Church of the New Jerusalem is the result of a reorganization in 1897 of the General Church of The Advent of the Lord. It stresses the full acceptance of the doctrines of Emanuel Swedenborg.

Churches: 33. Inclusive Membership: 2,143. Sunday or Sabbath Schools: 8. Total Enrollment: 168. Ordained clergy: 31.

GENERAL ORGANIZATION

General Assembly (International), meets every three or four years.

Headquarters: Bryn Athyn, PA 19009. Tel. (215) 947-4660.

OFFICERS

Presiding Bishop, Rt. Rev. W. D. Pendleton.

Sec., Rev. Norbert H. Rogers.

Treas., L. E. Gyllenhaal.

PERIODICAL

New Church Life (m), Bryn Athyn, PA 19009. Rev. W. Cairns Henderson, Ed.

General Conference of the Evangelical Baptist Church, Inc.

This denomination is an Arminian, premillennial group whose form of government is congregational.

It was organized in 1935, and was formerly known as the Church of the Full Gospel, Inc.

GENERAL ORGANIZATION

General Conference: annual.

Headquarters: 2306 E. Ash St., Goldsboro, NC 27530. Tel. (919) 735-4760.

OFFICERS

Pres., Dr. Wm. Howard Carter., 2306 E. Ash St., Goldsboro, NC 27530.

1st Vice-Pres., Dr. C. B. Peacock, Sr., P. O. Box 4351, Rocky Mount, NC 27801.

2nd Vice-Pres., Rev. T. T. Floyd, R-8, Res. 1008 Oswego Rd., Sumter, SC 29150.

3rd Vice-Pres., Dr. L. S. Miller, 1200 Park Dr., Elizabeth City, NC 27909.

Sec., Mrs. Harold K. Thomas, 204 S. Lee Dr., Goldsboro, NC 27530.

Treas., Mrs. Jessie Byrd Carter, 711 E. Pou St., Goldsboro, NC 27530.

Admin. Sec., Miss Clyde Dawson, 2306 E. Ash St., Goldsboro, NC 27530.

Dir. of Evangelism, Rev. B. L. Proctor, Rt. 3, Box 350, Nashville, NC 27856.

Dir. of Women's Auxiliaries, Mrs. Georgia Benton, 508 Tyree Rd., Kinston, NC 28501.

PERIODICAL

The Evangelical Baptist, 2306 E. Ash St., Goldsboro, NC 27530. Dr. William Howard Carter, Ed.

General Conference of Mennonite Brethren Churches

An immigration of Mennonite Brethren from Russia in the year 1874. (In 1960, the Krimmer Mennonite Brethren Conference merged with this body.)

GENERAL ORGANIZATION

General Convention: Triennial. (Next meeting, 1975.)

OFFICERS

Chmn., Rev. Marvin Hein, Hillsboro, KS 67063.

Vice-Chmn., Dr. J. A. Toews, 2625 James St., Clearbrook, British Columbia, Canada.

Sec., Rev. Henry H. Voth, 479 Ragland Rd., Winnipeg, Manitoba, Canada.

PERIODICAL

Christian Leader (bi-w), Hillsboro, KS 67063. Rev. Orlando Harms, Ed.

General Convention The Swedenborgian Church

Followers of Emanuel Swedenborg, Swedish scientist, philosopher, and theologian (1688-1772). They organized their first church society in the U.S. in 1792 in Baltimore. Their church is officially called The Church of the New Jerusalem, but they are usually referred to as Swedenborgians.

GENERAL ORGANIZATION

General Convention: annual (June).

OFFICERS

Pres., Rev. Ernest O. Martin, 48 Sargent St., Newton, MA 02158.

Vice-Pres., Adolph T. Liebert, 626 Park Pl., Pittsburgh, PA 15237.

Sec., Mrs. Wilfred Rice, 31 Poole St., Brockton, MA 02401.

Treas., Chester T. Cook, P.O. Box 25, Deer Isle, ME 04627.

PERIODICAL

The Messenger (m), 48 Sargent St., Newton, MA 02158, Robert H. Kirven, Ed.

General Six Principle Baptists

A Baptist Group, organized in Rhode Island in 1653, drawing its name from Heb. 6:1-2.

GENERAL ORGANIZATION

Conferences in Rhode Island and Pennsylvania: annually, in August or September.

OFFICERS

Rhode Island Conference: Pres., Deacon Raymond L. Josefson, 146 Brunswick Dr., Warwick, RI 02886.

Clk., Gladys I. Bailey, 2068 S. County Trail, East Greenwich, RI 02818.

Pennsylvania Association: Pres., Elder Daniel E. Carpenetti, Nicholson, PA 18446.

Clk., Mrs. Eleanor Warner, R.F.D. 1, Tunkhannock, PA 18657.

The Gospel Mission Corps

A nonsectarian, united, evangelistic church and home missionary society incorporated in 1962 in New Jersey. The ordinances of believer's baptism and holy communion are observed. Emphasis is placed on the doctrines and experience of full salvation and practical Christian living. Gospel Mission Christians desire to be biblical in both their faith and their work.

Churches: 7. Inclusive Membership: 175. Sunday or Sabbath Schools: 5. Total Enrollment: N.R. Ordained clergy: 7

GENERAL ORGANIZATION
Annual Meetings: Spring Encampment, Fall Conference.
Headquarters: Box 175, Highstown, NJ 08520. Tel. (609) 448-4387 and 448-4596.

OFFICERS
Hon. Pres., Pastor Clarence F. Kresge, Ocean Grove, NJ 07756.
Vice-Pres., Dist. Supt. Pastor Robert S. Turton III, Hightstown, NJ 08520.
Sec., Irene M. Bradford; Joan T. McBee.
Treas., Grace B. Turton; Sandra B. Turton.
Dir., Marine Gospel Mission, Pastor Eric McLaughlin, Seaside Heights, NJ 08751.

PERIODICALS
The Gospel Missionary (bi-m), P.O. Box 16, Cranbury, NJ 08512.
Loyalty to the Gospel (q), P.O. Box 175, Hightstown, NJ 08520.

Greek Orthodox Archdiocese of North and South America

The Greek Orthodox Archdiocese of North and South America is under the jurisdiction of the Ecumenical Patriarchate of Constantinople, in Istanbul. It was chartered in 1922 by the State of New York and has parishes in the United States, Canada, Central and South America. The first Greek Orthodox Church was founded in New Orleans, Louisiana in 1864.

Churches: 502. Inclusive Membership: 1,950,-000. Sunday or Sabbath Schools: 639. Total Enrollment: 75,191. Ordained clergy: 675.

GENERAL ORGANIZATION
Headquarters: 8-10 East 79th St., New York, NY 10021. Tel. (212) 628-2500.
22nd Biennial Congress of the Greek Archdiocese of North and South America will be convened July 6, 1974 in Chicago, Illinois.

OFFICERS
Archdiocesan Council:
Pres., His Eminence Archbishop Iakovos.
Vice-Pres., Bishop Silas; Mr. Pierre De Mets (Chicago, IL).
Sec., Mr. Peter Kourides (New York, NY).
Treas., Mr. Sotiros Katchules.

BISHOPS
His Eminence Archbishop Iakovos, Primate of

THE HOLINESS CHURCH OF GOD, INC.

the Greek Orthodox Church in the Americas.
His Grace Bishop Silas of Amphipolis, 8-10 E. 79th St., New York, NY 10021.
His Grace Bishop Philotheos of Meloa, 8-10 E. 79th St., New York, NY 10021.
His Grace Bishop Timothy of Rodostolon, 40 E. Burton Pl., Chicago, IL 60610.
His Grace Bishop Demetrios of Olympus, 180 Pond St., Jamaica Plain, MA 02130.
His Grace Bishop Meletios of Christianoupolis, 372 Santa Clara Ave., San Francisco, CA 94127.
His Grace Bishop Aimilianos of Harioupolis, 528 East Boulevard, Charlotte, NC 28203.
His Grace Bishop Gerasimos of Abydos, 5201 Ellsworth Ave., Pittsburgh, PA 15232.
His Grace Bishop Iakovos of Apameia, 19405 Renfew, Detroit, MI 48221.
His Grace Bishop John of Thermon, 4039 Grammercy Ave., Houston, TX 77025.

ARCHDIOCESAN DEPARTMENTS
(All located at 8-10 E. 79th St., New York, NY 10021.)
Chancellor: Very Rev. George Bacopulos
Education (Parochial, Afternoon Greek Language Schools, Sunday Schools, Adult Classes in Religion); Interchurch Relations; Laity; Registry (Marriage, Baptismal records, etc.); Youth Ministry (Boy Scouts, G.O.Y.A., Junior G.O.Y.A. Campus Commission); Economic Development; Financial, Public Affairs (Press, Radio and Television); Foreign Missions; Social Health and Welfare Center; Chaplaincy; Publications.

PERIODICAL
The Orthodox Observer (bi-m), 8-10 E. 79th St., New York, NY 10021.

The Holiness Church of God, Inc.

Established at Madison, North Carolina, in 1920; incorporated in 1928 at Winston-Salem, North Carolina.

GENERAL ORGANIZATION
General Assembly: annual.
Headquarters: Winston-Salem, NC

OFFICERS
Pres., Bishop B. McKinney, 602 E. Elm St., Graham, NC 27253.
Vice-Bishop, O. M. Gray, 2509 Druid Hill Dr., Winston-Salem, NC 27105.
Gen. Sec., Mrs. L. M. McNair, 1838 Gola Dr., Fayetteville, NC 28301.
Asst. Sec., Mrs. Esther M. Wright, 118 E. Glenn Ave., Winston-Salem, NC 27105.
Overseer, Northern Area of N.E. Dist., Elder James Radcliff, 21 Jackson St., Mount Vernon, NY 10553.
Overseer, Southern Area of N.E. Dist. Elder Ray Alston, R. 1, Box 190, Graham, NC 27253.
Overseer, So. Dist., Bishop B. McKinney, 6023 E. Elm St., Graham, NC 27253.
Overseer, Va. & W. Va., Area of N.W. Dist., Elder P. D. Kellum, Thorpe, WV 24888.
Overseer, North Carolina Area of N.W. Dist., Bishop O. M. Gray, 2509 Druid Hill Dr., Winston-Salem, NC 27105.

HOLY ORTHODOX CHURCH IN AMERICA

Holy Orthodox Church in America (Eastern Catholic and Apostolic)

This body was instituted in 1934 for the presentation in the English language of the Eastern Liturgies and primitive Christianity. Its orders were derived through the Syro-Russian line.

GENERAL ORGANIZATION
Holy Synod: semi-annual.
Headquarters: See House, 321 W. 101st St., New York, NY 10025. Tel. (212) 864-3729.

Holy Ukrainian Autocephalic Orthodox Church in Exile

Organized in a parish in New York in 1951. The laymen and clergy who organized it came from among the Ukrainians who settled in the Western Hemisphere after World War II. In 1954 two bishops, immigrants from Europe, met with clergy and laymen and formally organized the religious body.

GENERAL ORGANIZATION
Headquarters: Holy Trinity Cathedral Church, 185 S. 5th St., Brooklyn, NY 11211.
Administrator: Very Rev. Serhij K Pastukhiv

House of God, Which Is the Church of the Living God, the Pillar and Ground of the Truth, Inc.

Organized 1919.

GENERAL ORGANIZATION
Meets annually, in October.

OFFICERS
Bishop A. H. White, 6107 Cobbs Creek Pkwy., Philadelphia, PA 19143.
Gen. Sec., Sister Mildred Johnson, 41 N. 50th St., Philadelphia, PA 19139.

PERIODICAL
Spirit of Truth Magazine (m), 3943 Fairmont Ave., Philadelphia, PA 19104. Bishop A. H. White, Ed.

Hungarian Reformed Church in America

A Hungarian Reformed Church was organized in New York in 1904 in connection with the Reformed Church of Hungary. In 1922 the Church in Hungary transferred most of her congregations in the U.S. to the Reformed Church in the U.S. Some, however, preferred to continue as an autonomous, self-supporting American denomination, and these formed the Free Magyar Reformed Church in America. This group changed its name in 1958 to Hungarian Reformed Church in America.

OFFICERS
Bishop, Rt. Rev. Dezso Abraham, 331 Kirkland Pl., Perth Amboy, NJ 08861. Tel. (201) 442-7799.
Chief Lay-Curator, Charles Kiss, 1002 Douglas Rd., Coral Gables, FL 33134.
Gen. Sec., The Very Rev. Stephen Kovacs, 180 Home Ave., Trenton, NJ 08611.

Dean, New York Classis, The Very Rev. Gabor Csordas, 229 E. 82nd St., New York, NY 10028.
Dean, Western Classis, The Very Rev. Tibor Dömötör, 1657 Centerview Dr., Akron, OH 44321.
Dean, Eastern Classis, The Very Rev. Dr. Andrew Harsanyi, 175 Pershing Ave., Carteret, NJ 07008.
Legal Adviser, Alex B. Eger Jr., 214 Smith St., Perth Amboy, NJ 08861.

PERIODICAL
Magyar Egyhaz (Magyar Church) (m), 1657 Centerview Dr., Akron, OH 44321. The Very Rev. Tibor Dömötör, Ed.

† Hutterian Brethren

Small groups of Hutterites deriving their names from an early martyr, Jacob Huter (1536). They have all things in common and share income and expenses. There are 28 groups in South Dakota and one in Minnesota.

CORRESPONDENTS
Rev. Daniel S. Wipf, Alexandria, SD 57311. Tel. (605) 239-4422.
Rev. Andrew Hofer, Fordville, ND 58231.

Independent Assemblies of God, International

A body formerly known as Scandinavian Assemblies in the U.S., Canada, and other lands.

GENERAL ORGANIZATION
Convention: annual.
Headquarters: 3840 5th Ave., San Diego, CA 92103. Tel. (714) 295-1028.

OFFICERS
Sec., International: Rev. A. W. Rasmussen, Rev. T. A. Lanes, Assoc., 3840 5th Ave., San Diego, CA 92103.
Sec., S.E. U.S.: Rev. Edward A. Bender, 1707 Lonesome Pine Lane, Tarpon Springs, FL 33589.
Sec., Eastern Canada: Rev. Harry Nunn, Sr., 15 Beecher St., St. Catherines, Ontario, Canada.

STATE SECRETARIES
Rev. Les Gilpin, Rt. 4, Box 233C, Madison Hgts., VA 24572.
Rev. C. L. Gruver, 1104 Rocksprings Dr., Alton, IL 62003.
Rev. C. M. McCullough, 4900 Hern Dr., St. Louis, MO 63134.
Rev. Herbert Sweat, R.D. # 3, Box 340, Washington, PA 15301.

Independent Fundamental Churches of America

Organized 1930, at Cicero, Illinois, by representatives of various independent churches.

Churches: 904. Inclusive Membership: 139,932. Sunday or Sabbath Schools: 904. Total Enrollment: 203,812. Ordained clergy: 1,231.

GENERAL ORGANIZATION

Headquarters: 1860 Mannheim Rd., Westchester, IL 60153.

EXECUTIVE OFFICERS

Pres., Rev. Robert L. Gray, 10610 Cermak Rd., Westchester, IL 60153.
National Exec. Dir., Rev. Bryan J. Jones, 1860 Mannheim Rd., Westchester, IL 60135. Tel. (312) 562-0234.
1st Vice-Pres., Rev. Harold Longenecker, 1246 Ponderosa Dr., Billings, MT 59102.
2nd Vice-Pres., Rev. Bernard Didden, 926 Philadelphia Terr., Birdsboro, PA 19508.
Treas., Rev. Joseph Dedic, Jr., 2097 Iverness Rd., Downers Grove, IL 60515.

PERIODICAL

The Voice (m), 1860 Mannheim Rd., Westchester, IL 60153. Glen Lehman, Ed.

International Church of the Foursquare Gospel

An evangelistic missionary body organized by Aimee Semple McPherson in 1927. The parent church is Angelus Temple in Los Angeles, organized in 1923, with mission stations and meeting places in 27 foreign countries.

GENERAL ORGANIZATION

International Foursquare Convention: annual.
Headquarters: Angelus Temple, 1100 Glendale Blvd., Los Angeles, CA 90026. Tel. (213) 484-1100.

OFFICERS

Pres., Dr. Rolf K. McPherson.
Vice-Pres., and Gen. Supervisor, Dr. Howard P. Courtney.
Sec., Dr. Herman D. Mitzner.
Dir. of Foreign Missions, Dr. Leland E. Edwards.
Boards of Directors: Dr. Rolf K. McPherson, Dr. Howard P. Courtney, Rev. Lorna De McPherson, Dr. Vincent R. Bird, Dr. Leland E. Edwards, Rev. Curtis V. Correll, Dr. Paul Jones, Dr. Herman D. Mitzner, Dr. Clarence E. Hall.
District Supervisors:
Eastern, Dr. Howard Clark.
Great Lakes, Dr. Merrill Nicholls.
Midwest, Rev. D. J. Ballinger.
Northwest, Rev. Roy H. Hicks.
South Central, Dr. J. Craig Bigg.
Southeast, Dr. A. B. Teffeteller, Jr.
Southern California, Dr. Paul Jones.
Southwest, Dr. N. M. Van Cleave.
Western, Rev. Fred Wymore.
Western Canada, Rev. John Holland.
Missionary Cabinet: Composed of Board of Directors, District Supervisors, Rev. Barney Northcote, Leona Williams, Karl Williams.

OTHER ORGANIZATIONS

International Department of Youth and Christian Education: Dir., Vincent R. Bird.

PERIODICALS

(All published at 1100 Glendale Blvd., Los Angeles, CA 90026.)
Foursquare World Advance (m), Rev. Jennie Acuff, Ed.

Carry-On (a) Student Council, Ed.
Crusading (q), Rev. Dora Glenn, Ed.
United Foursquare Women's Magazine, Rev. Leona Williams, Ed.

International General Assembly of Spiritualists

Organized, Buffalo, New York, 1936, for the purpose of chartering Spiritualist churches.

GENERAL ORGANIZATION

Convention: annual (June).
Headquarters: 1809 E. Bayview Blvd., Norfolk, VA 23503.

OFFICERS

Pres., Fred Jordan, 1809 E. Bayview Blvd., Norfolk, VA 23503. Tel. (home) (703) 588-7251.
Sec.-Treas., C. C. Doyle, 1809 E. Bayview Blvd., Norfolk, VA 23503.

International Pentecostal Assemblies

The successor of the Association of Pentecostal Assemblies and the National and International Pentecostal Missionary Union.

Churches: 55. Inclusive Membership: 10,000 Sunday or Sabbath Schools: 55. Total Enrollment: 12,330. Ordained clergy: 201.

GENERAL ORGANIZATION

General Offices: 892 Berne St. S.E., Atlanta, GA 30316. Exec. Sec., P.O. Box 9056, Richmond, VA 23225.
Missionary Headquarters: 892 Berne St. S.E., Atlanta, GA 30316.

OFFICERS

Gen. Supt., Rev. T. G. Grinder, 892 Berne St. S.E., Atlanta, GA 30316.
Asst. Gen. Supt., Rev. Wm. Houck, Jr., P.O. Box 1052, Flint, MI 48501.
World Missions Dir., Dr. J. B. Keiller, 892 Berne St. S.E., Atlanta, GA 30316.
Natl. Sec.-Treas., Dr. Robert L. Cannon, P.O. Box 9056, Richmond, VA 23225.
Natl. Youth Dir., Rev. Curtis Mock, 27212 S.E. Powell Valley Rd., Gresham, OR 97030.

PERIODICAL

The Bridgegroom's Messenger (m), 892 Berne St. S.E., Atlanta, GA. Rev. John T. Reed, Ed.

Israelite House of David

Established at Benton Harbor, Michigan, by Benjamin Purnell, in 1903.
No statistics available.

GENERAL ORGANIZATION

Headquarters: P.O. Box 1067, Benton Harbor, MI 49022. Tel. (616) 926-6695.

OFFICERS

Pillar, Mabel Blackburn.
Chmn. of Bd., Lloyd H. Dalager.
Pillar & Sec., H. Thomas Dewhirst.

Jehovah's Witnesses

It is the belief of Jehovah's Witnesses that they adhere to the oldest religion on earth, the worship of Almighty God revealed in his Bible as Jehovah.

They use the Watch Tower and Tract Society of Pennsylvania, Watchtower Bible and Tract Society of New York, Inc., International Bible Students Association, and other corporations in their earthwide preaching activity, and preach to all regardless of denomination.

All of Jehovah's Witnesses are considered to be ministers of the gospel and have no human leader. Their Yearbook shows them active during 1971 in 207 countries of the earth, where there are approximately 1,590,793 such ministers preaching, teaching the people of all nations that God's word is true and that their only hope is in the Kingdom of Jehovah under Christ Jesus which has been established to rule over earth and which will replace all governments of man.

There are 5,676 congregations and 416,789 ministers in the U.S.

Churches: 5,676. Inclusive Membership: 416,789. Sunday or Sabbath Schools: N.R. Total Enrollment: N.R. Ordained clergy: N.R.

GENERAL ORGANIZATION
Headquarters: 124 Columbia Heights, Brooklyn, NY 11201. Tel. (212) 625-1240.

OFFICER
Pres. Nathan H. Knorr.

PERIODICALS
The Watchtower and Awake! 124 Columbia Heights, Brooklyn, NY 11201.

Jewish Congregations

Jews arrived in the colonies before 1650. The first congregation is recorded in 1654, in New York City, the Shearith Israel (Remnant of Israel).

Synagogues: 5,000. Inclusive Membership: 5,870,000. Sabbath Schools: N.R. Total Enrollment: N.R. Rabbis: 6,400.

CONGREGATIONAL AND RABBINICAL ORGANIZATIONS
*Union of American Hebrew Congregations: 838 Fifth Ave., New York, NY 10021; Chmn. of the Board, Sidney I. Cole; Pres., Maurice N. Eisendrath.
*United Synagogue of America: 3080 Broadway, New York, NY 10027; Pres., Jacob Stein; Exec. Dir., Rabbi Bernard Segal.
*Union of Orthodox Jewish Congregations of America: 84 Fifth Ave., New York, NY 10011; Pres., Rabbi Joseph Karasick; Exec. Vice-Pres., Rabbi Berelwein.
*Central Conference of American Rabbis: 790 Madison Ave., New York, NY 10021; Pres., Rabbi David Polish; Exec. Vice-Pres., Rabbi Joseph Glaser.
Rabbinical Alliance of America: 156 Fifth Ave., New York, NY 10011; Pres.. Rabbi Abraham Gross.
*The Rabbinical Assembly, 3080 Broadway, New York, NY 10027; Pres., Rabbi Gershon

Levy; Exec. Vice-Pres., Rabbi Wolfe Kelman.
*Rabbinical Council of America, Inc.: 84 Fifth Ave., New York, NY 10011; Pres., Rabbi Louis Bernstein; Exec. Vice-Pres., Rabbi Israel Klavan.
Union of Orthodox Rabbis of the United States and Canada: 235 E. Broadway, New York, NY 10002; Pres., Rabbi Moshe Feinstein; Exec. Dir., Rabbi Meyer Cohen.
*Synagogue Council of America: 432 Park Ave., So. New York, NY 10016; Pres., Rabbi Irving Lehrman; Exec. Vice-Pres., Rabbi Henry Siegman. Meets annually.

---

*Synagogue Council of America represents the organizations starred above.

EDUCATIONAL AND SOCIAL SERVICE ORGANIZATIONS
American Association for Jewish Education: 101 5th Ave., New York, NY 10003, Pres., Rabbi Isidore Breslau; Exec. Vice-Pres., Rabbi Isaac Toubin.
American Council for Judaism, The: 201 E. 57th St., New York, NY 10022, Pres., Richard Korn; Exec. Dir., Stuart Gottlieb.
American Jewish Committee: 165 E. 56th St., New York, NY 10022, Pres., Philip E. Hoffman; Exec. Vice-Pres., Bertram H. Gold.
American Jewish Congress: 15 East 84th St., New York, NY 10028, Pres., Rabbi Arthur J. Lelyveld; Exec. Dir., Will Maslow.
American Jewish Historical Society: 2 Thornton Rd., Waltham, MA 02154, Pres., Philip D. Sang; Dir., Bernard Wax.
American Jewish Joint Distribution Committee, 60 E. 42nd St., New York, NY 10017. Chmn., Louis Briodo; Exec. Vice-Chmn., Samuel L. Haber.
Anti-Defamation League of B'nai B'rith: 315 Lexington Ave., New York, NY 10016, Hon. Chmn., Dore Schary; Natl. Dir., Benjamin R. Epstein.
B'nai B'rith Hillel Foundation, Inc.: 1640 Rhode Island Ave. N.W., Washington, DC 20036, Chmn. Natl. Hillel Commission, Dr. Louis Gottschalk; Natl. Dir., Rabbi Benjamin M. Kahn.
Conference of Presidents of Major American Jewish Organizations, 515 Park Ave., New York, NY 10022. Chmn., Jordan C. Band; Exec. Vice-Chmn., Isaiah M. Minkoff.
Council of Jewish Federations and Welfare Funds, 315 Park Ave., So., New York, NY 10010. Pres., Max M. Fisher; Exec. Vice-Pres., Philip Bernstein.
Hadassah-Women's Zionist Organization of America, 65 East 52nd St., New York, NY 10022, Pres., Mrs. Mortimer Jacobson; Exec. Dir., Miss Hannah L. Goldberg.
Jewish Publication Society of America: 222 N. 15th St., Philadelphia, PA 19102, Pres., Joseph M. First; Exec. Dir., Lesser Zussman.
Jewish War Veterans of the United States of America, Inc.: 1712 New Hampshire Ave. N.W., Washington, DC 20009, Natl. Comdr., Samuel Samuels; Natl. Exec. Dir., Munroe R. Sheinberg.
National Council for Jewish Education: 101 5th Ave., New York, NY 10003, Pres., Daniel Isaacman; Exec. Sec., Jack M. Horden.
National Federation of Jewish Men's Clubs of

the United Synagogue of America: 3080 Broadway, New York, NY 10027, Pres., Morton Tabas; Sec., Joseph Gurmankin.

National Federation of Temple Brotherhoods: 838 Fifth Ave., New York, NY 10021, Pres., Milton E. Harris; Exec. Dir., Sylvan Lebow.

National Federation of Temple Sisterhoods: 838 Fifth Ave., New York, NY 10021, Pres., Mrs. David M. Levitt; Exec. Dir., Jane Evans.

National Jewish Community Relations Advisory Council, 55 W. 42nd St., New York, NY 10036. Chmn., Jordan C. Band; Exec. Vice-Chmn., Isaiah M. Minkoff.

National Jewish Welfare Board, 15 East 26th St., New York, NY 10010. Pres., Morton L. Mandel; Exec. Vice-Pres., Herbert Millman.

National Women's League of United Synagogue of America: 3080 Broadway, New York, NY 10027, Pres., Mrs. Sol Henkind, Natl. Sec., Mrs. Joseph Wagenheim.

United Hias Service: 200 Park Ave., S., New York, NY 10003. Pres., Harold Friedman; Exec. Vice-Pres., Gaynor I. Jacobson.

United Jewish Appeal: 1290 Ave. of Americas, New York, NY 10019, Gen. Chmn., Edward Ginsberg; Exec. Chmn., Rabbi Herbert A. Friedman.

Women's Branch of the Union of Orthodox Jewish Congregations of America: 84 Fifth Ave., New York, NY 10011, Pres., Mrs. Nathan A. Wadler; Exec. Vice-Pres., Mrs. Mordecai A. Stern.

Zionist Organization of America: 145 E. 32nd St., New York, NY 10016, Pres., Jacques Torczyner, Natl. Sec., Leon J. Ilutovich.

PERIODICALS

ORTHODOX

Jewish Life (bi-m), 84 5th Ave., New York, NY 10011, Saul Bernstein, Ed.

Traditional (q), 84 5th Ave., New York, NY 10011, Rabbi W. S. Wurzburger, Ed.

CONSERVATIVE

Adult Jewish Education (2 or 3 issues a year), 218 E. 70th St., New York, NY 10021, Rabbi Marvin S. Wiener, Ed.

United Synagogue Review (q), 3080 Broadway, New York, NY 10027, Rabbi Alvin Kass, Ed.

The Torch (q), 3080 Broadway, New York, NY 10027, Milton Berger, Ed.

Conservative Judaism (q), 3080 Broadway, New York, NY 10027, Rabbi S. Gershon Levi, Ed.

The Reconstructionist (once in 3 weeks), 15 W. 86th St., New York, NY 10024, Rabbi Ira Eisenstein, Ed.

REFORM

American Judiasm (q), 838 Fifth Ave., New York, NY 10021, Paul Kresh, Ed.

CCAR Journal (q), 790 Madison Ave., New York, 10021, Rabbi Daniel Jeremy Silver, Ed.

Dimensions of American Judaism (q), 838 Fifth Ave., New York, NY 10021, Myrna Pollak, Ed.

Jewish Audio-Visual Review (annual), National Council on Jewish Audio-Visual Materials, 101 Fifth Ave., New York, NY 10003. Dr. Zalmen Slesinger, Ed.

Jewish Education (q), National Council for Jewish Education, 101 5th Ave., New York, NY 10003, Dr. Samuel Dinin, Ed.

The Pedagogic Reporter (q), American Assn. for Jewish Education, 101 5th Ave., New York, NY 10003, Dr. Zalmen Slesinger, Ed.

The Synagogue School (q), United Synagogue Comm. on Jewish Education, 218 E. 70th St., New York, NY 10021, Dr. Morton Siegel, Ed.

American Jewish Historical Quarterly (q), American Jewish Historical Society, 2 Thornton Rd., Waltham, MA 02154, Dr. Isidore S. Meyer, Ed.

Kodesh Church of Immanuel

Founded 1929 by Rev. Frank Russell Killingsworth, from among a group withdrawing from the African Methodist Episcopal Zion Church, and others.

GENERAL ORGANIZATION

General Assembly or Quadrennial Assembly. Also Annual Assembly.

OFFICERS

Supervising Elder, Rev. F. R. Killingsworth, 1509 S St. N.W., Washington, DC 20009

OTHER ORGANIZATIONS

Church Extension Board: Chmn., Mrs. Thelma P. Homes, Pittsburgh, PA.

Home and Foreign Missions Board: Chmn., Mrs. Florence E. Woodruff.

Young People's Societies: Gen. Pres., Mrs. Catherine B. Harris, Philadelphia, PA.

Sunday Schools: Gen. Supt., Mrs. Esther Cooke, Philadelphia, PA.

Liberal Catholic Church (California)

An independent and autonomous body, organized in England in 1916, whose bishops derive their orders through the Old Catholic Church of Holland. It seeks to combine the ancient form of sacramental worship with liberality of thought.

GENERAL ORGANIZATION

International Headquarters: Bear Butte Rd. & U. S. 101 Freeway, P.O. Box 185, Miranda, CA 95553.

OFFICER

Presiding Bishop, The Most Rev. Edward M. Matthews.

The Liberal Catholic Church (World Headquarters, London, England)

Founded February 13, 1916 by the Rt. Rev. James Ingall Wedgwood. The first ordination in the United States of a priest was that of the Rev. Charles Hampton, at Los Angeles on August 16, 1917.

Churches: 18. Inclusive Membership: 1,500. Sunday or Sabbath Schools: N.R. Total Enrollment: N.R. Ordained clergy: 84.

GENERAL ORGANIZATION

Board of Trustees, meets July 1, annually. Triennial Assembly.

LUTHERAN CHURCH IN AMERICA

OFFICERS

Pres., The Rt. Rev. William H. Pitkin, 34 Taormina La., Ojai, CA 93023. Tel. (805) 646-2324.

Vice-Pres., Dr. Kenneth C. Hitchcock, 3149 Queens Chapel Rd., #103, Mt. Rainier, MD 20822.

Sec., The Rev. Alfred Strauss, 414 N. Lima St., Sierra Madre, CA 91024.

Treas., The Rev. Victor A. Neuman, 8435 Bloomington Ave., Minneapolis, MN 55420.

PERIODICAL

The Liberal Catholic (q), E. J. Burton, Ed. (published in London, England).

Lutheran Church in America

This body was organized June 28, 1962, by consolidation of the American Evangelical Lutheran Church, 1874; the Augustana Evangelical Lutheran Church, 1860; the Finnish Evangelical Lutheran Church, 1890; and the United Lutheran Church in America, 1918. The new body began to function formally on January 1, 1963. It includes congregations, ministers, and synods in both Canada and the U. S. A.

Churches: 5,797. Inclusive Membership: 3,069-679. Sunday or Sabbath Schools: 5,596. Total Enrollment: 889,212. Ordained clergy: 7,377.

GENERAL ORGANIZATION

Convention: biennial. Next meeting, July 3-10, 1974, Baltimore, MD.

Headquarters: 231 Madison Ave., New York, NY 10016. Tel. (212) 532-3410.

OFFICERS

Pres., Rev. Robert J. Marshall.
Sec., Rev. George F. Harkins.
Treas., Carl M. Anderson.

OTHER ORGANIZATIONS

Division for Mission in North America: 231 Madison Ave., New York, NY 10016, Exec. Dir., Rev. Kenneth C. Senft.

Division for Parish Services: 231 Madison Ave., New York, NY 10016, Exec. Dir., Rev. W. Kent Gilbert.

Division for Professional Services: 2900 Queen La., Philadelphia, PA 19129, Exec. Dir., Rev. Louis T. Almén.

Division for World Mission and Ecumenism: 231 Madison Ave., New York, NY 10016, Exec. Dir., Rev. Robert W. Stackel.

Office for Administration and Finance: 231 Madison Ave., New York, NY 10016, Exec. Dir., Rev. Martin E. Carlson.

Office for Communications: 231 Madison Ave., New York, NY 10016, Exec. Dir.,_____

Office for Research and Planning: 231 Madison Ave., New York, NY 10016, Exec. Dir., John V. Lindholm.

Lutheran Church Women: 2900 Queen La., Philadelphia, PA 19129, Pres., Mrs. Clarence Van Loo; Exec. Sec., Miss Dorothy J. Marple.

PERIODICAL

The Lutheran (bi-w), 2900 Queen La., Philadelphia, PA 19129, Rev. Albert P. Stauderman, Ed.

SYNODICAL PRESIDENTS

Caribbean, Rev. Victor M. Rodriquez, 148 Calle del Parque, San Juan, PR 00911.

Central Canada, Rev. Otto A. Olson, Jr., 2281 Portage Ave., Rm. 211, Winnipeg 12, Manitoba, Canada.

Central Pa., Rev. Howard J. McCarney, 900 S. Arlington Ave., Room 208, Harrisburg,PA 17109.

Central States, Rev. Harvey L. Prinz, Ste. 500, Congress Bldg., 3527 Broadway, Kansas City, MO 64111.

Eastern Canada, Rev. Otto F. Reble, 251 King St. W., Rm. 509, Kitchener, Ontario, Canada.

Florida, Rev. Royall A. Yount, Synod Office Bldg. (P.O. Box 10611), 3838 W. Cypress St., Tampa, FL 33609.

Illinois, Rev. Gerald K. Johnson, 53 W. Jackson Blvd., Suite 850, Chicago, IL 60604.

Ind.-Ky., Rev. Walter M. Wick, 3733 N. Meridian St., Indianapolis, IN 46208.

Iowa, Rev. Raynold J. Lingwall, Lutheran Church Center, 3125 Cottage Grove Ave., Des Moines, IA 50311.

Md., Rev. Paul M. Orso, 7604 York Rd., Baltimore, MD 21204.

Metropolitan N. Y., Rev. James A. Graefe, 123 E. 15th St., New York, NY 10003.

Mich., Rev. Frank P. Madsen, 19711 Greenfield Rd., Detroit, MI 48235.

Minn., Rev. Melvin A. Hammarberg, 122 W. Franklin Ave., Minneapolis, MN 55404.

Nebr., Rev. Reuben T. Swanson, Ste. 204, 124 S. 24th St., Omaha, NB 68102.

New England, Rev. Eugene A. Brodeen, 886 Washington St., Dedham, MA 02026.

N. J., Rev. Edwin L. Ehlers, 1930 State Hwy. 33 Hamilton Square, Trenton, NJ 08690.

N. C., Rev. George R. Whittecar, Klumac Rd. (P.O. Box 240), Salisbury, NC 28144.

Northeastern Pa., Rev. Wilson E. Touhsaent, 13 E. Main St., Wescosville, PA 18106.

Ohio, Rev. John W. Rilling, 1233 Dublin Rd., Columbus, OH 43215.

Pacific N.W., Rev. A. G. Fjellman, 5519 Phinney Ave., N., Seattle, WA 98103.

Pacific S.W., Rev. Carl W. Segerhammar, 1340 S. Bonnie Brae St., Los Angeles, CA 90006.

Red River Valley, Rev. Carl W. Larson, 1022-8th St., Ste. #6, Box 758, Moorhead, MN 56560.

Rocky Mountain, Rev. Franklin C. Heglund, Suite 201, 105 Fillmore St., Denver, CO 80206.

Slovak Zion, Rev. John Zornan, 173 Arla Dr., Greentree, Pittsburgh, PA 15220.

S.C. Rev. Herman W. Cauble, 1003 Richland St. (P.O. Box 43), Columbia, SC 29201.

Southeastern, Rev. Harvey L. Huntley, 1644 Tully Circle, N.E., Ste. 124, Atlanta, GA 30329.

Southeastern Pa., Rev. William A. Janson Jr., 2900 Queen Lane, Philadelphia, PA 19129.

Texas-La., Rev. Philip L. Wahlberg, Jr., 408 W. 45th St. (P.O. Box 4367), Austin, TX 78765.

Upper N. Y., Rev. Edward Kersten Perry, 3049 E. Genesee St., Syracuse, NY 13224.

Va., Rev. J. Luther Mauney, 317 Washington Ave., S.W., Roanoke, VA 24016.

Western Canada, Rev. Donald W. Sjoberg, 9901

107th St., Edmonton Alberta T5K 1G4, Canada.
Western Pa.-W. Va., Rev. William C. Hankey, 9625 Perry Hwy., Pittsburgh, PA 15237.
Wis.-Upper Mich., Rev. Theodore E. Matson, 1933 W. Wisconsin Ave., Milwaukee, WI 53233.

The Lutheran Church—Missouri Synod

This body, the second largest Lutheran church in America, was organized in 1847. It holds to an unwavering confessionalism, and is the leader in the conservative group among the Lutherans.

Churches: 5,724. Inclusive Membership: 2,788,-110. Sunday or Sabbath Schools: 5,552. Total Enrollment: 815,522. Ordained clergy: 7,041.

GENERAL ORGANIZATION
General Convention: Biennial. (Next meeting, New Orleans, LA 1973.)
Headquarters: The Lutheran Building, 210 N. Broadway, St. Louis, MO 63102. Tel. (314) 231-6969.

OFFICERS
Pres., Dr. Jacob A. O. Preus.
Sec., Rev. Herbert A. Mueller.
Treas., Milton Carpenter.
Adm. Officer of Bd. of Dir.,_____.
Controller, Ray C. Rauscher.
Asst. Treas., Erwin Wesche.
Stewardship Counselor, Rev. A. Lorenz Grumm.
Dir. of Res., Rev. Paul Picard.
Dir. of Personnel: Rev. John F. Gaertner.
Board of Directors: Pres., Sec., and Treas. of the Synod, and the following: Rev. Alvin W. Mueller, 841 W. Wood St., Decatur, IL 62522; Rev. Ernst H. Stahlke, 7712 53rd Ave., N., Minneapolis, MN 55428; Rupert Dunklau, 2146 Phelps Ave., Fremont, NE 68025; Rev. Gerhardt E. Nitz, 10015 Lance Dr., St. Louis, MO 63137; Harry G. Barr, P.O. Box 26, Fort Smith, AR 72901; Walter Hinck, Northwestern Natl. Bank, 7th and Marquette, Minneapolis, MN 55440; William Zehnder, Jr., 713 S. Main St., Frankenmuth, MI 48734; Carl Muhlenbruch, 4071 Fairway Dr., Wilmette, IL 60091; Gus Melde, 4511 Cherokee Trail, Dallas, TX 75209; Robert W. Hirsch, 2110 Mulberry, Yankton, SD 57078; Walter F. Steinberg, 3130 W. 87th St., Chicago, IL 60652.

BOARDS AND COMMISSIONS
(All at 210 N. Broadway, St. Louis, MO 63102, unless different address is given).
Board for Missions: Executive Sec., Dr. Wm. H. Kohn.
Board for Higher Education: Exec. Sec., Dr. A.M. Ahlschwede.
Board of Parish Education: Offices at 3558 S. Jefferson Ave., St. Louis, MO 63118. Exec. Sec., Dr. Arthur L. Miller.
Board of Social Ministry and World Relief: Exec. Sec., Rev. Leslie Weber.
Board of Stewardship: Exec. Sec., Rev. A. Lorenz Grumm.
Board of Support and Pensions: Exec. Sec., Rev. John Knippenberg.
Board of Managers, The Concordia Plans Manager, Earl Haake.

MENNONITE CHURCH

Armed Forces Commission: Exec. Sec., Rev. Milton S. Ernstmeyer.
Church Extension Board: Exec. Sec., Mr. Fred E. Lietz.

AUXILIARY ORGANIZATIONS
Concordia Publishing House: 3558 S. Jefferson Ave., St. Louis, MO 63118. Pres., Dr. Ralph Reinke.
Concordia Historical Institute: Concordia Seminary, 801 De Mun Ave., St. Louis, MO 63105. Dir., Rev. Aug. R. Suelflow.
Lutheran Deaconess Association: Deaconess Hall, Valparaiso, IN 46383. Ex. Dir., Dr. Lucille Wassman.
Lutheran Laymen's League: 2185 Hampton Ave., St. Louis, MO 63110. Exec. Dir., Ben F. Jutzi.
Lutheran Women's Missionary League: 3558 S. Jefferson Ave., St. Louis, MO 63118 Pres., Mrs. C. R. (Florence) Montz.
Walther League: 875 N. Dearborn St., Chicago, IL 60610. Exec. Sec., Mark T. Hellman.

PERIODICALS
The Lutheran Witness (m), 3558 S. Jefferson Ave., St. Louis, MO 63118. Dr. Martin W. Mueller, Ed.
The Lutheran Witness Reporter (bi-w), 3558 S. Jefferson Ave., St. Louis, MO 63118. Dr. Martin W. Mueller, Ed.
Concordia Theological Monthly (m), Concordia Seminary, 801 De Mun Ave., St. Louis, MO 63105. Dr. Herbert T. Mayer, Man. Ed.
Lutheran Education (m. Sept. to June), Concordia Teachers College, 7400 Augusta Ave., River Forest, IL 60305. Prof. Merle L Radke, Ed.
Advance (m), Lutheran Building, 210 N. Broadway, St. Louis, MO 63102.
Der Lutheraner (m), 3558 S. Jefferson Ave., St. Louis, MO 63118. Dr. Herman A. Mayer, Ed.

Mennonite Church

The largest group of the Mennonites who began arriving in the U. S. as early as 1683, settling in Germantown, Pennsylvania. They derive their name from Menno Simons, their outstanding leader, b. 1496.

Churches: 1,041. Inclusive Membership: 88,947. Sunday or Sabbath Schools: 967. Total Enrollment: 110,475. Ordained clergy: 2,335.

GENERAL ORGANIZATION
General Office: 10600 W. Higgins Rd., Rm. 104, Rosemont, IL 60018. Tel. (312) 297-1655.

OFFICERS
Mod., A. Don Augsberger, 1601 Hillcrest Dr., Harrisonburg, VA 22801. Mod.-Elect, Newton L. Gingrich, Tavistock, Ontario, Canada.
Sec.-Treas., Paul A. Leatherman, 111 S. Tenth St., Akron, PA 17501.
Gen. Sec., Paul M. Kraybill, 10600 W. Higgins Rd., Rm. 104, Rosemont, IL 60018.

OTHER ORGANIZATIONS
General Board: Chmn., Paul Mininger, Rt. 6, Box 392, Goshen, IN 46526.
Council on Faith, Life, and Strategy: Chmn., David W. Thomas, Rt. 6, Lancaster, PA. 17603.

MENNONITE CHURCH, THE GENERAL CONFERENCE

Board of Congregational Ministries: Exec. Sec., Ross T. Bender, 1110 N. Main, Goshen, IN 46526.

Board of Education: Exec. Sec., Albert Meyer, 1700 S. Main St., Goshen, IN 46526.

Board of Missions: Exec. Sec., H. Ernest Bennett, 1711 Prairie St., Elkhart, IN 46514.

Mutual Aid Board: Harold L. Swartzendruber, 1110 North Main, Goshen, IN 46526.

Mennonite Publication Board: Publisher, Ben Cutrell, 616 Walnut Ave., Scottdale, PA. 15683.

PERIODICALS

Gospel Herald (w), Scottdale, PA 15683. John M. Drescher, Ed.

Christian Living (m), Scottdale, PA 15683. Dan Hertzler, Ed.

Builder (m), Scottdale, PA 15683. Paul M. Lederach, Ed.

Rejoice! (q) Scottdale, PA. James E. Horsch, Associate Ed.

Mennonite Yearbook (annual), Scottdale, PA 15683. Levi Miller, Ed.

Mennonite Quarterly Review (q), Goshen, IN 46526. John S. Oyer, Ed.

With (m), Scottdale, PA 15683. J. Lorne Peachey, Ed.

Purpose (w), Scottdale, PA 15683. David E. Hostetler, Ed.

On the Line (w), Scottdale, PA 15683. Helen Alderfer, Ed.

Story Friends (w), Scottdale, PA 15683. Alice Hershberger, Ed.

Information: Levi Miller, Ed., Mennonite Yearbook, Scottdale, PA. 15683.

Mennonite Church, The General Conference

One of the oldest Mennonite conferences in the United States. The present denominational organization dates from 1860 (in Iowa).

Churches: 192. Inclusive Membership: 36,314. Sunday or Sabbath Schools: 192. Total Enrollment: 31,809. Ordained clergy: 314.

GENERAL ORGANIZATION

General Conference: triennial. Next meeting, 1974.

Central Office: 722 Main, Newton, KS 67114. Tel. (316) 283-5100.

OFFICERS

Pres., Henry Poettcker, 600 Shaftesbury Blvd., Winnipeg, Manitoba R3P OM4, Canada.

Vice-Pres., Jacob T. Friesen, 225 S. Lawn, Bluffton, OH 45817.

Sec., Hedy Sawadsky, Henderson, NB 68371.

Gen. Sec., Heinz D. Janzen, 722 Main St., Newton, KS 67114.

OTHER ORGANIZATIONS
(All at central office)

Commission on Home Ministries: Exec. Sec., Palmer Becker.

Commission on Overseas Mission: Exec. Sec., Howard Habegger.

Women's Missionary Association: Exec. Sec., Dorothea Dyck.

Commission on Education: Actg. Exec. Sec., Frank Ward.

Division of Administration: Exec. Sec., Wm. L. Friesen.

PERIODICALS

The Mennonite (w), 600 Shaftesbury Blvd., Winnipeg, Manitoba R3P OM4 Canada, Larry Kehler, Ed.

Builder (m), 722 Main St., Newton, KS 67114.

Missions Today (m), Marie Dyck, Ed.

Der Bote (w), 716-South Ave., N. Saskatoon, Saskatchewan, Canada.

The Metropolitan Church Association

Organized as the result of a revival movement in Chicago in 1894, as the Metropolitan Holiness Church, and in 1899 chartered as the Metropolitan Church Association. It has a Wesleyan theology.

GENERAL ORGANIZATION

General Assembly: annual.

International Headquarters: 323 Broad St., Lake Geneva, WI 53147.

OFFICERS

Pres., Rev. W. T. Pettengell.

Vice-Pres., Rev. C. J. Sammis.

Sec.-Treas., Rev. Murdo MacKay.

PERIODICAL

The Burning Bush (m), Lake Geneva, WI, Rev. W. T. Pettengell, Ed. (Publishing House, The Metropolitan Church Association, Lake Geneva, WI 53147).

The Missionary Church

The Missionary Church was formed in 1969 through a merger of the United Missionary Church (organized in 1883) and the Missionary Church Association (founded in 1898). It is evangelical and conservative with a strong emphasis on missionary work at home and abroad.

There are three levels of church government with local, district, and general conferences. There are nine church districts in the United States and two in Canada. The general conference meets every two years. The denomination operates two colleges in the U. S.

Churches: 365. Inclusive Membership: 22,071. Sunday or Sabbath Schools: 365. Total Enrollment: 45,301. Ordained clergy: 573.

GENERAL ORGANIZATION

International Headquarters: 3901 S. Wayne Ave., Ft. Wayne, IN 46807. Tel. (219) 744-1291.

Publishing Headquarters: Bethel Publishing Co., 1819 S. Main St., Elkhart, IN 46514. Tel. (219) 293-8585.

OFFICERS

Pres., Dr. Kenneth E. Geiger.

Vice-Pres., Rev. Tillman Habegger.

Sec., Timothy M. Warner.

Treas., Edwin W. Crewson.

Dir., Overseas Missions, Rev. Paul A. Erdel.

Dir., Evangelism and Church Extension, Rev. Tillman Habegger.

Dir., Christian Education, Rev. Vernon Petersen.

Dir., Youth, Rev. Robert Fansler.

Dir., Children, Mrs. Paul Grabill.
Missionary Men International: Pres., Robert Weyenseth Rohrer.
Women's Missionary Societies: Pres., Mrs. Marlin Ditmer, Rt. 4, Box 390, Elkhart, IN 46514.
Broadcasting Ministries: Dir., Rev. Quinton J. Everest, Box 2026, South Bend, IN 46615.
Board of Publications: Dir., Jerry R. Freed, 1819 S. Main St., Elkhart, IN 46514.

PERIODICAL
Emphasis (s-m), 3901 S. Wayne Ave., Ft. Wayne, IN 46807. Dr. W. O. Klopfenstein, Ed.

Moravian Church in America (Unitas Fratrum)

In 1735 Moravian missionaries of the pre-Reformation faith of John Hus came to Georgia, in 1740 to Pennsylvania, and in 1753 to North Carolina. They established the Moravian Church, which is broadly evangelical, liturgical, with an episcopacy as a spiritual office and in form of government "conferential."

GENERAL ORGANIZATION
Two Provincial Synods (Northern and Southern).

PERIODICAL
The North American Moravian (m), 5 W. Market St., Bethlehem, PA 18018.

NORTHERN PROVINCE
Headquarters: 69 W. Church St., Bethlehem, PA 18018. Tel. (215) 867-7566.

Churches: 100. Inclusive Membership: 34,555. Sunday or Sabbath Schools: 98. Total Enrollment: 10,069. Ordained clergy: 159.

OFFICERS
Provincial Elders' Conference:
Pres., Dr. John S. Groenfeldt.
Vice-Pres. (Eastern District), Dr. Thorlief Harberg.
Vice-Pres. (Western District), The Rt. Rev. Milo A. Loppnow, Madison, WI.
Sec., Theodore F. Hartmann.
Treas., Ralph R. Schlough, 69 W. Church St., Bethlehem, PA 18018.

SOUTHERN PROVINCE
Headquarters: 459 S. Church St., Winston-Salem, NC 27108. Tel. (919) 725-5811.

Churches: 49. Inclusive Membership: 22,784. Sunday or Sabbath Schools: 49. Total Enrollment: 10,771. Ordained clergy: 58.

OFFICERS
Provincial Elders' Conference:
Pres., Dr. Clayton H. Persons.
Vice-Pres., Dr. Richard F. Amos.
Sec., The Rev. Burton J. Rights.
Treas., D. A. Daetwyler, 500 S. Church St., Winston-Salem, NC 27101.

PERIODICAL
The North American Moravian, 5 W. Market St., Bethlehem, PA 18018, Rev. Bernard E. Michel, Ed.

BISHOPS
Walter Vivian Moses, 16 Carrera St., St. Augustine, FL 32084.
Kenneth G. Hamilton, 428 Second Ave., Bethlehem, PA 18018.
I. Richard Mewaldt, 4718 Tokay Blvd., Madison, WI 53711.
Carl J. Helmich, Box 211, Gnadenhutten, OH 44629
Percival R. Henkelmann, 7349 Via Amorita, Downey, CA 90241.
Milo Alvin Loppnow, 5305 Queensbridge Rd., Madison, WI 53714.
W. Herbert Spaugh, 130 N. Canterbury Road, Charlotte, NC 28211.
Allen W. Schattschneider, 415 Woodcrest, Lititz, PA 17543.
Frederick Wolff, 1825 Center St., Dover House 108, Bethlehem, PA 18017.
George G. Higgins, Box 2373 Westfield Ave., Winston-Salem, NC 27103.
Samuel J. Tesch, 635 Cascade Ave., Winston-Salem, NC 27107.
James Gordon Weingarth, 1028 Hill St., York, PA 17403.
Edward Wilde, Rt. 1, Box 158, Sister Bay, WI 54234.
Edwin W. Kortz, 69 W. Church St., Bethlehem, PA 18018.

Muslims

There are perhaps 15 or 20 local centers of worship among Muslims in the U. S.

Islamic Center, 2551 Massachusetts Ave., N.W., Washington, DC 20008. Dir., Dr. Abdul Rauf.

National Baptist Convention of America

This is the "unincorporated" body of National Baptists which was organized in 1880 following a dispute over control of the publishing board in which another Convention was organized. Membership of the churches is largely Negro.

GENERAL ORGANIZATION
Convention: Annual (September).

OFFICERS
Pres., Dr. James C. Sams, 1724 Jefferson St., Jacksonville, FL 32209.
Corr. Sec., Rev. Billy H. Wilson, 2620 S. Marsallis Ave., Dallas, TX 75216.
Treas., Dr. A. A. Lucas, 5109 Farmer St., Houston, TX 77020.
Hist., Rev. Marvin C. Griffin, 915 N. 6th St., Waco, TX 76707.

OTHER ORGANIZATIONS
Benevolent Board: Corr. Sec., Rev. George J. Johnson, Mary Allen College, Crockett, TX 75835; Chmn., Rev. John W. Williams, 1414 E. 15th St., Kansas City, MO 64106.
Evangelical Board: Corr. Sec., Rev. E. H. Branch, 2343 Benton Rd., Kansas City, MO 64128; Chmn., Rev. H. H. Robinson, 116 W. 8th St., Jacksonville, FL 32206.
Foreign Mission Board: Corr. Sec., Rev. E. S. Branch, 2708 Webster St., Houston, TX 77004.

NATIONAL BAPTIST CONVENTION, U.S.A., INC.

Home Mission Board: Corr. Sec., Rev. Ira. M. Hendon, 3993 So. Parkway, Chicago, IL 60653.

Publishing Board: Chmn., Rev. J. B. Ridley, 319 21st Ave. N., Nashville, TN 37206.

Educational Board: Chmn., Rev. P. S. Wilkinson, 1011 Delaware St., San Antonio, TX 78210.

B.Y.P.U. Board: Chmn., Rev. L. W. Mingo, 217 E. Monroe St., Carbondale, IL 69201.

Senior Woman's Auxiliary: Corr. Sec., Mrs. E. B. White, 2315 Harlem Ave., Baltimore, MD 21216.

Junior Woman's Auxiliary, Corr. Sec., Miss Mora D. Dailey, P. O. Box 105, Athena, TX 75751.

National Baptist Convention, U.S.A., Inc.

The older and parent convention of Negro Baptists. This body is to be distinguished from the National Baptist Convention of America, usually referred to as the "unincorporated" body.

GENERAL ORGANIZATION
Convention: annual.

OFFICERS
Pres., Rev. J. H. Jackson, 405 E. 31st St., Chicago, IL 60616.

Vice-Pres.-at-large, Rev. E. D. Billoups, 904 N. 33rd St., Baton Rouge, LA 70802.

Vice-Pres.: Rev. C. H. Hampton, 605 S. 32nd St., San Diego, CA 92113; Rev. David Matthews, P.O. Box 627, Indianola, MS; Rev. A. E. Campbell, 2500 Carnes Ave., Memphis, TN 38114; Rev. Sandy F. Ray, 574 Madison St., Brooklyn, NY 11221.

Sec., Rev. T. J. Jemison, 915 Spain St., Baton Rouge, LA 70802.

Treas., Rev. L. G. Carr, 5317 Masters St., Philadelphia, PA 19131.

Stat., Dr. B. Joseph Johnson, Sr., 1211 Hunter St., N.W., Atlanta, GA 30314.

Hist., Rev. E. T. Caviness. 10515 Tacoma Ave., Cleveland, OH 44108.

OFFICERS OF BOARDS
Foreign Mission Board: 701 S. 19th St., Philadelphia, PA 19146. Sec., Rev. William J. Harvey, III.

Home Mission Board: 1323 E. Second St., Plainfield, NJ 07062. Exec. Sec., Rev. Charles P. Harris.

Sunday School Publishing Board; 330 Charlotte Ave., Nashville, TN 37201. Exec. Dir., Rev. D. C. Washington.

B.T.U. Board: 412 4th Ave., Nashville, TN 37219. Sec., Rev. C. R. Williams.

Benefit Board: 932 Ft. Wood St., Chattanooga, TN 37403. Sec., Rev. M. Kirby.

Education Board: 903 Looney St., Memphis, TN 38107. Chmn., Rev. W. H. Brewster.

Evangelism Board: 7201 Claremont St., Albuquerque, NM 87110. Sec., Rev. W. C. Trotter.

Laymen's Movement: Pres., Walter Cade, 537 N. 82nd St., Kansas City, KS.

Woman's Auxiliary Convention: 584 Arden Pk., Detroit, MI 48202. Pres., Mrs. Mary O. Ross.

National S. S. AND B.T.U. Congress: 3620 Oak St., Kansas City, KS 66104. Pres., Dr. E. A. Freeman.

PERIODICAL
National Baptist Voice (s-m), 902 N. Good St., Dallas, TX 75204. Rev. C. A. Clark, Ed.

National Baptist Evangelical Life and Soul Saving Assembly of U.S.A.

Organized in 1921, by A. A. Banks, as a charitable, educational, and evangelical organization.

GENERAL ORGANIZATION
Assembly: general.

Headquarters: 441 Monroe Ave., Detroit, MI 48226.

OFFICERS
Exec. Sec., Captain, A. A. Banks, Jr., 2340 Chicago Blvd., Detroit, MI 48206.

Asst. Capt., J. C. Huey, 522 W. Walker St., Denison, TX 75020.

Directress of Women's Dept., Madam F. W. Land, P.O. Box 324, Tchula, MS 39169.

PERIODICAL
The Peoples' Soul Saving Radio Magazine, A. A. Banks, Man. Ed.

National Primitive Baptist Convention, Inc.

A group of Baptists having associations, state conventions, and a National Convention (organized in 1907).

Churches: 2,198. Inclusive Membership: 1,645,-000. Sunday or Sabbath Schools: 2,150. Total Enrollment: 32,200. Ordained clergy: 601.

GENERAL ORGANIZATION
Headquarters: Post Office Box 2355, Tallahassee, FL.

CHIEF OFFICERS
National Convention: Pres., Rev. Percy D. Brantley, 1795 N.W. 58th St., Miami, FL 33142; Rec. Sec., Rev. F.L. Livingston, 1334 Carson, Dallas, TX 75216; Sec. Board of Directors, Rev. M. G. Miles, 1525 S. Bronough St., Tallahassee, FL 32301.

National Church School Training Union: Pres., Rev. R. H. Frazier, 2536 Bancroft St., Charlotte, NC 28206; Sec., Mrs. Icylene B. Horne, 2222 Metropolitan St., Dallas, TX 75215.

National Ushers Congress: Pres., Willie Campbell, 1321 E. Scott St., Pensacola, FL 32503; Sec., Mrs. R. H. Howard, 3305 25th Ave., Tampa, FL 33605.

Publication Board: Chmn., Rev. R. H. Frazier, 2536 Bancroft St., Charlotte, NC 28206; Sec., Rev. Z. D. Coatson, 2906 Price St., Ft. Myers, FL 33901.

Women's Congress: Pres., Mrs. E. C. Raye, 2112 Russell St., Charlotte, NC 28208; Sec., Mrs. W. M. Miles, 1525 S. Bronough St., Tallahassee, FL 32301.

National Laymen's Council: Pres., Dea. J. L. Warren, 4209 Curtis St., Tampa, FL; Sec., Bro. J. L. Byrd, 4829 Fairmount Ave., Elyria, OH 44035.

The National Spiritual Alliance of the U.S.A.

This body, founded in 1913, believes in supernormal, personal and impersonal manifestations and in intercommunication between denizens of different worlds.

Churches: 34. Inclusive Membership: 3,230. Sunday or Sabbath Schools: N.R. Total Enrollment: N.R. Ordained clergy: N.R.

GENERAL ORGANIZATION
Convention: annual (July).
Headquarters: R.F.D. 1, Keene, NH 03431. Tel. (603) 352-2739.

OFFICERS
Pres., Mrs. Jeannette R. Brown, 16 Congress Pl., Fitchburg, MA 01420.
Sec., Mrs. Wilma M. Doucette, 14 Edgewood St., Stafford Springs, CT 06076.

National Spiritualist Association of Churches

This organization is made up of believers that Spiritualism is a science, philosophy, and religion based upon the demonstrated facts of communication between this world and the next.

GENERAL ORGANIZATION
Convention: annual (October).
Ralph D. Cutlip, Sr., P.O. Box 128, Cassadaga, FL 32706.
Rev. Edwin Ford, 1521 W. Edgemont, Phoenix, AR 85007.

OTHER ORGANIZATIONS
Bureau of Education: 11811 Watertown Plank Rd., Milwaukee, WI 53226.
Bureau of Public Relations: The Stow Memorial Foundation, Cassadaga, FL 32706, Ralph D. Cutlip, Sr., Sec.-Treas.
Spiritualist Benevolent Society, Inc.: Cassadaga, FL 32706.

PERIODICAL
The National Spiritualist (m), Robert J. Macdonald, P. O. Box 147, Cassadaga, FL 32706. Robert J. Macdonald, Ed.

Netherlands Reformed Congregations

Formed from among immigrations from Holland; a secession from the State Church there. The present body dates from 1907. The doctrines are the Netherlands Confession, the Heidelberg Catechism, and the Canons of Dort.
Churches: 22. Inclusive Membership: 7,319. Sunday or Sabbath Schools: N.R. Total Enrollment: N.R. Ordained clergy: N.R.

GENERAL ORGANIZATION
Synod meets every two years (next meeting, 1974).

OFFICERS
Pres. of Synod: Rev. William C. Lamain, 2115 Romence Dr., N.E., Grand Rapids, MI 49503. Tel. (616) 456-6323.

PERIODICAL
The Banner of Truth (bi-m).

New Apostolic Church of North America

This body is a variant of the Catholic Apostolic Church, which movement began in England in 1830. The New Apostolic Church distinguished itself from the parent body in 1863 by recognizing a succession of Apostles.
Churches: 262. Inclusive Membership: 20,195. Sunday or Sabbath Schools: 262. Total Enrollment: 7,186. Ordained clergy: 383.

GENERAL ORGANIZATION
Headquarters: 3753 N. Troy St., Chicago, IL 60618.

OFFICERS
Pres., Rev. Michael Kraus, 267 Lincoln Rd., Waterloo, Ontario, Canada.
First Vice-Pres., Rev. John W. Fendt, 36 Colony La., Manhasset, NY 11030.
Second Vice-Pres., Rev. Erwin Wagner, 330 Arlene Pl., Waterloo, Ontario, Canada.
Sec., Rev. William K. Schmeerbauch, 312 Ladue Woods Court, St. Louis, MO 63141.
Treas. and Asst. Sec., A. Walter Eckhardt, 6380 N. Indian Rd., Chicago, IL 60646.

PERIODICALS
(All published at 3753 N. Troy St., Chicago, IL 60618.)
Word of Life (s-m).
Youth Guide (m).
New Apostolic Review (s-m).
The Good Shepherd (m).
Our Family (m).

North American Baptist General Conference

These churches emanated from German Baptist immigrants of more than a century ago. Some are still bilingual in their ministry. Although scattered on the North American continent, they are bound together by a common heritage, a strong spiritual unity, a Bible-centered faith, and a deep interest in missions.

Churches: 341. Inclusive Membership: 54,441. Sunday or Sabbath Schools: 332. Total Enrollment: 55,815. Ordained clergy: 423.

GENERAL ORGANIZATION
General Conference: Triennial. Next meeting, 1973.
Headquarters: 7308 Madison St., Forest Park, IL 60130. Tel. (312) 771-8700.

OFFICERS
Mod., Rev. Aaron Buhler.
Vice-Mod., Mr. Henry Fluth.
Exec. Sec., Dr. Gideon K. Zimmerman.
Sec. of Stewardship and Com., Rev. John Binder.
Treas., Milton Hildebrandt.
Comptroller, Miss Mary H. Leypoldt.

OTHER ORGANIZATIONS
General Missionary Society: Gen. Sec., Dr. R. Schilke.
Dept. of Christian Education: Gen. Sec., Rev. Bruce Rich.

NORTH AMERICAN OLD ROMAN CATHOLIC CHURCH

Roger Williams Press, Bus. Mgr., Rev. Eldon L. Janzen.
Woman's Missionary Union: Pres., Mrs. Walter Stein; Sec., Mrs. Charles Littman; Treas., Mrs. Ernest A. Hoffmann.
Ministers' Fellowship: Pres., Rev. Bernard Fritzke; Sec.-Treas., Rev. Merle Brenner.

PERIODICAL
The Baptist Herald (m), Rev. Reinhold Kerstan, Ed. published by the Roger Williams Press, 7308 Madison St., Forest Park, IL 60130.

North American Old Roman Catholic Church

A body with the doctrine of the Old Catholics in right and succession of Catholic orders. Knott Missal used for Masses. Pontificale used for all Order Rights. Not under Papal jurisdiction.

Churches: 121. Inclusive Membership: 60,098. Sunday or Sabbath Schools: 15. Total Enrollment: 8,022. Ordained clergy: 112.

OFFICERS
Presiding Bishop of the Americas and Canada, Most Rev. John E. Schweikert, 4200 N. Kedvale Ave., Chicago, IL 60641.

North American Old Roman Catholic Church

This body is identical with the Roman Catholic Church in worship, faith, etc., but differs from it in discipline. It was received into union with the Eastern Orthodox Church by the Archbishop of Beirut on August 5, 1911, and by the Orthodox Patriarch of Alexandria on February 26, 1912.

GENERAL ORGANIZATION
Synod: Biennial; 1973.
Chancery Address: Box 1647, G.P.O., Brooklyn, NY 11207. Tel. (212) 384-1400.

OFFICERS
Primate Metropolitan, The Most Rev. Archbishop James H. Rogers, 238 Wyona St., Brooklyn, NY 11207.
Vicar Gen.-Treas., The Most Rev. George T. Koerner.
Chancellor, Rt. Rev. Albert J. Berube.
Vice-Chancellor, Very Rev. Gregory Boschen.
Sec. of Synod, Rev. Jonathan E. Trela.

PERIODICAL
The Augustinian (q), Box 1647, G.P.O., Brooklyn, NY 11207.

Old German Baptist Brethren

A group which separated from the Church of the Brethren (formerly German Baptist Brethren) in 1881 as a protest against a liberalizing tendency.

GENERAL ORGANIZATION
Conference, annual.

OFFICERS
Foreman, Elder Morris B. Wagoner, R.D. 4,

Delphi, IN 46923. Tel.: Buck Creek (317) 489-3696.
Reading Clk., Elder C. J. Rumble, 2737 W. Rumble Rd., Modesto, CA 95350.
Writing Clk., Elder Clement Skiles, Rt. 1, Box 140, Bringhurst, IN 46913.

PERIODICAL
The Vindicator, Covington, OH, Lester Fisher, Ed.

Old Order Amish Church

The congregations of this Mennonite group have no annual conference. They worship in private homes. They adhere to the older forms of worship and attire. This body has bishops, ministers, and deacons.

Churches: 368. Inclusive Membership: 14,720. Sunday or Sabbath Schools: N.R. Total Enrollment: N.R. Ordained clergy: 1,497.

NO GENERAL ORGANIZATION

INFORMATION
Der Neue Amerikanische Calendar, c/o Raber's Book Store, Baltic, OH 43804.

Old Order (Wisler) Mennonite Church

This body arose from a separation of Mennonites dated 1870, under Jacob Wisler, in opposition to what were thought to be innovations.
At present, this group is located in the Eastern United States and Canada. There are approximately 8,000 members and 58 congregations, with 19 bishops, 74 ministers, and 48 deacons.
Each state, or district, has its own organization or government and holds a yearly conference.

Churches: 38. Inclusive Membership: 8,000. Sunday or Sabbath Schools: None. Total Enrollment: None. Ordained clergy: 101.

NO GENERAL ORGANIZATION

INFORMATION
Henry W. Riehl, Rt. 1, Columbiana, OH 44408. Tel. (216) 482-4832.

The Old Roman Catholic Church (English Rite)

The old Roman Catholic Church regards itself as the "historical Roman Catholic Church, in principle, doctrine, sacraments, rules and holy orders" but separated from the Papal See since 1711 on matters of administration only.
This church came to America in 1916, when the Prince deLandes Berghes consecrated the late Msgr. Carmel Henry Carfora as Archbishop-Primate for the American Province. Msgr. Carfora consecrated the present Archbishop-Metropolitan on August 25, 1956, and he was elected to succeed Msgr. Carfora as Archbishop-Metropolitan for all of North America after the death of Msgr. Carfora in 1959.
In 1963, Msgr. Burns entered into status of Union with the British Church under Msgr.

Barrington-Evans and the American Province has steadily grown since that date.

Churches: 186. Inclusive Membership: 65,128. Sunday or Sabbath Schools: N.R. Total Enrollment: N.R. Ordained clergy: 201.

OFFICER

Archbishop Metropolitan for North America: The Most Rev. Robert Alfred Burns, 840 N Oakley Blvd., Chicago, IL 60622. Tel. (312) 235-5675.

Open Bible Standard Church, Inc.

An evangelical, full gospel denomination emphasizing evangelism, missions, and the message of the Open Bible. Originally composed of two separate groups, namely Bible Standard Churches and Open Bible Evangelistic Association, a merger took place July 26, 1935, and the name Open Bible Standard Churches, Inc., was adopted.

Churches: 275. Inclusive Membership: 25,000. Sunday or Sabbath Schools: 275. Total Enrollment: 24,000. Ordained clergy: 725.

GENERAL ORGANIZATION

General Conference: annual (June).
Headquarters: Bell Ave. at Fleur Dr., P.O. Box 1737, Des Moines, IA 50306. Tel. (515) 244-2251.

OFFICERS

Gen. Supt., Ray E. Smith, Des Moines, Iowa.
Asst. Supt., Frank W. Smith, Des Moines, Iowa.
Sec.-Treas., O. Ralph Isbill.
Miss. Sec., R. Bryant Mitchell, Des Moines, Iowa.
National Sunday School Supt. and National Youth Dir., Daniel LeLaCheur, Des Moines, Iowa.

PERIODICALS

Message of the Open Bible (m), 1159—24th St., Des Moines, IA 50311. Clifford and Dolores Rainey, Eds.
The Overcomer (q), 1120 Walnut, P.O. Box 1737, Des Moines, IA, 50306, Daniel LeLa Cheur, Ed.
World Vision (bi-m), 1120 Walnut, P.O. Box 1737, Des Moines, IA, 50306, R. Bryant Mitchell, Ed.

The (Original) Church of God, Inc.

This body was organized in 1886 as the first church in the U.S.A., to take the name "The Church of God." In 1917 a difference of opinion led this particular group to include the word (Original) in its name. It is a holiness body and believes in the whole Bible, rightly divided, using the New Testament as its rule and government.

Churches: 70. Inclusive Membership: 20,000. Sunday or Sabbath Schools: 40. Total Enrollment: 129. Ordained clergy: 124.

GENERAL ORGANIZATION

General Convention: annual (October) at Chattanooga, TN
Headquarters: 2214 E. 17th St., Chattanooga, TN 37404.

THE ORTHODOX PRESBYTERIAN CHURCH

OFFICERS

Gen. Supt., Rev. O. E. Lambeth.
Asst. Gen. Supt., Rev. I. R. Rodgers.
Bus. Mgr., Rev. O. E. Scott.
Sec.-Treas., Rev. O. F. Barnes.
Supt. Y.P.C.U.W., Roy Wm. Kyzer.
Sec.-Treas., Juanita Perkins.

PERIODICALS

The Messenger (m), 2214 E. 17th St., Chattanooga, TN, 37404, Rev. O. E. Scott, Ed.
Youth Messenger (m), Billy Perkins, Ed.

The Orthodox Church in America

The Russian Orthodox Greek Catholic Church of America entered Alaska in 1792 before its purchase by the U.S.A. in 1867. Its canonical status of independence (autocephaly) was granted by its Mother Church, the Russian Orthodox Church, on April 10, 1970, and is now known as The Orthodox Church in America.

Churches: 387. Inclusive Membership: 1,000,000. Sunday or Sabbath Schools: N.R. Total Enrollment: N.R. Ordained clergy: 448.

GENERAL ORGANIZATION

All-American Council (Biennial, next meeting, October, 1973).
Primate: His Beatitude, Metropolitan Ireney, Archbishop of New York, Metropolitan of All America and Canada; Sec'y to the Metropolitan: Serge Troubetzkoy, 59 E. 2nd St., New York, NY 10003.
Chancellor:_____; Sec.-Treas., V. Rev. Daniel Hubiak.

SYNOD

The Most Rev. John, Archbishop of Chicago and Minneapolis, 1121 N. Leavitt St., Chicago, IL 60622.
The Most Rev. Nikon, Archbishop of Brooklyn.
The Most Rev. John, Archbishop of San Franoisco and Western U.S., 2040 Anza St., San Francisco, CA 94118.
The Most Rev. Sylvester, Archbishop of Montreal and Canada, 1175 Champlain St., Montreal, Canada.
The Most Rev. Valerian, Archbishop of Detroit and Michigan, 2522 Grey Tower Rd., RFD 7, Jackson, MI 49201.
The Most Rev. Kiprian, Archbishop of Philadelphia and Pennsylvania, St. Tikhon Monastery, South Canaan, PA 18459.
The Rt. Rev. Stephen, Bishop of Boston, 529 E. Broadway, South Boston, MA 02127.
The Rt. Rev. Theodosius, Bishop of Pittsburgh and West Virginia, 300 S. Dallas Ave., Pittsburgh, PA 15208.
The Rt. Rev. Ioasaph, Bishop of Edmonton, 5910-11 8th Ave., Edmonton, Alberta, Canada.
The Rt. Rev. Dmitri, Bishop of Berkeley, 2040 Anza St., San Francisco, CA 94118.

The Orthodox Presbyterian Church

On June 11, 1936, certain ministers, elders, and lay members of the Presbyterian Church in the U.S.A. withdrew under the leadership of the conservative scholar, the late Rev. J. Gresham Machen.

PENTECOSTAL ASSEMBLIES OF THE WORLD, INC.

GENERAL ORGANIZATION

General Assembly: annual.
Headquarters: 7401 Old York Rd., Philadelphia, PA 19126. Tel. (215) 224-1883.

OFFICERS

Mod., Jack J. Peterson, 7401 Old York Rd., Philadelphia, PA 19126.
Stated Clk., Richard A. Barker, 7401 Old York Rd., Philadelphia, PA 19126.

† Pentecostal Assemblies of the World, Inc.

An interracial Pentecostal holiness group, originating in the early part of the century in the Middle West and now spread throughout the country.

GENERAL ORGANIZATION

Convention: annual (August).
Headquarters: 3040 N. Illinois St., Indianapolis, IN 46208.

OFFICERS

Bishops: R. P. Paddock, Asst. Presiding Bishop, 1342 N. Burdick St., Kalamazoo, MI 49007; A. Wm. Lewis, 1501 W. 9th St., Santa Ana, CA 92703; David Schultz, 3107 Virginia Ave., Louisville, KY 40211; K. F. Smith, 357 Sherborn Dr., Columbus, OH 43219; Oscar Sanders, 902 S. Hackley St., Muncie, IN 47302; Freeman M. Thomas, 7308 Race St., Pittsburgh, PA 15208; William Crossley, 247 Northland Ave., Buffalo, N Y 14208; Noble Pace, 600 E. 4th St., Hartford City, IN 47348; David Johnson, 621 22nd St., Superior, WI 54880; Austin Layne, 3809 San Francisco Ct., St. Louis, MO 63115; John Caldwell, 2546 "L" St., San Diego, CA 92102; J. S. Holly, 7337 Eberhart, Chicago, IL 60619; Ralph Bass, 1545 Tampa, Dayton, Ohio 45408; B. Nelson, Box 196, Red Wing, MN 55066; O. Pettford, 2145 Isleta Rd., Albuquerque, NM 87105; L. E. Brisbin, 212 56th St., S.E., Grand Rapids, MI 49508; B. T. Moore, 316 33rd Ave., Seattle, Wash. 98144; F. R. Bowdan, 1740 Victoria Ave., Los Angeles, CA 90066.
Gen. Sec., Elder J. Johnson, 3040 N. Illinois St., Indianapolis, IN 46208.
Treas., Elder L. Beard, 3040 N. Illinois St., Indianapolis, IN 46208.

PERIODICAL

Christian Outlook (m), 228 S. Orange Ave., South Orange, NJ 07079. Elder Thomas Streitferdt, Ed.

Pentecostal Church of Christ

Founded by John Stroup at Flatwoods, Kentucky, May 10, 1917. Incorporated at Portsmouth, Ohio, 1927. Doctrinally this group subscribes to belief in the Trinity, personal spiritual experiences—regeneration, sanctification, baptism by the Holy Spirit—and divine healing for the body.

Churches: 43. Inclusive Membership: 1,209. Sunday or Sabbath Schools: 40. Total Enrollment: 3,171. Ordained clergy: 45.

GENERAL ORGANIZATION

Headquarters: Box 263, London, OH. Tel. (614) 852-2421.

OFFICERS

Gen. Overseer, Chester I. Miller, Box 263, London, OH 43140.
Gen. Sec., T. L. Dooley, 1600 Mill Rd. S. W., Canton, OH 44706.
Gen. Treas., L. T. Hayes, P.O. Box 324, London, OH 43140.

PERIODICAL

Pentecostal Witness (m), 1600 Mill Rd., S. W.., Canton, OH 44706. Mrs. Sarabelle Dooley, Ed.

Pentecostal Church of God of America, Inc.

Organized in 1919 at Chicago, Illinois, the first convention was held in October, 1933.

GENERAL ORGANIZATION

Headquarters: 312-316 Joplin Ave., Joplin, MO 64801.

OFFICERS

Gen. Supt., Rev. R. D. Heard.
Gen. Sec., Rev. John W. Stalls.

† Pentecostal Fire-Baptized Holiness Church

Organized in 1918, in 1920 consolidated with Pentecostal Free Will Baptists. Maintains rigid discipline over members.

GENERAL ORGANIZATION

General Convention every two years. (Next meeting, 1973).
Headquarters: Toccoa, GA

OFFICERS

Gen. Mod., Rev. D. E. Beauchamp, Rt. 4, Commerce, GA 30529.
Gen. Treas., Rev. H. J. Barrett, Rt. 3, Danielsville, GA 30633.
Gen. Sec., Foreign Mission Board, W. B. Pitman, Jr., 5800 Fornof Rd., Midland, GA 31820.

PERIODICAL

Faith and Truth (m), Rt. 4, Commerce, GA 30529. Rev. D. E. Beauchamp, Ed.

The Pentecostal Free-Will Baptist Church, Inc.

Organized 1855, as the Cape Fear Conference of Free Will Baptists. Reorganized in 1959, and renamed the Pentecostal Free Will Baptist Church, Inc. The doctrines include regeneration, sanctification, the Pentecostal baptism of the Holy Ghost, the Second Coming of Christ, and divine healing.

GENERAL ORGANIZATION

General Meeting: annual, 3rd Wednesday and Thursday of August.

OFFICERS

Gen. Supt., Rev. Herbert Carter, P.O. Box 966,

Dunn, NC 28334. Tel. (919) 892-4161.
Gen. Sec., Rev. Don Sauls, P.O. Box 966, Dunn, NC 28334.
Gen. Treas., Rev. Stacy Lanier, P.O. Box 966, Dunn, NC 28334.
Youth Dir., Rev. Elbert Hollowell, P.O. Box 966, Dunn, NC 28334.
Ministerial Dir., Rev. Don Sauls.
Ladies' Auxiliary Dir., Mrs. Tom Dorman.
Brotherhood Dir., Don Worley.
World Missions Dir., Rev. Ned Sauls.

Pentecostal Holiness Church, Inc.

This body grew out of the holiness movement in the South and Middle West from 1895 to 1900. It is premillennial in belief, emphasizes Christian perfection as taught by John Wesley, and believes in the Pentecostal baptism with the Holy Spirit, accompanied by glossolalia.

Churches: 1,341. Inclusive Membership: 72,696. Sunday or Sabbath Schools: N.R. Total Enrollment: 155,843. Ordained clergy 2,422.

GENERAL ORGANIZATION
General Conference: quadrennial. (Next meeting, 1973).
Headquarters: Franklin Springs, GA 30639. Tel. (404) 245-6111.

OFFICERS
Gen. Supt., Bishop J. Floyd Williams, P.O. Box 295, Franklin Springs, GA 30639.
Asst. Gen. Supts.: Dr. R. O. Corvin, 3228 S. Delaware Pl., Tulsa, OK 74105; Rev. R. L. Rex, P.O. Box 276, Franklin Springs, GA 30639; Rev. B. E. Underwood, Franklin Springs, GA 30639; Rev. Leon Stewart, Franklin Springs, GA.
Gen. Sec., Rev. C. E. Bradshaw, Franklin Springs, GA.
Gen. Treas., Rev. A. D. Beacham, P.O. Box 68, Franklin Springs, GA. 30639.

OTHER ORGANIZATIONS
The Publishing House (Advocate Press), Franklin Springs, GA 30639. Rev. Charles E. Bradshaw, Gen. Administrator.
Lifeliners (Youth): Gen. Dir., Rev. C. L. Turpin, P.O. Box 281, Franklin Springs, GA 30639.
General Sunday School Dept.: Pres., Rev. K. W. Bunkley, Franklin Springs, GA 30639.
General Woman's Auxiliary: Pres., Mrs. C. F. Isaac, P.O. Box 525, Greenville, PA 16125.

PERIODICALS
The Pentecostal Holiness Advocate (bi-w), Franklin Springs, GA 30639, Rev. A. M. Long, Ed.
Reach (m), Franklin Springs, GA 30639.
Helping Hand (m), P.O. Box 87, Franklin Springs, GA 30639, Mrs. H. P. Robinson, Ed.

† Pillar of Fire

This is a holiness, Methodistic group, organized by Mrs. Alma White in 1901 under the name Pentecostal Union. The name was changed in 1917, as above.

PLYMOUTH BRETHREN

GENERAL ORGANIZATION
Headquarters: Zarephath, NJ 08890.
Western Headquarters: 1845 Champa St., Denver, CO 80202.

OFFICERS
Pres., Bishop Arthur K. White, Vice-Pres. and Asst. Supt., Kathleen M. White; Sec., Arlene Lawrence; Treas., L. S. Wolfgang.

PERIODICALS
Pillar of Fire (w), Zarephath, NJ
Rocky Mountain Pillar of Fire (s-m), 1845 Champa St., Denver, CO 80202.
Woman's Chains (m), Zarephath, NJ 08890.
Pillar of Fire Junior (w), Zarephath, NJ 08890.
Pillar of Fire Bay Chronicle (m), 24 Beulah St., San Francisco, CA 94117.
Dry Legion (m), 1845 Champa St., Denver, CO 80202.
Arthur K. White, Editor of all periodicals listed above.

† Plymouth Brethren

An orthodox and evangelical movement to unite Christians from various denominations which began in the British Isles in the 1820's and is now worldwide. The name "Plymouth Brethren" was given by others because the group in Plymouth, England was a large congregation; in the United States, Plymouth Brethren usually refer to congregations in their fellowship as Assemblies.

The congregations meet in "Bible Chapels," "Gospel Halls," etc., observe the Lord's Supper as a separate meeting each Sunday and do not view their full-time ministers (over 300 in the U.S., over half of whom are itinerant) as being a separate clerical order. Much ministry is given by qualified men of spiritual gift, secularly employed.

In the 1840's the movement divided. The "exclusive" branch, which is now smaller, stresses the interdependency of congregations. It has subdivided and has had partial reunions. There are now about six groups in the U.S., with a dozen to a few score congregations each.

By contrast, the "Open" branch stresses congregational independency, each assembly guided by the oversight of local elders. The "Open" branch has a large foreign missions effort and is cooperative with other evangelicals; they hold regional ministry conferences and youth camps.

Churches: 740. Inclusive Membership: 37,500. Sunday or Sabbath Schools: 700. Total Enrollment: 33,000. Ordained clergy: None.
The following data pertain only to the "Open" branch:

NO GENERAL ORGANIZATION

OTHER ORGANIZATIONS
Christian Missions in Many Lands, 16 Hudson St., New York, NY 10013.
Literature Crusades, Prospect Heights, IL 60070.
Stewards Foundation, 218 Willow, Wheaton, IL 60187.
Publishers:

Loizeaux Brothers, Inc., 1238 Corlies Ave., Neptune, NJ 17753.
Walterick Publishers, P.O. Box 2216, Kansas City, KS 66110.

PERIODICALS

The Fields (m), 16 Hudson St., New York, NY 10013. John Smart, Ed.
Help and Food (q), Mt. Carmel Rd., Parkton, MD 21120. Paul F. Loizeaux, Ed.
Interest (m), Box 294, Wheaton, IL 60187. C. Donald Cole, Ed.
The Uplook (m), Box 2041, Grand Rapids, MI 49501. Peter and William Pell, Eds.
Words in Season (m), 1289 Chase Ave., Lakewood, OH 44107. William H. Ferguson, Ed.

CORRESPONDENT

Paul F. Loizeaux, Parkton, MD 21120.

Polish National Catholic Church of America

After a long period of dissatisfaction with Roman Catholic administration and ideology and, in addition, through the strong desire for religious freedom, this body was organized in 1897.

GENERAL ORGANIZATION

General Synod: every four years. (Next General Synod, 1975).
Headquarters: 529 East Locust St., Scranton, PA 18505.

OFFICERS

Prime Bishop, Most Rev. Thaddeus F. Zielinski, 115 Lake Scranton Rd., Scranton, PA 18505.
Bishop of the Central Diocese, Rt. Rev. Anthony M. Rysz, 529 E. Locust St., Scranton, PA 18505.
Bishop of the Eastern Diocese, Rt. Rev. Walter A. Slowakiewicz, 635 Union St., Manchester, NH 03104.
Bishop of the Buffalo-Pittsburgh Diocese, Rt. Rev. Daniel F. Cyganowski, 182 Sobieski St., Buffalo, NY 14212.
Bishop of Western Diocese, Rt. Rev. Francis Rowinski, 2019 W. Charleston St., Chicago, IL 60647.
Bishop of the Canadian Diocese, Rt. Rev. Joseph I. Nieminski, 186 Cowan Ave., Toronto 146, Ontario, Canada.

Presbyterian Church in the U.S.

This body is a branch of the Presbyterian Church established in separate existence in 1861.

Churches: 4,230. Inclusive Membership: 949,-857. Sunday or Sabbath Schools: N.R. Total Enrollment: 509,602. Ordained clergy: 4,858.

GENERAL ORGANIZATION

The General Assembly: annual.
Office of General Assembly: 341 Ponce de Leon Ave. N.E., Atlanta, GA 30308. Tel. (404) 875-8921.

OFFICERS

Mod., Dr. L. Nelson Bell.
Stated Clk.-Treas., Rev. James A. Millard, Jr.
Asst. to Stated Clk.: Rev. James E. Andrews.

AGENCIES

The General Council
Office, 341 Ponce de Leon Ave. N.E., Atlanta, GA 30308. Tel. (404) 875-8921.
Exec. Sec., Rev. Lawrence I. Stell.
Sec. of Stewardship, Rev. James H. Daughdrill, Jr.
Sec. of Program, Mrs. H. Kerr Taylor.
Sec. of Information, Wm. P. Lamkin.
Treas., Mrs. Celeste L. Jackson.
Board of Annuities and Relief
Office: 341 Ponce de Leon Ave. N.E., Atlanta, GA 30308. Tel. (404) 875-8921.
Exec. Sec., Rev. George Vick.
Asst. to Exec., Rev. George R. Wright.
Treas., H. H. Guerrant.
Board of Christian Education
Office, 801 East Main St., P.O. Box 1176, Richmond, VA 23209. Tel. (703) 649-9021.
Exec., Sec., Rev. John B. Evans.
Admin. Asst., Rev. James A. Nisbet.
Treas., T. Marshall Gordon.
Board of National Ministries
Office, 341 Ponce de Leon Ave. N.E., Atlanta, GA 30308. Tel. (404) 875-8921, Ext. 201.
Exec. Sec., Rev. John F. Anderson, Jr.
Exec. Coordinator, D. H. Speck.
Treas., John L. Kittle.
Board of Women's Work
Office, 341 Ponce de Leon Ave. N.E., Atlanta, GA 30308. Tel. (404) 875-8921.
Exec. Sec., Dr. Evelyn L. Green.
Treas., Mrs. Evelyn S. Brannon.
Business Manager, Mrs. Esther N. Anderson.
Board of World Missions.
Office, 2400 21st Ave. S., Nashville, TN 37202.
Exec. Sec., Rev. T. Watson.
Dir. Division of Finance, J. A. Halverstadt.
Dir. Div. of Interpretation, Rev. James T. Magruder.
Dir. Div. of Personnel, Rev. J. M. Coffin.
Dir. Div. of Program, Rev. D. W. A. Taylor.
Historical Foundation
Montreat, NC 28757. Tel. (704) 669-7061.
Dir., Rev. Kenneth J. Foreman, Jr.
Mountain Retreat Association
Montreat, NC 28757. Tel. (704) 669-7046.
Pres., Silas M. Vaughn.
The Presbyterian Foundation, Inc. (U.S.) Tel. (704) 375-6667.
Exec. Dir., Rev. Warner L. Hall, 1402 Wachovia Bldg., Charlotte, NC 28202.
Presbyterian School of Christian Education
Pres., Rev. Chas. E. S. Kraemer, 1205 Palmyra Ave., Richmond, VA 23227. Tel (703) 359-5031.
TRAV
Office, 341 Ponce de Leon Ave. N.E., Atlanta, GA 30308. Tel. (404) 875-8921, Ext. 294.
Exec. Sec., Bluford B. Hestir, Jr.
Dir. of Radio, Rev. Bill W. Huie.
Dir. of TV, Rev. D. Kirk Hammond.
Dir. of Training, Rev. Charles E. Swann.
Dir. of Operations, Robert E. McClure, Jr.
Assembly's Committee on the Minister and His work. Office, 341 Ponce de Leon Ave. N.E., Atlanta, GA 30308. Tel. (404) 875-8921.
Exec. Sec., William A. Urch.
Asst. to Exec. Sec., Charles R. Harris.

PERIODICALS

Presbyterian Survey (m), 341 Ponce de Leon Ave. N.E., Atlanta, GA 30308. Tel. (404)

875-8921, Ext. 335, Exec. Dir., E. A. Dean.

SYNODICAL OFFICERS

The listings follow this order: Synod, Stated Clerk, Address.

Alabama, Rev. James O. Speed, 4565 Montevallo Rd., Birmingham, AL 35210.
Appalachia, Rev. W. F. Wadsworth, Box 26, Tazewell, VA 24651.
Arkansas-Oklahoma, Rev. Edward S. Bayless, Box 6008, Little Rock, AR 72206.
Florida, Rev. Harvard A. Anderson, 1221 Lee Rd., Ste. 214, Orlando, FL, 32810.
Georgia, John J. Deifell, 341 Ponce de Leon Ave. N.E., Atlanta, GA 30308.
Kentucky, Rev. M. Ralph Weedon, 1044 Alta Vista Rd., Louisville, KY, 40205.
Louisiana, Rev. George J. Fischer, Jr., Box 12, Kenner, LA 70062.
Mississippi, Rev. A.H. Freundt, Jr., 1009 Laurelwood Dr., Clinton, MS 39056.
Missouri, Rev. Robert Rodisch, 7353 E. High St., Jefferson City, MO
North Carolina, Mr. Vernol R. Jansen, Box 10785, Raleigh, NC 27605.
South Carolina, Rev. Frank B. Estes, Box 735, Summerville, SC 29483.
Tennessee, Rev. Charles D. Harvey, 3469 Stone, Memphis, TN 38118.
Texas, Rev. James M. Campbell, Box 4428, Austin, TX 78751.
Virginia, Rev. James A. Payne, Jr., 3503 Seminary Ave., Richmond, VA 23227.
West Virginia, Rev. Dorsey D. Ellis, 905 Village Dr., South Charleston, WV 25309.

Primitive Advent Christian Church

A development from the Advent Christian Church; all churches are located in West Virginia.

GENERAL ORGANIZATION

OFFICERS

Pres., Elza Moss, Sissonville, WV 25185. Tel. (304) 984-3528.
Vice-Pres., Bretram Young, South Charleston, WV 25303.
Sec. and Treas., Hugh W. Good, Rt. 2, Box 422, Elkview, WV 25071.

† Primitive Baptists

A large group of Baptists, mainly through the South, who are opposed to all centralization and to modern missionary societies.

GENERAL ORGANIZATION

Headquarters: Cayce Publ. Co., S. Second St., Thornton, AR 71766. Tel. (501) 352-3694.

OFFICERS

Elder W. H. Cayce, S. Second St., Thornton, 71766. Tel. (501) 352-2269.

PERIODICALS

Primitive Baptist (semi-m), Thornton, AR W. H. Cayce, Ed.
For the Poor (m), Thornton, AR 71766. Mrs. C. H. Cayce and W. H. Cayce, Eds.
Lucky Shopper (w), Thornton, AR 71766. W. H. Cayce, Ed.

Bus. Mgrs., Mrs. C. H. Cayce, Thornton, AR and W. H. Cayce, Thornton, AR 71766.

Primitive Methodist Church, U.S.A.

This body was established at Mow Cop in England as an offshoot of the Wesleyan Connection. It was brought to America by immigrants in 1829, and organized into a General Conference in 1889.

GENERAL ORGANIZATION

General Conference: quadrennial. (Next meeting, 1974).

OFFICERS

Pres., Dr. Richard L. Purnell, 13 Nelson St., Centerdale, RI 02911. Tel. (401) 231-0444.
Sec., Rev. G. Kenneth Tyson, 6147 Glenwood Ave., Youngstown, OH 44512.
Treas., Rev. Gillard I. Evans, 425 Ford St., West Conshohocken, PA 19428.

PERIODICAL

The Primitive Methodist Journal (m), 425 Norwood Ave., New Castle, PA 16101, Rev. Evan P. Thomas, Ed.

Progressive National Baptist Convention, Inc.

A body which held its organizational meeting at Cincinnati, November, 1961, and subsequent regional sessions, followed by the first annual session in Philadelphia in 1962.

GENERAL ORGANIZATION

Convention: annual.

Pres., Dr. L. Venchael Booth, 630 Glenwood Ave., Cincinnati, OH 45229.
1st Vice-Pres., Rev. Nelson H. Smith, 903 6th Ave. S., Birmingham, AL 35233.
Exec. Sec., Dr. S. S. Hodges, 1239 Vermont Ave. N.W., Ste 204, Washington, DC 20005.
Dir., Publicity, Rev. Samuel B. Kyles, 704 S. Pkwy. E., Memphis, TN 38106.

OTHER ORGANIZATIONS

Dept. of Christian Education: Sec., Dr. S.D. Edward, 2237 Francis Ave., Flint, MI 48595.
Women's Auxiliary: Pres., Miss Violet M. Ankrum, 149 W. St., N.W., Washington, DC 20001.
Home Mission Bd., Rev. J. Barry Williams, 1732 N. Steele St., Tacoma, WA 98401
Baptist Foreign Mission Bureau: Exec. Sec., Dr. J. H. Beatty, 163 N. 60th St., Philadelphia, PA 19139.
Congress of Christian Education: Pres., Rev. James O. Rich, 324 W. Reed St., Anderson, SC 29621.

PERIODICAL

Baptist Progress, 6300 Hartford Ave., Detroit, MI 48210. Rev. Charles G. Adams, Ed.

The Protestant Conference (Lutheran), Inc.

Organized in 1927 in Wisconsin as a result of differences with the Evangelical Lutheran Joint Synod of Wisconsin and Other States.

Churches: 7. Inclusive Membership: 2,600. Sunday or Sabbath Schools: 7. Total Enrollment: 600. Ordained clergy: 15.

GENERAL ORGANIZATION

Conference: meets 3 times annually.

OFFICERS

Rec. Sec., Pastor Gerald Hinz, Shiocton, WI 54170.
Fin. Sec.-Treas., Michael Meier, 1023 Colan Blvd., Rice Lake, WI 54868.

PERIODICAL

Faith-Life (bi-m), 728 N. 9th St., Manitowoc, WI 54220. Pastor Paul Hensel, Ed.

Protestant Reformed Churches in America

Organized in 1926 in Grand Rapids, Michigan. The doctrinal tenets are those of Calvinism, the Belgic Confession, the Heidelberg Catechism, and the Canons of Dordrecht.

GENERAL ORGANIZATION

General Synod: meets annually (June).
Headquarters: 463 E. 154th Place, South Holland, IL 60473. Tel. (312) 333-1314.

OFFICER

Stat. Clk., Rev. D. H. Kuiper, 1314 Main St., Pella, IA 50219.

Reformed Church in America

This body was established by the earliest Dutch settlers of New York as the Reformed Protestant Dutch Church in 1628. It is evangelical in theology and Presbyterian in government and has 939 churches located in 26 states of the United States.

Churches: 921. Inclusive Membership: 369,951. Sunday or Sabbath Schools: 905. Total Enrollment: 127,359. Ordained clergy: 1,277.

GENERAL ORGANIZATION

General Synod: annual. (Next meeting, June 11-17, 1973, Pella, Iowa)
Headquarters: 475 Riverside Dr., New York, NY 10027.

OFFICERS AND STAFF OF GENERAL SYNOD

Pres., Mr. Harry E. DeBruyn, 6721 Wyandot Dr., Palos Heights, IL 60463.
Gen. Sec., Rev. Marion de Velder, 475 Riverside Dr., New York, NY 10027.
Exec. Sec., Arie R. Brouwer, 475 Riverside Dr. New York, NY 10027.
Treas. and Dir. of Office of Administration and Finance: J. Robert R. Harrison, 475 Riverside Dr., New York, NY 10027.
Sec. for Operations, Rev. Marvin D. Hoff, 475 Riverside Dr., New York, NY 10027.
Exec. Comm.: Chmn., Dr. Christian H. Walvoord. V. Chmn., Harry E. DeBruyn.

OTHER ORGANIZATIONS

Board of Direction: Pres., Arad Riggs, 339 Pondfield Rd., Bronxville, NY 10708; Treas.,

J. Robert R. Harrison, 475 Riverside Dr., New York, NY 10027.
General Program Council: Chmn., Mr. Carl VerBeek. Executive Staff; Exec. Sec., Rev. Arie R. Brouwer; Sec. for World Ministries, Rev. John E. Buteyn; Sec. for Missionary Personnel, Rev. Leonard De Beer; Sec. for Program Interpretation, Rev. Isaac C. Rottenberg; Sec. for Church Life and Mission, Rev. Arthur O. Van Eck; Sec. for Church Planning and Development, Rev. Russell J. Redeker.
Promotion and Communications: Dir., Rev. Paul E. Mitchell.
Board of Pensions: Pres., Mr. Elmer Dill, Cream St., Poughkeepsie, NY 12601. Vice-Pres., Rev. H. Paul Morehouse, Box 183, R.D. 3, Schenectady, N. Y. 12306. Exec. Sec., Theodore F. Zandstra, 475 Riverside Dr., New York, NY 10027.
National Department of Women's Work: Dir., Mrs. J. Foster Welwood, 475 Riverside Dr., New York, NY 10027.

PERIODICAL

The Church Herald (w), 630 Myrtle St., N.W. Grand Rapids, MI 49504. Rev. L. H. Benes, Ed.

Reformed Church in the United States

The Eureka Classis, organized in 1910 in South Dakota, continued as the Reformed Church in the United States, when that body merged into the Evangelical and Reformed Church in 1934. The doctrines are Calvinistic as set forth in the Heidelberg Catechism.

Churches: 25. Inclusive Membership: 4,038. Sunday or Sabbath Schools: 24. Total Enrollment: 807. Ordained clergy: 25.

GENERAL ORGANIZATION

Classis: annual.

OFFICERS

Pres., Rev. N.C. Hoeflinger, Rt. 3, Manitowoc, WI 54220. Tel. (414) 726-4464.
Vice-Pres., Rev. R. D. Stuebbe, Menno, SD 57045.
Clerk, Rev. D. W. Treick, 1408 S. Lincoln St., Aberdeen, SD 57401.
Treas., Donald Greiman, Route 3, Garner, IA 50438.

PERIODICAL

The Reformed Herald (m), Rt. 3, Manitowoc, WI 54220, N. C. Hoeflinger, Ed.

Reformed Episcopal Church

In 1873, Bishop Cummins withdrew from the Protestant Episcopal Church in protest against certain sacramentalist and ritualistic tendencies and, with other clergymen and laymen, organized the church as above.

GENERAL ORGANIZATION

General Council: triennial. (Next meeting, 1975).
Sec., Gen. Council, Rev. D. Ellsworth Raudenbush, 560 Fountain St., Havre de Grace, MD 21078. Tel. (301) 939-3210.

OFFICERS

Pres. and Presid. Bishop, Rev. Howard D. Higgins, 109 Glenwood Rd., Merion Station, PA 19066.

Vice-Pres., G. Arnold Pfaffenbach, 209 N. Union Ave., Havre de Grace, MD 21078.

Sec., Rev. D. Ellsworth Raudenbush, 560 Fountain St., Havre de Grace, MD 21078.

Treas., David B. Boon, 4106 Hain Dr., Lafayette Hill, PA 19444.

OTHER ORGANIZATIONS

Board of Foreign Missions: Pres., Rev. Edwin A. Bustard, 600 Collingdale Ave., Collingdale, PA 19023; Sec., Rev. Samuel M. Forster; Treas., Richard B. Miekley.

Board of Home Missions: Pres., Rev. D. Ellsworth Raudenbush, 560 Fountain St., Havre de Grace, MD 21078; Sec., Rev. Frank C. Roppelt; Treas., Henry M. Bates, Hatfield, PA 19440.

Trustees Sustentation Fund: Pres., _____; Treas., Harry Moock, 7458 Beverly Rd., Phila., PA 19138.

Publication Society: Sec., Rev. Theophilus J. Herter, 25 S. 43rd St., Philadelphia, PA 19104.

Women's Auxiliary to the Board of Home Missions: Pres., Mrs. Wilford L. Ottey, Jr., 921 Bartram Ave., Collingdale, PA 19023.

Women's Auxiliary to the Board of Foreign Missions: Pres., Miss Martha Derr, 206B—Kenwood Apts., 243 W. Tulpehocken St., Philadelphia, PA 19144.

PERIODICAL

Episcopal Recorder (m), 25 S. 43rd St., Philadelphia, PA 19104. Bishop Howard D. Higgins, Ed.

BISHOPS

Joseph E. Kearney, Summerville, SC 29483.

Howard D. Higgins, 109 Glenwood Rd., Merion Station, PA 19066.

William H. S. Jerdan, Summerville, SC 29483.

Sanco K. Rembert, 121 Moultrie St., Charleston, SC 29403.

Theophilus J. Herter, 26 Strath Haven Dr., Broomall, PA 19008.

Reformed Mennonite Church

This group was reorganized in 1812 under John Herr because they did not know of any other organization that fully carried out New Testament teachings. They believe there can be only one true church, consisting of regenerated persons who are united in love and doctrine.

OFFICER

Bishop J. Henry Fisher, 35 Greenfield Rd., Lancaster, PA 17602.

Reformed Methodist Union Episcopal Church

Organized in 1885 at Georgetown, S. C. among persons withdrawing from the African Methodist Episcopal Church; the doctrines were generally those of the Methodist Episcopal Church.

GENERAL ORGANIZATION

General Conference: annual.

Headquarters: Charleston, SC 29407.

OFFICERS

Rt. Rev. Eddie Ogden Gibbs, Rt. 17, Box 1057, Seaside La., Charleston, SC 29407, Tel. (803) 795-0179.

Sec., Rev. Leroy Gethers, 1136 Brody Ave., Charleston, SC 29407.

Sec. of Education, Fred E. German.

Treas., Joseph Patterson.

Sec. of Books Concerns, Earnest McKeever.

Sec. of Pension Fund, Eddie McCulough.

Sec. of Church Extension, Joseph Gadsden.

Sec. of Church Contingent, Rufus German.

Reformed Presbyterian Church, Evangelical Synod

This church was formed on April 6, 1965 by a union of the Reformed Presbyterian Church in North America, General Synod, and the Evangelical Presbyterian Church. It is Biblical in its theology, subscribes to the Westminister Confession of Faith and Catechisms as its doctrinal standards, subordinate to Holy Scripture.

Churches: 129. Inclusive Membership: 17,798. Sunday or Sabbath Schools: 129. Total Enrollment: 10,426. Ordained clergy: 320.

GENERAL ORGANIZATION

General Synod: annual.

OFFICERS

Mod., Dr. Marion D. Barnes, 109 E. Brow Rd., Lookout Mountain, TN 37350.

Vice-Mod., Rev. William McColley, 3116 49th St., SW, Calgary, Alberta, Canada T3E 3Y3.

Stated Clk., Rev. Paul R. Gilchrist, 107 Hardy Rd., Lookout Mountain, TN 37350.

Asst. Clk., Rev. Frank P. Crane, 3412 Torquay Rd., Muncie, IN 47304.

PERIODICAL

Mandate, 415 Krupski Loop, Lookout Mountain, TN 37350, Joel Belz, Ed.

Reformed Presbyterian Church of North America

Also known as the Church of the Covenanters. Origin dates back to the Reformation days of Scotland when the Covenanters signed their "Covenants" in resistance to the king and the Roman Church in the enforcement of state church practices. The Church in America has signed two "Covenants" in particular, those of 1871 and 1954.

GENERAL ORGANIZATION

Synod: annual (June).

OFFICERS

Mod., Rev. D. Howard Elliott, 2007 Crest Dr., Topeka, KS 66604. Tel. (913) 272-2554.

Clk., Rev. Bruce C. Stewart, 5139 Argus Dr., Los Angeles, CA 90041. Tel. (213) 255-1230.

Asst. Clk., Rev. Robert B. McCracken, 1145 "A" Ave., Marion, IA 52302. Tel. (319) 377-0197.

Stated Clk., Louis D. Hutmire, 7418 Penn Ave., Pittsburgh, PA 15208. Tel. (412) 731-1177.

PERIODICALS

The Covenanter Witness (bi-w), 738 Rebecca

REFORMED ZION UNION APOSTOLIC CHURCH

Ave., Pittsburgh, PA 15221. Rev. Ronald Nickerson, Ed.
Blue Banner Faith and Life (q), 3408 7th Ave., Beaver Falls, PA 15010. Dr. J. G. Vos, Ed.

† Reformed Zion Union Apostolic Church

Organized in 1869, at Boydton, Va., by Elder James R. Howell of New York, a minister of the A.M.E. Zion Church; with doctrines of the Methodist Episcopal Church.

GENERAL ORGANIZATION
Two Annual Conferences (in August and September).
General Conference: quadrennial. (Next meeting, 1974.)

OFFICER
Fin. Sec., Deacon James B. Harrison.

PERIODICAL
Union Searchlight, South Hill, VA 23970, Rev. T. J. Johnson, Ed.

Religious Society of Friends (Conservative)

In 1845 and 1854, under the leadership of John Wilbur, separations from the main body of Friends occurred. The motive for the separation was a desire to maintain the primitive teachings of the Friends.

Churches: 26. Inclusive Membership: 1,835. Sunday or Sabbath Schools: N.R. Enrollment: N.R. Ordained clergy: None.

YEARLY MEETINGS
North Carolina YM, Mr. George C. Parker, Woodland, NC 27897.
Iowa YM, Mary E. Autenrieth, R. R. 1, Paullina, IA 51046.
Ohio YM, Mr. Edward N. Kirk, R. R. 2, Columbiana, OH 44408.

Religious Society of Friends (Unaffiliated Meetings)

Elements of the early Friends movement are to be found in this small but significant category of meetings and groups which are marked by spontaneity, fluidity, variety, and experimentation. These groups are not formally associated in traditional ways with the larger organizations within the Society. Some of these unaffiliated groups have begun within the past twenty-five years.

Churches: 72. Inclusive Membership: 2,896. Sunday or Sabbath Schools: N.R. Total Enrollment: N.R. Ordained clergy: N.R.

UNAFFILIATED YEARLY MEETINGS
Southern Appalachian YM, Mr. Nelson Fuson, 911-18th Ave, N., Nashville, TN 37208.
Mexico, General Meeting, Casa De Los Amigos, Ignacio Mariscal 132, Mexico 1, D.F., Mexico
Alaska YM, Mr. Samuel Williams, Kotzebue, AK 99752.
Pacific YM, Mr. Edwin A. Sanders, 6208 Temple City Blvd., Temple City, CA 91780.

Central YM, Mr. Arthur Hollingsworth, Box 215, Westfield, IN 46074.
Missouri Valley Conference YM, Mr. Arthur Evans, 619 Monroe Way, Denver, CO 80209.
Central America YM, Sr. Ruben Galvez, Apartado 8, Chiquimula, Quatemala, Central America.

Reorganized Church of Jesus Christ of Latter Day Saints

A division among the Latter Day Saints (non-Mormon) occurred on the death of Joseph Smith in 1844. His son, Joseph Smith, became presiding officer of this group, which has established headquarters at Independence, Missouri.

Churches: 1,027. Inclusive Membership: 154,481. Sunday or Sabbath Schools: N.R. Total Enrollment: N.R. Ordained clergy: 14,634.

GENERAL ORGANIZATION
Conference: biennial. (Next meeting March 31-April 7, 1974).
Headquarters: The Auditorium, Independence, MO 64051. Tel. (816) 833-1000.

OFFICERS
Pres., W. Wallace Smith.
First Presidency: W. Wallace Smith, Maurice L. Draper, Duane E. Couey.
Pres. of Council of 12 Apostles, Clifford A. Cole.
Presiding Bishop: Francis E. Hansen, Harold W. Cackler, Gene M. Hummel.
Presiding Evangelist, Roy A. Cheville.

PERIODICALS
Saints Herald (m), Independence, MO. W. Wallace Smith, Maurice L. Draper, Duane E. Couey, and Paul Wellington, Eds.
Stepping Stones (child, w), Independence, MO Barbara Howard.
Zion's Hope (little tots, w), Independence, MO, Barbara Howard.
Restoration Witness (missionary, m), Independence, MO, Norman Ruoff.
Dimensions (put out by Department of Christian Education), James Cable.
Distaff (Dept. of Women), Marjorie Troeh.

The Roman Catholic Church

The largest single body of Christians in the U.S., the Roman Catholic Church, is under the spiritual leadership of His Holiness the Pope. Its establishment in America dates back to the priests who accompanied Columbus on his second voyage to the New World. A settlement, later discontinued, was made at St. Augustine, Florida. The continuous history of this Church in the Colonies began at St. Mary's in Maryland, in 1634.

Churches: 23,796 Inclusive Membership: 48,390,990. Sunday or Sabbath Schools: 11,792. Total Enrollment: 10,104,507. Ordained clergy: 57,778.

(The following information has been furnished by the editor of The Official Catholic Directory, published by P. J. Kenedy & Sons, P.O. Box 729, New York, NY 10022. Reference to this complete volume will provide more adequate information.)

INTERNATIONAL ORGANIZATION

His Holiness the Pope, Bishop of Rome, Vicar of Jesus Christ, Supreme Pontiff of the Catholic Church.

POPE PAUL VI, Giovanni Battista Montini (born, Sept. 26, 1897; crowned, June 30, 1963).

APOSTOLIC DELEGATE TO THE UNITED STATES

(Vacant at time of publication)

U.S. ORGANIZATION

National Conference of Catholic Bishops, 1312 Massachusetts Ave. N.W., Washington, DC 20005. Tel. (202) 659-6600.

The National Conference of Catholic Bishops (NCCB) is a canonical entity operating in accordance with the Vatican II Decree, **Christus Dominus.** Its purpose is to foster the Church's mission to mankind by providing the Bishops of this country with an opportunity to exchange views and insights of prudence and experience and to exercise in a joint manner their pastoral office.

OFFICERS

Pres., John Cardinal Krol.
Vice-Pres., Archbishop Leo Byrne.
Sec., Bishop James Rausch.
Treas., Archbishop Thomas A. Donnellan.

GENERAL SECRETARIAT

Gen. Sec., Bishop James Rausch.
Assoc. Gen. Sec., Rev. Thomas Kelly, O.P.

COMMITTEES

Ecumenical and Interreligious Affairs (Ecumenism): Chmn., —————

Secretariat: Exec. Dir., Rev. John Hotchkin.
  Asst. Exec. Dir., Rev. Daniel McKenzie.
Liturgy:
  Chmn., Bishop Walter W. Curtis, Bishop of Bridgeport.
  Secretariat: Dir., Rev. Frederick R. McManus. Asst. Rev. John Rotelle.
Priestly Formation:
  Chmn., Bishop Louis Watters.
  Secretariat: Dir., Msgr. Robert Bacher.
Permanent Diaconate:
  Chmn., —————.
  Secretariat: Dir., —————.
Priestly Life and Ministry:
  Chmn., Archbishop Philip Hannan.
  Secretariat: Dir., Msgr. Colin MacDonald.

United States Catholic Conference, 1312 Massachusetts Ave. N.W., Washington, DC 20005. Tel. (202) 659-6600.

The United States Catholic Conference (USCC) is a civil entity of the American Catholic Bishops assisting them in their service to the Church in this country by uniting the people of God where voluntary, collective action on a broad diocesan level is needed. The USCC provides an organization structure and the resources needed to insure coordination, cooperation, and assistance in the public, educational, and social concerns of the Church at the national, regional, state, interdiocesan and, as appropriate, diocesan levels.

OFFICERS

Pres., John Cardinal Krol.
Vice-Pres., Archbishop Leo Byrne.
Sec., Bishop Joseph L. Bernardin.
Treas., Archbishop Thomas Donnellan.

GENERAL SECRETARIAT

Gen. Sec., Rev. James Rausch.
Assoc. Gen. Sec., —————
Ass't Gen. Sec., Rev. Michael Sheehan.
Sec. for Planning, John J. O'Neill.
Sec. for Research, Msgr. George Higgins.

DEPARTMENTS AND DIVISIONS

Office of Finance & Administration, Dir., Thomas Hinton.
  Accounting, Dir., Lloyd Johnson.
  General Services, Dir., Steve Connally.
  Personnel, Dir., James Zofcin.
  Print Shop, Dir., Charles Garris.
  Publications, Dir., Marie Houser.
Office of General Counsel, Dir., William Consedine.
Office of Government Liaison, Dir., James Robinson.
Office of Communications, Dir., Robert Buesse.
  NC News Service, Dir., A. P. Wall.
  Nat'l Catholic Office for Information, Dir., Russell Shaw.
  Div. for Film & Broadcasting, Dir., Rev. Patrick Sullivan.
  Div. for Creative Services, Dir., James Prior.
Department of Education, Secretary, Msgr. Olin Murdick.
  Elementary & Secondary, Dir., Dr. Edward R. D'Alessio.
  Higher Education, Dir., Rev. Laurence Murphy.
  Religious Education, Dir., —————.

Youth Activities, Dir., Msgr. Thomas Leonard.
Family Life, Dir., Msgr. James McHugh.
Department of Social Development and World Peace, Sec., Msgr. Harrold Murray.
  Justice & Peace, Dir., —————.

Rural Life, Dir., Rev. John McRaith, Rev. Msgr. John George Weber.
Spanish Speaking, Dir., Paul Sedillo.
Urban Affairs, Dir., John E. Cosgrove.
Health Affairs, Dir., Sr. Virginia Schwager.
Chaplin Services, Dir., —————.

Other Divisions:
  Latin America, Dir., Rev. Frederick McGuire.
  Migration & Refugee Service, Dir., John McCarthy.
Lay Organizations:
  Council of Catholic Laity, Dir., Miss Margaret Mealey.
  National Catholic Community Service, Dir., Michael Menster.

AFFILIATED OFFICES

Catholic Relief Services:
  Exec. Dir., Bishop Edward E. Swanstrom.
  Asst. Dir., Rev. Msgr. Andrew P. Landi, 350 Fifth Ave., New York, NY 10001. Tel. (212) 594-9300.

THE ROMAN CATHOLIC CHURCH

ASSOCIATIONS

The Canon Law Society of America: President, Rev. Thomas Lynch, 134 Farmington Ave., Hartford, CT 06105. Center for Urban Ethnic Affairs: Pres., Rev. Msgr. Geno C. Baroni.

The Conference of Major Religious Superiors of Men's Institutes of the United States, Inc.: Permanent Sec., Rev. Francis X. Gokey, S.S.E., 724 Dupont Circle Bldg., Washington, DC 20036.

The Conference of the Major Religious Superiors of Womens' Institutes of America, Inc.: Exec. Sec., Sister M. Claudia Zeller, O.S.F., 2158 Florida Ave., N.W., Washington, DC 20008.

National Catholic Educational Associaton: Exec. Sec., Rev. Albert Koob, O. Praem., 1 Dupont Circle, N.W., Washington, DC 20036.

National Conference of Catholic Charities: Sec., Rev. Msgr. Lawrence J. Corcoran, 1346 Connecticut Ave., N.W., Washington, DC 20006.

ARCHDIOCESES AND DIOCESES

There follows an alphabetical listing of Archdioceses and Dioceses of The Roman Catholic Church. Each Archdiocese or Diocese contains the following information in sequence: Name of incumbent Bishop; name of Auxiliary Bishop with right to succession, if any; name of the Apostolic Administrator for vacant Sees; name of Episcopal Vicars, if any, and their territorial jurisdiction; name and address of Ecumenical officers, if any; address and telephone number of the Chancery office. Archdioceses are designated in the text.

Cardinals are addressed as "His Eminence" and Archbishops and Bishops as "Most Reverend."

Albany, Bishop Edwin B. Broderick. Ecumenical Officer, Rev., Msgr. Joseph P. Conway, V.G. 465 State St., Albany, NY 12203. Chancery Office, 465 State St., Albany, NY 12206. Tel. (518) 434-7883.

Alexandria, Bishop Charles P. Greco. Chancery Office, 2315 Texas Ave., P.O. Box 5665, Alexandria, LA 71301. Tel. (318) 445-2401.

Allentown, Bishop Joseph McShea. Ecumenical Officer, Rev. Richard J. Ford, 925 Centre Ave.; Reading, PA 19601. Chancery Office, 1729 Turner St., Allentown, PA 18104. Tel. (215) 437-0755.

Altoona-Johnstown, Bishop James J. Hogan. Ecumenical Officer, Rev. Philip P. Saylor, 309 Lotz Ave., Lakemont, Altoona, PA 16602. Chancery Office, Logan Blvd., Hollidaysburg, PA 16648. Tel. (814) 695-5579.

Amarillo, Bishop Lawrence M. De Falco. Ecumenical Officer, Rev. Msgr. J. E. Fitzgerald, 4011 54th St., Lubbock, TX 79413. Chancery Office, 1800 N. Spring St., P.O. Box 5644, Amarillo, TX 79107. Tel. (806) 383-2243.

Archdiocese of Anchorage, Archbishop Joseph T. Ryan. Chancery Office, 811 Sixth Ave., P.O. Box 2239, Anchorage, AK 99501. Tel. (907) 272-6581.

Archdiocese of Atlanta, Archbishop Thomas A. Donnellan. Chancery Office, 756 W. Peachtree St., N.W., Atlanta, GA 30308. Tel. (404) 873-3056.

Austin, Bishop Vincent M. Harris. Chancery Office, N. Congress and 16th, P.O. Box 13327 Capital Sta. Austin, TX 78711. Tel. (512) 476-4888.

Baker, Bishop Thomas J. Connolly. Chancery Office, Baker and First Sts., P.O. Box 826, Baker, OR 97814. Tel. (503) 523-2373.

Archdiocese of Baltimore, Lawrence Cardinal Shehan. Ecumenical Officer, Rev. Msgr. E. Melville Taylor, 5300 N. Charles St., Baltimore, MD 21210. Tel. (301) 433-8800, Chancery Office, 320 Cathedral St., Baltimore, MD 21201. Tel. (301) 727-7777.

Baton Rouge, Bishop Robert E. Tracy. Ecumenical Officer, Rev. Msgr. Louis E. Marionneaux, River Rd. Hwy. 75., St. Gabriel, LA 70776. Tel. (504) 642-5435. Chancery Office, P.O. Box 2028, Baton Rouge, LA 70821. Tel. (504)348-0561.

Beaumont, Bishop Warren L. Boudreaux. Ecumenical Officer, Rev. John K. Broussard, 3503 Gulfway Drive, Port Arthur, TX 77640. Chancery Office, P.O. Box 3948, Beaumont, TX 77704. Tel. (713) 838-0451.

Belleville, Bishop Albert B. Zuroweste. Chancery Office, 222 S. Third St., Box 546, Belleville, IL 62221. Tel. (618) 233-1100.

Birmingham, Bishop Joseph G. Vath. Ecumenical Officer, Rev. John P. Sheehan, 2112 Ave. H., Birmingham, AL 35218. Tel. (205) 785-1230. Chancery Office, P.O. Box 2086, Birmingham, AL 35201. Tel. (205) 322-2501.

Bismarck, Bishop Hilary B. Hacker. Chancery Office, 420 Raymond St., Box 1575, Bismarck, ND 58501. Tel. (701) 223-1347.

Boise, Bishop Sylvester W. Treinen. Ecumenical Officer, Rev. William F. Ordway, Box 310 Mountain Home, ID 83647. Tel. (208) 587-3046. Chancery Office, Box 769, 420 Idaho St., Boise, ID 83701. Tel. (208) 342-1311.

Archdiocese of Boston, Archbishop Humberto Cardinal S. Medeiros; Episcopal Vicars: Rev. Msgr. Thomas H. Kennedy (Norfolk); Most Rev. Jeremiah F. Minihan (Suffolk); Most Rev. Thomas J. Riley (Southern Middlesex); Rt. Rev. Cornelius T. H. Sherlock (Essex); Rt. Rev. Alfred F. Julien (Northern Middlesex); Rt. Rev. John J. Sheehan Plymouth). Ecumenical Officer, Rev. James Hickey, 201 Lake St., Arlington, MA 02174. Tel. (617) 648-0736. Chancery Office, 2121 Commonwealth Ave., Brighton, MA 02135. Tel. (617) 254-0100.

Bridgeport, Bishop Walter W. Curtis. Ecumenical Officers: Revs. Martin J. O'Connor, Thomas J. Driscoll, Thomas J. Green, Richard L. Rooney, S. J. Office 389 Kossuth St. Bridgeport, CT 06608, Tel. (203) 334-3821. Chancery Office, 250 Waldemere Ave., Bridgeport, CT 06604. Tel. (203) 367-3631.

Brooklyn, Bishop Francis J. Mugavero. Episcopal Vicars: Rev. Peter L. Altman (S.W. Brooklyn); Rev. Martin P. Bannan (Central Brooklyn); Rev. William J. Cullen (N.E. Kings & N.W. Queens); Rev. George T. Deas (S.W. Queens & Adj. Kings); Rev. Vincent J. Powell (East Queens). Ecumenical Officer: Rev. Terrence J. Mulkerin, 92-96 220th St., Queens Village, NY 11428. Tel. (212) 479-5111. Chancery Office, 75 Greene Ave., Brooklyn, NY 11238. Tel. (212) 638-5500.

Brownsville, Bishop John J. Fitzpatrick, Chancery Office, P.O. Box 1150, 1910 E. Elizabeth St., Brownsville, TX 78520. Tel. (512) 542-2501.

Buffalo, Bishop James A. McNulty, Chancery Office, 35 Lincoln Parkway, Buffalo, NY 14222. Tel. (716) 883-1372.

Burlington, Bishop John A. Marshal. Ecumenical Officer, Rt. Rev. Edwin T. Buckley, S.T.D., 1251 North Avenue, Burlington, VT 05401. Tel. (802) 864-7686. Chancery Office, 52 William St., Burlington, VT 05401. Tel. (802) 864-5777.

Camden, Bishop George H. Guilfoyle. Ecumenical Officer, Rev. John G. Flanagan, 49-12 Dune St. Avalon, NJ 08202. Tel. (609) 967-3746. Chancery Office, 721 Cooper St., Camden, NJ 08101. Tel. (609) 963-5210.

Charleston, Bishop Ernest L. Unterkoefler. Ecumenical Officer, Rev. Msgr. Charles J. Baum, 338 W. Washington St., Greenville, SC 29601. Tel. (803) 232-1201. Chancery Office, 119 Broad St., Charleston, SC 29401. Tel. (803) 723-3488.

Charlotte, Bishop Michael S. Begley, Chancery Office P.O. Box 3776 Charlotte, NC 28203.

Cheyenne, Bishop Hubert M. Newell. Ecumenical Officer, Rev. John Corrigan, Box 1141, Cheyenne, WY 82001. Chancery Office, Box 426, Cheyenne, WY 82001. Tel. (307) 638-9394.

Archdiocese of Chicago, John Cardinal Cody. Ecumenical Officer: Rev. Edward M. Egan, 730 N. Wabash Ave., Chicago, IL 60611. Tel. (312) 787-8040. Chancery Office, 211 E. Chicago Ave., Chicago, IL 60611. Tel. (312) 787-2315.

Archdiocese of Cincinnati, Archbishop Joseph L. Bernadin. Ecumenical Officer, Rev. Msgr. Robert J. Sherry, 29 E. 8th St., Cincinnati, OH 45202. Chancery Office, 29 E. Eighth St., Cincinnati, OH 45202. Tel. (513) 721-1532.

Cleveland, Bishop Clarence George Issenmann. Ecumenical Officer, Rev. John F. Wessel, 8700 Brecksville Rd., Cleveland, OH 44141. Tel. (216) 526-1686. Chancery Office, 350 Chancery Bldg., Cathedral Square, 1027 Superior Ave., Cleveland, OH 44114. Tel. (216) 696-6525.

Columbus, Bishop Clarence E. Elwell. Ecumenical Officer, Revs. William McEwan, Edward F. Trenor, 212 E. Broad St., Columbus, OH 43215. Tel. (614) 224-1295. Chancery Office, 198 E. Broad St., Columbus, OH 43215. Tel. (614) 224-2251.

Corpus Christi, Bishop Thomas J. Drury. Ecumenical Officer, Mr. Daniel D. Meaney, 1201 Lantana St., Corpus Christi, TX 78407. Chancery Office, 620 Lipan St., Corpus Christi, TX 78401. Tel. (512) 882-6191.

Covington, Bishop Richard H. Ackerman. Ecumenical Officer, Rev. Msgr. Edward T. Hickey, 1680 Dixie Hwy., Lookout Heights, Covington, KY 41011. Chancery Office, 1140 Madison Ave., P.O. Box 192, Covington, KY 41012. Tel. (606) 291-4240.

Crookston, Bishop Kenneth Povish. Chancery Office, 1200 Memorial Dr., P.O. Box 610, Crookston, MN 56716. Tel. (218) 281-4533.

Dallas, Bishop Thomas Tschoepe, Ecumenical Officer, Rev. Robert C. Rehkemper, 2330 Cheyenne, Irving, TX 75060. Chancery Office, 3915 Lemmon Ave., P.O. Box 19507,

Dallas, TX 75219. Tel. (214) 528-2240.

Davenport, Bishop Gerald Francis O'Keefe. Ecumenical Officer, Rev. John F. Hynes, 615 Marquette St., Davenport, IA 52802. Tel. (319) 322-3473. Chancery Office, 811 Kaha Bldg., 410 Brady St., Davenport, IA 52801. Tel. (319) 322-7155.

Archdiocese of Denver, Archbishop James V. Casey, Ecumenical Officer, Very Rev. James W. Rasby, 1501 Pennsylvania St., Denver, CO 80203. Tel. (303) 623-0233. Chancery Office, 934 Bannock St., Denver, CO 80204. Tel. (303) 892-6857.

Des Moines, Bishop Maurice J. Dingman. Chancery Office, 2910 Grand Ave., P.O. Box 1816, Des Moines, IA 50306. Tel. (515) 243-7653.

Archdiocese of Detroit, John Cardinal Dearden.

Vicars—

Birmingham-Blmfld-Troy—Rev. William L. Anderson.

College & University—Rev. Kean D. Cronin, Pro-Vicar.

Core City—Rev. John F. Morel, C.I.C.M.

Dearborn—Rev. Gerard S. Brennan.

Detroit-Grosse Pointe—Rev. Edward L. Scheuerman.

Downriver—Rev. William J. Murphy.

East Side—Rev. Paul F. Fettig, C.PP.S.

Farmington-Southfield—Rev. Francis X. Dietz.

Grand River Area—Rev. Thomas J. Finnigan.

Gratiot Area—Rev. Thomas H. Villerot.

Monroe—Rev. Arthur W. Fauser.

North Central—Rev. Kenneth P. Mac-Kinnon.

Northern—Rev. John R. Hogan.

North Macomb—Rev. John T. Gordon.

Northwest Wayne—Rev. Thomas J. Cain.

Pontiac Area—Rev. Edmund M. Brennan, C.S.B.

Serf—Rev. Anthony M. Tocco.

Southeast Oakland—Rev. Dennis Harrity.

Southland—Rev. Donald E. Dacey.

Southwest—Rev. Jacob J. Samonie.

Vicariate of the Lakes—Rev. Richard A. McGarry.

Warren—Center Line—Rev. Walter A. Hurley.

West Detroit—Rev. Thomas J. Sutherland.

Western Wayne—Rev. Thomas J. Van Antwerp.

West Side Inner City—Rev. Francis J. Granger.

College and University Pro-Vicariate—Rev. Kean D. Cronin.

Chancery Office, 1234 Washington Blvd., Detroit, MI 48226. Tel. (313) 963-3680.

Dodge City, Bishop Marion F. Forst. Ecumenical Officer, Rev. John Lavrih, 706 E. Sixth St., Kinsley, KS 67547. Chancery Office, 910 Central Ave., P.O. Box 849, Dodge City, KS 67801. Tel. (316) 227-3011.

Archdiocese of Dubuque, Archbishop James J. Byrne. Chancery Office, 1229 Mt. Loretta Ave., Dubuque, IA 52001. Tel. (319) 556-2580.

Duluth, Bishop Paul F. Anderson, Chancery Office, 215 W. Fourth St., Duluth, MN 55806. Tel. (218) 727-6861.

El Paso, Bishop Sidney Matthew Metzger, Ecumenical Officer, Rev. Andrew C. Burke,

Chancery Office, 1012 N. Mesa St., El Paso, TX 79902. Tel. (915) 533-5549.

Erie, Bishop Alfred M. Watson. Chancery Office, 205 W. Ninth St., Erie, PA 16501. Tel. (814) 454-4563.

Evansville, Bishop Francis R. Shea. Ecumenical Officer, Rev. James J. Lex, RR 7, Box 281, Evansville, IN 47712. Tel. (812) 963-3273. Chancery Office, 219 N.W. Third St., Evansville, IN 47708. Tel. (812) 424-5536.

Fairbanks, Bishop Robert Louis Whelan. Ecumenical Officer, Rev. F. E. Mueller, S.J., 1316 Peger Rd., Fairbanks, AK 99701. Tel. (907) 456-6753. Chancery Office, 1316 Peger Rd., Fairbanks, AK 99701. Tel. (907) 456-6753.

Fall River, Bishop Daniel A. Cronin. Chancery Office, 362 Highland Ave., Box 30, Fall River MA 02722. Tel. (617) 677-9862.

Fargo, Bishop Justin A. Driscoll. Ecumenical Officer, Rev. Al Bitz, St. Alphonsus Church, Langdon, ND 58249. Tel. (701) 256-2129. Chancery Office, 504 Black Bldg., Box 1750, Fargo, ND 58102. Tel. (701) 235-6429.

Fort Wayne–South Bend, Bishop Leo Aloysius Pursley, Ecumenical Officer, Rev. Daniel E. Peil, 1130 W. Thomas St., South Bend, IN 46625. Tel. (219) 289-3033. Chancery Office, 1103 S. Calhoun St., P.O. Box 390. Fort Wayne, IN 46801. Tel. (219) 422-4611.

Fort Worth, Bishop John J. Cassata. Ecumenical Officer, Rev. Leon Flusche, 3717 Stadium Dr., Ft. Worth, TX 76109. Tel. (817) 927-5383. Chancery Office, 1206 Throckmorton St., Fort Worth, TX 76102. Tel. (817) 335-2697.

Fresno, Bishop Hugh A. Donohoe. Chancery Office, P.O. Box 1668, 1550 N. Fresno St., Fresno, CA 93717. Tel. (209) 237-5125.

Gallup, Bishop Jerome J. Hastrich. Ecumenical Officer, Very Rev. James Dunphy, Box 250, Holbrook, AZ 86025. Tel. (602) 524-3261. Chancery Office, 406 W. Aztec St., P.O. Box 1338, Gallup, NM 87301. Tel. (505) 863-5083.

Galveston-Houston, Bishop Wendelin J. Nold & Bishop John L. Morkovsky. Ecumenical Officer: Rev. Joseph H. Crosthwait, 3700 Brinkman Rd., Houston, TX 77018. Tel. (713) 692-9123. Chancery Office, 1700 San Jacinto St., Houston, TX 77002. Tel. (713) 224-5461.

Gary, Bishop Andrew Gregory Grutka. Chancery Office, P.O. Box 474, 668 Pierce St., Gary, IN 46401. Tel. (219) 886-3141.

Gaylord, Bishop Edmund C. Szoka. Chancery Office M-32 West, P.O. Box 700, Gaylord, MI 49735. Tel. (517) 732-5147.

Grand Island, Bishop John J. Sullivan, Chancery Office, 607 W. Division St., P.O. Box 996, Grand Island, NB 68801. Tel. (308) 382-6565.

Grand Rapids, Bishop Joseph M. Breitenbeck. Ecumenical Officer, Mr. Robert Carpenter, 100 Waters Bldg., Grand Rapids, MI 49502. Tel. (616) 454-9231. Chancery Office, 265 Sheldon Ave., S.E., Grand Rapids, MI 49502. Tel. (312) 459-4509.

Great Falls, Bishop Eldon Bernard Schuster. Ecumenical Officer, Rev. Robert Fox, 1325 Smelter Ave., Black Eagle, MT 59414. Tel. (406) 453-8425. Chancery Office, 725 Third Ave., N. P. O. Box 1399, Great Falls, MT 59401. Tel. (406) 453-9389.

Green Bay, Bishop Aloysius J. Wycislo. Ecu-

menical Officer, Rev. Orville H. Janssen, 1600 Orchard Dr., Appleton, WI 54911. Tel. (414) 734-9115. Chancery Office, Box 66, Green Bay, WI 54305. Tel. (414) 435-4406.

Greensburg, Bishop William G. Connare. Ecumenical Officer, Rev. John A. Regoli, P.O. Box 312 Saltsburg, PA 15681 Tel. (412) 639-9338. Chancery Office, 723 E. Pittsburgh St., Greensburg, PA 15601. Tel. (412) 837-0901.

Harrisburg, Bishop Joseph T. Daley. Ecumenical Officer, Rev. Clair A. Redding, 4000 Derry St., Harrisburg, PA 17111. Tel. (717) 564-1321. Chancery Office. 111 State St., Harrisburg, PA 17105. Tel. (717) 238-1621.

Archdiocese of Hartford, Archbishop John F. Whealon. Ecumenical Officer, Rev. John Stack, 1678 Asylum Ave., West Hartford, CT 06117. Tel. (203) 523-4283. Chancery Office, 134 Farmington Ave., Hartford, CT 06105. Tel. (203) 527-4201.

Helena, Bishop Raymond G. Hunthausen. Ecumenical Officer, Rev. William Greytak, Carroll College, Helena, MT 59601. Chancery Office, 612 Harrison Ave., P.O. Box 1729, Helena, MT 59601. Tel. (406) 442-5820.

Honolulu, Bishop John J. Scanlan, Ecumenical Officer, Rev. David H. Schuyler, S.M., 3140 Waialae Ave., Honolulu, HI 96816. Tel. (808) 732-1471. Chancery Office, 1184 Bishop St., Honolulu, HI 96813. Tel. (808) 533-1791.

Archdiocese of Indianapolis, Archbishop George J. Biskup. Chancery Office, 1350 N. Pennsylvania St., P.O. Box 1776 Indianapolis, IN 46206. Tel. (317) 635-2579.

Jefferson City, Bishop Michael F. McAuliffe, Ecumenical Officer, Rev. Joseph Starmann, 701 Maryland Ave., Columbia, MO 65201. Tel. (314) 449-2611. Chancery Office, 605 Clark Ave., P.O. Box 417, Jefferson City, MO 65101. Tel. (314) 635-9127.

Joliet, Bishop Romeo Blanchette. Chancery Office, 425 Summit St., Joliet, IL 60435. Tel. (815) 722-6606.

Juneau, Bishop Francis T. Hurley. Ecumenical Officer, Rev. Ernest Muellereile, Box 495, Sitka, AK 99835. Tel. (907) 747-8371 Chancery Office, 329 5th St. Juneau, AK 99801. Tel. (907) 586-2221.

Kalamazoo, Bishop Paul V. Dorovan. Chancery Office, 215 N. Westnedge, Kalamazoo, MI 49005. Tel. (616) 349-8714.

Archdiocese of Kansas City in Kansas, Archbishop Ignatius J. Strecker. Chancery Office, 2220 Central Ave., P.O. Box 2328, Kansas City, KS 66110. Tel. (913) 621-4131.

Kansas City-St. Joseph, Bishop Charles H. Helmsing. Ecumenical Officer; Rev. Msgr. Ernest J. Fiedler, 5141 Main St., Kansas City, MO 64112. Tel. (816) 753-7422. Chancery Office, P.O. Box 1037, Kansas City, MO 64141. Tel. (816) 531-1475.

La Crosse, Bishop Frederick W. Freking. Chancery Office, 421 Main St., P.O. Box 982, La Crosse, WI 54601. Tel. (608) 784-8700.

Lafayette in Indiana, Bishop Raymond J. Gallagher. Ecumenical Officer, Mr. John Groppe. Chancery Office, 610 Lingle Ave., Lafayette, IN 47902. Tel. (317) 742-0275.

Lafayette, Bishop Gerard L. Frey. Ecumenical Officer, Rev. Msgr. Richard von Phul Mouton, P.O. Drawer E, Lafayette, LA 70504. Chan-

84

cery Office, Diocesan Office Bldg., P.O. Drawer 3387, Lafayette, LA 70501. Tel. (318) 232-5150.

Lansing, Bishop Alexander M. Zaleski. Ecumenical Officer, Rev. James A. Murray, 300 W. Ottawa, Lansing, MI 48933. Chancery Office, 300 W. Ottawa, Lansing, MI 48933. Tel. (517) 372-8540.

Lincoln, Bishop Glennon P. Flavin, Ecumenical Officer, Rev. Msgr. Raymond B. Hain, P.O. Box 512. Plattsmouth, NB 68048. Tel. (402) 296-3139. Chancery Office, 3400 Sheridan Blvd., P.O. Box 80328, Lincoln, NB 68501. Tel. (402) 488-0921.

Little Rock, Bishop Andrew J. McDonald. Ecumenical Officer: Rev. Msgr. James P. Gaffney, 100 Central Ave., Hot Springs, AR 71901. Chancery Office, 2415 N. Tyler St., Little Rock, AR 72207. Tel. (501) 664-0340.

Archdiocese of Los Angeles, Archbishop Timothy Cardinal Manning. Ecumenical Officer, Rev. Msgr. John Chedid, 333 S. San Vincente Blvd., Los Angeles, CA 90048. Tel. (213) 272-2028. Chancery Office, 1531 W. Ninth St., Los Angeles, CA 90015. Tel. (213) 388-8101.

Archdiocese of Louisville, Archbishop Thomas J. McDonough. Ecumenical Officer, Rev. Stanley Schmidt, 501 Cherrywood Rd., Louisville, KY 40207. Tel. (502) 897-5207. Chancery Office, 212 E. College St., Louisville, KY 40203. Tel. (502) 585-3291.

Madison, Bishop Cletus F. O'Donnell. Chancery Office, 15 E. Wilson St., Madison, WI 53701. Tel. (608) 256-2677.

Manchester, Bishop Ernest J. Primeau. Ecumenical Officer, Rev. Placidus H. Riley, O.S.B., St. Anselm's College, Manchester, NH 03102. Tel. (603) 669-1030. Chancery Office, 153 Ash St., Manchester, NH 03104. Tel. (603) 669-3100.

Maronite Apostolic Exarchate, Bishop Francis M. Zayek. Chancery Office, 11470 Kercheval and St. Jean, Detroit, MI 48214. Tel. (313) 822-2280.

Marquette, Bishop Charles A. Salatka. Ecumenical Officer, Rev. Charles E. Olivier. Chancery Office, 444 S. Fourth St., P.O. Box 550, Marquette, MI 49855. Tel. (906) 225-1141.

Melkite Apostolic Exarchate, Bishop Joseph Tawil. Chancery Office, 19 Dartmouth St, P.O. Box 83, West Newton, MA 02165. Tel. (617) 969-8957.

Memphis Bishop Carroll T. Dozier. Ecumenical Officer, Rev. Thomas Kirk, 1644 Jackson Ave. Memphis, TN 38107. Tel. (901) 276-1412. Chancery Office, 1325 Jefferson Ave., Memphis, TN 38104. Tel. (901) 278-6400.

Archdiocese of Miami, Archbishop Coleman F. Carroll. Ecumenical Officer, Rev. Donald F. X. Connolly, 2355 S. Miami Ave., Miami, FL 33129. Tel. (305) 854-1521. Chancery Office, 6301 Biscayne Blvd., Miami, FL 33138. Tel. (305) 757-6241.

Archdiocese of Milwaukee, Archbishop William E. Cousins. Ecumenical Officer, Rev. Harvey W. Brahm. Chancery Office, 345 N. 95th St., Milwaukee, WI 53226. Tel. (414) 476-2101.

Mobile, Bishop John L. May. Ecumenical Officer, Rev. Charles T. Miller. Chancery Office, 400 Government St., P.O. Box 1966, Mobile, AL 36601. Tel. (205) 433-2241.

Monterey, Bishop Harry Anselm Clinch. Ecumenical Officer, Rev. Harry Freiermuth, 527 Corralitos Rd., Watsonville, CA 95076. Tel. (408) 722-5490. Chancery Office, 580 Fremont Blvd., Monterey, CA 93940. Tel. (408) 373-4345.

Munhall Archeparchy, Bishop Stephen J. Kocisko. Chancery Office, 54 Riverview Ave., Pittsburgh, PA 15214. Tel. (412) 322-7300.

Nashville, Bishop Joseph A. Durick. Ecumenical Officer, Rev. Robert Hofstetter, Gallatin Rd., S. Madison, TN 37115. Tel. (615) 865-1071. Chancery Office, 421 Charlotte Ave., Nashville, TN 37219. Tel. (615) 255-8776.

Natchez-Jackson, Bishop Joseph B. Brunini. Chancery Office, 237 E. Amite St., P.O. Box 2248, Jackson, MS 39205. Tel. (601) 948-6553.

Archdiocese of Newark, Archbishop Thomas A. Boland. Episcopal Vicars: Most Rev. Martin W. Stanton (Bergen and Hudson Counties); Most Rev. John J. Dougherty, (Essex and Union Counties). Rev. Msgr. Joseph L. Przezdziecki (Essex County), Rev. Thomas A. Gillick, Rev. John H. VanWie (Bergen County), Rev. Msgr. Charles B. Murphy, Rev. Denis J. Whelan (Union County), Rev. Harold P. Darcy (Hudson County). Episcopal Vicar, Spanish Speaking Apostolate, Rev. Thomas W. Heck. Office: 31 Mulberry St., Newark, NJ 07102. Tel. (201) 623-8308. Ecumenical Officer, Rev. Msgr. Thomas W. Cunningham, 30 N. Fullerton Ave., Montclair, NJ 07042. Chancery Office, 31 Mulberry St., Newark, NJ 07102. Tel. (201) 623-8308.

Archdiocese of New Orleans, Archbishop Philip M. Hannan. Ecumenical Officer, Rev. Msgr. Charles J. Plauche, 7887 Walmsley Ave., New Orleans, LA 70125. Chancery Office, 7887 Walmsley Ave., New Orleans, LA 70125. Tel. (504) 861-9521.

New Ulm, Bishop Alphonse J. Schladweiler. Ecumenical Officer, Rev. John M. Murphy, 509 So. Lincoln St.,. Redwood Falls, MN 56283. Tel. (507) 637-2278. Chancery Office, Chancery Drive, New Ulm, MN 56073. Tel. (507) 354-2323.

Archdiocese of New York, Terence Cardinal Cooke. Episcopal Vicars of the Archdiocese: Manhattan: (Upper) Bishop Edward D. Head, 122 E. 22nd St., N. Y., NY 10010. Tel. (212) 677-5000. Southern Manhattan (S. of 14th St.): Rt. Rev. Msgr. Leonard J. Hunt, 414 E. 14th St., New York, NY 10009. Bronx: Bishop Patrick V. Ahern, 2860 Webb Ave., Bronx, NY 10468. Tel. (212) 548-3005 Co-Vicar, Rt. Rev. Msgr. Gustav J. Schultheiss, 1759 Castle Hill Ave., Bronx, NY 10462. Tel. (212) 792-4044. Richmond: Rt. Rev. Msgr. Andrew F. Quinn, 981 Castleton Ave., Staten Island, NY 10310. Tel. (212) 442-0058. Westchester: Rev. Msgr. John C. Dougherty, 32 Massitoa Rd., Yonkers, NY 10710. Tel. (914) 779-5460. Dutchess and Putnam: Most Rev. Joseph M. Pernicone, 775 Main St., Poughkeepsie, NY 12603. Tel. (914) 452-1863. Orange and Rockland: Most Rev. John M. Fearns, 55 Grand St., Newburgh, NY 12550. Tel. (914) 561-0885. Ulster: Rev. Msgr. James V. Keating, Presentation Church, Minturn St., Port Ewen, NY 12466. Tel. (914) 331-0053. Sullivan: Rev. Msgr. Robert D. Browny. Broadway and Liberty St., Monticello, NY 12701. Tel. (914) 794-5577.

THE ROMAN CATHOLIC CHURCH

Ecumenical Officer: Rev. Msgr. James F. Rigney, 451 Madison Ave., New York, NY 10022; Chancery Office, 451 Madison Ave., New York, NY 10022. Tel. (212) 759-1400.

Norwich, Bishop Vincent J. Hines, Ecumenical Officer, Rev. James J. O'Brien, 201 Broadway, Norwich, CT 06360. Chancery Office, 201 Broadway, P.O. Box 587, Norwich, CT 06360. Tel. (203) 887-9294.

Oakland, Bishop Floyd L. Begin. Ecumenical Officer, Rev. Anthony Harear, 5641 Esmond Ave., Richmond, CA 94805. Tel. (415) 237-1531. Chancery Office, 2900 Lakeshore Ave., Oakland, CA 94610. Tel. (415) 893-4711.

Ogdensburg, Bishop Stanislaus J. Brzana. Ecumenical Officer, Rev. Msgr. Robert A. Farmer, 7 Margaret St., Plattsburgh, NY 12901. Tel. (518) 563-0730. Chancery Office, 622 Washington St., Ogdensburg, NY 13669. Tel. (315) 393-2920.

Oklahoma City and Tulsa, Bishop John R. Quinn, Ecumenical Officer, Rev. Stephen Wells. Center for Christian Renewal, P.O. Box 332, Oklahoma City, OK 73101. Tel. (405) 721-5651. Chancery Office, 1521 N. Hudson, Oklahoma City, OK 73103, Tel. (405) 235-3688.

Archdiocese of Omaha, Archbishop Daniel E. Shephan. Ecumenical Officer, Rev. Robert P. Hupp, 654 S. 86th St., Omaha, NB 68114. Tel. (402) 391-3606. Chancery Office, 100 N. 62nd St., Omaha, NB 68132. Tel. (402) 558-3100.

Orlando, Bishop William D. Borders. Ecumenical Officer, Rev. Joseph A. Nolin, P.O. Box 699, Kissimmee, FL 32741. Tel. (305) 847-2500. Chancery Office, 5330 Diplomat Circle, P.O. Box 3069, Orlando, FL 32802. Tel. (305) 645-1516.

Owensboro, Bishop Henry J. Soenneker. Ecumenical Officer, Very Rev. Anthony G. Higdon. RR 5, Box 517, Paducah, KY 42001. Tel. (502) 554-3810. Chancery Office, c/o Chancellor's Residence, 4003 Frederica St., P.O. Box 773, Owensboro, KY 42301. Tel. (502) 683-1545.

Parma Eparchy, Bishop Emil Mihalik. Chancery Office, 1900 Carlton Rd., Parma, OH 44134. Tel. (216) 741-8773.

Passaic (Greek Rite), Bishop Michael J. Dudick. Ecumenical Officer, Rev. Msgr. George Durisin, 96 First St., Passaic, NJ 07055. Tel. (201) 777-2553. Chancery Office, 101 Market St., Passaic, NJ 07055. Tel. (201) 778-9595.

Paterson, Bishop Lawrence B. Casey. Ecumenical Officer, Rev. James L. Fallon, 250 Speedwell Ave., Morris Plains, NJ 07950. Tel. (201) 538-1418. Chancery Office, 24 De Grasse St., Paterson, NJ 07505. Tel. (201) 274-0400.

Peoria, Bishop Edward W. O'Rourke. Ecumenical Officer, Rev. Msgr. Robert G. Peters, 409 N.E. Monroe Ave., Peoria, IL 61603. Chancery Office, 607 N.E. Madison Ave., Peoria, IL 61603. Tel. (309) 673-6318.

Archdiocese of Philadelphia, John Cardinal Krol. Chancery Office, 1712 Summer St., Philadelphia, PA 19103. Tel. (215) 563-6810.

Ukrainian Rite—Philadelphia, Bishop Ambrose Senyshyn. Chancery Office, 815 N. Franklin St., Philadelphia, PA 19123. Tel. (215) 627-0143.

Phoenix, Bishop Edward A. McCarthy. Ecumenical Officer, Rev. Msgr. Robert J. Donohoe, 1954 N. 24 St., Phoenix, AZ 85008. Tel. (602) 253-4148. Chancery Office, 400 E. Monroe St. Phoenix, AZ 85004. Tel. (602) 258-6933.

Pittsburgh, Bishop Vincent M. Leonard. Ecumenical Officer, Rev. Msgr. Francis A. Glenn, 111 Blvd. of Allies, Pittsburgh, PA 15222. Chancery Office, 111 Blvd. of Allies, Pittsburgh, PA 15222. Tel. (412) 391-1002.

Portland, Bishop Peter Leo Gerety. Ecumenical Officer, Rev. Clement D. Thibodeau, Waterboro Rd., Alfred, ME 04002. Chancery Office, 510 Ocean Ave., Portland, ME 04103. Tel. (207) 773-6471.

Archdiocese of Portland in Oregon, Archbishop Robert J. Dwyer. Ecumenical Officer, Rev. Edward Zinner, P.O. Box 351, Portland, OR 97207. Chancery Office, 2838 E. Burnside St., Portland, OR 97214. Tel. (503) 234-5334.

Providence, Bishop Louis E. Gelineau. Ecumenical Officer, Rev. Lionel A. Blain, Our Lady of Providence Seminary, Warwick Neck, RI 02889. Chancery Office, Cathedral Square, Providence, RI 02903. Tel. (401) 861-9800.

Pueblo, Bishop Charles A. Buswell. Ecumenical Officer, Rev. William T. Gleeson, 650 Elm St., Las Animas, CO 81054. Tel. (303) 456-0357. Chancery Office, 1426 Grand Ave., Pueblo, CO 81003. Tel. (303) 544-9861.

Raleigh, Bishop Vincent S. Waters. Chancery Office, P.O. Box 1949, Raleigh, NC 27602. Tel. (919) 832-0375.

Rapid City, Bishop Harold J. Dimmerling. Chancery Office, 520 Cathedral Dr., P.O. Box 752, Rapid City, SD 57701. Tel. (605) 343-3541.

Reno, Bishop Joseph Green. Chancery Office, 515 Court St., Reno, NV 89501. Tel. (702) 329-9274.

Richmond, Bishop John J. Russell. Ecumenical Officer, Rev. N. Robert Quirin, 9506 Gayton Rd., Richmond, VA 23229. Tel. (703) 288-9244. Chancery Office, 807 Cathedral Pl., Richmond, VA 23220. Tel. (703) 649-9353.

Rochester, Bishop Joseph L. Hogan. Ecumenical Officer, Rev. Msgr. Charles V. Boyle, 549 Humboldt St., Rochester, NY 14610. Tel. (716) 482-6211. Chancery Office, 50 Chestnut St., Rochester, NY 14604. Tel. (716) 454-1155.

Rockford, Bishop Arthur J. O'Neill. Ecumenical Officer, Rev. William P. Knott, 921 W. State St., Rockford, IL 61102. Chancery Office, 1245 N. Court St., Rockford, IL 61101. Tel. (815) 962-3709.

Rockville Centre, Bishop Walter P. Kellenberg. Ecumenical Officer, Rev. Daniel Hamilton, P.O. Box 395, Rockville Centre, NY 11571. Tel. (516) 766-4191. Chancery Office, 253 Sunrise Highway, Rockville Centre, NY 11570. Tel. (516) 764-9800.

Sacramento, Bishop Alden J. Bell. Ecumenical Officer, Rev. Msgr. Richard C. Dwyer, 10497 Coloma Rd., Rancho Cordova, CO 95670. Tel. (916) 362-1385. Chancery Office, 1119 K St., P.O. Box 1706, Sacramento, CA 95808. Tel. (916) 443-1996.

Saginaw, Bishop Francis F. Reh. Chancery Office, 2555 Wieneke Rd., Saginaw, MI 48603. Tel. (517) 799-7910.

St. Augustine, Bishop Paul F. Tanner. Chancery Office, Ste. 1648, Gulf Life Tower, Jacksonville, FL 32207. Tel. (904) 359-2509.

St. Cloud, Bishop George H. Speltz and Bishop Peter W. Bartholome. Ecumenical Officer, Rev. Robert Voight, St. Anna Rt. 1, Avon, MN 56310. Chancery Office, P.O. Box 1248, St. Cloud, MN 56301. Tel. (612) 251-2340.

Archdiocese of St. Louis, John Cardinal Carberry. Ecumenical Officer, Rev. Msgr. Joseph W. Baker, 4445 Lindell Blvd., St. Louis, MO 63108. Chancery Office, 4445 Lindell Blvd., St. Louis, MO 63108. Tel. (314) 533-1887.

St. Nicholas in Chicago for the Ukrainians, Bishop Jaroslav Gabro. Chancery Office, 2245 W. Rice St., Chicago, IL 60622. Tel. (312) 276-5080.

Archdiocese of St. Paul and Minneapolis, Archbishop Leo Binz. Leo C. Byrne, Archbiship with right of succession. Chancery Office, 226 Summit Ave., St. Paul, MN 55102. Tel. (612) 222-1745.

St. Petersburg, Bishop Charles B. McLaughlin. Ecumenical Officer, Rev. Edward Mulligan, 4000 43rd St., N., St. Petersburg, FL 33714. Tel. (813) 525-0262. Chancery Office, 5201 Central Ave., P.O. Box 13109. St. Petersburg, FL 33733. Tel. (813) 342-8911.

Salina, Bishop Cyril J. Vogel. Chancery Office, 421 Country Club Rd., P.O. Box 999, Salina, KS 67401. Tel. (913) 827-8746.

Salt Lake City, Bishop Joseph Lennox Federal. Ecumenical Officer, Rev. Lawrence P. Sweeney, 333 E. South Temple, Salt Lake City, UT 84111. Chancery Office, 333 E. South Temple, Salt Lake City, UT 84111. Tel. (801) 328-8641.

San Angelo, Bishop Stephen A. Leven. Chancery Office, 116 S. Oakes (Mailing Address Box 1829) San Angelo, TX 76901. Tel. (915) 653-2466.

Archdiocese of San Antonio, Archbishop Francis J. Furey. Ecumenical Officer, Rev. Robert P. Kownacki, 6425 West Ave. San Antonio, TX 78213. Tel. (512) 344-9265. Chancery Office, 9123 Lorene Lane, P.O. Box 13190, San Antonio, TX 78213. Tel. (512) 344-2331.

San Diego, Bishop Leo T. Maher. Ecumenical Officer, Rev. Msgr. John R. Portman. DeSales Hall, Alcala Park, CA 92110. Tel. (714) 291-6480. Chancery Office, Alcala Park, San Diego, CA 92110. Tel. (714) 298-7711.

Archdiocese of San Francisco, Archbishop Joseph T. McGucken. Ecumenical Officer, Rev. Edward J. Dingberg, P.O. Box 6166, San Rafael, CA 94903. Chancery Office, 445 Church St., San Francisco, CA 94114. Tel. (415) 863-5112.

Archdiocese of Santa Fe, Archbishop James Peter Davis. Chancery Office, 202 Morningside Dr., S.E., Albuquerque, NM 87108. Tel. (505) 268-4572.

Santa Rosa, Bishop Mark J. Hurley. Chancery Office, 398 10th St., P.O. Box 1499, Santa Rosa, CA 95403. Tel. (707) 545-7610.

Savannah, Bishop Gerard L. Frey. Ecumenical Officer, Rev. Msgr. Andrew J. McDonald, P.O. Box 3427, Savannah, GA 31405. Chancery Office, 225 Abercorn St., P.O. Box 8789, Savannah, GA 31402. Tel. (912) 234-0601.

Scranton, Bishop J. Carroll McCormick, Ecumenical Officer, Rev. Constantine V. Siconolfi,

300 Wyoming Ave., Scranton, PA 18503. Chancery Office, 300 Wyoming Ave., Scranton, PA 18503. Tel. (717) 346-9681.

Archdiocese of Seattle, Archbishop Thomas A. Connolly. Ecumenical Officer, Rev. William Treacy, 1021 S. Boundary, Box 766, Olympia, WA 98507. Tel. (206) 357-5513. Chancery Office, 907 Terry Ave., Seattle, WA 98104. Tel. (206) 622-8880.

Sioux City, Bishop Frank H. Greteman. Chancery Office, 1822 Jackson St., P.O. Box 3105, Sioux City, IA 51102. Tel. (712) 255-9412.

Sioux Falls, Bishop Lambert A. Hock. Ecumenical Officer, Rev. Msgr. Louis J. Delahoyde, 423 N. Duluth Ave., Sioux Falls, SD 57104. Chancery Office, 423 N. Duluth Ave., Sioux Falls, SD 57104. Tel. (605) 334-9861.

Spokane, Bishop Bernard J. Topel. Ecumenical Officer, Most Rev. Bernard J. Topel, P.O. Box 1453, Spokane, WA 99201. Chancery Office, 1023 W. Riverside Ave., Spokane, WA 99201. Tel. (509) 624-8994.

Springfield-Cape Girardeau, _____. Chancery Office, 410 Landers Bldg., Springfield, MO 65806. Tel. (417) 866-0842.

Springfield in Illinois, Bishop William Aloysius O'Connor. Ecumenical Officer, Rev. Msgr. Lawrence Wiskirchen, 1412 9th St., Highland, IL 62249. Tel. (618) 654-2339. Chancery Office, 524 E. Lawrence Ave., Springfield, IL 62705. Tel. (217) 522-7781.

Springfield, Bishop Christopher J. Weldon. Ecumenical Officer, Rev. Patrick A. Sullivan, S. J. 27 Onota St., Pittsfield, MA 01201. Chancery Office, 76 Elliot St., P.O. Box 1730, Springfield, MA 01101. Tel. (413) 732-3175.

Byzantine Ukrainian Rite—Stamford, Bishop Joseph M. Schmondiuk. Chancery Office, 161 Glenbrook Rd., Stamford, CT 06902. Tel. (203) 324-7698.

Steubenville, Bishop John King Mussio. Chancery Office, 422 Washington St., P.O. Box 969, Steubenville, OH 43952. Tel. (614) 282-3631.

Stockton, Bishop Merlin J. Guilfoyle. Chancery Office, 1105 N. Lincoln St., Stockton, CA 95203, P.O. Box 4237, Stockton, CA 95204. Tel. (209) 466-0636.

Superior, Bishop George A. Hammes. Ecumenical Officer, Rev. George Gleason, 419 So. Third St., Chetek, WI 54728. Tel. (715) 924-3514. Chancery Office, 1201 Hughitt Ave., Superior, WI 54880. Tel. (715) 392-2937.

Syracuse, Bishop David F. Cunningham. Ecumenical Officer: Rev. George E. Arseneau, 44 N. Main St., Cortland, NY 13045. Tel. (607) 756-9967. Chancery Office, 240 E. Onondaga St., Syracuse, NY 13202. Tel. (315) 422-7203.

Toledo, Bishop John A. Donovan. Ecumenical Officer, Rev. Loren B. McClanahan, 1842 Airport Hwy., Toledo, OH 43609. Tel. (419) 385-7431. Chancery Office, 2544 Parkwood Ave., Toledo, OH 43610. Tel. (419) 255-1670.

Trenton, Bishop George W. Ahr. Episcopal Vicars: New Brunswick Area, Middlesex County; Rev. J. Morgan Kelly; Amboy Area, Middlesex County; Rev. Joseph R. Brzozowski; Burlington County, Rev. William J. Kokoszka; Mercer County; Rev. Thomas C. Ryan; Monmouth County; Very Rev. Msgr.

Robert T. Bulman; Ocean County; Rev. George E. Everitt; Hunterdon, Warren Counties; Vacant. Somerset County; Rev. John R. Torney. Office 901 W. State St., Trenton, NJ 08618. Tel. (609) 882-7125. Ecumenical Officer, Rev. Msgr. John Endebrock, 214 Nassau St., Princeton, NJ 08540. Tel. (609) 924-1743. Chancery Office, 701 Lawrenceville Rd., Trenton, NJ 08638. Tel. (609) 882-7125.

Tucson, Bishop Francis J. Green. Ecumenical Officer, Rev. James T. Weber, 3201 E. Presidio St., Tucson, AZ 85716. Tel. (602) 326-7670. Chancery Office, 192 S. Stone Ave., Box 31, Tucson, AZ 85702. Tel. (602) 792-3410.

Archdiocese of Washington, Archbishop William Baum. Ecumenical Officer, ————. Chancery Office, 1721 Rhode Island Ave., N.W., Washington, DC 22036. Tel. (202) 783-1465.

Wheeling, Bishop Joseph H. Hodges. Ecumenical Officer: Rev. John H. McDonnell, P.O. Box 230, Wheeling, WV 26003. Tel. (304) 233-0880. Chancery Office, 1300 Byron St., Wheeling WV 26003. Tel. (304) 233-0880.

Wichita, Bishop David M. Maloney. Ecumenical Officer, Rev. Msgr. Charles F. Walsh, 307 E. Central Ave., Wichita, KS 67202. Tel. (316) 263-6574. Chancery Office, 424 N. Broadway, Wichita, KS 67202. Tel. (316) 363-6262.

Wilmington, Bishop Thomas J. Mardaga. Chancery Office, P.O. Box 2030, Wilmington, DE 19899. Tel. (302) 656-2578.

Winona, Bishop Loras J. Watters. Chancery Office, 275 Harriet St., Winona, MN 55987. Tel. (507) 454-4643.

Worcester, Bishop Bernard J. Flanagan. Ecumenical Officer, Rev. John Burke, 38 High St., Worcester, MA 01605. Tel. (617) 799-4193. Chancery Office, 49 Elm St., Worcester, MA 01609. Tel. (617) 791-7171.

Yakima, Bishop Cornelius M. Power. Ecumenical Officer, Rev. Anthony S. Hannick. 1609 Landon Ave., Yakima, WA 98902. Tel. (509) 248-2241. Chancery Office, 228 Liberty Bldg., P.O. Box 901, Yakima, WA 98907. Tel. (509) 452-8503.

Youngstown, Bishop James W. Malone. Chancery Office, 144 W. Wood St., Youngstown, OH 44503. Tel. (216) 744-5341.

The Romanian Orthodox Church in America

The Romanian Orthodox Church in America is an autonomous Episcopate chartered under the name of the "Romanian Orthodox Missionary Episcopate in America."

It was founded in 1929 and approved by the Holy Synod of the Romanian Orthodox Church in Romania in 1934. By a decision of the Holy Synod of the Romanian Church of July 12, 1950 it was granted the status of ecclesiastical autonomy in America, continuing to hold only dogmatical and canonical ties with the Holy Synod and the Romanian Orthodox Patriarchate of Romania.

In 1951, a group of approximately 40 parishes with their clergy separated from this church and eventually joined in 1960 the Russian Orthodox Greek Catholic Metropolia now called the Orthodox Church in America.

The Bishop of the Romanian Orthodox Church in America is a member of the Standing Conference of Canonical Orthodox Bishops in America.

GENERAL ORGANIZATION

Headquarters: 19959 Riopelle, Detroit, MI 48203. Tel. (313) 366-1998.

Annual Congress in July, and bi-annual Diocesan Council.

OFFICERS

Bishop, His Grace The Rt. Rev. Bishop Victorin (Ursache), 19959 Riopelle, Detroit, MI 48203.

Vicar, Very Rev. Archpriest John Bugariu, 4319 Elm St., East Chicago, IN 46312.

Chancellor, Very Rev. Archim. Bartholomew V. Anania, 19959 Riopelle, Detroit, MI 48203.

PERIODICALS

Credinta—The Faith (m), 19959 Riopelle, Detroit, MI 48203. Very Rev. Archim. B. V. Anania.

Calendarul Credinta (yearbook), 19959 Riopelle, Detroit, MI 48203. Very Rev. Archim. B. V. Anania.

The Romanian Orthodox Episcopate of America

This body of Eastern Orthodox Christians of Romanian descent was organized in 1929 as an autonomous Diocese under the jurisdiction of the Romanian Patriarchate. In 1951 it severed all relations with the Orthodox Church of Romania. The Diocese is under the canonical jurisdiction of the autocephalous Orthodox Church in America, but enjoys full administrative autonomy and is headed by its own bishop.

Churches: 45. Inclusive Membership: 50,000. Sunday or Sabbath Schools: 39. Total Enrollment: 1,693. Ordained clergy: 50.

GENERAL ORGANIZATION

Church Congress: annual (July).

Headquarters: 2522 Grey Tower Road, Jackson, MI 49201. Tel. (517) 522-4800.

OFFICERS

The Bishop: His Grace Bishop Valerian (D. Trifa).

The Council of the Episcopate: Pres., His Grace Bishop Valerian; Sec., Rev. Fr. Eugene Lazar, 626 Wick Ave., Youngstown, OH 44502; Treas., John Bondar, 13134 Walter Road, Warren, MI 48093.

OTHER ORGANIZATIONS

The American Romanian Orthodox Youth (AROY): Pres., Robert L. Cipu, 4 Autumn Ridge Rd., Fairfield, CT 06430; Sec., Miss Mary J. Buta, 525 W. Glen Dr., Youngstown, OH 44512; Spiritual Adviser, Rev. Fr. Nicholas Craciun, 3319 Ridgewood Rd., Akron, OH 44313.

Association of Romanian Orthodox Ladies' Auxiliaries (ARFORA): Pres., Leona Barbu, 3188 W. 142nd St., Cleveland, OH 44111; Sec., Mrs. Aurelia Buner, 316 Second St., Ellwood City, PA 16117.

Orthodox Brotherhood: Chmn., Harold Shantz, 2201 S. Short Hills Dr., Akron, OH 44313.

PERIODICAL

SOLIA, Romanian News (m), 11341 Woodward Ave., Detroit, MI 48202.

Russian Orthodox Church in the U.S.A., Patriarchal Parishes of the

This group of parishes is under the direct jurisdiction of the Patriarch of Moscow and All Russia, His Holiness Pimen, in the person of a Vicar Bishop, the Most Rev. Makary, Bishop of Uman.

GENERAL ORGANIZATION

Headquarters: St. Nicholas Patriarchal Cathedral, 15 E. 97th St., New York, NY 10029. Tel. (212) 289-1915.
Vicar Bishop: The Most Rev. Makary, Bishop of Uman.

PERIODICAL

One Church (bi-m), P.O. Box 363, East Lansing, MI 48823. Rt. Rev. Photius F. M. Donahue, Ed.
Journal of the Moscow Patriachate (in English) (m), Subscription List, St. Nicholas Cathedral, New York, NY 10029.

The Russian Orthodox Church Outside Russia

(Formerly The Russian Orthodox Church Abroad)

Organized in 1920 to unite in one body of dioceses the missions and parishes of the Russian Orthodox Church outside of Russia. The Governing body was set up in Constantinople sponsored by the Ecumenical Patriarchate. In November 1950, it came to the United States. The Russian Orthodox Church Outside Russia lays emphasis on being true to the old traditions of the Russian Church, but it does not compromise with official church leaders in Moscow, "since that would amount to being under the influence and direction of a godless State."

GENERAL ORGANIZATION

Headquarters: 75 E. 93rd St., New York, NY 10028.
(Summer residence): Hermitage of Our Lady of Kursk, Lake Mahopac, NY 10541, and 1600 Carmelita Ave., Burlingame, CA 94010.
Council of Bishops, Synod (elected by the Council): Pres., His Eminence, the Most Rev. Metropolitan Philaret.
Other Members: Most Rev. Archbishop Nikon, Archbishop of Washington and Florida, Rt. Rev. Bishop Laurus, Sect.
Consultant and Director of Public and Foreign Relations Dept., Archpriest George Grabbe, 75 E. 93rd St., New York, NY 10028.

PERIODICAL

Orthodox Life, in English (bi-m). Abbot Constantine, Ed.

The Salvation Army

An evangelistic organization with a military government, first set up by General William Booth (1829-1912) in England in 1865 and introduced into America in 1880.

Churches: 1,104. Inclusive Membership: 335,684. Sunday or Sabbath Schools: 1,112. Total Enrollment: 108,910. Ordained clergy 5,180.

GENERAL ORGANIZATION

National Headquarters: 120-130 W. 14th St., New York, NY 10011. Tel. (212) 243-8700.

OFFICERS

Natl. Commander, Commissioner Paul J. Carlson.
Natl. Chief Sec., Col. C. Emil Nelson.

TERRITORIAL ORGANIZATIONS

Eastern Territory, 120-130 W. 14th St., New York, NY 10011; Territorial Commander, Lt. Commissioner Bramwell Tripp; Chief Sec., Col. Harold Barry.
Central Territory, 860 N. Dearborn St., Chicago, IL 60610; Territorial Commander, Commissioner J. Clyde Cox; Chief Sec., Col. Henry J. Koerner.
Western Territory, 101 Valencia St., San Francisco, CA 94103. Territorial Commander, Lt. Commissioner Paul S. Kaiser; Chief Sec., Col. Ernest Holz.
Southern Territory, 675 Seminole Ave. N.E., Atlanta, GA 30307. Territorial Commander, Commissioner William E. Chamberlain; Chief Sec., Col. W. R. H. Goodier.

PERIODICALS

War Cry (w), The Young Soldier (w), El Grito (w). National Publications Dept., 860 N. Dearborn St., Chicago, IL 60610. Lt. Col. William Burrows, Ed.

The Schwenkfelder Church

Descendants of a German migration from Silesia into Pennsylvania in 1734, followers of a Reformation leader, Caspar Schwenckfeld Von Ossig.

GENERAL ORGANIZATION

General Conference: semi-annual.
Headquarters: Pennsburg, PA 18073.

OFFICERS

Mod., Vincent W. Nyce, 2017 Berkley Rd., Norristown, PA 19401.
Sec., Miss Florence Schultz, 920 Stanbridge Rd., Drexel Hill, PA 19026.
Treas., Lester S. Heebner, 1865 W. Marshall St., Norristown, PA 19401.

PERIODICAL

The Schwenkfeldian (q), Pennsburg, PA 18073. Jack R. Rothenberger, Ed.

† Second Cumberland Presbyterian Church in U.S.

In 1869 the Negro churches of the Cumberland Presbyterian Church were set apart by the General Assembly with their own ecclesiastical organization.

GENERAL ORGANIZATION

General Assembly: annual (June).

OFFICERS

Mod., R. L. Blackburn.
Stat. Clk., Roy Tinsley, Princeton, KY 42445.

SEPARATE BAPTISTS IN CHRIST

Separate Baptists in Christ

A group of Baptists found in Indiana, Ohio, Kentucky, Tennessee, and Illinois, dating back to an association formed in 1758 in North Carolina.

GENERAL ORGANIZATION

General Association.

OFFICERS

Mod., Rev. Roger Popplewell, Rt. 5, Russell Springs, KY 42642.
Asst. Mod., Rev. F. T. Pepper, Greensburg, KY 42743.
Clk., Bro. Floyd Wilson, 59 Greensprings Rd., Indianapolis, IN 46224.

Serbian Eastern Orthodox Church for the U.S.A. and Canada

GENERAL ORGANIZATION

National Assembly.
Chancery: 5701 N. Redwood Dr., Chicago IL
Tel. (312) 693-3309.

OFFICERS

Diocese of the Mid-West, Rt. Rev. Bishop Firmilian, 8347 W. Summerdale Ave., Chicago, IL 60656.
Diocese for the Eastern States of America and Canada, Bishop Sava, 5095 Broadview, Richfield, OH 44286.
Western Diocese, Rt. Rev. Bishop Gregory, 2511 W. Garvey Ave., Alhambra, CA 91803.

OTHER ORGANIZATIONS

Brotherhood of Serbian Orthodox Clergy in the U.S. and Canada, Pres., V. Rev. Mitan Brieich, Joliet, IL.
Circle of Serbian Sisters.
Serbian Orthodox Teacher's and Youth Association.

Seventh-day Adventists

This Protestant body developed out of an interdenominational movement that appeared in different countries of Christendom in the early decades of the nineteenth century, stressing the imminence of the Second Advent of Christ. However, Seventh-day Adventists were not formally organized until 1863. Taking the Bible as their sole rule of faith and practice, they are fundamentally evangelical, holding to the full inspiration of the Scriptures and the deity of Christ. Their two cardinal points of faith are: (1) belief in the personal, imminent, premillennial return of Christ, and (2) observance of the seventh day as the Sabbath.

Churches: 3,235. Inclusive Membership: 433,906. Sunday or Sabbath Schools: 3,315. Total Enrollment: 375,031. Ordained clergy: 3,365.

GENERAL ORGANIZATION

General Conference: quadrennial. (Next meeting, 1975.)
Headquarters: 6840 Eastern Avenue N.W., Washington, DC 20012. Tel. (202) 723-0800.

OFFICERS

Pres., Robert H. Pierson.
Sec., Clyde O. Franz.
Treas., K. H. Emmerson.

OTHER ORGANIZATIONS

Bureau of Public Relations: Sec., E. W. Tarr.
Dept. of Educ.: Sec., Charles B. Hirsch.
Dept. of Public Affairs: Sec., M. E. Loewen.
Health Dept.: Sec., Ralph Waddell, M. D.
Lay Activities Dept. (Welfare): Sec., V. W. Schoen.
Ministerial Association: Sec., N. R. Dower.
Publishing Dept.: Sec., D. A. McAdams.
Radio and TV Dept.: Sec., J. J. Aitken.
Regional Dept. (Colored): Sec., H. D. Singleton.
Sabbath School Dept.: Sec., Fernon Rezer.
Stewardship and Development Dept.: Sec., W. M. Starks.
Young People's Dept.: Sec., John H. Hancock.
And other general Activities:
American Temperance Society: Sec., E.H.J. Steed.
Association of Self-Supporting Institutions: Sec., C. H. Lauda.
Faith for Today (Television): Sec., W. A. Fagal.
Home Study Institute (correspondence school): Sec., D. W. Holbrook.
Statistical: Sec., Jesse O. Gibson.
Voice of Prophecy (Radio): Sec., Alvin G. Munson.

NORTH AMERICAN ORGANIZATIONS

The North American Division of Seventh-day Adventists, 6840 Eastern Ave., N.W., Washington, DC 20012, President, Neal C. Wilson; Secretaries, L. L. Bock and C. E. Bradford. This Division includes the United States and Canada and is divided into 61 Conferences which are grouped together into 10 organized Union Conferences. The various Conferences work under the general direction of these Union Conferences. The Canadian Union Conference is listed under the Canadian Section of this **Yearbook.** Following is a list of the 9 Union Conferences in which the Seventh-day Adventist Churches are organized in the United States.

Atlantic Union Conference, P.O. Box 458, South Lancaster, MA 01561. Pres., J. L. Dittberner; Sec., A. N. Brogden; Treas., Ben Trout. (Territory: Connecticut, Maine, Massachusetts, New Hampshire, New York, Rhode Island, Vermont, and the Bermuda Islands.)
Central Union Conference, P.O. Box 6127, Lincoln, NB 68506. Pres. R. H. Nightingale; Sec.-Treas., R. E. Spangle. (Territory: Colorado, Kansas, Missouri, Nebraska, Wyoming, and San Juan County in New Mexico.)
Columbia Union Conference, 7710 Carroll Ave., Takoma Park, MD 20012. Pres., Cree Sandefur; Sec., W. A. Thompson; Treas., A. B. Butler. (Territory: Delaware, Maryland, New Jersey, Ohio, Pennsylvania, Virginia, West Virginia, and District of Columbia.)
Lake Union Conference, P.O. Box C, Berrien Springs, MI 49103. Pres., F. W. Wernick; Sec., F. L. Jones; Treas., W. F. Miller. (Territory: Illinois, Indiana, Michigan, and Wisconsin.)
North Pacific Union Conference, P.O. Box 16677, Portland, OR 97216. Pres., E. R.

Walde; Sec., M. C. Torkelsen; Treas., L. W. Crooker. (Territory: Alaska, Idaho, Montana, Oregon, and Washington.)

Northern Union Conference, 400 North Lilac Dr., Minneapolis, MN 55422. Pres., Arthur Kiesz; Sec.-Treas., L. H. Netteburg. (Territory: Iowa, Minnesota, North Dakota, and South Dakota.

Pacific Union Conference, P.O. Box 146, Glendale, CA 91209. Pres., W. J. Blacker; Sec., W. D. Walton; Treas., R. L. Cone. (Territory: Arizona, California, Hawaii, Nevada, and Utah.)

Southern Union Conference, P.O. Box 849, Decatur, GA 30031. Pres., H. H. Schmidt; Sec., H. F. Roll; Treas., J. H. Whitehead. (Territory: Alabama, Florida, Georgia, Kentucky, Mississippi, North Carolina, South Carolina, and Tennessee.)

Southwestern Union Conference, P.O. Box 400, Richardson, TX 75080. Pres., B. E. Leach; Sec., Cyril Miller; Treas., V. L. Roberts. (Territory: Arkansas, Louisiana, New Mexico [excepting San Juan County], Oklahoma, and Texas.)

PERIODICALS

Adventist Home and School (three issues yearly, P.O. Box 59, Nashville, TN 37202. W. John Cannon, Ed.

Alert (q), Pacific Press Publishing Association, Mountain View, CA 94040. F. A. Soper, Ed.

Christian Record, 3705 South 48th St., Lincoln, NB 20006. R. A. Gibson, Ed.

The Adventist Layman (m), 6840 Eastern Ave. N.W., Washington, DC 20012. L. A. Shipowick, Ed.

Guide (w), 6856 Eastern Ave. N.W., Washington, DC 20012. Lowell Litten, Ed.

Insight, 6656 Eastern Ave., N.W., Washington, DC 20012. Michael Jones, Ed.

Journal of Adventist Education (five issues yearly), 6856 Eastern Ave. N.W., Washington, DC 20012. G. J. Millet, Ed.

Liberty (bi-m), 6856 Eastern Ave. N.W., Washington, DC 20012. R. R. Hegstad, Ed.

Life and Health (m), 6856 Eastern Ave. N.W., Washington, DC 20012. Mervyn G. Hardinge, M.D., Ed.

Listen (m), Pacific Press Publishing Association, Mountain View, CA 94040. F. A. Soper, Ed.

MV Program Kit (q), P.O. Box 59, Nashville, TN 37202. Donald Jones, Ed.

Message Magazine (bi-m), P.O. Box 59, Nashville, TN 37202. W. R. Robinson, Ed.

Ministry, The (m), 6840 Eastern Ave. N.W., Washington, DC 20012. J. R. Spangler, Ed.

Our Little Friend (w), Pacific Press Publishing Association, Mountain View, CA 94040. L. P. Schutter, Ed.

Primary Treasure (w), Pacific Press Publishing Association, Mountain View, CA 94040. L. P. Schutter, Ed.

Review and Herald (w), 6856 Eastern Ave. N.W., Washington, DC 20012. K. H. Wood, Ed.

Sabbath School Lesson Quarterlies, Pacific Press Publishing Association, Mountain View, CA 94040.

Signs of the Times (m), Pacific Press Publishing Association, Mountain View, CA 94040. Lawrence Maxwell, Ed.

Smoke Signals, 6840 Eastern Ave. N.W., Washington, DC 20012. F. A. Soper, Ed.

These Times (m), P.O. Box 59, Nashville, TN 37202. K. J. Holland, Ed.

Worker: Journal of Sabbath School Action, (m), 6856 Eastern Ave., Washington, DC 20012. Fernon Retzer, Ed.

Seventh Day Baptist General Conference

A group of Baptists organized in Rhode Island in 1671; they are distinguished from other groups by their observance of Saturday as the Sabbath.

Churches: 66. Inclusive Membership: 5,376. Sunday or Sabbath Schools: 47. Total Enrollment: 2,837. Ordained clergy: 81.

GENERAL ORGANIZATION

General Conference: annual.

Headquarters: Seventh Day Baptists Bldg., 510 Watchung Ave., Plainfield, NJ 07061. Tel. (201) 756-1325.

OFFICERS

Pres., Rev. Paul B. Osborn, Box 366, Nortonville, KS 66060.

Rec. Sec., Richard C. Bond, 351 Arcadia Blvd., Battle Creek, MI 49017.

Gen. Sec., Rev. Alton L. Wheeler, 510 Watchung Ave., Plainfield, NJ 07061.

Treas., John L. Harris, 24 Canterbury Dr., Pennsville, NJ 08070.

Treas., Denom. Budget, Gordon Sanford, R. 1, Little Genesee, NY 14754.

OTHER ORGANIZATIONS

Seventh Day Baptist Missionary Society: Exec. Vice-Pres., Rev. Leon R. Lawton, 401 Washington Trust Bldg., Westerly, RI 02891.

Seventh Day Baptist Board of Christian Education: Exec. Sec., Rev. David S. Clarke, Alfred Station, NY 14803.

Women's Society of the General Conference: Pres., Mrs. Elmo Fitz Randolph, 1648 9th St., Boulder, CO 80302, Corr. Sec., Mrs. Tom Buttoms, 1118 Ravenwood Rd., Boulder, CO 80303.

American Sabbath Tract Society: Corr. Sec., Rev. Leon M. Maltby, 510 Watchung Ave., Plainfield, NJ 07061.

Seventh Day Baptist Publishing House, 510 Watchung Ave., Plainfield, NJ 07061.

Seventh Day Baptists Historical Society: 510 Watchung Ave., Plainfield, NJ 07061. Librarian, Rev. Albert N. Rogers.

PERIODICAL

Sabbath Recorder (w), Seventh Day Baptist Bldg., Plainfield, NJ 07061. Rev. Leon Maltby, Ed.

Social Brethren

Organized 1867 among members of various bodies; confession of faith has thirteen articles; evangelical.

Churches: 31. Inclusive Membership: 1,672. Sunday or Sabbath Schools: 30. Total Enrollment: N.R. Ordained clergy: 42.

GENERAL ORGANIZATION

General Assembly: biennial.

SOUTHERN BAPTIST CONVENTION

OFFICERS

Mod., of General Assembly, Rev. Bernie Cowgill, Harrisburg, IL 62946.
Mod. (Union Association), Rev. John Bailey, R.F.D. 2, Simpson, IL 62985.
Mod. (Illinois Association), Rev. Earl E. Vaugh, 215 E. 4th St., Flora, IL 62839.
Mod. (Midwestern Association), Rev. Edward Darnell, Marion, IN 46952.

Southern Baptist Convention

In 1845 Southern Baptist withdrew from the General Missionary Convention over the question of slavery and other matters and formed the Southern Baptist Convention.

Churches: 34,420. Inclusive Membership: 11,824,676. Sunday or Sabbath Schools: 33,435. Total Enrollment: 7,138,741. Ordained clergy: N.R.

GENERAL ORGANIZATION
Convention: annual.

OFFICERS

Pres., Owen Cooper, Box 388 Yazoo City, MS 39194. Rec. Sec., Clifton J. Allen, Executive Committee: Offices, 460 James Robertson Pkwy., Nashville, TN 37219. Tel. (615) 244-2355; Exec. Sec., Porter Routh; Program Planning Sec., Albert McClellan; Fin. Planning Sec., John H. Williams; Public Relations Sec., W. C. Fields.

OTHER ORGANIZATIONS

Foreign Mission Board: Address, 3806 Monument Ave., Richmond, VA 23230. Exec. Sec., Baker James Cauthen.
Home Mission Board: Office, 1350 Spring St. N.W., Atlanta GA 30303, Exec. Sec. & Treas., Arthur B. Rutledge.
Sunday School Board: Office, 127 9th Ave. N., Nashville, TN 37203, Exec. Sec. & Treas., James L. Sullivan.
Annuity Board: Office, 511 N. Akard, Dallas, TX 75201, Exec. Sec., Darold H. Morgan.
Baptist Brotherhood Commission: Office, 1548 Poplar Ave., Memphis, TN 38104, Exec. Sec. George W. Schroeder.
Woman's Missionary Union: Office, 600 N. 20th St., Birmingham, AL 35203, Exec. Sec., Alma Hunt; Pres., Mrs. Marie Mathis, Student Union Building, Baylor University, Waco, TX 76703.
Southern Baptist Foundation: Office, 460 James Robertson Pkwy., Nashville, TN 37219, Exec. Sec., Kendall Berry.
Education Commission: Office, 460 James Robertson Pkwy., Nashville, TN 37219, Exec. Sec., Ben C. Fisher.
Christian Life Commission: Office, 460 James Robertson Pkwy., Nashville, TN 37219, Exec. Sec., Foy Valentine.
Radio & Television Commission: Dir., Paul M. Stevens, 6350 W. Freeway, Fort Worth, TX 76116.
Stewardship Commission: Office, 460 James Robertson Pkwy., Nashville, TN 37219, Dir., James Lackey.
Historical Commission: Office, 127 9th Ave., N. Nashville, TN 37203, Exec. Sec., Lynn E. May, Jr.
Commission on the American Baptist Theological Seminary, Nashville, TN Exec. Sec.-Treas., Ben C. Fisher.

STATE CONVENTIONS

Alabama, George E. Bagley, 4001 E. South Blvd., Montogomery 36106.
Alaska, Troy Prince, Box 80, Anchorage 99501.
Arizona, Roy Sutton, 316 W. McDowell Rd., Phoenix 85003.
Arkansas, Charles H. Ashcraft, Baptist Bldg., Little Rock 72201.
California, Robert D. Hughes, 678 E. Shaw Ave., Fresno 93726.
Colorado, Glen Braswell, P.O. Box 22005, Denver 80222.
District of Columbia, James Langley, 1628 16th St., N.W., Washington 20009.
Florida, Harold C. Bennett, 1230 Hendricks Ave., Jacksonville 32207.
Georgia, Searcy S. Garrison, 291 Peachtree St., N.E., Atlanta 30303.
Hawaii, Edmond Walker, 1225 Nehou St., Honolulu 96822.
Illinois, James H. Smith, Baptist Bldg., P.O. Box 271, Carbondale 62901.
Indiana, E. H. Moore, 900 N. High School Rd., Indianapolis 46224.
Kansas, Pat McDaniel, 525 W. Douglas, Wichita 67213.
Kentucky, Franklin Owen, Kentucky Baptist Bldg., Middletown 40043.
Louisiana, Robt. L. Lee, Box 311, Alexandria 71301.
Maryland, Roy D. Gresham, 1313 York Rd., Lutherville 21093.
Michigan, Robert Wilson, 2619 Cass Ave., Detroit 48201.
Mississippi, W. Douglas Hudgins, P.O. Box 530, Jackson 39205.
Missouri, Earl Harding, Baptist Bldg., 213 Adams St., Jefferson City 65101.
New Mexico, R. Y. Bradford, P.O. Box 485, Albuquerque 87103.
New York, Paul S. James, Ste. 610 Powelson Bldg., Syracuse 13202.
North Carolina, Perry Crouch, 301 Hillsboro Rd., Raleigh 27603.
Northern Plains, John Baker, P.O. Box 1232, Rapid City, SD 57701.
Northwest Baptist Convention, Dan C. Stringer, 811 N.W. 20th Ave., Portland 97209.
Ohio, Ray E. Roberts, 1680 E. Broad St., Columbus 43203.
Oklahoma, Joe L. Ingram, 1141 N. Robinson, Oklahoma City 73103.
Pennsylvania-South Jersey, C. E. Price, Acting 3805 Paxton Street, Harrisburg, PA 17111.
South Carolina, A. Harold Cole, 907 Richland St., Columbia 29201.
Tennessee, W. Fred Kendall, 1812 Belmont Blvd., Nashville 37212.
Texas, Thomas A. Patterson, Baptist Bldg., Dallas 75201.
Utah-Idaho, Darwin E. Welsh, Sec., P.O. Box 2545, Salt Lake City 84110.
Virginia, Richard M. Stephenson, Va. Baptist Bldg., Monument Ave. at Willow Lawn, Richmond 23226.
West Virginia, John Snedden, 801 Sixth Ave., St. Albans, WV 25177.

PERIODICALS

Accent, 600 No. 20th, Birmingham, AL. Oneta Gentry, Ed.

Alabama Baptist (w), 807 S. 20th St., Birmingham, AL 35205. Hudson Baggett, Ed.

Alaska Baptist Messenger, Box 80, Anchorage, AK 99501. Troy Prince, Ed.

Ambassador Life, 1548 Poplar Ave., Memphis, TN 38104.

Arkansas Baptist Newsmagazine (w), Baptist Bldg., Little Rock, AR 72201. J. Everett Sneed, Ed.

Aware, 600 No. 20th, Birmingham AL 35203. Mrs. Jesse A. Tucker, Ed.

Baptist and Reflector (w), P.O. Box 647, Brentwood, TN 37027. James Lester, Ed.

Baptist Beacon (w), 400 W. Camelback Rd., Phoenix, AZ 85013. Irving Childress, Ed.

Baptist Courier (w), Box 2168, Greenville, SC 29602. John Roberts, Ed.

Baptist Digest (w), Box 729, Wichita, KS 67201. Pat McDaniel, Ed.

Baptist Message (w), Box 311, Alexandria, LA 71301. James F. Cole, Ed.

Baptist Messenger (w), 1141 N. Robinson, Oklahoma City, OK 73103. Jack L. Gritz, Ed.

Baptist New Mexican (w), Box 485, Albuquerque, NM 87103. C. Eugene Whitlow, Ed.

Baptist Record (w), P.O. Box 530, Jackson, MS 39205. Joe T. Odle, Ed.

Baptist Standard (w), 2222 San Jacinto St., Dallas, TX 75201. John J. Hurt, Ed.

Biblical Recorder (w), P.O. Box 688, Raleigh, N. C. 27603. Marse Grant, Ed.

California Southern Baptist (w), P.O. Box 5168, Fresno, CA 93755. Don T. McGregor, Ed.

Capital Baptist, 1628 16th St., N.W., Washington, DC 20009. James O. Duncan, Ed.

Christian Index (w), 291 Peachtree, N.E., Atlanta, GA 30303. Jack U. Harwell, Ed.

Commission, The, 3806 Monument Ave., Richmond, VA 23230. Floyd North, Ed.

Contempo, 600 N. 20th, Birmingham, AL 35203. Laurella Owens, Ed.

Discovery, 600 N. 20th, Birmingham, AL 35203. Mrs. Jesse A. Tucker, Ed.

Florida Baptist Witness (w), 1230 Hendricks Ave., Jacksonville, FL 32207. Edgar Cooper, Ed.

Hawaii Baptist, 1225 Nehoa St., Honolulu 96822. Edmond Walker, Ed.

Home Missions, 1350 Spring St., N.W., Atlanta, GA 30303. Walker L. Knight, Ed.

Illinois Baptist (w), Box 271, Carbondale, Ill. 62901. Robert J. Hastings, Ed.

Indiana Baptist (m), P.O. Box 24038, Indianapolis, IN 46224. Alvin Shackleford, Ed.

Maryland Baptist (w), 1313 York Rd., Lutherville, MD 21093. R. Gene Puckett, Ed.

Michigan Baptist Advocate, 2619 Cass Ave., Detroit, MI 48201. Robert Wilson, Ed.

Ohio Baptist Messenger (m), 1680 E. Broad, Columbus, OH 43203. L. H. Moore, Ed.

Pacific Coast Baptist (semi-m), 811 N.W. 20th Ave., Portland, OR 97209. C. E. Boyle, Ed.

Quarterly Review (q), 127 Ninth Ave. N., Nashville, TN 37203. Reggie McDonough, Ed.

Religious Herald (w), P.O. Box 8377, Richmond, VA 23226. Julian Pentecost, Ed.

Review and Expositor (q), 2825 Lexington Rd., Louisville, KY 40206.

Rocky Mountain Baptist, P.O. Box 22005, Denver, CO 80222. O. L. Bayless, Ed.

Royal Service, 600 North 20th St., Birmingham, AL 35203. Rosanne Osborn, Ed.

Southwestern News, P.O. Box 22000, Seminary Hill, Fort Worth, TX 76122. John Seelig, Ed.

Start, 600 N. 20th, Birmingham, AL 35203. Mrs. Helen M. Allan, Ed.

Western Recorder (w), Baptist Bldg., Middletown, KY 40043. C. R. Daley, Ed.

Word and Way (w), Mo. Baptist Bldg., Jefferson City, MO 65101. W. Ross Edwards, Ed.

Southern Methodist Church

Organized in 1939, this body is composed of congregations that declined to be a party to the merger of the M. E. Church, The M. E. Church, South, and the Methodist Protestant Church into The Methodist Church.

Churches: 150. Inclusive Membership: 9,917. Sunday or Sabbath Schools: 150. Total Enrollment: 9,630. Ordained clergy 63.

GENERAL ORGANIZATION

General Conference: Quadrennial. (Next meeting, 1974).

Annual Conferences: 1) South Carolina Conference (Virginia, North Carolina, South Carolina); 2) Alabama, Florida, Georgia Conference; 3) Mid-South Conference (Mississippi, Tennessee); 4) South-Western Conference (Arkansas, Louisiana, Texas)

OFFICERS

Pres., Rev. Glenn S. Comfort, P.O. Box 132, Orangeburg, SC 29115. Tel. (803) 536-1378.

Vice-Presidents:

South Carolina Conf., Rev. Lynn Corbett, 168 Raysor St., Orangeburg, SC 29115.

Alabama, Florida, Georgia Conf., Rev. Webber M. Walker, P.O. Box 386, Centreville, AL 35042.

Mid-South Conf., Dr. Ronald R. Carrier, 5035 Hillsboro Rd., Nashville, TN 37215.

South-Western Conf., Rev. Frank Beauchamp, 5960 Thornhill, Shreveport, LA 71109.

Treas., Gen. Conference, Mr. Ray P. Oden, Jr., 833 Thora Blvd., Shreveport, LA 71106.

PERIODICAL

The Southern Methodist (m), P.O. Drawer A, Orangeburg, SC 29115.

Syrian Orthodox Church of Antioch (Archdiocese of the U.S.A. and Canada)

An archdiocese in America in a direct ecclesiastical line of the Syrian Orthodox Church. In the Middle East and India there are 35 archdioceses, numerous churches, schools, and seminaries, which trace their history to the earliest Patriarchate established in Antioch.

In the United States, there are 10 parishes in the archdiocese located in California, Illinois, Massachusetts, Michigan, New Jersey, and Rhode Island. In the Province of Quebec, there are two parishes; one at Quebec and one at Sherbrooke.

Churches: 8. Inclusive Membership: 35,000. Sunday or Sabbath Schools: 8. Total Enrollment: 2,050. Ordained clergy: 10.

OFFICER

Archbishop Mar Athanasius Y. Samuel, 293 Hamilton Pl., Hackensack, NJ 07601.

Triumph the Church and Kingdom of God in Christ

Organized in 1902 in Georgia, by Elder E. D. Smith, emphasizing sanctification and the Second Coming of Christ.

Churches: 495. Inclusive Membership: 54,307. Sunday or Sabbath Schools: 495. Total Enrollment: 51,777. Ordained clergy: 1,375.

GENERAL ORGANIZATION
Quarterly and annual Conferences. International Religious Congress: quadrennial.
Headquarters: 213 Farrington Ave. S.E., Atlanta, GA 30315.

OFFICERS
Chief Bishop, Bishop D. H. Harris, 7122 Campania Ave., Pittsburgh, PA 15206.
Gen. Rec. Sec., Bishop L. W. Coleman, R.F.D. 3, Box 260-C, Greensburg, PA 15601.

Ukrainian Orthodox Church in the U.S.A.

Formally organized in U.S.A. in 1919. Archbishop John Theodorovich arrived from Ukraine in 1924.

GENERAL ORGANIZATION
The Sobor, which elects a Council of Bishops, meets every three years. Next meeting of the Sobor, 1973.
Headquarters: South Bound Brook, NJ 08880.

OFFICERS
Metropolitan: Most Rev. Mstyslav S. Skrypnyk, South Bound Brook, NJ 08880; Archbishop Mark Hundiak, 641 Roosevelt Ave., Carteret, NJ 07008; Bishop Constantine Buggan, 2238 W. Cortex St., Chicago, IL 60622.
Consistory: Pres., Protopresbyter Artem Selepyna; Vice Pres., Protopresbyter Stephen Bilak, 6729 N. 5th St., Philadelphia, PA 19126; Sec. Protopresbyter Theo. Forosty, 635 Broad St., Clifton, NJ 07013; Treas., Very Rev. Michael Zemlachenko, Box 358-A, R.D. 2, Neshanic, NJ 08853.

PERIODICAL
Ukrainian Orthodox Word, South Bound Brook, NJ 08880.

Ukrainian Orthodox Church of America (Ecumenical Patriarchate)

This body was organized in America in 1928, when the first convention was held. In 1932 Dr. Joseph Zuk was consecrated as first Bishop. His successor was the Most Rev. Bishop Bohdan, Primate, who was consecrated by the order of the Ecumenical Patriarchate of Constantinople on February 28, 1937, in New York City. The present primate is the Most Rev. Bishop Andrei Kuschak.

GENERAL ORGANIZATION
Sobor meets on call.
Headquarters: St. Andrew's Ukrainian Orthodox Diocese, 90-34 139th St., Jamaica, N. Y. 11435. Tel. (212) 297-2407.

OFFICERS
Primate: Most Rev. Bishop Andrei Kuschak.

Chancellor: Hilarion Wroblewsky.
Dean: Jacob Kostecky.

PERIODICAL
Ukrainian Orthodox Herald (q), Fr. Ivan Tkaczuk, Ed.

Unitarian Universalist Association

The Unitarian Universalist Association is the consolidated body of the former American Unitarian Association and the Universalist Church of America. The Unitarian movement arose in Congregationalism in the 18th century, producing the American Unitarian Association in 1825. In 1865 a national conference was organized. The philosophy of Universalism originated with the doctrine of universal salvation in the first century, and was brought to America in the 18th century. Universalists were first formally organized in 1793. In May, 1961, the Unitarian and Universalist bodies were consolidated to become the Unitarian Universalist Association. The movement is non-creedal.

GENERAL ORGANIZATION
General Assembly: annual.
Headquarters: 25 Beacon St., Boston, MA 02108. District offices, 21 in number.

OFFICERS
Pres., Rev. Robert Nelson West.
Exec. Vice-Pres., Dr. Raymond C. Hopkins.
Mod., Dr. Joseph L. Fisher.
Vice-Mods., Mrs. Karl H. Hanson and Dr. Chas. W. Davidson.
Sec., John M. Hines.
Treas., Arthur J. Root.
Vice-Pres. for Development and Fund Raising, Rev. Philip Giles.
Ministry, Churchmanship and Extension, Dr. George Spencer; Education and Program, Dr. Norman F. Benson; Publications, Doris Pullen; Beacon Press, Gobin Stair. Extension Dept., Christopher Raible.
Minister, Church of the Larger Fellowship: Rev. George N. Marshall.

OTHER ORGANIZATIONS
(Address unless otherwise noted, 25 Beacon St., Boston, MA 02108)
Unitarian Universalist Ministers' Association: Pres., Rev. Russell R. Bletzer.
Unitarian Universalist Women's Federation: Exec. Dir., Mrs. Elizabeth Scarlatos.
The Laymen's League: Treas., William A. Donovan.
Liberal Religious Youth: Pres., Charles Rosene.
Student Religious Liberals: Sec., Tim Cahn.
Unitarian Universalist Service Committee, Inc.: 78 Beacon St., Boston, MA 02108. Exec. Dir., Richard Scobie.
Universalist Historical Society: Pres., Rev. Theodore A. Webb.
Unitarian Historical Society: Pres., Dr. Conrad Wright, Harvard Divinity School, Francis Ave., Cambridge, MA 02138.

PERIODICALS
UU World (twice monthly), William Gagnon, Ed., 25 Beacon St., Boston, MA 02108.
Wayside Community Pulpit, Helen Barnes, Ed., 25 Beacon St., Boston, MA 02108.

Journal of the Liberal Ministry, Rev. Arthur Graham, Ed., Box 485, Oak Ridge, TN 37830.

United Brethren in Christ

The Church of the United Brethren in Christ had its beginning with Philip William Otterbein and Martin Boehm, who were leaders in the revivalistic movement in Pennsylvania and Maryland during the late 1760s and which continued into the early 1800s.

On September 25, 1800, they and others associated with them, formed a society under the name of United Brethren in Christ. Subsequent conferences adopted a Confession of Faith in 1815 and a constitution in 1841. The Church of the United Brethren in Christ adheres to the original constitution as amended in 1957 and 1961.

Churches: 296. Inclusive Membership: 26,643. Sunday or Sabbath Schools: N.R. Total Enrollment: 30,618. Ordained clergy: N.R.

GENERAL ORGANIZATION

General Conference, quadrennial. (Next meeting, 1973).

Headquarters: 402 United Brethren Bldg., Huntington, IN 46750. Tel. (219) 356-2312.

OFFICERS

Bishops: Chmn., George E. Weaver, Duane A. Reahm, Raymond Waldfogel.
Sec.-Treas., Mrs. Anne E. Bruner.
Sec. Educ., E. DeWitt Baker.
Bus. Mgr., Publications, Mr. Eugene Riebe.
Sec. Christian Educ., W. Burkholder.
Sec., Woman's Missionary, Mrs. Wm. Wood.
Sec., Board of Missions, Rev. Emmett Cox.

PERIODICAL

The United Brethren (bi-w), Huntington, IN 46750, Stanley Peters, Ed.

United Christian Church

A group which separated in 1862-70 from the United Brethren in Christ; organized at Campbelltown, PA 1878.

Churches: 12. Inclusive Membership: 400. Sunday or Sabbath Schools: 11. Total Enrollment: 866. Ordained clergy: 13.

GENERAL ORGANIZATION

General Conference: annual (1st Monday in May).

OFFICERS

Mod., Elder Henry C. Heagy, Lebanon, R.D. 4, Lebanon County, PA 17042. Tel. (717) 867-2611.
Presiding Elder, Elder Henry C. Heagy, Lebanon, R.D. 4, Lebanon County, PA 17042.

OTHER ORGANIZATIONS

Mission Board: Pres., Elder Henry C. Heagy; Sec., Elder David S. Sellers; Treas., Elder John P. Ludwig.

United Church of Christ

A union in 1957 of the Evangelical and Reformed Church and the General Council of the Congregational Christian Churches. The union was completed in July 1961, when the Constitution was adopted in Philadelphia.

Churches: 6,688. Inclusive Membership: 1,928,-674. Sunday or Sabbath Schools: N.R. Total Enrollment: 711,757. Ordained clergy: 9,378.

GENERAL ORGANIZATION

Synod: biennial.
Headquarters: 297 Park Avenue S., New York, NY 10010. Tel. (212) 475-2121.

OFFICERS

Pres., Rev. Robert V. Moss.
Sec., Rev. Joseph H. Evans.
Dir. of Finance & Treas., Charles H. Lockyear.
Exec. Asst. to the Pres., Rev. Jack E. Yates.
Asst. to Pres.: Rev. Mineo Katagiri., Spec. Asst. to Pres., Rev. Ms. Barbara McCall; Rev. Norman W. Jackson.
Chmn., Exec. Council, Rev. Kenneth B. Smith.
Mod., Rev. David G. Colwell.
Asst. Mod., Dr. Manford Byrd, Jr.
Asst. Mod., Mrs. F. E. Shotwell.

ORGANIZATIONS

Board for World Ministries: Offices, 475 Riverside Dr., New York, NY 10027. Tel. (212) 870-2637. 14 Beacon St., Boston, MA 02108; 1720 Chouteau Ave., St. Louis, MO 63103; 222 S. Downey Ave., Indianapolis, IN 46129. Exec. Vice-Pres., Rev. David M. Stowe; Asst. to the Exec. Vice-Pres., Dalton Smith.
Division of World Missions: Regional Secs.: Near East, Margaret R. Blemker; Pacific Area, Rev. Paul R. Gregory; Southern Asia; Rev. Telfer Mook; Latin America, Alfred Bartholomew; Africa, Rev. Chester L. Marcus; Europe, Rev. Howard Schomer, Assoc. Regional Secs.: Pacific Area, Rev. Elinor G. Galusha; Africa: Rev. Lawrence W. Henderson; Southern Asia, Rev. Joseph M. Smith (Indiana)
Division of World Service: Gen. Sec., Rev. B. Kenneth Anthony; Assoc. Gen. Sec., Dr. Alfred C. Bartholomew; Sec. for Program, Mr. J. Richard Butler; World Issues Sec., Dr. Howard Schomer.
Division of Interpretation and Personnel; Gen. Sec., Rev. Theodore A. Braun; Sec. for Program Development, Rev. Neill Richards.
Treasury; Treas., Rev. Myles H. Walburn; Asst. Treas., Rev. Everett A. Babcock, 14 Beacon St., Boston, MA 02108; Asst. Treas., George W. Keitel, Jr.; Dir. of Accounting, Adolf W. Simonides; Dir. of Transportation and Purchasing, Marcella M. Begovic.
Board for Homeland Ministries: Offices, 287 Park Ave. S., New York, NY 10010; 1505 Race St., Philadelphia, PA 19102. Exec. Vice-Pres., Rev. Howard E. Spragg; Sec. for Adm., William J. Nelson; Asst. Sec. for Adm., Nils E. Forstner; Exec. Asst. for Planning and Strategy, Rev. Paul H. Sherry; Planning Assoc., Rev. Theodore H. Erickson; Treas., Richard H. Dubie; Asst. Treas., Stanley R. Ketcham; Asst. Treas., Miss Paula Hamburger; Clk., Bd. of Dir., Mrs. Gladys W. Williams; Gen. Sec., Div. of Higher Education and The American Missionary Association, Rev. Wesley A. Hotchkiss; Dir. of

UNITED CHURCH OF CHRIST

Evangelism and Church Extension, Rev. Serge F. Hummon; Gen. Sec., Div. of Health and Welfare, Rev. Hobart A. Burch; Gen. Sec., Div. of Publication, Rev. Thomas D. Garner (Philadelphia,) Gen. Sec., Div. of Christian Education, Rev. Edward A. Powers. (Philadelphia).

Division of Church Extension: Offices, 287 Park Ave. S., New York, NY 10010; 216 Clayton St., Denver, CO 80206; 651 Flood Bldg., 870 Market St., San Francisco, CA 94102; Rev. Serge F. Hummon.

Dept. of Church Development and Building, Evangelism: Chmn., Rev. John C. DeBoer, Rev. Ira D. Black; Ray O. Bachman (St. Louis); Rev. Harris E. Heverly (Denver); Rev. Gerald J. Jud; John R. Potts.

Dept. of Ministries to Communities in Special Need: Chmn. Rev. Joseph W. Merchant; Rev. Howard S. Fuller (San Francisco); Rev. Serge F. Hummon; Rev. Daniel O. Parker (Denver); Rev. Milton L. Upton.

Division of Health and Welfare: 287 Park Ave. So., New York, NY 10010; Gen. Sec., Rev. Hobart A. Burch; Sec., Mrs. Helen Webber.

Division of Publication: 1505 Race St., Philadelphia, PA 19102; P.O. Box 7286, St. Louis, MO 63177; Gen. Sec., Rev. Thomas D. Garner; Adm. Asst., Rev. William D. Powell.

Dept. of Book Publication: Senior Book Ed., Miss Marion M. Meyer; Editor-in-Chief, Rev. Theodore A. McConnell.

Dept. of Sales and Promotion: Dir., Donald Widmayer; Circulation Mgr., Virginia L. Blauser; Central Distribution Dir., Bill L. Shaw; Mgr. St. Louis, Mrs. Maxine M. Fischer; Mgr., Phila., Scott Williams; Mgr. Office, Hugh Dadd.

Dept. of Promotion and Design, Mgr. Robert W. O'Leary, Designer, Miss Lenoire Brown.

A.D.—United Church Herald Edition: Offices, 297 Park Ave. S., New York, NY 10010; P. O. Box 7095, St. Louis, MO 63177. Ed., Rev. J. Martin Bailey; Assoc. Eds., Rev. Frank A. Kostyu, Rev. Thomas O. Bentz; Dir. of Circulation, L. J. Shaw; Art Dir., Raymond Waites.

Also see A.D.—Presbyterian Life Edition

Central Distribution Service: Offices, 1505 Race St., Philadelphia, PA 19102; P.O. Box 7286, St. Louis, MO 63177. Dir., Bill L. Shaw.

Division of Higher Education and The American Missionary Association: Offices, 287 Park Ave. S., New York, NY 10010; Gen. Sec., Rev. Wesley A. Hotchkiss; Campus Ministry, Sec., Rev. Verlyn L. Barker; Church and Culture, Consultant, Robert Newman; College Relationships, Joseph T. McMillan, Jr.; Special Programs, Rev. John R. Moyer. United Ministries in Higher Educ., Rev. Richard R. Hicks; Amistad Research Center, Mr. Clifton Johnson (Dillard Univ., New Orleans, LA 70113).

Division of Christian Education: Offices, 1505 Race St., Philadelphia, PA 19102; R.D. 2 Pottstown, PA 19464. Gen. Sec., Rev. Edward A. Powers; Ed.-in-Chief, Rev. Robert E. Koenig; Dir., Field Program, Rev. Percel O. Alston. Planning Coordinator, Miss Bettie Currie.

Dept. of Educational Resources: Ed. Youth Magazine, Herman C. Ahrens, Jr.; Ed. Adult Publications, Ed. Youth Publications, Rev. Robert L. Burt; Sec., Educational Media, Carolyn E. Goddard; Ed. Children's Publications, Mrs. June W. McCarron; Ed. Children's Publications, Ruth L. Sprague; Ed. Colloquy, Rev. John H. Westerhoff III.

Dept. of Education Program: Sec. Specialized Ministries, Carl A. Bade; Sec. for Youth Ministries, Rev. Russell G. Claussen; Sec. for Special Program Development, Dr. Frances W. Eastman; Sec., Children's Program, Elizabeth Helz; Sec., Specialized Ministries, Rev. Edward L. Schlingman; Sec., Camps and Confs., Ethel Shellenberger; Sec. for Young Adult Ministries, Rev. Ralph W. Weltge, Sec., Urban Educ. Program, Miss Yvonne V. Delk, Sec. Adult Educ., Rev. Charles R. McCollough.

Council for Christian Social Action: Offices, 289 Park Ave. So., New York, NY 10010; 110 Maryland Ave. N.E., Washington, DC 20002. Acting Exec. Dir. Tilford E. Dudley. (Council is in the process of being reorganized.)

Office of Communication: 289 Park Ave. So., New York, NY 10010. Dir., Rev. Everett C. Parker; Assoc. Dirs., Mrs. Dorothea M. Lindsey, Rev. Eugene A. Schneider, Editorial Assoc., Martha Underhill; Research Analyst, Ralph M. Jennings; Television Assoc., William C. Winslow.

Commission for Racial Justice: 287 Park Ave. So., New York, NY 10010, P.O. Box 1721; Raleigh, NC 27601; 1330 Mass. Ave. Ste. 2000 Washington, DC 20005. Rev. Charles E. Cobb, Exec. Dir. Asst. to Dir., William Land; Adm. Asst., Mrs. Marilyn E. Moore. Dir. of Special Higher Educ., Mrs. Toni Killings; Dir. of New Approaches to White Comm., Rev. Allan Fisher; Dir. of Comm. Org. & Mobilization, Irv Joyner; Rev. Leon White, Exec. Dir., Field Office (NC) Consultant, Rev. Benjamin E. Lewis, Field Office (Wash.)

Council for Church and Ministry: 290 Park Ave. So., New York, NY 10010. Exec. Dir., Rev. Harold H. Wilke; Gen. Sec. for Administration and Sec. for Pastoral Relations, Rev. J. Stanley Stevens; Sec. for Chaplains—Religion and Health, Rev. Leon A. Dickinson, Jr.; Sec. for Church Vocations—Student Care, Rev. George Nishimoto; Sec. for Black Ministries, Rev. James H. Hargett.

Council for Lay Life and Work: 297 Park Ave., So., New York, NY 10010. Exec. Sec., Rev. Hartland H. Helmich; Assoc. Sec., Thomas R. Tupper, P.O. Box, 179, St. Louis, MO; Assoc. Sec., Richard B. Griffis, Assoc. Sec. Rev. Ms. Barbara W. McCall (on leave), Admin. Asst., Leo G. Vonfeld; Assoc. Sec., Mrs. F. C. Lester, 1113 N. Rotary Dr., High Point, NC 27262; Rev. Teruo Kawata, 651 Flood Bldg., 870 Market St. San Francisco, CA.

Stewardship Council: 1505 Race St., Philadelphia, PA 19102. Exec. Sec., Rev. Sheldon E. Mackey; Gen. Sec. for Administration, Duane R. Baker; Gen. Sec. for Program Development, Rev. Theodore S. Horvath; Business Mgr., Mrs. Anne M. Gerrow; Ed., Sunday Bulletin Service, Rev. Charles W. Cooper,

Jr.; Sec. for Program Information, Mrs. Jean E. Schwertfager; Sec. for Stewardship Education, Rev. George S. Siudy, Jr.; Sec., Speakers' Bureau, Rev. William A. Slater; Dir., Office for Audio-Visuals, Rev. William E. Wimer, Sec. for Promotion, Rev. Milton E. Gockley; Editorial Sec., John M. Haverstick; Sec. for Special Appeals, John B. Herod. Ed. Desk Calendar and Plan Book, Rev. Earl D. Miller; Sec. Christian Enlistment, Rev. C. David Langerhans; Regional Secs.: New England, Rev. Eugene Van Kranenburgh; Middle Atlantic, Rev. Truman D. Whitaker, 1505 Race St., Philadelphia, PA 19102; Southern, Rev. Karlton C. Johnson, P.O. Box 29665, Atlanta, GA 30329; West Central, Rev. Earl W. Krueger, 429 Scott Bldg., 2640 Pine St., St. Louis, MO 63103; Western, LeRoy E. Eide, 651 Flood Bldg., 870 Market St., San Francisco, CA 94102.

Film Libraries, Office for Audio-Visuals, United Church of Christ (rentals): 600 Grand Ave., Ridgefield, NJ 07657 and 512 Burlington Ave., LaGrange, IL 60525.

Pension Boards: 297 Park Ave. So., New York, NY 10010. Exec. Vice-Pres., William Kincaid Newman; Sec., Rev. Don A. Bundy; Supervisor of Actuarial Dept., Mrs. Ruth Wahl; Treas., Richard H. Dubie; Asst.-Treas., Ralph Russell; Benefits Sec., Rev. Harold C. Baer.

Historical Societies: Congregational Christian Historical Society, 14 Beacon St., Boston, MA 02108; Evangelical and Reformed Historical Society, Philip Schaff Library, Lancaster Theol. Sem., 555 W. James St., Lancaster, PA 17603; Congregational Library, Rm. 207, 14 Beacon St., Boston, MA 02108.

CONFERENCES AND ACTING CONFERENCES

Western Region:

California, Northern, Rev. Richard C. Norberg, 677 Flood Bldg., 870 Market St., San Francisco 94102.

California, Southern, Rev. Fred P. Register, 466 East Walnut St., Pasadena 91101.

Colorado, Rev. George W. Otto, 222 Clayton St., Denver 80206.

Hawaii, Rev. Chester G. Terpstra, 2103 Nuuanu Ave., Honolulu 96817.

Intermountain, Rev. Bradley F. Skinner, P.O. Box 8225, 2201 E. 13th St. So., Salt Lake City, UT 84108.

Montana, Rev. George P. Barber, 104 N. 28th St., Billings 59101.

Oregon, Rev. Ruben H. Huenemann, 0245 S.W. Bancroft St., Portland 97201.

Southwest, Rev. Henry A. Culbertson, 10 E. Roanoke, Phoenix, AZ 85004

Washington-North Idaho, Rev. W. James Halfaker, 720 14th Ave. E., Seattle, WA 98102.

West Central Region:

Iowa, Rev. Scott S. Libbey, 600 42nd St., Des Moines 50312.

Kansas-Oklahoma, Rev. Andrew K. Craig, 5303 East Central Ave., Wichita, KS 67208.

Minnesota, Rev. Carl A. Hansen, 122 West Franklin Ave., Minneapolis 55404.

Missouri, Rev. Charles C. Hoskinson, 1720 Chouteau Ave., St. Louis 63103.

Nebraska, Rev. David J. Amieson, 2055 "E" St., Lincoln 68510.

North Dakota, Rev. Lester L. Soberg, 202½ Third St. No., Bismarck 58501.

South Dakota, Rev. Ralph J. Hoffman, 2065 Campbell Dr. Southwest, P.O. Box 138, Huron 57350.

Great Lakes Regions:

Illinois, Rev. Erston M. Butterfield, Third and Grant St., Hinsdale 60521.

Illinois South, Rev. John L. Schmidt, Interim Conf. Minister, 1312 Broadway, Highland 62249.

Indiana-Kentucky, Rev. Harry W. Bredeweg, 1100 W. 42nd St., Indianapolis, IN 46208.

Michigan, Rev. Duane N. Vore, P.O. Box 1006, East Lansing 48823.

Ohio, Rev. Charles L. Burns, Jr., 41 Croswell Rd., Columbus 43214.

Northwest Ohio, 33½ S. Washington St., Tiffin 44883.

Western Reserve, 3209 Broadview Road, Cleveland 44109.

Eastern Ohio, 2560 Clearview Ave., N.W., Canton 44718.

Central Southeast Ohio, 41 Croswell Road, Columbus 43214.

Southwest Ohio, 249 Sanderson Dr., Dayton 45459.

Wisconsin, Rev. Ralph P. Ley, 2719 Marshall Court, Madison 53705.

Southeast, 3025 N. Pilgrim Rd., Brookfield, WI 53005.

Southwest, 2719 Marshall Ct., Madison, WI 53705.

Northeast, 501 E. Parkway Blvd., Appleton, WI 54911.

Northwest, 2704 Keith St., Eau Claire, WI 54701.

Southern Region:

Florida, Rev. Robbins Ralph, P.O. Box 1056, Avon Park 33825.

South Central, Rev. Russell Mueller, Acting, 1104 W. Koenig La., Austin, TX 78756.

Southeast, Rev. William J. Andes, P.O. Box 29883, Atlanta, GA 30329.

Southern, Rev. James H. Lightbourne, Jr., 328 W. Davis St., Burlington, NC 27215.

Middle Atlantic Region:

Central Atlantic, Rev. Francis X. Pirazzini, 620 Pershing Dr., Silver Spring, MD 20910.

Shenandoah-Western Maryland Area, Hood College, Frederick, MD 21701.

Baltimore-Washington Area, 5202 Baltimore National Pike, Baltimore, MD 21229.

New Jersey Area, 40 So. Fullerton Ave., Montclair, NJ 07042.

New York, Rev. James R. Smucker, The Church Center, Rm. 260, 3049 E. Genesee St., Syracuse 13224.

Penn Central, Rev. James W. Moyer, The United Church Center, Rm. 126, 900 South Arlington Ave., Harrisburg, PA 17109.

Penn Northeast, Rev. William T. Longsdorf, 470 Delaware Ave., Palmerton, PA 18071.

Pennsylvania Southeast, Rev. John C. Shetler, 620 Main St., Collegeville 19426.

Penn West. Rev. Paul L. Westcoat, Jr. 320 South Maple Ave., Greensburg, PA 15601

Puerto Rico, Rev. Serafin Garcia-Guevara, 54 El Roble St., Rio Piedras 00925.

New England Region:

Connecticut, Rev. Nathanael M. Guptill, 125 Sherman St., Hartford 06105.

THE UNITED FREE WILL BAPTIST CHURCH

Maine, Rev. William M. Thompson, 53 Baxter Blvd., Portland 04101.
Massachusetts, Rev. Avery D. Post, 14 Beacon St., Boston 02108.
New Hampshire, Rev. Everett R. Barrows, 85 N. State St., Concord 03301.
Rhode Island, 2 Stimson Ave., Providence 02906.
Vermont, Rev. Edward S. Treat, 285 Maple St., Burlington 05401.

Nongeographic:
Calvin Synod, Rev. Arpad L. Bertz, 7520 Woodmar Ave., Hammond, IN 46323.

† The United Free Will Baptist Church

A body which set up its organization in 1870.

GENERAL ORGANIZATION
General Conference: every 3 years.
Headquarters: Kinston College, 1000 University St., Kinston, NC 28501.

OFFICERS
Vice-Mod., Rev. O. L. Williams, 1052 N. Missouri Ave., Lakeland, FL 33801.
Chmn. Exec. Board, Rev. W. F. Cox, 1106 Holt St., Durham, NC 27701.
Gen. Fin. Sec., Rev. W. L. Jones, 606 Bancraff Ave., Greenville, NC 27834.
Gen. Rec. Sec., Rev. J. H. O'Neal, 203 De Soto St., Daytona Beach, FL 32014.
Gen. Pres., Women's Home Mission Dept., Mrs. J. M. Reaves, Ayden, NC 28513
Mgr. Lit. Dept., Rev. J. C. Smith, 209 Freemon St., Raleigh, NC 27601.

PERIODICAL
The Free Will Baptist Advocate (s-m), Kinston, NC 28501. E. L. Brown, New Bern, NC, Ed.

United Holy Chuch of America, Inc.

Organized in 1886 at Method, North Carolina. Ordinances of baptism by immersion, the Lord's Supper and Feet Washing are observed. We accept the premillennial teaching of the Second Coming of Christ. Divine healing, but not to the exclusion of medicine, justification by faith, sanctification as a second word of grace, and spirit Baptism.

GENERAL ORGANIZATION
Convocation: quadrennial. (Next meeting, May, 1973).
Headquarters: 159 W. Coulter St., Philadelphia, PA 19144.
General Convocation, annual.

OFFICERS
Gen. Pres., Bishop W. N. Strobhar, 268 Orange Rd., Montclair, NJ 07042.
Gen. Vice-Pres., Bishop J. A. Forbes, New York.
Gen. Sec., Mrs. Margaret Griffith, 210 Whitefoord Ave. N.E., Atlanta, GA 30307.
Gen. Satistician, Thomas Mills, California.
Pres., Missionary Department, Rev. Ella Yarbough.
Gen. Supt., Bible Church School, Mr. David Williams, Philadelphia, PA.
Pres., Youth Dept., Rev. Elroy Lewis.
Gen. Chmn., Education Dept., Rev. J. A. Forbes, Jr., Richmond, VA.

PERIODICAL
The Holiness Union (m), 194-96 Claremont Ave., Montclair, NJ 07042. Mrs. B. Lewis Jones, Ed.

The United Methodist Church

The United Methodist Church was formed April 23, 1968 in Dallas, Texas, by the union of The Methodist Church and The Evangelical United Brethren Church. The two churches shared a common historical and spiritual heritage. The Methodist Church resulted in 1939 from the unification of three branches of Methodism—the Methodist Episcopal Church; the Methodist Episcopal Church, South; and the Methodist Protestant Church. The Methodist movement began in 18th-century England under the preaching of John Wesley, but the so-called Christmas Conference of 1784 in Baltimore is regarded as the date on which the organized Methodist Church was founded as an ecclesiastical organization. It was there that Francis Asbury was elected the first bishop in this country. The Evangelical United Brethren Church was formed in 1946 with the merger of the Evangelical Church and the Church of the United Brethren in Christ, both of which had their beginnings in Pennsylvania in the evangelistic movement of the 18th and early 19th centuries. Philip William Otterbein and Jacob Albright were early leaders of this movement among the German-speaking settlers of the Middle Colonies.

Churches: 40,054. Inclusive Membership: 10,509,198. Sunday or Sabbath Schools: 37,803. Total Enrollment: 5,634,662. Ordained clergy: 34,822.

GENERAL ORGANIZATION
General Conference: quadrennial. (Next meeting will be held April 25-May 8, 1976 in Portland, OR.)

OFFICERS
The Bishops (see list below) preside in turn.
Sec. of Gen. Conference, John B. Holt, Perkins School of Theology, Southern Methodist University, Dallas, TX 75222.
Council of Bishops: Pres., Bishop O. Eugene Slater, P.O. Box 28409 (535 Bandera Rd.), San Antonio, TX 78228; Pres.-designate, Bishop Charles F. Golden, 5250 Santa Monica Blvd., Los Angeles, CA 90029; Sec., Bishop Ralph T. Alton, 1100 W. 42nd St., Indianapolis, IN 46208. Tel. (317) 924-1321.

BISHOPS IN U.S.A.
L. Scott Allen, 502 Gay St., S.W., Ste. 314, Knoxville, TN 37902.
Ralph T. Alton, 1100 W. 42nd St., Indianapolis, IN 46208.
A. James Armstrong, Berkshire Plaza, 405 N.W. 8th Ave., Aberdeen, SD 57401.
James M. Ault, 1701 Arch St., Philadelphia, PA 19103.
Robert M. Blackburn, Methodist Bldg., 1307 Glenwood Ave., Raleigh, NC 27605.
William R. Cannon, 159 Forrest Ave., N.E., Ste. 208, Atlanta, GA 30303.
Alsie H. Carleton, 1201 First National Bank Bldg., E., Albuquerque, NM 87108.

Edward G. Carroll, 581 Boylston St., Rm. 84, Boston, MA 02116.

Wilbur W. Y. Choy, 800 Olympic National Bldg., 920 Second Ave., Seattle, WA 98104.

Wayne K. Clymer, 122 W. Franklin Ave., Minneapolis, MN 55404.

Kenneth W. Copeland, 5214 S. Main St., Houston, TX 77002.

Finis A. Crutchfield, 1915 American Bank Bldg., 200 Carondelet St., New Orleans, LA 70130.

Jesse R. DeWitt, 325 Emerald Terrace, Sun Prairie, WI 53590.

Ernest T. Dixon, 4201 W. 15th St., Topeka, KS 66604

F. Gerald Ensley, 395 E. Broad St., Columbus, OH 43215.

H. Ellis Finger, Jr., Cavalier Bldg., Rm. 415, 95 White Bridge Rd., Nashville, TN 37205.

Eugene M. Frank, 723 Center St., Little Rock, AR 72201.

Charles F. Golden, 5250 Santa Monica Blvd., Los Angeles, CA 90029.

Robert E. Goodrich, Jr., Centenary Methodist Bldg., 55 Plaza Square, St. Louis, MO 63103.

W. Kenneth Goodson, 108-10 Methodist Bldg., 4016 W. Broad St., Richmond, VA 23230.

Don W. Holter, 2641 N. 49th St., Lincoln, NB 68504

Earl G. Hunt, Jr., 310 Cole Bldg., 207 Hawthorne Lane, Charlotte, NC 28204.

Francis E. Kearns, 1226 Market Ave., N., Canton OH 44714.

Dwight E. Loder, Francis Palms Bldg., 2111 Woodward Ave., Detroit, MI 48201.

James K. Mathews, 100 Maryland Ave., N.E., Washington, DC 20002.

Joel D. McDavid, P.O. Box 1747, Lakeland, FL 33802.

Paul W. Milhouse, 606 Cravens Bldg., Oklahoma City, OK 73102.

Roy C. Nichols, 305 Seventh Ave., Pittsburgh, PA 15222

Frank L. Robertson, 1115 S. Fourth St., Louisville, KY 40203.

Carl J. Sanders, 1801 Sixth Ave., N., Birmingham, AL 35203.

O. Eugene Slater, P.O. Box 28509 (535 Bandera Rd.), San Antonio, TX 78228.

Mack B. Stokes, P.O. Box 931, Jackson, MS 39205.

W. McFerrin Stowe, P.O. Box 8124 (3300 Mockingbird Lane), Dallas, TX 75205.

R. Marvin Stuart, P.O. Box 467 (330 Ellis St.) San Francisco, CA 94101.

Prince A. Taylor, Jr., Opinion Research Bldg., N. Harrison & Terhune Rd., Princeton, NJ 08540.

James S. Thomas, 1019 Chestnut St., Des Moines, IA 50309.

Jack M. Tuell, 1838 S.W. Jefferson St., Rm. 135, Portland, OR 97201.

Edward L. Tullis, 1420 Lady St., Columbia, SC 29201.

W. Ralph Ward, United Methodist Center, 210 Boston Post Rd., Rye, NY 10580.

John B. Warman, 3 Riverside Office Center, 3101 N. Front St., Harrisburg, PA 17110.

Paul A. Washburn, 77 W. Washington St., Ste. 1806, Chicago, IL 62701.

Lance Webb, The United Methodist Church, 501 E. Capitol Ave., Springfield, IL 62701.

D. Frederick Wertz, 900 Washington St., E., Charleston, WV 25301.

Melvin E. Wheatley, Jr., 2200 S. University Blvd., Denver, CO 80210.

Joseph H. Yeakel, 3049 E. Genesee St., Syracuse, NY 13224.

OTHER ORGANIZATIONS

Judicial Council: Pres., Ralph M. Houston; Vice-Pres., Theodore M. Berry; Sec., Mrs. D. Dwight Grove, 5025 N. Marvine St., Philadelphia, PA 19141.

Council on Finance and Administration: 1200 Davis St., Evanston, IL 60201. Tel. (312) 869-3345. Pres., Bishop F. Gerald Ensley; Vice-Pres., Bishop H. Ellis Finger; Rec. Sec., Mrs. John W. Carrell; Gen. Sec. and Treas., R. Bryan Brawner; Assoc. Gen. Secs., Norman L. Conard, Ewing T. Wayland; Asst. Gen. Secs., Systems and Procedures, Vernon L. Sidler; Records and Statistics, John L. Schreiber; Insurance, Legal, Property Management Services, John C. Espie; Controller, Wilbert A. Blum; Chief Accountant, Mrs. Frances L. Braker; Asst. Treas., Douglas Crozier; Admin. Asst., Marie Kitazumi; Dirs., Council Operations, Jason E. Robinson; Dept. of Records, Mrs. Dorothy Marshall; Payroll and Fringe Benefits, Mrs. Marjorie R. Philbrick.

General Council on Ministries: 601 W. Riverview Ave., Dayton, OH 45406. Tel. (513) 222-2531. Pres., John T. King; Vice-Pres., R. Jervis Cooke; Rec. Sec., Mrs. W. T. Roberts; Gen. Sec., Paul V. Church; Acting Treas., William H. Jenkins.

Advance Committee: (to be organized).

Joint Committee on Communications: Pres., Thomas P. Moore: Vice Pres., John E. Carrington; Rec. Sec., Dolphus Whitten, Jr.; Treas., R. Bryan Brawner.

Program and Benevolence Interpretation: 1200 Davis St., Evanston, IL 60201. Tel. (312) 869-3770. Assoc. Exec. Sec., Howard Greenwalt; Asst. Exec. Sec. for Field Cultivation, Arthur V. Long; Asst. Exec. Sec. and Edit. Dir., Edwin H. Maynard; Bus. Mgr. and Asst. Sec. for Field Cultivation, Warren M. Jenkins; Asst. Secs. for Field Cultivation, Alex Porteus, Nelson E. Stants; Eds., Promotional Materials, Earl K. Wood; Program Materials, Harold H. Hazenfield; Art Dir., Edward J. Mikula; Service Dept. Dir., Thomas A. Adams. (Dayton Office) Ed. of The Interpreter, Darrell R. Shamblin; Mng. Ed., Ralph E. Baker.

Television, Radio & Film Communication (TRAFCO): 1525 McGavock St., Nashville, TN 37203. Tel. (615) 242-3561. Assoc. Exec. Sec., Harry C. Spencer; Treas. and Bus. Mgr., Joe W. Davis. Dept. of Communications Education: Dir., Sam S. Barefield. Section of Media Resources: Asst. Exec. Sec., James C. Campbell: Dirs., Dept of Information Services, Sue Couch; Dept. of Audiovisual Media, Edgar A. Gossard; Producers, J. Fred Rowles, C. B. Anderson, Ben T. Logan. Bureau of Special Projects, Supt., Donald E. Hughes. Dept. of Technical Services, Dir. and Supt., Bureaus of Photography and Manufacturing, Anton J. Pilversack; Supt.,

Bureau of Sound Recording, Vilmars Zile. Dept, of Utilization, Dir., Wilford V. Bane, Jr. Dept. of Annual Conference Relationships, 601 W. Riverview Ave., Dayton, OH 45406. Tel. (513) 222-2531. Dir., Gene W. Carter. Section of Broadcasting Communication, 475 Riverside Dr., New York, NY 10027. Tel. (212) 663-8900. Asst. Exec. Sec., Nelson Price. Dept. of Radio and Television, Dir. ————; Producers, Ben T. Logan, Bruce C. Mosher, Peter Francis, William R. Richards (Nashville).

United Methodist Information and Public Relations: 601 W. Riverview Ave., Dayton, OH 45406. Tel. (513) 222-2531. Assoc. Exec. Sec., Arthur West; National Dirs., Robert Lear, 1200 Davis St., Evanston, IL 60201. Tel. (312) 869-4210; Thomas S. McAnally, P. O. Box 871, Nashville, TN 37202. Tel. (615) 327-0631; Leonard M. Perryman, 475 Riverside Dr., New York, NY 10027. Tel. (212) 749-0700; Winston H. Taylor, 100 Maryland Ave., Washington, DC 20002. Tel. (202) 543-5038. Admin. Asst., Mrs. Charlotte O'Neal (New York).

Board of Church and Society: 100 Maryland Ave., N.E., Washington, DC 20002. Tel. (202) 546-1000. Pres., Bishop A. James Armstrong; Vice-Pres., Bishop Wilbur W. Y. Choy, E. McKinnon White, Joel N. Martinez, Mrs. William A. Hudson, Bishop Roy C. Nichols, Bryan Crenshaw; Rec. Sec., Samuel T. Middleton; Treas., Mrs. Arthur Styron; Gen. Sec., A. Dudley Ward; Asst. Gen. Sec., Warren R. Ebinger; Dirs., Office of Publication and Ed. of engage/Social Action, Allan R. Brockway; Office of Communication, Lee R. Ranck; Washington Study Program, Vaudra Rushing.

Division of General Welfare: Chprsn., Bishop Wilbur W. Y. Choy; Vice-Chprsn., P. B. Revels; Rec. Sec., Mrs. Monroe Cooke; Assoc. Gen. Sec., Grover C. Bagby; Dirs., Dept. of Alcohol and Drug Issues, Thomas E. Price; Dept. of Law, Justice, and Community Relations, John P. Adams.

Division of Human Resources: Chprsn., Joel N. Martinez; Vice-Chprsn., Mrs. Lamar Wilson; Rec. Sec., Walker Railey; Assoc. Gen. Sec., Earnest A. Smith; Dirs., Dept. of Economic Life, Luther E. Tyson; Dept. of Church-Government Relations, J. Elliott Corbett.

Division of Emerging Social Issues: Chprsn., Mrs. William A. Hudson; Vice-Chprsn., Kenneth Watson; Rec. Sec., Orion N. Hutchinson, Jr. (Staff to be elected.)

Division of World Peace: Chmn., E. McKinnon White; Vice-Chprsn., Mrs. Emmett Conrad; Rec. Sec., Richard Tholin; Assoc. Gen. Sec., Herman Will, Jr.; Dir., Dept. of World Development, Rodney Shaw. United Methodist U.N. Office, 777 U.N. Plaza, New York, NY 10017. Tel. (212) 682-3633.

Board of Discipleship: P.O. Box 840 (1908 Grand Ave.,), Nashville, TN 37202. Tel. (615) 327-0971. Pres., Bishop W. Kenneth Goodson; Vice-Pres., Div. of Evangelism, Worship and Stewardship, Edward L. Duncan; Div. of Education, Bishop James S. Thomas; Div. of Lay Life and Work, James F. W. Talley; Rec. Sec., Mrs. Charles N. Gilreath.

(The following agencies are merged in this board and their staffs continued on an interim basis.)

General Board of Evangelism: Gen. Sec., Ira Gallaway; Admin. Asst., Lou Dozier; Treas., Carl D. Case; Dirs., Production Services, Kenneth Diehl; Accounting Services, Isaac Brown; Communications, Ronn Kerr. Christian Community Section: Asst. Gen. Sec., David J. Randolph; Dirs., Appalachian Ministry, Glenn Evans; Leisure Ministries, Robert Ochsenrider; New Life Missioners, ————; Urban Ministries, Cornelius L. Henderson. Connectional Ministries Section: Asst. Gen. Sec., George H. Outen; Dirs., Service and Guidance to Designated Leaders, Charles D. Whittle; Bilingual Ministries, Roberto Escamilla; Ecumenical Evangelism, Joe Hale; Urban Young Adult Action, Earl R. Barr, Jr. Local Church Section: Asst. Gen. Sec., Ross E. Whetstone; Coordinator Local Church Evangelism Ministries, Chester E. Custer; Dir., Dept. of Koinonia Ministries, Ross E. Whetstone; Assoc. Dir., Vance D. Archer, Jr.; Dir., Discipleship Cultivation, Harold Rogers.

Division of Devotional and Evangelistic Resources: Assoc. Gen. Sec. and Ed. of The Upper Room, Wilson O. Weldon; Mng. Ed., Russell Q. Chilcote; Ed. Assocs., Ronald Patterson, Mary Ruth Coffman, Mrs. Gregory Grana; Ed. Assoc. and Dean of Upper Room Chapel, Maurice W. King; Dirs., Devotional Literature, Sulon G. Ferree; Devotional Library and Museum, Brooks B. Little; Family Worship ————; Upper Room Fellowship, Mrs. Harold Baggett; Sales and Promotion, Chaplains, Other Languages, R. W. Ricker; Art Services, Gordon Haug; Radio-TV Parish, Mary Ruth Coffman; Military Membership Roll, Lois Pottle; Asst. Gen. Sec. and Ed. of Tidings, Reuben P. Job; Edit. Assocs., Harold Bales, William Reed, Jr.

General Board of the Laity; 1200 Davis St., Evanston, IL 60201. Tel. (312) 869-4950. Gen. Sec., David W. Self; Treas. and Bus. Mgr., John L. Hereford.

Division of Lay Life and Work: Assoc. Gen. Sec., Sidney R. Nichols. Section on Lay Ministries: Dir., Richard S. Smith. Section on United Methodist Men, Asst. Gen. Sec., Charles P. Kellogg, Sr.; Dir., Charles P. Jaeger.

Division of Stewardship and Finance: Assoc. Gen. Sec., Clifford B. Lott. Section on Financial Resources, Asst. Gen. Sec., Gordon D. Danielson; Dirs., Dwight E. Newberg, Albert V. Hooke. Section on Stewardship Education, Asst. Gen. Sec., Hilbert J. Berger; Dir., Earl F. Barfoot.

Division of the Local Church: P.O. Box 871 (1001 Nineteenth Ave., S.), Nashville, TN 37202. Tel. (615) 327-2727. Gen. Sec., Howard M. Ham; Assts. for Educational Research and Program Development, Warren J. Hartman; Program Design and Coordination, Robert S. Clemmons; Financial Development and Dir., National United Methodist Foundation for Local Church Education, T. Poe Williams; Developing Ministry with the Black Community, Willard A. Williams. Exec. Dirs., Section of Innovation and Experimentation, George E. Koehler; Section of Services to Designated Leaders, Wayne M. Lindecker, Jr.; Dirs., Services to Conference Directors of Education, William J. Washington; Services to Dist. Supts. and Pastors, Alvin T. Maberry; Services to Local Church Professional Christian Educators and Leisure-Recreation Ministries, R. Harold Hipps; Services to Local Church Leaders, _____; Services to Churches of Small Membership, Jennie Youngblood; Camping and Christian Education Outdoors, Melvin A. Moody. Section of Age-Level and Family Ministries: Exec. Dir., Margie McCarty; Dirs., Ministries in Marriage, Leon Smith; Ministries to Infants and Young Children, Vera V. Zimmerman; Ministries with Early Elementary Boys and Girls and Dir. of Ministries to Exceptional Persons, LaDonna Bogardus; Ministries to Junior Highs, John W. Gattis; Ministries to Senior Highs, Charles W. Courtoy; Ministries to Parents, _____; Ministries to Young Adults, _____; Ministries to Middle Adults, Roy H. Ryan; Ministries to Older Adults and to the Homebound, Virginia Stafford. Section of Communication Processes and Learning Resources: Exec. Dir., James E. Alexander; Consultant on Buildings and Equipment, Glenn S. Gothard. Section on Training Enterprises: Exec Dir., _____; Dirs., Laboratory Enterprise, Aileen M. Sanborn; Leadership Schools, Richard E. Monroe; Performance Training, _____. Interboard Committee on Missionary Education: Exec. Sec., Thomas J. Van Loon; Dir., May L. Titus. General Committee on Family Life, Leon Smith.

Division of Curriculum Resources: 201 Eighth Ave., S., Nashville, TN 37202. Tel. (615) 327-2727. Gen. Sec., Ewart G. Watts; Exec. Ed., Dept. of General Publications, Mrs. Florence A. Lund; Assoc. Ed., Harold L. Fair; Exec. Eds., Children's Publications, Leo N. Kisrow; Youth Publications, Richard H. Rice; Adult Publications, Horace R. Weaver; Eds., H. Myron Braun, Lena Mereness, Thomas H. Nankervis; Coordinator of Interpretation, Howard E. Walker.

United Methodist Council on Youth Ministries: P.O. Box 7871, Nashville, TN 37202. (615) 327-2727. Chprsn., Barbe Spies; Vice-Chprsn., Tim Bagwell; Dir., James Ling.

Board of Global Ministries: 475 Riverside Dr., New York, NY 10027. Tel. (212) 749-0700.

Pres., Bishop Paul A. Washburn; Vice-Pres., Bishop L. Scott Allen, Mrs. C. Clifford Cummings, Mrs. Henry L. Georg, Bishop James K. Mathews, Bishop Carl J. Sanders, Bishop Jack M. Tuell, H. Claude Young. Gen. Sec., Tracey K. Jones, Jr., Assoc. Gen. Secs., Roger Burgess, J. Harry Haines, Theressa Hoover, Robert W. Huston, Lois C. Miller, Randolph Nugent, John F. Schaefer; Ombudsman, Harry B. Gibson, Jr.; Personnel Dir., Mary-Alice Thomas; Exec. Sec., Crusade Scholarship, Margaret Swift; Librarian, Miriam Parsell; Rec. Sec., Mrs. F. Lois Persons; Gen. Treas., Stephen F. Brimigion; Assoc. Div. Treas., Beverly C. Berry, Florence Little, Mrs. Florence Walter; Gen. Comptroller, Frank A. W. Morrison; Senior Acctnts., Nabil G. Abou-Daoud, Louis M. Kreismer, Emilio Natera; Acctg. Supr., Esther Tyma; Adminstr. of Legal Services, Maurice E. Persons; Missionary Services Supr., S. Joseph Bozek; Missionary Payroll Supr., Louis R. Spach; Mgr., Electronic Data Processing, Harold M. Jenkins; Systems Analysts, Janis G. Hoover, Mary E. Hetrich; Programmers, Laning Abramson, Peter J. McLaughlin; Purchasing and Gen. Services Dir., Hans L. Aurbakken; Traffic Mgr., Albert Barnes; Service Dept. Mgr., Raoul J. Rodriguez. Office of Missionary Personnel: Exec. Sec., John W. Johannaber; Sec., Avery C. Manchester.

Division on Ecumenical and Interreligious Concerns: Pres., Bishop James K. Mathews; Vice-Pres., Mrs. John Eby; Assoc. Gen. Sec., Robert W. Huston; Asst. Gen. Sec., Jeanne Audrey Powers.

Division of Education and Cultivation: Pres., H. Claude Young; Vice-Pres., Mrs. Robert F. Trost; Rec. Sec., Mrs. Jack Barneson; Assoc. Gen. Sec., Lois C. Miller; Asst. Gen. Sec., David W. Briddell. Section of Cultivation. Asst. Gen. Sec., Joe W. Walker; Exec. Secs., Howard T. Brinton, Warren A. Loesch; Assoc. Dir. of the Advance, Harry B. Poppe; Field Reps., David H. Blackburn, Dwight S. Busacca, William A. Cheyne, Billy M. Starnes; Coordr. of Field Itineration, Robert C. Holstein. Section of Communication: Asst. Gen. Sec., Betty A. Thompson; Coordr. of Fine Arts and Graphic Services, B. Elizabeth Marchant; Dir. of Interpretive Services, George M. Daniels; Service Center Dir., Mrs. Erma D. Owens; Audio-Visual Resources, Dir., Gilbert M. Galloway; Assoc. Dir., Beverly J. Chain; Literature, Dir., Blaise Levai; Ed., Juanita B. Wright; Eds., New/World Outlook, Arthur J. Moore, Jr.; response, Carol M. Herb; Assoc. Eds., Charles E. Brewster, Ellen Clark; Senior Staff Writer, Constance Myer; Senior Photographer, Toge Fujihira. Section of Education: Coords., Mission Education, Miriam Brattain; Mission Leaders, Donald E. Struchen; Consultative Services, Elinor Kajiwara.

Division of Health and Welfare Ministries: Pres., Mrs. Henry L. Georg; Vice-Pres., Bishop Francis E. Kearns; Rec. Sec., Alfred Pollar; Treas., Mrs. Florence H. Walter; Assoc. Gen. Sec., Roger Burgess;

Spec. Assts. to Gen. Sec., Mrs. Cathie Lyons, James Moore. Section on Agency Ministries: Asst. Gen. Sec., John Murdock; Dir., Dept. of Services to Children and Youth, Merlin Outcalt. Section on Church Program: Asst. Gen. Sec., John Norwood; Dirs., Dept. of Jurisdictional and Annual Conference Programs, Wendell Bassett; Dept. of Local Church Programs, Charles Frazier.

National Division: Pres., Bishop Jack M. Tuell; Vice-Pres., Mrs. E. L. Ferris, Eugene L. Smith; Rec. Sec., Robert L. Johnson; Treas., Beverley C. Berry; Assoc. Gen. Sec., Randolph Nugent; Asst. Gen. Secs., Administration, Betsy K. Ewing; Minority Concerns, Negail R. Riley; Asst. Rec. Sec., Florence E. Bell; Planning Dir., Neal F. Fisher; Comptroller, Enid M. Belle. Section of Agency and Community Concerns: Asst. Gen Sec., Norman W. Klump; Offices of: Neighborhood Centers and Residences, Exec. Sec., Dorothy Chapman; Field Rep., A. Louise Weeks; Deaconess/Home Missionary Service, Exec. Sec., Allene M. Ford; Health Ministries, Exec. Sec., Betty J. Letzig; University and Young Adult Ministries, Exec. Sec., John E. Jordan; Field Rep., John H. Graham; Children and Youth Services, Exec. Sec., _____; Goodwill Industries, Exec. Sec , _____. Section of Parish and Community Ministries: Asst. Gen. Sec., Paul A. Stauffer; Offices of: Community Developers, Exec. Sec., John W. Coleman; Ethnic and Language Ministries, Exec. Sec., Harry S. Komuro; Field Reps., Hispanic-American Ministries, Leo D. Nieto; American Indian Ministries, Homer Noley; Church and Community Ministries, Exec. Sec., Harold S. Huff; Field Rep. Shirley E. Greene; Urban Ministries, Exec. Secs., Negail R. Riley, Ernest V. May; Field Reps., John H. Hager, Kinmoth W. Jefferson, Cecil P. E. Pottieger; Voluntary Services, Exec. Sec., Randle B. Dew. Section of Specialized Services, Asst. Gen. Sec., _____, Offices of: Architecture, Exec. Sec., Jerry Ellis; Field Rep., Claire M. Jones; Construction Agent, Samuel G. Hollenhead; Church Extension, Exec. Sec., _____; Field Reps., W. Darwin Andrus, James R. Maxfield; New Church Development, Exec. Sec., James R. Maxfield; Research and Survey, Dir. James H. Davis; Assoc., Ezra Earl Jones; United Methodist Development Fund, Exec. Sec., H. Paul Smith; Finance and Field Service, Exec. Sec., Wilburn S. Yoder; Field Reps., Edmund R. Warne, Leon L. Blackman, Frank L. Countryman, D. George Davies, William J. Erwin, Floyd L. Hindshaw, Walter E. Hoover, Wesley E. McKelvey, Alton S. Miller, William A. Perry, Allen R. Regan, C. Clifford Sargent, Frederick H. Strathdee, Edgar E. Walker, Julius J. Webb, Charles W. Welch, Orville G. Wilson, Maurice L. Win. Low Income Housing, Consultant, _____.

United Methodist Committee on Relief:

Pres., Bishop Carl J. Sanders; Vice-Pres., Mrs. Ralph W. Wilde; Rec. Sec., Fletcher Scharer; Assoc. Gen. Sec. J. Harry Haines; Secs., Coordination and Interpretation, David W. Flude; Specialized Ministries, James J. Thomas; Programs and Administration, Jean Baer.

Women's Division: Pres., Mrs. C. Clifford Cummings; Vice-Pres., Mrs. Harold Quickel, Mrs. Harvey J. Winn, Mrs. Lowell H. Sohn, Mrs. Carlton Carruth; Rec. Sec., Sachi Kajiwara; Treas., Florence Little; Assoc. Gen. Sec., Theressa Hoover, Asst. Gen. Sec., Mrs. J. Boyd Terrell; Exec. Sec., _____; Staff Asst., Helen Abshire; Staff in Regions: Maryruth Nickels, Atlanta, GA., Marion L. Baker, Chicago, IL; John L. Clark, Dallas, TX; Bernice Dvorak, Dayton, OH; Gene E. Maxwell, Denver, CO; Mrs. David Cathcart, Nashville, TN; Mrs. Helen L. Swett, Portland, ME; Murden Woods, San Francisco, CA; Mae Frances Spencer, Washington, DC. Section of Christian Social Relations: Asst. Gen. Sec., Peggy Billings; Exec. Secs., U.N./International Affairs, Mrs. Else Marie Adjali; Development, Education and Training, _____; Secs., Community Action, Ruth Gilbert; Legislative Affairs and Welfare, Joyce V. Hamlin; Racial Justice, Mrs. Carolyn Wilhelm. Section of Finance: Div. Comptroller, Mrs. Jesse Lyons; Asst. Treas., Erna Slagg; Sec., Financial Promotion, Peggy Halsey. Section of Program and Education for Christian Mission: Asst. Gen. Sec., Elaine Gasser; Exec. Secs., Leadership Development, Barbara Campbell; Program, Mary Lou Van Buren; Secs., Membership and Interpretation, Nancy Ellen Kirby; Leadership, Schools/Mission Education, Ann Eaton.

World Division: Pres., Bishop L. Scott Allen; Vice-Pres., Mrs. Alvin L. Morrison, Robert M. Daugherty; Rec. Sec. and Dir. of Admin. Services, Mrs. Patricia Ewald; Treas., _____: Assoc. Gen. Sec., John F. Schaefer, Asst. Gen. Secs., for Program, _____: for Development and Planning, Ruth Harris; Africa Team, Asst. Gen. Sec. for African Affairs, Issac Bivens; Exec. Sec., Juel Nordby; Asia Team, Asst. Gen Sec. for Asian Affairs, Charles H. Germany; Exec. Secs., Edwin O. Fisher, Jr., Henry A. Lacy, Barbara Chase; Latin American Team, Asst. Gen. Sec. for Latin American Affairs, Paul F. McCleary; Exec. Secs., Joyce Hill, Lewistine M. McCoy; Functional Exec. Secs., Education, _____; Mass Communication, Doris Hess; Medicine, Duvon C. Corbitt, Jr.; Ministry of Women, Rose M. Catchings; Missionary Affairs, Patricia Patterson; University and Young Adult Ministries, Pharis Harvey; Treasury Staff, Assoc. Treas., Harry Greenberg; Budget Dir., Hunter D. Griffin.

Board of Higher Education and Ministry: P.O. Box 871 (1001 Nineteenth Ave., S.), Nashville, TN 37202. Tel. (615) 327-2727. Pres., Bishop Ernest T. Dixon; Vice-Pres., Bishop Don Holter, Ethel R. Johnson, Thomas K.

Kim, Bishop Prince A. Taylor, Jr.; Rec. Sec., Mrs. Fletcher Nelson; Treas. and Bus. Mgr., Edwin E. Smith; Acting Gen. Sec., Myron F. Wicke.

Division of Higher Education: Chprsn., Thomas K. Kim; Vice-Chprsn., William L. Apetz; Rec. Sec., Mrs. Caroline R. Adams; Assoc. Gen. Sec., Fred E. Harris. Section on Schools, Colleges and Universities, Chprsn., Isaac H. Miller, Jr.; Section on Campus Ministry, Chprsn., Thomas F. Trotter; Section on Loans and Scholarships, Chprsn., William L. Apetz.

Division on Chaplains and Related Ministries: 3900 Wisconsin Ave., N.W., Washington, DC 20016. Tel. (202) 537-1115. Chprsn., Bishop Prince A. Taylor, Jr.; Vice-Chprsn., Bishop W. Kenneth Goodson; Rec. Sec., James C. Stokes; Assoc. Gen. Sec., A. Purnell Bailey; Assoc. Secs., M. Douglas Blair; John W. Heyward, Jr.

Division of Lay Ministry: Chprsn., Ethel R. Johnson, Vice-Chprsn., Walter N. Kalaf; Rec. Sec., Mrs. Rena Yocom.

Division of Ordained Ministries: Chmn., Bishop Don W. Holter; Vice-Chmn., Robert W. Burtner; Rec. Sec., Donald H. Treese.

Office of Personnel: Chprsn., Roy B. Shilling, Rec. Sec., Mrs. Olin Troy; Exec. Sec., Richard H. Bauer. (Staff Serving During Interim of Reorganization) Assoc. Gen. Secs., E. Craig Brandenburg, John D. Humphrey; Office of Information and Publications, Dir. Woodrow A. Geier. National Methodist Foundation for Christian Higher Education, Exec. Dir., Maurice E. Gordon. Dept. of Educational Institutions, Assoc. Dirs., Donald S. Stanton, Daniel W. Wynn. Dept. of Campus Ministry, Dir., Eugene A. Ransom; Assoc. Dirs., Frank L. Horton, Glenn B. Hosman, Jr., Samuel M. Kirk. Dept. of the Ministry, Dir., Gerald O. McCulloh; Assoc. Dirs., William H. Likins, Harold T. Porter, Mark A. Rouch.

General Board of Pensions: 1200 Davis St., Evanston, IL 60201. Tel. (312) 869-4550. Pres., Bishop Alsie H. Carleton; Vice-Pres., J. Wesley Hole; Rec. Sec., Mrs. Betty L. Nusbaum; Asst. Rec. Sec., Vernon A. Sladek; Treas., Donald R. McKee; Asst. Treas., G. Warren Dare; Gen. Sec., Claire C. Hoyt; Actuary, Frank L. Markel, Jr.; Dirs.: Conference Service Section, Kenneth F. Thompson; Operation Section, Gerald A. Beam.

General Board of Publication: 201 Eighth Ave., S., Nashville, TN 37202. Tel. (615) 242-1621. Chmn., Jack B. Russell; Vice-Chmn., Harry J. Fravert; Rec. Sec., J. Kenneth Forbes. The Methodist Publishing House: Pres. and Publisher, John E. Procter, Exec. Vice-Pres. and Gen. Mgr., Donald A. Theuer; Treas., John H. Laird; Assoc. Publisher, H. Thornton Fowler; Admin. Asst. to Pres., Mrs. Sara R. Parks; Vice-Pres., Personnel and Public Relations, W. T. Handy, Jr.; Publishing Division, Thomas K. Potter, Jr.; Cokesbury Division, Thomas E. Carpenter; Ed., Church School Publications, Ewart G.

Watts; Book Ed. and Ed. of Abingdon Press, Emory Stevens Bucke. General Church Periodicals: (P.O. Box 423, Park Ridge, IL 60068) Editorial Dir. and Ed. of *Together*, Curtis A. Chambers; Ed., *Christian Advocate*, William C. Henzlik. (Nashville) Bus. Mgr., Gen. Church Periodicals, Warren P. Clark; Advertising Sales, John H. Fisher; Fulfillment, Jack Inman; Reader Service Supervisor, Mrs. June W. Luttrell; Dir., Public Relations, Stephen C. Tippens; Mgrs., Central Research, Thomas B. Newton; Central Real Estate, A. Q. Campbell; Manufacturing Operations, W. Wayne Hogen; Employee Relations, William J. Vaughn; Personnel Services, James O. Parrish; Wage and Salary, Mrs. Maureen R. Poole; Placement, Mrs. Mary Ellen Badger; Nashville Bldg. Hostess, Melba Martin. Accounting Div.: Chief Accountant, Aubrey L. Troxler; Mgrs., Credit, J. Clarence Register; Accts. Payable, Joseph C. Fuqua; Data Processing, Whit T. Terrell; Forms and Procedures, Garland P. Rose; Payroll, Mrs. Gladys T. Hill; Internal Aud., Johnny W. Fitzhugh; Cashier, Mrs. Esther E. Austin. Manufacturing Div., Mgr., The Parthenon Press, Sales, Robert C. Dickens; Planning and Estimating, Herbert V. Stone; Production Control, C. Eugene Thompson, Jr.; Production Engineering, John E. Ingram. Publishing Div.: Copyrights and Permissions, Carolyn Hite; Admin. Asst., Mrs. Betty D. Lankford; Mgrs., Central Art Services, H. Wilson Estes; Production Services, William C. Bosworth, III. Abingdon Press: Eds., Children's Books, ———; College Texts, Pierce S. Ellis, Jr.; General Books, Robert J. Hill, Jr.; Religious Books, Paul M. Pettit; Mgrs., Manuscript Dept., Jean P. Hager; Fine Arts, J. Richard Loller; Special Projects, Jon L. Setzer; Operations, Charles O. McNish; Asst. Mgr., C. Malcolm Kassell; Mgrs., Trade Relations, E. Guy Brownfield (55 E. 55 St., New York, NY 10022); Church Supplies, Ralph A. Wood; Sales, Kenneth L. MacNeill; Advertising and Publicity, F. Vernon Fox; Dir., Church Music Section, Robert O. Hoffelt. Graded Press: Mgr., Gary H. Vincent. Cokesbury Div.: Mgrs., Merchandising Dept., Gerald N. Battle; Advertising Dept., Tyler Ford, Jr. Regional Service Centers and Cokesbury Stores: Atlanta, Baltimore, Birmingham, Boston, Chicago, Cincinnati, Dallas, Dayton, Detroit, Harrisburg, Houston, Kansas City, Los Angeles, Nashville, New York, Park Ridge, IL, Pittsburgh, Richmond, San Francisco, Seattle, and Teaneck, NJ.

Commission on Archives and History: Box 488, Lake Junaluska, NC 28745. Tel. (704) 456-9433. Pres., Bishop O. Eugene Slater; Vice-Pres., Carroll Hart; Rec. Sec., Joseph Evers; Exec. Sec., John H. Ness, Jr.; Edit. Asst. Mrs. Louise Queen; Librarian, Mrs. Paul A. Sutton. (E.U.B. Depository) 601 W. Riverview Ave., Dayton, OH 45406. Tel. (513) 222-2531. Librarian, Esther George.

THE UNITED METHODIST CHURCH

Commission on Religion and Race: 100 Maryland Ave., Washington, DC 20002. Tel. (202) 547-4270. Pres., Bishop D. Frederick Wertz; Vice-Pres., Bishop James S. Thomas; Rec. Sec., Hector Navas; Exec. Sec., Woodie W. White; Assoc. Exec. Secs., Clayton E. Hammond, James L. Jones, Isabel Gomez.

Commission on the Status and Role of Women: Pres., Mrs. Alfred E. Thompson; Vice-Pres., Tom Graves, Bonnie Jones-Goldstein, Harriet Miller, Mrs. Douglas Underwood, Toni White; Rec. Sec., Jeanne Audrey Powers, 475 Riverside Dr., New York, NY. 10027. Tel. (212) 749-0700.

Fellowship of United Methodist Musicians: Pres., W. Howard Coble; Pres.-elect, Kenneth Tebow; Vice-Pres., Robert E. Scoggin; Sec., Marjorie Hershey; Exec. Sec., Glenn S. Gothard, P.O. Box 871, Nashville, TN 37202. Tel. (616) 327-2727.

PERIODICALS

Action (q), 501 E. Capitol Ave., Springfield, IL 62701. Robert L. Sands, Ed.

Arkansas Methodist (w), P.O. Box 3547, Little Rock, AR 72203. Alfred A. Knox, Ed.

California-Nevada United Methodist (m), P.O. Box 5133, Sacramento, CA 95817. David R. Swope, Ed.

Christian Advocate (bi-w), P.O. Box 423, Park Ridge, IL 60068. William C. Henzlik, Ed.

Christian Home, The (m), 201 Eighth Ave., S., Nashville, TN 37202. Mrs. Florence A. Lund, Ed.

Church School, The (m), 201 Eighth Ave., S., Nashville TN 37202. Lena Mereness, Ed.

Communicator, The (m), 405 N.W. Eighth Ave., Berkshire Plz., Aberdeen, SD 57401. Russell Dilley, Ed.

Dimensions (m), 2374 Prairie Ave., Beloit, WI 53591. Mrs. Sharon R. Mielke, Ed.

Engage/Social Action (m), 100 Maryland Ave., N.E. Washington, DC 20002. Allan R. Brockway, Ed.

Florida United Methodist (m), P.O. Box 70, Lakeland, FL 33802. Mrs. Doris J. Buhrman, Ed.

Hawkeye Methodist (m), 1019 Chestnut St., Des Moines, IA 50309. Edward S. Zelley, Ed.

Hoosier United Methodist (m), 1100 W. 42 St., Indianapolis, IN 46208. Newman Cryer, Ed.

Indian Missionary Advocate (m), 1707 N. Broadway, Oklahoma City, OK 73103. Noah Long, Ed.

Interpreter, The (m), 601 W. Riverview Ave., Dayton, OH 45406. Darrell R. Shamblin, Ed.

Link, The (m), 900 Arlington Ave., Harrisburg, PA 17109. Arthur W. Stambach, Ed.

Louisiana Methodist (w), Box 3547, Little Rock, AR 72203. Alfred A. Knox, Ed.

Maine United Methodist, The (m), Box 277, Winthrop, ME 04364. Edward F. Allen, Ed.

Mature Years (m), 201 Eighth Ave., S., Nashville, TN 37202. Mrs. Daisy D. Warren, Ed.

Methodist Christian Advocate (w), 1801 Sixth Ave., N., Birmingham, AL 35203. Herschel T. Hamner, Ed.

Methodist Churchman, The (m), 581 Boylston St., Boston, MA 01226. John L. Bryan, Ed.

Methodist History (q), Box 488, Lake Junaluska, NC 28745. John H. Ness, Jr., Ed.

Methodist Relay (m), 329 Marlton Pike, Cherry Hill, NJ 08034. Robert J. Beyer, Ed.

Michigan Christian Advocate (m), 316 Springbrook Ave., Adrian, MI 49221. John E. Marvin, Ed.

Minnesota United Methodist (m), 122 W. Franklin Ave., Minneapolis, MN 55404. Ray Boehlke, Ed.

Mississippi Methodist Advocate (w), Box 1093, Jackson, MS 39201. George Roy Lawrence, Ed.

Missouri Methodist (m), 101 N. Bemiston Ave., St. Louis, MO 63105. Charles A. McEowen, Ed.

Music Ministry (m), 201 Eighth Ave., S., Nashville, TN 37202. H. Myron Braun, Ed.

Nebraska United Methodist Messenger (m), 2641 N. 49 St., Lincoln, NB 68504. Miles W. Jackson, Ed.

New Mexico United Methodist (w), 525 San Pedro, N.E., Albuquerque, NM 87108. Hollis Shook, Ed.

New/World Outlook (m), 475 Riverside Dr., New York, NY 10027. Arthur J. Moore, Jr., Ed.

News Pulse (bi-w), 5250 Santa Monica Blvd., Los Angeles, CA 90029. Raymond H. Wilson, Ed.

North Carolina Christian Advocate (w), Box 508, Greensboro, NC 27402. James C. Stokes, Ed.

Northwest United Methodist (m), 9225 Twilight Ln., S.W., Tacoma, WA 98498. Mrs. Robert Davis, Ed.

Ohio East Area News (m), 1226 Market Ave., N., Canton, OH 44714. DeWayne Woodring, Ed.

Ohio West News (m), 395 E. Broad St., Columbus, OH 43215. John F. Young, Ed.

Religion in Life (q), 201 Eighth Ave., S., Nashville, TN 37202. Emory S. Bucke, Ed.

Response (m), 475 Riverside Dr., Rm. 1323, New York, NY 10027. Carol M. Herb, Ed.

Rocky Mountain United Methodist (w), 2200 S. University Blvd., Denver, CO 80210. Clarence W. Smith, Ed.

Seven Points (m), 1115 S. Fourth St., Louisville, KY 40203. Rual T. Perkins, Ed.

South Carolina Methodist Advocate (w), 1420 Lady St., (Box 11589, Capitol Station) Columbia, SC 29211. M. Eugene Mullikan, Ed.

Texas Methodist, The (w), Box 1076, Dallas, TX 75221. Spurgeon M. Dunnam, III, Ed.

Together (m), Box 423, Park Ridge, IL 60068. Curtis A. Chambers, Ed.

United Methodist, The (m), 1907 Acklen Ave., Nashville, TN 37212. Carl Elkins, Ed.

United Methodist, The (m), 77 W. Washington St., Rm. 1806, Chicago, IL 60602. James N. Moore and Darrell D. English, Eds.

United Methodist (m), 10 N.W. 19th Ave., Portland, OR 97209. Alden Munson, Ed.

United Methodist Contact (m), 609 Cravens Bldg., Oklahoma City, OK 73102. Luman Cockerill, Ed.

United Methodist of Holston (m), Box 1178, Johnson City, TN 37602. Frank A. Settle, Ed.

United Methodist of Western Pennsylvania (q), 408 Seventh Ave., Pittsburgh, PA 15222. ———, Ed.

Upper Room (bi-m), 1908 Grand Ave., Nashville, TN 37203. Wilson O. Weldon, Ed.

Virginia Advocate (w), 4016 W. Broad St., Richmond, VA 23230. W. Hewlett Stith, Jr., Ed.

Wesleyan Christian Advocate (w), 159 Forrest Ave., N.E., Atlanta, GA 30303. William M. Holt, Ed.

West Virginia United Methodist (w), P.O. Box 2313, Charleston, WV 25328. Elwood Fleming, Ed.

World Parish (m), Box 518, Lake Junaluska, NC 28745. Lee F. Tuttle, Ed.

Wyoming Conference United Methodist (m), 438 Chenango St., Binghamton, NY 13901. —————, Ed.

United Pentecostal Church, Inc.

Pentecostal Church, Inc., and Pentecostal Assemblies of Jesus Christ merged September 25, 1945 at St. Louis, Missouri.

Churches: 2,500 Inclusive Membership: 250,000. Sunday or Sabbath Schools: N.R. Total Enrollment: N.R. Ordained clergy: N.R.

GENERAL ORGANIZATION
Conference: annual.
Headquarters: 8855 Dunn Rd., Hazelwood, MO 63042. Tel. (314) 837-7300.

OFFICERS
Gen. Supt., Stanley W. Chambers, 8855 Dunn Rd., Hazelwood, MO 63042.
Asst. Gen. Supts., James Kilgore, Box 15175, Houston, TX 77020; N. A. Urshan, 1814 Orange, Indianapolis, IN 46203.
Gen. Sec., Cleveland M. Becton, 8855 Dunn Rd., Hazelwood, MO 63042.
Dir. of For. Miss., T. F. Tenney, 8855 Dunn Rd., Hazelwood, MO 63042.
Gen. Dir. of Home Miss., J. T. Pugh, 8855 Dunn Rd., Hazelwood, MO 63042.
Editor in Chief, Arthur L. Clanton, 8855 Dunn Rd., Hazelwood, MO 63042.
Gen. Sunday School Dir., J. O. Wallace, 8855 Dunn Rd., Hazelwood, MO 63042.

OTHER ORGANIZATIONS
The Pentecostal Publishing House, Hazelwood. Ray Agnew, Mgr.
Pentecostal Conquerors (Young People's Dept.): Pres., Kenneth Haney, Hazelwood.
Sunday School Dept.: Supt., J. O. Wallace, Hazelwood.
Ladies Auxiliary: Pres., Vera Kinzie, 4840 Elm Pl., Toledo, OH 43608.
Harvestime Radio Broadcast: Dir., F. L. Mc-Kenzie, Hazelwood.

PERIODICAL
The Pentecostal Herald, Hazelwood. A. L. Clanton, Ed.

The United Presbyterian Church in the United States of America

The United Presbyterian Church in the United States of America was formed in May 1958 through a merger of the United Presbyterian Church of North America and the Presbyterian Church in the United States of America. The uniting General Assembly was held in Pittsburgh, Pennsylvania from May 28 to June 3, 1958. Of the two uniting bodies the Presbyterian Church in the United States of America dated from the first Presbytery organized in Philadelphia in 1706. The first General Assembly was held in Philadelphia in 1789.

The United Presbyterian Church of North America was formed in 1858, when the Associate Reformed Presbyterian Church and Associate Presbyterian Church united.

Churches: 8,760. Inclusive Membership: 3,013,-808. Sunday or Sabbath Schools: 8,760. Total Enrollment: 1,203,488. Ordained Clergy: 13,451.

THE GENERAL ASSEMBLY
Meets annually: Next meeting May 14-23, 1973 Omaha, NB.

OFFICERS
Mod. (1972-73), C. Willard Heckel.
Vice-Mod., Rev. Kenneth C. Miller.
Stated Clerk, William P. Thompson.
Assoc. Stated Clerks, Rev. Samuel W. Shane, Otto K. Finkbeiner, Rev. Robert F. Stevenson.
Treas., The Fidelity Bank, Philadelphia, PA 19109.

THE OFFICE OF THE GENERAL ASSEMBLY
510 Witherspoon Bldg., Philadelphia, PA 19107.
A. Dept. of Administration, Otto K. Finkbeiner.
B. Department of History, William B. Miller, Mgr. 425 Lombard St., Philadelphia, PA 19147.
C. Presbyterian Council for Chaplains and Service Personnel (joint with the Associate Reformed Presbyterian Church, the Cumberland Presbyterian Church, and the Presbyterian Church in the United States), Chprsn., Rev. Alister Sinclair; Dir., Rev. Robert B. Harriman; Assoc. Dir., Rev. James J. Alexander; Asst. Dir., Rev. R. David Chambers. 4125 Nebraska Ave., N. W., Washington, DC 20016.

UNITED PRESBYTERIAN FOUNDATION
Pres., Glen A. Lloyd; Vice-Pres., Rev. Don E. Hall; Dir., Rev. James E. Spivey, 475 Riverside Dr., New York, NY 10027. Sec. William P. Thompson, 510 Witherspoon Bldg., Philadelphia, PA 19107.

THE GENERAL ASSEMBLY MISSION COUNCIL
Chprsn., Mrs. Lois H. Stair; Exec. Dir., Rev. Leon E. Fanniel, 475 Riverside Dr., New York, NY 10027.

THE PROGRAM AGENCY
Pres., George E. Bushnell, Jr.; Gen. Sec., Rev. J. Oscar McCloud, 475 Riverside Dr., New York, NY 10027.

THE VOCATION AGENCY
Chprsn, Lewis S. Mudge; Gen. Dir., Rev. Donald P. Smith, 475 Riverside Dr., New York, NY 10027.

THE SUPPORT AGENCY
Chprsn., Morris Plotkin; Gen. Dir., Edward F. Tablak, 475 Riverside Dr., New York, NY 10027.

THE COUNCIL ON ADMINISTRATIVE SERVICES
Chprsn., Rev. Kenneth C. Miller; Dir., Rev. James L. Hogue, 475 Riverside Dr., New York, NY 10027.

THE UNITED PRESBYTERIAN CHURCH IN THE U.S.A.

THE COUNCIL OF THEOLOGICAL SEMINARIES

Chprsn., G. Pierson Brauch; Exec. Sec., Rev. John W. Meister, 475 Riverside Dr., New York, NY 10027.

THE COUNCIL ON CHURCH AND RACE

Co-Chprsns, Rev. Edler G. Hawkins and J. Henry Neale; Assoc. Chprsn. for Operation, Rev. Wilbur K. Cox, 475 Riverside Dr., New York, NY 10027.

THE NATIONAL COMMITTEE ON THE SELF-DEVELOPMENT OF PEOPLE

Chprsn., Rev. Bryant George; Exec. Dir., Rev. St. Paul Epps, 475 Riverside Dr., New York, NY 10027.

THE ADVISORY COUNCIL ON DISCIPLESHIP AND WORSHIP

Chprsn, Rev. Lloyd J. Ogilville; Dir., _____; 475 Riverside Dr., New York, NY 10027.

THE ADVISORY COUNCIL ON CHURCH AND SOCIETY

Chprsn, Rev. Jack L. Stotts; Dir., _____, 475 Riverside Dr., New York, NY 10027.

PERIODICALS

Journal of Presbyterian History (q), 425 Lombard St., Philadelphia, PA 19147. Rev. James H. Smylie, Ed.

Monday Morning (bi-w), 518 Witherspoon Bldg., Philadelphia, PA 19107. Rev. Frank H. Heinze, Ed.

Concern (10 issues yearly), 475 Riverside Dr., New York, NY 10027.

A.D. (m), (Jointly with the United Church of Christ), Pres., Walter G. Barlow; Publisher, Rev. Robert H. Heinze; Ed., Rev. J. Martin Bailey, Witherspoon Bldg., Philadelphia, PA 19107.

Social Progress (bi-m), 830 Witherspoon Bldg., Philadelphia, PA 19107. Rev. Dean H. Lewis, Ed.

These Days (m), (jointly with the Cumberland Presbyterian Church, the Presbyterian Church in Canada, the Presbyterian Church in the United States and the United Church of Christ), Ed., Larry M. Carreau, Editorial Office, P. O. Box 1176, Richmond, VA 23209.

SYNOD EXECUTIVES

Alaska-Northwest, Rev. W. Wilson Rasco, 720 Senaca St., Seattle, WA 98101.

Covenant, Rev. Lawrence W. McMaster, Jr., Michigan Office, 10600 Puritan Ave., Detroit, MI 48238.

Lakes & Prairies, Rev. Ellis H. Butler, 3050 Metro Park, Ste. 301, Minneapolis, MN 55420.

Lincoln Trails, Rev. Gordon H. Skadra, 1100 W. 42nd St., Indianapolis, IN 46200.

Mid-America, Rev. Robert J. Rodisch, 57 Broadmoor St., Mission, KS 66202.

New England, Rev. Burrett E. McBee, 888 Washington St., Dedham, MA 20026.

New Jersey, Rev. James H. Chesnutt, 110 S. Munn Ave., East Orange, NJ 07018.

New York, Rev. George H. DeHority, Jr., 3049 Genesee St., Syracuse, NY 13224.

Pacific, Rev. Richard E. Moore, 330 Ellis St., San Francisco, CA 94102.

Pennsylvania-West Virginia, Rev. William G. Rusch, 3040 Market St., Camp Hill, PA 17011.

Piedmont, Rev. William R. Phillippe, 320 Hillen Rd., Baltimore, MD 21204.

Puerto Rico, Rev. Jorge Acevedo-Cruz, P.O. Box C, Mayaguez, PR 00708.

Rocky Mts., Rev. Lloyd A. Peterson, 1737 Vine St., Denver, CO 80206.

South, Rev. Charles E. Carson, Rm. 217-C, 1001 Virginia Ave., Atlanta, GA 30354.

Southern Calif., Rev. Wallace W. Gibbs, 1501 Wilshire Blvd., Los Angeles, CA 90017.

Southwest, Rev. Richard K. Smith, 10 E. Roanoke Ave., Phoenix, AZ 85004.

Sun, Rev. Hugh D. Nelson, Box 901, Denton, TX 76201.

† United Seventh Day Brethren

A merger of two small independent churches in 1947. They are evangelical, premillennial, and Sabbatarian.

GENERAL ORGANIZATION

General Association: meets annually.

OFFICERS

Pres., Elder Myrtle Ortiz, Box 225, Enid, OK 73701.

Vice-Pres., W. R. Kaps, 608 E. Maine St., Enid, OK 73701.

Rec. Sec., Lois Crouse, Arthur, NB 69121.

Sec-Treas., Nobel Lewis, Box 3, Pomona, MO 65780.

The United Wesleyan Methodist Church of America

Founded in 1905 to meet needs of Methodists coming to the U.S. from the West Indies who wished to continue the traditions of British Methodism.

Churches: 6. Inclusive Membership: 400. Sunday or Sabbath Schools: 5. Total Enrollment: N.R. Ordained clergy: 8.

General Conference: Every two years.

OFFICERS

Pres., Rev. David S. Bruno, 270 W. 126th St., New York, NY 10027.

Gen. Sec., Rev. A. V. Arno, 47 Rogers Ave., Brooklyn, NY 11216. Tel. (212) 778-0665.

United Zion Church

A branch of the Brethren in Christ, which settled in Lancaster County, Pennsylvania, and was organized under the leadership of Matthias Brinser, in 1855.

Churches: 17. Inclusive Membership: 875. Sunday or Sabbath Schools: 13. Total Enrollment: 1,327. Ordained clergy: 24.

GENERAL ORGANIZATION

Conference: annual.

OFFICERS

Bishops: Luke Showalter, 202 Akron Rd. Ephrata, PA 17522. Brinser Heistand, R.D. 3, Elizabethtown, PA 17022; Amos Weidman, R.D. 2, Manhiem, PA 17545.

Gen. Conf. Sec.: Rev. J. Paul Martin, Box 212D, R.D. 1, Annville, PA 17003.

Unity of the Brethren

Czech and Moravian immigrants in Texas (beginning about 1855) established congregations which grew into an Evangelical Union in 1903, and with the accession of other Brethren in Texas, into the Evangelical Unity of the Czech-Moravian Brethren in North America. In 1959, it shortened the name to the original name used in 1457, the Unity of the Brethren (Unitas Fratrum, or Jednota Bratrska).

GENERAL ORGANIZATION
Synod: Every two years.

OFFICERS
Pres., Rev. Daniel J. Marek, 700 Sloan St., Taylor, TX 76574.
1st Vice Pres., Rev. John Baletka, Austin, TX.
Sec., Stanley F. Mrnustik, 205 N. Shaw, Caldwell, TX 77836.
Fin. Sec., Antone Elsik, 2210 So. 45th, Temple, TX 76501.
Treas., Arthur Lostak, 100 Fifth St., Highlands, TX 77562.

ORGANIZATIONS
Sunday School Union: Chmn., Stanley F. Mrnustik, 205 N. Shaw, Caldwell, TX 77836; Sec., Marvin Chlapek, 2513 Rever, Pasadena, TX 77502; Chmn., Board of Christian Education: Rev. Milton Maly, P.O. Box 175, Rosenberg, TX 77471.
Christian Sisters Society: Pres., Mrs. Jesse Skrivanek, 5905 Carleen Dr., Austin, TX 78731; Sec., Mrs. Ruben Malina, 1010 Marleen St., Houston, TX 77034.
Brethren Youth Fellowship: Pres., Mark Baletka, 2609 Green Lawn Pkwy., Austin, TX 78757.

PERIODICAL
Brethren Journal (m), 5905 Carleen Dr., Austin, TX 78731, Rev. Jesse E. Skrivanek, Ed.

Vedanta Society of New York

Followers of the Vedas, the scriptures of the Indo-Aryans, doctrines expounded by Swami Vivekananda at the Parliament of Religions, Chicago, 1893. There are altogether 13 such Centers in the U.S.A. All are under the control of the Ramakrishna Mission, organized by Swami Vivekananda in India.

Churches: 13. Inclusive Membership: 1,000. Sunday or Sabbath Schools: N.R. Total Enrollment: N.R. Ordained clergy: N.R.

GENERAL ORGANIZATION
Headquarters: 34 W. 71st St., New York, NY 10023.

LEADER
Swami Pavitrananda.

Volunteers of America

A religious social welfare organization, founded in 1896 by Ballington and Maud Booth; it provides spiritual and material aid for those in need, through approximately 700 service units in the continental U.S.

GENERAL ORGANIZATION
National Headquarters: 340 West 85th St., New York, NY 10024. Tel. (212) 873-2600.

NATIONAL OFFICERS
Commander-in-Chief, Gen. John F. McMahon.
National Fin. Sec., Lt. Col. Walter G. Nash.
National Religious Activities Sec., Col. Elizabeth J. Hartman
National Sec. for the Aging, Lt. Col. Ruth Fox Vottero.
National Correctional Services Sec., Lt. Maj. J. Clint Cheveallier.
National Social Welfare Sec., Lt. Col. Belle Leach.
National Youth Services Sec., Adjutant, David A. Wild.
National Rehabilitation Services Sec., Lt. Maj. David W. Bordenkircher.
Eastern Region Headquarters: 18 Exchange St., Binghamton, NY 13901; Regional Dir., Col. Clifford S. Hartman.
Midwest Region Headquarters: 2825 E. Lake St., Minneapolis, MN 55406; Regional Dir., Col. Robert E. Nolte.
Southern Region Headquarters: 3801 Pitt St., New Orleans, LA 70115; Regional Dir., Col. Ray C. Tremont.
Western Region Headquarters: 2300 East 14th St., Oakland, CA Regional Dir., Col. Oliver P. Strickland.
Metropolitan Division Headquarters: 340 W. 85th St., New York, NY 10024.

PERIODICAL
The Volunteer (m), published at National Headquarters.

The Wesleyan Church

The Wesleyan Church originated through the uniting of the Pilgrim Holiness Church (1897) and The Wesleyan Methodist Church of America (1843) at a merging conference held on June 26, 1968. The Wesleyan Church emphasizes scriptural truth concerning the new birth, the entire sanctification of believers, the personal return of Christ, and worldwide holiness evangelism.

GENERAL ORGANIZATION
General Conference: quadrennial. (Next session, 1976).
Headquarters: P.O. Box 2000, Marion, IN 46952. Tel. (317) 674-3301.

OFFICERS
Gen. Supts.: Dr. John D. Abbott, Dr. Virgil A. Mitchell, Dr. B. H. Phaup, Dr. Melvin H. Snyder.
Gen. Sec., Rev. D. Wayne Brown.
Gen. Treas., Dr. Willard Smith.
Gen. Ed., Dr. Robert W. McIntyre.
Gen. Publisher, Mr. Raymond J. Halt.
Gen. Sec. Extension and Evangelism, Dr. C. Wesley Lovin.
Gen. Sec. World Missions, Rev. Robert N. Lytle.
Gen. Sec. S.S., Dr. O. D. Emery.
Gen. Sec. Youth, Rev. David Keith.
Gen. Sec. Educational Institutions, Dr. Melvin E. Dieter.

WESLEYAN HOLINESS ASSOCIATION OF CHURCHES

PERIODICALS
The Wesleyan Advocate, Dr. Robert W. McIntyre, Ed.
Win, Rev. David Keith.
Wesleyan World, Rev. Paul Swauger, Ed.

Wesleyan Holiness Association of Churches

This body was founded Aug. 4, 1959 near Muncie, Indiana by a group of ministers and laymen who were drawn together for the purpose of spreading and conserving sweet, radical, scriptural holiness. These men came from various church bodies. This group is Wesleyan in doctrine and standards.

Churches: 67. Inclusive Membership: 2,000. Sunday or Sabbath Schools:. 67. Total Enrollment: N.R. Ordained clergy: 112.

GENERAL ORGANIZATION
General Conference meets every two years (Next meeting, July 20-21, 1973, Macksville, KS).
Headquarters: 726 W. 13th St., Tempe, AZ 85281. Tel. (602) 967-2734.

OFFICERS
Gen. Supt., Rev. Glenn Griffith, 3213 W. Camelback Rd., Phoenix, AZ 85019. Tel. (602) 937-2367.
Asst. Gen. Supt., Rev. L. Wayne States, 3213 W. Camelback Rd., Phoenix, AZ 85019. Tel. (602) 937-8644.
Gen. Sec.-Treas., Rev. Duane H. Watkins, 726 W. 13th St., Tempe, AZ 85281. Tel. (602) 967-2734.

PERIODICAL
Eleventh Hour Messenger (m), Rev. Glenn Griffith, Ed.

Wisconsin Evangelical Lutheran Synod

This body was organized in Wisconsin in 1850.

Churches: 987. Inclusive Membership: 383,263. Sunday or Sabbath Schools: 920. Total Enrollment: 57,569. Ordained clergy: 967.

GENERAL ORGANIZATION
Synod: biennial. (Next meeting, 1973.)

OFFICERS
Pres., Rev. Oscar Naumann, 3512 W. North Ave., Milwaukee, WI 53208.

1st Vice-Pres., Rev. Carl H. Mischke, 429 S. Main, Juneau, WI 53039.
2nd Vice-Pres., Rev. Manfred J. Lenz, 134 N. 3rd St., Box 68, Delano, MN 55328.
Sec., Prof. Heinrich J. Vogel, 11757N Seminary Dr. 65W., Mequon, WI 53092.

OTHER ORGANIZATIONS
Board of Trustees:
Chmn., Rev. Elton H. Huebner, 817 May St., Beaver Dam, WI 53916; Vice-Chmn., Rev. Erhardt G. Schultz, 109 W. Monroe St., Durand, MI 48429; Sec., Rev. Carl Leyrer, 3773 S. 2 St., Milwaukee, WI 53207.
Staff: 3512 W. North Ave., Milwaukee, WI 53208. Exec. Sec., Rev. Harold H. Eckert; Treas. and Comptroller: Mr. Norris Koopmann; Fiscal Exec., Mr. Paul A. Unke; Real Estate Mgr., Mr. Arthur W. Schaefer.
Board of Education: Office, 3614 West North Ave., Milwaukee, WI 53208.
Exec. Sec., Adolph Fehlauer; Sec. of Schools, Mr. LeDell Plath; Sec. of Part-time Education, Rev. Wm. E. Fischer.
Gen. Board for Home Missions:
Exec. Sec., Rev. Norman W. Berg, 3512 W. North Ave., Milwaukee, WI 53208.
Gen. Board for World Missions:
Exec. Sec., Rev. Edgar Hoenecke, 4960 Academy St., San Diego, CA 92109.
Stewardship Board: Chmn., Rev. Robert Baer, 35556 Oakwood La., Westland, MI 48185.
Exec. Sec., Rev. James P. Schaefer, 3512 W. North Ave., Milwaukee, WI 53208.
Special Ministries Board:
Chmn.: Rev. Ernst F. Lehninger, 9302 Ridge Blvd., Wauwatosa, WI 53226.
Public Relations Committee:
Chmn.: Rev. Alfred C. Schewe, 2416 N. Grant Blvd., Milwaukee, WI 53210; Dir. of Publ. Inf., Rev. James P. Schaefer, 3512 W. North Ave., Milwaukee, WI 53208.

PERIODICALS
Wisconsin Theological Quarterly (q), 11844 N. Seminary Dr., 65 W. Mequon, WI 53092. Prof. Armin Schuetze, Mng. Ed.
Northwestern Lutheran (bi-w), 3624 W. North Ave., Milwaukee, WI 53208. Rev. Harold E. Wicke, Ed.
Junior Northwestern (m), Editorial Committee: Arthur Schulz, Roland H. Hoenecke, C. J. Trapp; Dr. Martin Luther College, New Ulm, MN 56073.
Yearbook, 3624 W. North Ave., Milwaukee, WI 53208. Rev. S. Fenske, Ed.
The Lutheran Educator, 3614 W. North Ave., Milwaukee, WI 53208. A. F. Fehlauer, Ed.

RELIGIOUS BODIES IN THE UNITED STATES ARRANGED BY FAMILIES

The following list of religious bodies appearing in the Directory Section of this **Yearbook** shows the "families," or related clusters into which American religious bodies can be grouped. For example, there are many communions that can be grouped under the heading "Baptist" for historical and theological reasons. It is not to be assumed, however, that all denominations under one family heading are similar in belief or practice. Often, any similarity is purely coincidental. The family clusters tend to represent historical factors more often than theological or practical ones. The family categories provide one of the major pitfalls of church statistics because of the tendency to combine the statistics by "families" for analytical and comparative purposes. Such combined totals are almost meaningless, although often used as variables for sociological analysis. **Religious bodies not grouped under family headings appear alphabetically and are not indented in the following list.**

ADVENTIST BODIES
Advent Christian Church
Church of God General Conference (Oregon, Ill.)
Primitive Advent Christian Church
Seventh-day Adventists

The African Orthodox Church
Amana Church Society
American Evangelical Christian Churches
American Rescue Workers
The Anglican Orthodox Church of North America
Baha'i Faith

BAPTIST BODIES
American Baptist Association
American Baptist Churches in the U.S.A.
Baptist General Conference
Baptist Missionary Association of America
Bethel Ministerial Association, Inc.
Christian Unity Baptist Association
Conservative Baptist Association of America
Duck River (and Kindred) Associations of Baptists
Free Will Baptists
The General Association of Regular Baptist Churches
General Baptists, General Association of
General Conference of the Evangelical Baptist Church, Inc.
General Six-Principle Baptists
National Baptist Convention of America
National Baptist Convention, U.S.A., Inc.
National Baptist Evangelical Life and Soul Saving Assembly of U.S.A.
National Primitive Baptist Convention, Inc.
North American Baptist General Conference
Primitive Baptists
Progressive National Baptist Convention, Inc.
Separate Baptists in Christ
Seventh Day Baptist General Conference
Southern Baptist Convention
The United Free Will Baptist Church

Berean Fundamental Church

BRETHREN (German Baptists)
Brethren Church (Ashland, Ohio)
Brethren Churches, National Fellowship of
Church of the Brethren
Old German Baptist Brethren

BRETHREN, RIVER
Brethren in Christ Church
United Zion Church

Buddhist Churches of America
Christadelphians

The Christian and Missionary Alliance
Christian Catholic Church
Christian Church (Disciples of Christ)
Christian Churches and Churches of Christ
Christian Nation Church U.S.A.
Christian Union
Christ's Sanctified Holy Church
Church of Christ (Holiness), U.S.A.
Church of Christ, Scientist
The Church of Illumination
Church of the Nazarene
The Church of Revelation
Churches of Christ
Churches of Christ in Christian Union

CHURCHES OF GOD
Church of God (Anderson, Ind.)
The Church of God (Seventh day)
The Church of God (Seventh Day), Denver, Colo.
Church of God and Saints of Christ
Church of God by Faith
Churches of God in North America, General Eldership

CHURCHES OF THE LIVING GOD
Church of the Living God
House of God, Which is the Church of the Living God, the Pillar and Ground of the Truth, Inc.

CHURCHES OF THE NEW JERUSALEM
General Church of the New Jerusalem
General Convention The Swedenborgian Church

Community Churches
Congregational Christian Churches, National Association of
Conservative Congregational Christian Conference

EASTERN CHURCHES
Albanian Orthodox Archdiocese in America
Albanian Orthodox Diocese of America
The American Carpatho-Russian Orthodox Greek Catholic Church
Antiochian Orthodox Archdiocese of Toledo, Ohio and Dependencies in N.A.
The Antiochian Orthodox Christian Archdiocese of N.Y. and all N.A.
Armenian Apostolic Church of America
Armenian Church of North America, Diocese of the (Including Diocese of California)
Bulgarian Eastern Orthodox Church
Church of the East (Assyrians)
Eastern Orthodox Catholic Church in America
Greek Orthodox Archdiocese of North and South America

EVANGELISTIC ASSOCIATIONS

Holy Orthodox Church in America
Holy Ukrainian Autocephalic Orthodox Church in Exile
The Orthodox Church in America
Romanian Orthodox Church in America
The Romanian Orthodox Episcopate of America
Russian Orthodox Church in the U.S.A., Patriarchal Parishes of the
The Russian Orthodox Church Outside Russia
Serbian Eastern Orthodox Church for the U.S.A. and Canada
Syrian Orthodox Church of Antioch (Archdiocese of the U.S.A. and Canada)
Ukrainian Orthodox Church in America
Ukrainian Orthodox Church of America (Ecumenical Patriarchate)

The Episcopal Church
Ethical Culture Movement
Evangelical Church of North America
Evangelical Congregational Church
The Evangelical Covenant Church of America
The Evangelical Free Church of America

EVANGELISTIC ASSOCIATIONS

Apostolic Christian Church (Nazarean)
Apostolic Christian Churches of America
The Christian Congregation
Church of Daniel's Band
The Gospel Mission Corps
The Missionary Church
Pillar of Fire

The Fire-Baptized Holiness Church (Wesleyan)
Free Christian Zion Church of Christ

FRIENDS

Evangelical Friends Alliance
Friends General Conference
Friends United Meeting
Religious Society of Friends (Conservative)
Religious Society of Friends (Unaffiliated Meetings)

The Holiness Church of God, Inc.
Independent Fundamental Churches of America
Israelite House of David
Jehovah's Witnesses
Jewish Congregations
Kodesh Church of Immanuel

LATTER DAY SAINTS

Church of Christ
The Church of Jesus Christ (Bickertonites)
The Church of Jesus Christ of Latter-day Saints
Reorganized Church of Jesus Christ of Latter Day Saints

Liberal Catholic Church (California)
The Liberal Catholic Church (World Headquarters—London, England)

LUTHERANS

The American Lutheran Church
Apostolic Lutheran Church of America
Church of the Lutheran Brethren of America
Evangelical Lutheran Church in America (Eielsen Synod)
Evangelical Lutheran Synod
Lutheran Church in America
The Lutheran Church—Missouri Synod

The Protestant Conference (Lutheran)
Wisconsin Evangelical Lutheran Synod

MENNONITE BODIES

Beachy Amish Mennonite Churches
Church of God in Christ (Mennonite)
Evangelical Mennonite Brethren Conference
Evangelical Mennonite Church
General Conference of Mennonite Brethren Churches
Hutterian Brethren
Mennonite Church
Mennonite Church, The General Conference
Old Order Amish Church
Old Order (Wisler) Mennonite Church
Reformed Mennonite Church

METHODIST BODIES

African Methodist Episcopal Church
African Methodist Episcopal Zion Church
Bible Protestant Church
Christian Methodist Episcopal Church
Evangelical Methodist Church
Free Methodist Church of North America
Fundamental Methodist Church, Inc.
Primitive Methodist Church, U.S.A.
Reformed Methodist Union Episcopal Church
Reformed Zion Union Apostolic Church
Southern Methodist Church
The United Methodist Church
The United Wesleyan Methodist Church of America

The Metropolitan Church Association

MORAVIAN BODIES

Moravian Church in America (Unitas Fratrum)
Unity of the Brethren

Muslims
New Apostolic Church of North America
North American Old Roman Catholic Church

OLD CATHOLIC CHURCHES

The American Catholic Church, Archdiocese of New York
The American Catholic Church (Syro-Antiochian)
Christ Catholic Church (Diocese of Boston)
Christ Catholic Exarchate of Americas and Eastern Hemisphere
North American Old Roman Catholic Church

The Old Roman Catholic Church (English Rite)

PENTECOSTAL BODIES

*Holiness-Pentecostal Denominations**

The Apostolic Faith
The Church of God
Church of God (Cleveland, TN)
The Church of God in Christ
Church of God in Christ, International
The Church of God of Prophecy
The Church of God of the Mountain Assembly
Congregational Holiness Church
International Pentecostal Assemblies
The (Original) Church of God
Pentecostal Church of Christ
Pentecostal Fire-Baptized Holiness Church
Pentecostal Free-Will Baptist Church, Inc.

Pentecostal Holiness Church, Inc.
United Holy Church of America

*Baptistic-Pentecostal Denominations**

Assemblies of God
Christian Church of North America, General
Council
Elim Fellowship
Independent Assemblies of God, International
International Church of the Foursquare
Gospel
Open Bible Standard Churches
Pentecostal Church of God of America, Inc.

*Unitarian (Oneness)-Pentecostal Denominations**

Apostolic Overcoming Holy Church of God
Bible Way Church of Our Lord Jesus Christ,
World Wide, Inc.
Church of Our Lord Jesus Christ of the
Apostolic Faith
Pentecostal Assemblies of the World
United Pentecostal Church

(*The above typology for Pentecostal Bodies
was supplied by Dr. H. Vinson Synan, Emmanuel College, Franklin Springs, Georgia to
whom the editor is grateful. According to Dr.
Synan, "Holiness-Pentecostal" bodies are those
that teach the three stages theory of Christian
experience (i.e. conversion, sanctification, baptism of the Holy Spirit). "Baptistic-Pentecostal"
denominations are those that teach a two-stage
theory (i.e., conversion and baptism of the
Holy Spirit). "Unitarian-Pentecostal" bodies
deny the traditional concept of the Trinity
and teach that Jesus Christ alone is God.)

Plymouth Brethren
Polish National Catholic Church of America

PRESBYTERIAN BODIES
Associate Reformed Presbyterian Church
(General Synod)
Cumberland Presbyterian Church

The Orthodox Presbyterian Church
Presbyterian Church in the U.S.
Reformed Presbyterian Church, Evangelical
Synod
Reformed Presbyterian Church of North
America
Second Cumberland Presbyterian Church in
U.S.
The United Presbyterian Church in the U.S.A.

REFORMED BODIES
Christian Reformed Church
Hungarian Reformed Church in America
Netherlands Reformed Congregations
Protestant Reformed Churches in America
Reformed Church in America
Reformed Church in the U.S.

Reformed Episcopal Church
The Roman Catholic Church
The Salvation Army
The Schwenkfelder Church
Social Brethren Church

SPIRITUALIST BODIES
International General Assembly of Spiritualists
The National Spiritual Alliance of the U.S.A.
National Spiritualist Association of Churches

Triumph the Church and Kingdom of God in
Christ
Unitarian Universalist Association

UNITED BRETHREN BODIES
United Brethren in Christ
United Christian Church

United Church of Christ
United Seventh Day Brethren
Vedanta Society of New York
Volunteers of America
The Wesleyan Church
Wesleyan Holiness Association of Churches

4. RELIGIOUS BODIES IN CANADA

A large number of Canadian religious bodies were organized by immigrants from Europe and elsewhere and a smaller number of them sprang up originally on Canadian soil. In the case of Canada, moreover, many denominations overlapping the U.S.-Canadian border have headquarters in the United States.

In the past year, a concerted effort has been made to develop completeness in this directory and much improvement over the previous listing in the 1972 edition has been made. The editor of the **Yearbook of American and Canadian Churches** would be grateful for information on any Canadian religious body not now included.

What follows is, first, an alphabetical directory of religious bodies in Canada that have supplied information for this edition of the **Yearbook.** The second section is an alphabetical list, with addresses and other information, of bodies known to exist in Canada that have not yet supplied directory information. This second section is entitled "Other Religious Bodies in Canada."

Those directories which have not been corrected for this edition of the **Yearbook** by denominational officials carry the symbol (†) in front of the title of the denomination.

The Anglican Church of Canada

Anglicanism came to Canada with the early explorers such as Martin Frobisher and Henry Hudson. Continuous services began in Newfoundland about 1700 and in Nova Scotia in 1710. The first Bishop, Charles Inglis, was appointed to Nova Scotia in 1787. The numerical strength of Anglicanism was increased by the coming of American Loyalists and by massive immigration both after the Napoleonic wars and in the later 19th and early 20th centuries.

The Anglican Church of Canada has enjoyed self-government for over a century and is an autonomous member of the worldwide Anglican Communion. The General Synod, which normally meets biennially, consists of the Archbishops, Bishops, and elected clerical and lay representatives of the 28 dioceses. Each of the Ecclesiastical Provinces—Canada, Ontario, Rupert's Land, and British Columbia—is organized under a Metropolitan and has its own Provincial Synod and Executive Council. Each diocese has its own Diocesan Synod meeting usually annually.

Churches: 1,736. Inclusive Membership: 1,126,-570. Sunday or Sabbath Schools: 2,197. Total Enrollment: 150,776. Ordained clergy: 2,658.

GENERAL SYNOD OFFICERS

Primate of the Anglican Church of Canada, Most Rev. E. W. Scott, 600 Jarvis St., Toronto 285, Ontario
Prolocutor, Miss Betty C. Graham, Toronto, Ontario
Gen. Sec., Ven. E. S. Light, 600 Jarvis St., Toronto 285, Ontario.
Gen Treas. and Treas. of all Departments, John R. Ligertwood, 600 Jarvis St., Toronto 285, Ontario.

DEPARTMENTS AND DIVISIONS

Offices: Church House, 600 Jarvis St., Toronto 285, Ontario, Canada.
Exec. Dir. of Program, L. C. Raymond.
Missionary Society of the Anglican Church of Canada. Exec. Sec., T. M. Anthony.
Division of National and World Program: Dir., T. M. Anthony.
Division of Parish and Diocesan Services: Dir., P. C. Jefferson.

Division of Communications: Dir., Michael O'-Meara.
Division of Planning: Dir., W. E. Lowe.
Division of Pensions: Dir., G. E. Hobson.
Department of Administration and Finance: Dir., J. R. Ligertwood.
Anglican Book Centre: Mgr., M. J. Lloyd.

METROPOLITANS (ARCHBISHOPS)
(Address: The Most Reverend)
Ecclesiastical Province of:
Canada: W. W. Davis, 5732 College St, Halifax, Nova Scotia.
Rupert's Land: G. F. C. Jackson, 1501 College Ave., Regina, Saskatchewan. S4P IB8
British Columbia: R. S. Dean, 360 Nicola St., Kamloops, British Columbia.
Ontario: W. L. Wright, Bishophurst, Box 637, Sault Ste. Marie, Ontario.

DIOCESAN ARCHBISHOPS AND BISHOPS
(Address: the Most Reverend; the Right Reverend)
Algoma: W. L. Wright (Archbishop), Bishophurst, Box 637, Sault Ste. Marie, Ontario.
Artic: D. B. Marsh, 1055 Avenue Rd., Toronto 12, Ontario.
Athabasca: R. J. Pierce, Box 279, Peace River, Alberta TOH 2X0.
Brandon: T. W. Wilkinson, Synod Office 341-13th St., Brandon, Manitoba. 47A 4P8
British Columbia: F. R. Gartrell, 912 Vancouver St., Victoria, British Columbia.
Caledonia: D. W. Hambridge, 208 Fourth Ave., Prince Rupert, British Columbia.
Calgary: M. L. Goodman, 3015 Clencoe Rd. S. W., Calgary, Alberta T2S 2L9.
Cariboo: R. S. Dean, (Archbishop) 360 Nicola St., Kamloops, British Columbia.
Edmonton: W. G. Burch, 9707-107th St., Edmonton, Alberta T5K IE3
Fredericton: H. L. Nutter, 791 Brunswick St., Fredericton, New Brunswick, Ontario.
Huron: C. J. Queen, Box 308, London, Ontario.
Keewatin: H. V. Stiff, Box 118, Kenora, Ontario
Kootenay: R. E. F. Berry, 608 Sutherland Ave., Kelowna, British Columbia.
Montreal: R. K. Maguire 1444 Union Ave., Montreal, Quebec.
Moosonee: J. A. Watton, Bishopstope, Box 841, Schumacher, Ontario.
Newfoundland: R. L. Seaborn, 22 King's Bridge Rd., St. John's, Newfoundland.

New Westminister: T. D. Somerville, 692 Burrard St., Vancouver, British Columbia.

Niagara: W. E. Bagnall, 67 Victoria Ave. S., Hamilton, Ontario.

Nova Scotia: W. W. Davis, (Archbishop) 5732 College St., Halifax, Nova Scotia.

Ontario: J. B. Creeggan, 90 Johnson St., Kingston, Ontario.

Ottawa: W. J. Robinson, Bishop's Court, 71 Bronson Ave., Ottawa, Ontario K1R 6G6.

Quebec: T. J. Matthews, 36 rue Desjardins, Quebec 4, Quebec.

Qu'Appelle: G. F. G. Jackson (Archbishop), Bishopscourt, 1501 College Ave., Regina, Saskatchewan S4P 1B8.

Rupert's Land: Barry Valentine, 66 St. Cross St., Winnipeg, Manitoba R2W 3X8.

Saskatchewan: H. V. R. Short, Bishopthrope, Box 1088, Prince Albert, Saskatchewan S6V 5S6.

Saskatoon: D. A. Ford, 334-5th Ave. N., Saskatoon, Saskatchewan S7K 2P4.

Toronto: G. B. Snell, 135 Adelaide St., E., Toronto 1, Ontario.

Yukon: J. T. Frame, Box 4247, Whitehorse, Yukon.

The Antiochian Orthodox Christian Archdiocese of New York and All North America

There are approximately 25,000 members of the Antiochian Orthodox community living in Canada. They are under the jurisdiction of the Patriarch of Antioch and All the East, with headquarters in Damascus, Syria. There are churches in Ottawa, Toronto, and Montreal and a number of missions in other cities.

Churches: 4. Inclusive Membership: 25,000. Sunday or Sabbath Schools: N.R. Total Enrollment: N.R. Ordained clergy: 3.

GENERAL ORGANIZATION
Metropolitan Archbishop, Philip (Saliba), 358 Mountain Rd., Englewood, NJ 07631.

In Canada: Rev. Fr. Emile Hanna, St. George's Orthodox Church, 555-575 Jean Talon St., E., Montreal 328, Quebec.

The Apostolic Church in Canada

Founded in Wales in 1904 and brought over to Canada thereafter.

GENERAL ORGANIZATION
The Apostolic Church Council, twice yearly.

OFFICERS
Pres., Rev. D. S. Morris, 388 Gerald St., La Salle, Quebec.

Natl. Sec., Rev. Vernon E. Wood, 715 Huron, London 25, Ontario.

The Armenian Church of North America, Diocese of Canada

The Canadian branch of the Ancient Church of Armenia founded in A.D. 301 by St. Gregory the Illuminator. It was established in Canada at St. Catherines, Ontario, in 1930.

The diocesan organization is under the jurisdiction of the Holy See of Etchmiadzin, Armenia, U.S.S.R. The Diocese of Canada is normally under the jurisdiction of a suffragan bishop within the Diocese of the Armenian Church of North America.

Churches: 3. Inclusive Membership: 15,000. Sunday or Sabbath Schools: N.R. Total Enrollment: 700. Ordained clergy 4.

GENERAL ORGANIZATION
Diocesan Offices: St. Gregory the Illuminator Cathedral, 615 Stuart Ave., Montreal 154, Quebec.

OFFICER
Vicar: Rt. Rev. Zaven Arzoomanian, 615 Stuart Ave., Montreal 154, Quebec.

PERIODICALS
Nor Serout (m) in Armenian and English, 14 Woodlawn Ave., Toronto 190, Ontario.

Pourastan (m) in Armenian, 615 Stuart Ave., Montreal 154, Quebec.

Associated Gospel Churches

Founded in 1922 by Dr. Peter Philpott and H. E. Irwin, K. C., in Hamilton and Toronto, Ontario. Letters of Patent obtained from the Canadian Government in 1925. This body stresses historical, conservative theology.

Churches: 104. Inclusive Membership: 10,000. Sunday or Sabbath Schools: 101. Total Enrollment: N.R. Ordained clergy 167.

GENERAL ORGANIZATION
Annual Conference. Next meeting, June, 1973. A 20-member Executive Committee acts in the interim.

Headquarters: 280 Plains Rd. W., Burlington, Ontario.

OFFICERS
Pres., Rev. L. K. Redinger, Box 341. Beamsville, Ontario.

Vice-Pres., Rev. L. Grant Wright, 7 Duffield Rd., Weston, Ontario.

Sec.-Treas., Rev. J. L. Hockney, 280 Plains Rd. W., Burlington, Ontario.

PERIODICAL
Advance (bi-m), 84 Merrick St., Hamilton 11, Ontario. Rev. Alex B. Stein, Ed.

The Association of Regular Baptist Churches (Canada)

Organized in 1957 by a group of churches for the purpose of mutual cooperation in missionary activities. The Association believes the Bible to be God's word, stands for historic Baptist principles, and opposes modern ecumenism.

Headquarters: 337 Jarvis St., Toronto, Ontario. Tel. (416) 925-3261.

OFFICERS
Pres., Dr. H. C. Slade, 337 Jarvis St., Toronto, Ontario.

BAHA'I FAITH

Sec., Rev. J. C. McCombe, 130 Gerrard St., E., Toronto 225, Ontario.

PERIODICAL

The Gospel Witness, 130 Gerrard St. E., Toronto, Ontario. Dr. H. C. Slade, Ed.

Baha'i Faith

(National Spiritual Assembly of Baha'is in Canada).

Followers of Baha'u'llah (1817-1892) whose religion upholds the basic principles of progressive revelation, religious unity, and a new world order.

The Bahá'is administrative order consists of local communities, each with local assemblies, elective national assemblies, and a spiritual and administrative world center at Haifa, Israel.

This body was incorporated by Act of Parliament in 1949. There are approximately 800 Baha'i centers in Canada, one-fifth of them electing local spiritual assemblies.

GENERAL ORGANIZATION

National Spiritual Assembly Headquarters: 7290 Leslie St., Willowdale, Ontario. Sec., Mr. M. E. Muttart.

Baptist Federation of Canada

The Baptist Federation of Canada has four federated member bodies: 1) Baptist Convention of Ontario and Quebec, 2) Baptist Union of Western Canada, 3) the United Baptist Convention of the Atlantic Provinces, 4) French Baptist Union. Its main purpose is to act as a coordinating agency for the four groups.

Churches: 1,110. Inclusive Membership: 132,003. Sunday or Sabbath Schools: 973. Total Enrollment: 54,899 Ordained clergy: 860.

GENERAL ORGANIZATION

Office: 91 Queen St., Box 1298, Brantford, Ontario. Tel. (519) 752-9114.

OFFICERS

Pres., Dr. T. B. McDormand, 50 Elmwood Dr., Amherst, Nova Scotia.
Vice-Presidents, Rev. J. Frank Patch, 235 Metcalfe Ave., Apt. 306, Westmont, Montreal 215, Quebec; Mrs. R. Gavin, 11204-125 St., Edmonton, Alberta.
Gen. Sec.-Treas., Dr. R. F. Bullen, Box 901, Brantford, Ontario.
Gen. Sec., Canadian Baptist Overseas Mission Board, 217 St. George St., Toronto, Ontario, Dr. John Keith.

1. *Baptist Convention of Ontario and Quebec*
Office: 217 St. George St., Toronto 180, Ontario Canada. Tel. (416) 922-5163.

Churches: 380. Inclusive Membership: 46,709. Sunday or Sabbath Schools: 380. Total Enrollment: 17,644. Ordained clergy: 389.

Note: *The above statistics are a subtotal for the Baptist Federation of Canada whose total statistics are reported initially.*

OFFICERS

Pres., Mr. David Simmonds, R.R. 1, Port Perry, Ontario.
1st Vice-Pres., Rev. D. Timpany, Smith Falls, Ontario.
2nd Vice-Pres., Mrs. V. Pearson, Stratford, Ontario.
Gen. Sec., Dr. Ronald F. Watts, Oakville, Ontario.
Treas., Michael E. C. Lang, Burlington, Ontario.

DEPARTMENTS

Dept. of Canadian Missions: Chmn., Rev. James Taylor, Tillsonburg, Ontario; Sec., Rev. A. R. Goldie, Toronto, Ontario.
Dept. of Christian Education: Chmn., Rev. Elmer G. Anderson, Dundas, Ontario; Sec., Rev. Ronald D. Harmer, Burlington, Ontario.
Dept. of Ministry: Chmn., Rev. K. W. Morrison, Dunville, Ontario; Sec., Rev. Fred M. Ward, Richmond Hill, Ontario.
Dept. of Overseas Missions: Chmn., George McMillan, Brantford, Ontario; Sec., Dr. John F. Keith, Burlington, Ontario.

PERIODICAL

The Canadian Baptist, 217 St. George St., Toronto 180, Ontario, Harold U. Trinier, Ed.

2. *Baptist Union of Western Canada*
Office: 8925-82nd Ave., Edmonton, Alberta. Tel. (403) 465-2025. Mailing address: P. O. Box 5828, Stn. L., Edmonton, Alberta.

Churches: 134. Inclusive Membership: 17,151 Sunday or Sabbath Schools: 132. Total Enrollment: 14,522. Ordained clergy: 159.

Note: *The above statistics are a subtotal for for the Baptist Federation of Canada whose total statistics are reported initially.*

OFFICERS

Pres., Mr. J. E. Law.
Exec. Minister, Rev. Harry A. Renfree.
Area Minister, Alberta, Rev. R. C. Standerwick, 2304 Lancing Ave., S. W., Calgary.
Area Minister, British Columbia, Rev. Philip Collins, 1460 W. 49th Ave., Vancouver 13.
Area Minister, Manitoba, Rev. E. M. Thompson, 581 Linden Ave., Winnipeg 15.
Area Minister, Saskatchewan, Rev. B. F. Haskins, 2270 Queen St., Regina.

3. *United Baptist Convention of the Atlantic Provinces*
Office: 112 Princess St., P. O. Drawer 1053, Saint John, New Brunswick.

Churches: 596. Inclusive Membership: 68,143. Sunday or Sabbath Schools: 461. Total Enrollment: 22,683. Ordained clergy: 312.
Note: *The above statistics are a subtotal for the Baptist Federation of Canada whose total statistics are reported initially.*

OFFICERS

Pres., Mr. G. E. Phillips, Woodstock, New Brunswick.
Gen. Sec., Rev. Keith R. Hobson, 112 Princess St., Saint John, New Brunswick.

Treas., Miss Edna I. Potter, Box 1053, Saint John, New Brunswick.
Supt. Home Missions, Rev. W. E. O'Grady, 112 Princess St., Saint John, New Brunswick.
Field Sec., Bd. of Christian Education, Rev. Byron W. Fenwick, 112 Princess St., Saint John, New Brunswick.
Assts. to Gen. Sec., Rev. Daniel Dryer; Rev. Wrenfred Bryant, 112 Princess St., Saint Saint John, New Brunswick.
Dir. of Evangelism, Rev. B. G. Redding, Box 91, Saint John, New Brunswick.

PERIODICAL
The Atlantic Baptist, Box 756, Kentville, Nova Scotia. Rev. George E. Simpson, Ed.

4. *French Baptist Union* (Union d'Eglises Baptistes Françaises au Canada)
Headquarters: 3674 rue Ontario est, Montreal 403, Quebec. Gen. Sec., Rev. Maurice C. Boillat.

Baptist General Conference

Founded in Canada by missionaries from the United States. Originally a Swedish body, but no longer an ethnic body. The BGC includes people of many nationalities and is conservative and evangelical in doctrine and practice.

The Baptist General Conference has three conferences in Canada, all separately incorporated as follows:
1. *The Central Canada Baptist Conference* (Manitoba, Saskatchewan, and part of Ontario).
2. *Baptist General Conference of Alberta.*
3. *Columbia Conference* (partly in British Columbia and the remainder in the Northwest U.S.).

Churches: 111. Inclusive Membership: 12,432. Sunday or Sabbath Schools: 111. Total Enrollment: 15,768. Ordained clergy: N.R.

1. *The Central Canada Baptist Conference.*
Annual Conference in May.
Headquarters: 421 Berkley St., N., Winnipeg, Manitoba R3R 1J7. Tel. (214) 837-2921.

OFFICERS
Mod., Rev. George Bell, 16 Elderwood Dr., Brandon, Manitoba.
Exec. Sec., David L. Clink, 421 Berkley St., N., Winnipeg, Manitoba R3R 1J7.

PERIODICAL
The Christian Link (m), Box 524, Red Lake, Ontario. Rev. John Brown, Ed.

2. *Baptist General Conference of Alberta.*
Annual Conference in June.
Headquarters: 5011-122A St., Edmonton, Alberta. Tel. (403) 435-4974.

OFFICERS
Mod., Wesley F. Long, Box 2053, Hinton, Alberta.
Exec. Sec., Abe Funk, 5011-122A St., Edmonton, Alberta.

PERIODICALS
The Challenge, 5011-122A St., Edmonton, Alberta. Rev. Abe Funk, Ed.

3. *Columbia Baptist Conference.*
Annual Conference in May.
Headquarters: 14032 Aurora Ave., N., Seattle, WA 98133 or P. O. Box 65, White Rock, British Columbia. Tel. (206) 365-9890.

OFFICERS
Mod., Donald Stoops, 327 "C" St., Ephrata, WA 98823.
Exec. Sec., John H. Bergeson, 14032 Aurora Ave., N., Seattle, WA 98133.

PERIODICAL
The Conference Call, 14032 Aurora Ave., N., Seattle, WA 98133. Rev. John Bergeson, Ed.

Bible Holiness Movement

A missionary and evangelistic movement organized at Vancouver, British Columbia in 1949. It emphasizes the original Methodist faith of salvation and Scriptural holiness with principles of exacting discipleship, nonconformity, and nonresistance. Overseas indigenous missionary centers have been developed.

Churches: 7. Inclusive Membership: 112. Sunday or Sabbath Schools: N.R. Total Enrollment: N.R. Ordained clergy 5.

International Headquarters:
Box 223 Postal Stn. A, Vancouver 1, British Columbia.

DIRECTORS
Evangelist Wesley H. Wakefield, Pres. (International Leader).
Evangelist M. J. Wakefield.
Evangelist Napoleon Sneed, 155 Windemere, Calgary, Alberta.
Evangelist A. E. Powell.

PERIODICAL
Truth on Fire (bi-m), Box 223 Postal Stn. A., Vancouver 1, British Columbia. Rev. Wesley H. Wakefield, Ed.

Brethren in Christ Church, Canadian Conference

The Brethren in Christ, known as Tunkers in Canada, arose out of a religious awakening in Lancaster County, Pa., late in the eighteenth century. Representatives of the new denomination reached Ontario in 1788 and established the church in the southern part of the present province. Presently the conference has congregations in Ontario and Saskatchewan. In doctrine the body is evangelical, Arminian, holiness, and premillennial.

Churches: 27. Inclusive Membership: 1,466. Sunday or Sabbath Schools: 27. Total Enrollment: 2,806. Ordained clergy: 47.

Headquarters: 301 N. Elm St., Nappanee, IN 46550. Tel. (219) 773-3164. Canadian Headquarters (Bishop's office): P. O. Box 65, Sherkston, Ontario. Tel. (416) 894-3602.

OFFICERS
Mod., Bishop Roy V. Sider, P.O. Box 65, Sherkston, Ontario.

THE CANADIAN BAPTIST CONFERENCE

Sec., W. Lloyd Hogg, R. R. 3, Stouffville, Ontario.

PERIODICAL
Evangelical Visitor (bi-w), Nappanee, IN 46550. Rev. John E. Zercher, Ed.

The Canadian Baptist Conference

This conference was founded in 1959 at Kamloops, British Columbia by pastors of existing churches. It is associated with the Northwest Baptist Convention of the Southern Baptist Convention with offices at 811 NW 20th, Portland, OR 97209.

Churches: 25. Inclusive Membership: 1,688. Sunday or Sabbath Schools: 25. Total Enrollment: 2,633. Ordained clergy: 23.

Headquarters: 11136 Knudson Rd., Delta, British Columbia. Tel. (604) 588-2413.

OFFICER
Supt. of Church Ministries, Rev. Bob Dove.

PERIODICAL
Pacific Coast Baptist (bi-m), 811 NW 20th, Portland, OR 97209. C. E. Boyle, Ed.

Canadian Jewish Congress

The Canadian Jewish Congress was founded in 1919 and reorganized in 1934. It is the national representative body of Canadian Jewry having as its functions the protection of the status, rights, and welfare of Canadian Jews; the promotion of understanding and goodwill among ethnic and religious groups, and the combatting of anti-semitism; the improvement, through the establishment of cooperative relationships with other Jewish agencies, of social, economic, and cultural conditions, and the rehabilitation of Jewish refugees and immigrants; the establishment of central community organizations to provide for the social, philanthropic, educational, and cultural needs of Jews.

Churches: N.R. Inclusive Membership: 280,000. Sunday or Sabbath Schools: N.R. Total Enrollment: N.R. Ordained clergy N.R.

GENERAL ORGANIZATION
Headquarters: 1590 McGregor Ave., Montreal 109, Quebec.

OFFICERS
Natl. Pres., Sol Kanee.
Exec. Vice-Pres., Saul Hayes.

PERIODICALS
Cahiers du Cercle Juif (bi-a), 1590 McGregor Ave., Montreal 109, Quebec. V. M. H. Rodriguez, Ed. Bulletin du Cercle Juif (m), 1590 McGregor Ave., Montreal 109, Quebec. V. M. H. Rodriguez, Ed.
Congress Bulletin (m), 1590 McGregor Ave., Montreal 109, Quebec. Perry Cohen, Ed.

The Canadian Yearly Meeting of the Religious Society of Friends

Founded in Canada in 1833, this body is associated with both the Friends United Meeting and the Friends General Conference (see listing in the section Religious Bodies in the U.S. in this edition).

Churches: 24. Inclusive Membership: 972. Sunday or Sabbath Schools: N.R. Total Enrollment: N.R. Ordained clergy: None.

GENERAL ORGANIZATION
Meeting: Annual.
Headquarters: 60 Lowther Ave., Toronto, Ontario. Tel. (416) 922-2632.

CLERK
Mr. Burton Hill, Box 33, Rockwood, Ontario.

PERIODICAL
The Canadian Friend, J. Elizabeth Hopkins, Ed.

The Christian and Missionary Alliance in Canada

The ministry of the Alliance first began in Canada in 1897 at Peterborough, Ontario. Meetings were held in Ottawa, Toronto, Peterborough, Montreal, and other Canadian cities. The founder, Rev. A. B. Simpson, D.D., was born in Prince Edward Island, educated in Toronto, and served in the Presbyterian ministry, having as his first church, Knox, in Hamilton, Ontario.

Churches: 188 Inclusive Membership: 21,355 Sunday or Sabbath Schools: 178 Total Enrollment: 25,951 Ordained clergy: 200.

GENERAL ORGANIZATION
Headquarters: 2026 Yonge St., Toronto 295, Ontario. Tel (416) 489-1659.
General Conference: Annual. Next meeting in Winnipeg, May, 1973.

OFFICERS
Pres., Rev. William J. Newell, 125 Panin Rd., Burlington, Ontario.
Vice-Pres., Rev. A. H. Orthner, 2821 Parliament Ave., Regina, Saskatchewan.
Sec., Rev. Roy McIntyre, 2528 Chicoutimi Dr., N. W., Calgary, Alberta.
Treas., Dr. B. S. King, 260 W. 44th St., New York, NY 10036.

Christian Church (Disciples of Christ)

Organized in May, 1922, the Committee serves the Churches of Christ (Disciples) in Canada, which were founded 160 years ago.

Churches: 41. Inclusive Membership: 4,836. Sunday or Sabbath Schools: 41. Total Enrollment: 2,554. Ordained clergy: 47.
Headquarters: 130 Merton St., Suite 301, Toronto 7, Ontario. Tel. (416) 488-1412.

OFFICERS
Chmn., Rev. R. K. Leland, Winger, Ontario.
Vice-Chmn., Mrs. K. McNeil, R.R. 2, Springfield, Ontario.
Treas., W. H. Luton, London, Ont.
Gen. Sec., K. S. Wills, Toronto, Ont.

PERIODICAL
Canadian Disciple (m), 130 Merton St., Suite 301, Toronto 7, Ontario. Mrs. J. W. Hutcheson, Ed.

Christian Churches and Churces of Christ in Canada

This undenominational fellowship, dedicated to the "restoration of the New Testament Church in doctrine, ordinances and life," has been operating in Canada since 1820. There is no general organization. Each church within the fellowship is completely independent. For detailed information see: *Directory of the Ministry,* Christian Churches and Churches of Christ, 1525 Cherry Rd., Springfield, IL 62704, U.S.A.

Churches: 77. Inclusive Membership: 5,036. Sunday or Sabbath Schools: 77. Total Enrollment: 3,265. Ordained clergy 56.

The Church of God of Prophecy in Canada

John Harris organized the first church of this group at Swan River, Manitoba in 1937. There are now established churches in British Columbia, Manitoba, Alberta, Saskatchewan, Ontario, and Quebec.

General Meetings: Annually held in the various Provinces in June and July.

Churches: 24. Inclusive Membership: 1,150. Sunday or Sabbath Schools: 29. Total Enrollment: 1,287. Ordained clergy: 42.

Headquarters: 3269 Academy Dr., Windsor 21, Ontario. Tel. (519) 969-6768.

OFFICERS
Natl. Overseer, Hugh R. Edwards.
Natl. Treas., Wanda Edwards.

PERIODICALS
Canadian Trumpeter (m), Hugh R. Edwards, Ed.
Active Christian (m), Wanda Edwards, Ed.

The Church of Jesus Christ of Latter-day Saints in Canada

This body has no central headquarters in Canada, only regional offices. All General Authorities of The Church of Jesus Christ of Latter-day Saints can be reached at 47 East South Temple St., Salt Lake City, UT 84111 [See U. S. Directory, "Religious Bodies in the United States" in this edition for further details.]

In Canada, there are 11 Stakes, 19 Districts, and Branches and 189 Wards. Those holding the Priesthood in Canada total 20,185 men. There are no career clergy, only lay clergy.

A listing of "Mission and Stake (Diocese) Officers of Church of Jesus Christ of Latter-day Saints in Canada" may be obtained from Church Information Service, 19 West South Temple St., Salt Lake City, UT 84111.

Churches: 214. Inclusive Membership: 58,683. Sunday or Sabbath Schools: 214. Total Enrollment: 29,400. Ordained clergy: 1,239.

The Evangelical Church in Canada

Founded early in the 19th century by Jacob Albright and William Otterbein in Pennsylvania as the Evangelical Church, this body became known later as the Evangelical United Brethren Church, which in the U.S. became a part of The United Methodist Church in 1968. This Canadian body is Methodist Episcopal in organization and Arminian, Wesleyan, and Methodist in doctrine. It was incorporated in 1928 by Dominion Charter as The Northwest Canada Conference Evangelical Church.

Churches: 50. Inclusive Membership: 3,736. Sunday or Sabbath Schools: 50. Total Enrollment: 5,226. Ordained Clergy: 62.

GENERAL ORGANIZATION
Council of Administration: Meets 2 to 4 times each year. Annual Conference. Quadrennial Conference, next meeting, June, 1974.

Headquarters: 164-5th St., S. E., Medicine Hat, Alberta T1A OM3 Tel. (403) 527-2754.

OFFICERS
Conference Supt., Rev. T. E. Jesske, 164-5th St., S. E., Medicine Hat, Alberta. T1A OM3.
Conference Chmn., Rev. A. W. Riegel, 2802-17th Ave., S. E., Medicine Hat, Alberta.
Conference Sec., Rev. A. Hein, 4335 Second St. N. W., Calgary, Alberta.

PERIODICAL
Northwest Canada Echoes (m), 2347-20th Ave. S.E., Medicine Hat, Alberta. Rev. A. R. Lieske, Ed.

The Evangelical Covenant Church of Canada

A Canadian denomination organized in Canada at Winnipeg in 1904 which is affiliated with the Evangelical Covenant Church of America and with the International Federation of Free Evangelical Churches, which includes churches in eleven European countries.

This body believes in the one triune God as confessed in the Apostles' Creed, that salvation is received through faith in Christ as Saviour, that the Bible is the authoritative guide in all matters of faith and practice. Christian Baptism and the Lord's Supper are accepted as divinely ordained sacraments of the church. As descendants of the 19th century pietistic awakening, the group believes in the need of a personal experience of commitment to Christ, the development of a virtuous life, and the urgency of spreading the gospel to the "ends of the world."

Most of the members of this group came from Northern Europe originally, primarily from Scandanavia.

Churches: 23. Inclusive Membership: 1,060. Sunday or Sabbath Schools: 21. Total Enrollment: 1,704. Ordained clergy: 11.

THE EVANGELICAL LUTHERAN CHURCH IN CANADA

GENERAL ORGANIZATION

Headquarters: 8501-82 Ave., Edmonton, Alberta T6C OY7. Tel. (403) 466-0462.

Conference: Annual. Next meeting, June 1973.

OFFICERS

Supt., Rev. Albert R. Josephson, 8501-82 Ave., Edmonton, Alberta T6C OY7.

Chmn., Rev. Wesley Morris, 2402 Kensington Rd., N. W., Calgary, Alberta T2N OY4.

Sec., Rev. James Stone, Box 828, Minnedosa, Manitoba ROJ 1EO.

Treas., Mr. Ralph Hubick, Site 8, R. R. 7, South Edmonton, Alberta.

PERIODICAL

The Covenant Messenger (m), 611 Quance Ave., Saskatoon, Saskatchewan S7H 3B5. Rev. Keith Fullerton, Ed.

The Evangelical Lutheran Church in Canada

This body was formerly the Canada District of The American Lutheran Church. On January 1, 1967, it became autonomous. The Confessional Statements are identical with those of The American Lutheran Church.

Churches: 318. Inclusive Membership: 83,274. Sunday or Sabbath Schools: 285. Total Enrollment: 23,746. Ordained clergy: 242.

GENERAL ORGANIZATION

Biennial Convention: 1974.

Headquarters: 212 Wiggins Ave., N., Saskatoon, Saskatchewan S7N 1K4. Tel. (306) 653-0133.

OFFICERS

Pres., Dr. S. T. Jacobson, 212 Wiggins Ave., N., Saskatoon, Saskatchewan S7N 1K4.

Vice-Pres., Dr. Roger W. Nostbakken (same address as above).

Sec., Rev. R. J. Busch (same address as above).

PERIODICAL

The Shepherd (m), 806-3rd St., N.E., Calgary, Alberta. Rev. Oscar Sommerfeld, Ed.

The Fellowship of Evangelical Baptist Churches in Canada

Formed in 1953 by the merging of the Union of Regular Baptist Churches of Ontario and Quebec with the Fellowship of Independent Baptist Churches of Canada.

Headquarters: 74 Sheppard Ave. W., Willowdale, Ontario. Tel. (416) 223-8696.

OFFICERS

Pres., Rev. W. N. Charlton.

Gen. Sec.-Treas., Dr. J. H. Watt.

PERIODICALS

Evangelical Baptist, 74 Sheppard Ave. W., Willowdale, Ontario. Le Phare, Box 72, Montreal 203, Quebec. Rev. W. H. Frey, Ed.

The Gospel Missionary Association

Initially organized in 1951 under the chairmanship of Rev. W. J. Laing of the Bethel Baptist Church and a group of clergymen of independent missions and churches; then incorporated by the Province of Alberta in 1956.

The doctrines of this body are: fundamental, premillennial, pre-tribulation rapture, evangelical, and congregational in church government.

Headquarters: c/o Bethel Baptist Church, 830 7th Ave., S.W., Calgary, Alberta T2P OZ9.

Annual Meeting: Fourth Wednesday in June.

OFFICERS

Pres., Rev. W. J. Laing, 830 7th Ave., S.W., Calgary, Alberta T2P OZ9.

Sec.-Treas., Rev. A. D. Cornell, 460 31st Ave., N.W., Calgary, Alberta T2M 2P4.

PERIODICAL

Impact.

Greek Orthodox Archdiocese of North and South America, Ninth Archdiocesan District

Greek Orthodox Christians in Canada under the jurisdiction of the Ecumenical Patriarchate of Constantinople (Istanbul).

Churches: 29. Inclusive Membership: 210,000. Sunday or Sabbath Schools: N.R. Total Enrollment: 10,500. Ordained clergy: 28.

GENERAL ORGANIZATION

Biennial Clergy-Laity Conference, July 6, 1974, at Chicago, Illinois.

Headquarters: 27 Teddington Park Ave., Toronto 12, Ontario. Tel. (416) 481-4643.

OFFICERS

Primate, The Most Rev. Iakovos. (See U. S. listing.)

The Rt. Rev. Bishop Theodosios of Ancona, 27 Teddington Park Ave., Toronto 12, Ontario.

Independent Assemblies of God—Canada

This fellowship of churches has been operating in Canada for over twenty-five years. It is a branch of the Pentecostal Church in Sweden. Each church within the fellowship is completely independent.

Churches: 45. Inclusive Membership: 5,500. Sunday or Sabbath Schools: 50. Total Enrollment: N.R. Ordained clergy: 165.

GENERAL ORGANIZATION

General Convention, annual.

Headquarters: 15 Beecher St., St. Catharines, Ontario. Tel. (416) 685-5392.

OFFICER

Sec.-Treas., Rev. Harry Nunn, Sr., 15 Beecher St., St. Catharines, Ontario.

PERIODICAL

The Mantle (m), 3840 Fifth Ave., San Diego, CA 92103. Rev. A. W. Rassmussen, Ed.

Independent Holiness Church

The former Holiness Movement of Canada merged with the Free Methodist Church in 1958. Some churches remained independent of this merger and they formed the Independent Holiness Church in 1960, in Kingston, Ontario. The doctrines are Methodist and Wesleyan.

Churches: 12. Inclusive Membership: N.R. Sunday or Sabbath Schools: N.R. Total Enrollment: N.R. Ordained clergy: 13.

Headquarters: R. R. 3, Metcalfe, Ontario.
General Conference: Every three years. Next meeting, 1974.

OFFICERS
Pres., Rev. Murdo Campbell, 5861 Berwick St., Burnaby, British Columbia.
Vice-Pres., Rev. J. R. Woodland, 161 Mack St., Kingston, Ontario.
Gen. Sec., R. E. Votary, R. R. 3, Metcalfe, Ontario.

PERIODICAL
Gospel Tidings (m), Box 254, Wellesley, Ontario, Rev. Lynn Synder, Ed.

The Italian Pentecostal Church of Canada

This body had its beginnings in Hamilton, Ontario, in 1913 when a few people of an Italian Presbyterian Church banded themselves together for prayer and received a Pentecostal experience of the Baptism in the Holy Spirit. Since 1913, there has been a close association with the teachings and practices of the Pentecostal Assemblies of Canada.

From Hamilton the work spread to Toronto, which became a center for all of Southern Ontario. The Church then spread to Montreal, where it also flourished.

In 1958, the Church was recognized by the Government of Canada and a charter granted. The early leaders of this body were the Rev. Luigi Ippolito and the Rev. Ferdinand Zaffuto. The churches have carried on active missionary work in Italy and among many thousands of immigrants recently arrived in Canada.

Churches: 14. Inclusive Membership: 2,000. Sunday or Sabbath Schools: 10. Total Enrollment: 1,402. Ordained clergy: 12.

GENERAL ORGANIZATION
General Conference, annual. Oct.
Headquarters: 6724 Fabre St., Montreal 35, Quebec. Tel. (514) 721-5614.

OFFICERS
Gen. Supt., Rev. Antonio DiBiase, Box 218, St. Louis des Terrebonne, Quebec.
Gen. Sec., Rev. Daniel Ippolito, 46 George Anderson Dr., Toronto 15, Ontario.
Gen. Treas., Rev. Rinaldo Remoli, 61 Hatton Dr., Ancaster, Ontario.
Overseers, Elio Madonia, 28 Hillcrest Dr., Toronto 4, Ontario; Mario Spiridigliozzi, 6730 Fabre St., Montreal 330, Quebec.

PERIODICAL
Communicato Missionario [Missionary News Bulletin] (q) Joseph Manafo, Daniel Ippolito, Eds.

Jehovah's Witnesses

For details on Jehovah's Witnesses see the directory in this edition "Religious Bodies in the United States."
There are 790 congregations and 49,204 ministers in Canada.

GENERAL ORGANIZATION
Headquarters: 124 Columbia Heights, Brooklyn, NY 11201. Tel. (212) 625-1240.
Canadian Branch Office: 150 Bridgeland Ave., Toronto 390, Ontario.

Lutheran Church—Canada

Founded April 23, 1959, at Edmonton, Alberta, by the Canadian congregations of the Lutheran Church—Missouri Synod.

Churches: 370. Inclusive Membership: 98,097. Sunday or Sabbath Schools: 337. Total Enrollment: 29,037. Ordained clergy: 287.

GENERAL ORGANIZATION
Biennial Convention. Next meeting, 1973.
Headquarters: Tel. (416) 354-8881.

OFFICERS
Pres., Rev. Harold Merklinger, 7205 Sharon Ave., Niagara Falls, Ontario.
Sec., Rev. Albin J. Stanfel, 15 Eastwood Dr., Kitchener, Ontario.
Treas., Mr. Carl Wagner, 1927 Grant Dr., Regina, Saskatchewan.
Dirs., Rev. George Rode, 7731 157th St., Edmonton 54, Alberta; Mr. Thomas Mundinger, R. R. 2, Eganville, Ontario.

Lutheran Church in America—Canada Section

The Lutheran Church in America's three synods in Canada jointly constitute its Canada Section. Where there is a common Canadian concern, it establishes inter-Lutheran, ecumenical and governmental relationships, and engages in social action programs and projects.

Churches: 332. Inclusive Membership: 121,212. Sunday or Sabbath Schools: 300. Total Enrollment: 28,906. Ordained clergy: 314.

OFFICERS
Pres., Dr. Otto A. Olson, Jr., 211-2281 Portage Ave. W., Rm. 311, Winnipeg, Manitoba. R3J OM1. Tel. (204) 837-3316.
Sec., Rev. Norman A. Berner, 509-251 King St. W. Kitchener, Ontario. Tel. (519) 743-1461.
Treas., Walter A. Schultz, 365 Hargrave St., Rm. 500, Winnipeg, Manitoba. R3B 2K3.

SYNOD PRESIDENTS
Central Canada Synod, Dr. Otto A. Olson, Jr., 211-2281 Portage Ave. W., Winnipeg, Manitoba. R3J OM1. Tel. (204) 837-3316.
Eastern Canada Synod, Dr. Otto F. Reble, 509-251 King St. W., Kitchener, Ontario. Tel. (519) 743-1461.
Western Canada Synod, Rev. Donald Sjoberg, 9901-107 St., Edmonton 14, Alberta. Tel. (403) 424-4677.

Mennonite Brethren Churches of North America, Canadian Conference of

Incorporated, November 22, 1945.

Churches: 125. Inclusive Membership: 17,982. Sunday or Sabbath Schools: 130. Total Enrollment: 18,293. Ordained clergy: 252.

GENERAL ORGANIZATION
Annual Conference: Next meeting, July, 1973. Headquarters: 159 Henderson Hwy., Winnipeg, Manitoba.

OFFICERS
Moderator, J. H. Quiring, 31906 Beech Ave., Clearbrook, British Columbia.
Ass't. Moderator, J.F. Froese, Box 237, Hepburn, Saskatchewan.
Sec., J. H. Neumann, 9985 Kenswood Dr., RR 2, Chilliwack, British Columbia.

PERIODICAL
Mennonite Brethren Herald (bi-w), 159 Henderson Hwy., Winnipeg, Manitoba. Harold Jantz, Ed.

Mennonite Church (Canada)

This body had its origins in Europe in 1525 as an outgrowth of the Anabaptist movement. It was organized in North America in 1898.

Churches: 68. Inclusive Membership: 8,577. Sunday or Sabbath Schools: 67. Total Enrollment: 10,004. Ordained clergy: 81.

GENERAL ORGANIZATION
The North American Assembly meets biennially. Next meeting in 1973. Headquarters: 10600 W. Higgins Rd., Rm. 104, Rosemont, IL 60018. Three conferences in Canada affiliate with the General Assembly of Mennonite Church. One of these three conferences is Ontario Conference with offices at 117 King St., W. Kitchener, Ontario. Tel. (519) 743-2673.

OFFICERS
Mod., Donald Augsburger, Eastern Mennonite College, Harrisonburg, VA 22801.
Mod., Elect, Newton L. Gingrick, Tavistock, Ontario.

The Missionary Church—Canada (Ontario District)

This body, organized in 1883, was formerly known as the Mennonite Brethren in Christ and changed its name to the United Missionary Church in 1947. In 1969, it merged with the Missionary Church Association and is now called The Missionary Church. It is an Anabaptist body.

Churches: 77. Inclusive Membership: 4,121. Sunday or Sabbath Schools: 77. Total Enrollment: 8,679. Ordained clergy: 91.

GENERAL ORGANIZATION
Note: The information below is for the Ontario District of The Missionary Church. For information on the Canada West District,

write to: John Gamble, Dist. Supt., Didsbury, Alberta.
District Conference meets annually. Next meeting, June 19-20, 1973.

OFFICERS
Dist. Supt., Rev. Grant Sloss, Ste. 203, Frederick St. Plaza, Kitchener, Ontario. Tel. (519) 744-4071.
Sec., Rev. Lyness Wark, R.R. 2, Mildmay, Ontario. Tel. (519) 367-2039.

Moravian Church in America, Northern Province, Canadian District of the

Churches: 9. Inclusive Membership: 1,583. Sunday or Sabbath Schools: 9. Total Enrollment: 670. Ordained clergy: 10.

Note: The work in Canada is under the general oversight and rules of the Moravian Church in America, Northern Province, general offices for which are located at 69 W. Church St., Bethlehem, PA 18018.

OFFICER
Pres. and Corr. Sec., Donald H. Laverty, 5719-114A St., Edmonton, Alberta.

North American Baptist General Conference

These churches emanated from German Baptist immigrants of more than a century ago. Many are still bilingual in their ministry. Although scattered on the North American continent, they are bound together by a common heritage, a strong spiritual unity, a Bible-centered faith, and a deep interest in missions.

Churches: 97. Inclusive Membership: 12,647. Sunday or Sabbath Schools: 92. Total Enrollment: 12,570. Ordained clergy: 102.

Note: The details of general organization, headquarters, officers, and periodicals of this body will be found in the North American Baptist General Conference directory in the United States directory. The office at 7308 Madison St., Forest Park, IL 60130 serves the Canadian churches.

The Pentecostal Assemblies of Canada

Incorporated under the laws of the Dominion of Canada in 1919.

Churches: 749. Inclusive Membership: 160,000. Sunday or Sabbath Schools: 831. Total Enrollment: 120,000. Ordained clergy: 886.

International Offices: 10 Overlea Blvd., Toronto 17, Ontario. Tel (416) 425-1010.

OFFICERS
Gen. Supt., Rev. Robert W. Taitinger.
Gen. Sec.-Treas., Rev. J. Montgomery.
Exec. Dir. Overseas Missions, Rev. C. W. Lynn.
Exec. Dir. Christian Education and Youth Departments, Rev. S. D. Feltmate.

Exec. Dir. Home Missions and Bible Colleges, Rev. R. M. Argue.

Dir. Women's Missionary Council, Mrs. Marion Parkinson.

Man. Full Gospel Publishing House, Mr. Victor T. Smalridge.

Man. Testimony Press, Mr. Henry Borodenko.

DISTRICT SUPERINTENDENTS

British Columbia, Rev. J. M. House, 339 E. Carisbrooke Rd., North Vancouver, British Columbia.

Alberta, Rev. C. Yates, 5924-142nd Ave., Edmonton 32, Alberta.

Saskatchewan, Rev. J. C. Tyler, 107 Howell Ave., Saskatoon, Saskatchewan.

Manitoba, Rev. W. G. Reinheimer, 3 Fieldstone Bay, Winnipeg, Manitoba R2Y OR1.

Western Ontario, Rev. D. A. Emmons, 3419 Mainway, Burlington, Ontario.

Eastern Ontario and Quebec, Rev. R. A. Bombay, 5 King George Sq., Belleville, Ontario.

Maritime Provinces, Rev. Ivan D. Raymer, Box 633, Truro, Nova Scotia.

CONFERENCES

German Conference, Rev. Gustav Kurtz, 1314 Victoria St., London, Ontario.

French Conference, Rev. R. C. Bergeron, 1705 Henri-Bourassa E., Montreal, Quebec.

Slavic Conferences: Eastern District, Rev. P. Horban, Apt. 311, 2543 Lakeshore Blvd W., Toronto; Western District, Rev. W. Melnychuk, 10521-97th St., Edmonton, Alberta.

Finnish Conference, Rev. V. Kyllonen, 302-1615 William St., Vancouver 6, British Columbia.

PERIODICAL

The Pentecostal Testimony, 10 Overlea Blvd., Toronto 17, Ontario. Rev. E. N. O. Kulbeck, Ed.

Polish National Catholic Church of Canada

This Diocese was created at the XII General Synod of the Polish National Catholic Church of America in October, 1967. Formerly, the Canadian parishes were a part of the Western Diocese and Buffalo-Pittsburgh Diocese of the Polish National Catholic Church in America.

Churches: 11. Inclusive Membership: 6,000. Sunday or Sabbath Schools: 10. Total Enrollment: N.R. Ordained clergy: 8.

GENERAL ORGANIZATION

Headquarters: St. John's Cathedral, 186 Cowan Ave., Toronto 146, Ontario.

OFFICER

The Rt. Rev. Joseph Nieminski, Bishop of the Canadian Diocese, 186 Cowan Ave., Toronto 146, Ontario.

The Presbyterian Church in Canada

The nonconcurring portion of the Presbyterian Church in Canada that did not become a part of the United Church in Canada in 1925.

Churches: 1,069. Inclusive Membership: 182,-559. Sunday or Sabbath Schools: N.R. Total Enrollment: 67,531. Ordained clergy: 866. Offices: 50 Wynford Dr., Don Mills, 403, Ontario. Tel. (416) 429-0110.

OFFICERS

Mod., Rev. M. V. Putnam.

Clerks of Assembly: Rev. E. A. Thompson; Rev. L. H. Fowler; Rev. D. C. MacDonald.

Treas., Russell Merifield, Q.C.

NATIONAL BOARDS

Board of World Missions: Sec., Rev. George Malcolm.

Board of Christian Education: Sec., Rev. A. E. Bailey.

Board of Stewardship and Budget: Sec., Rev. H. F. Davidson.

Board of Evangelism and Social Action: Sec., Rev. Wayne A. Smith; Men's Work, R. A. Hamilton and G. Fernie.

Women's Missionary Society (WD): Pres., Mrs. J. M. Burnett, Toronto, Ontario.

Women's Missionary Society (ED): Pres., Mrs. John Posno, Chatham, New Brunswick.

PERIODICAL

The Presbyterian Record (m). Rev. DeCourcy H. Rayner, Ed.

Primitive Baptist Conference of New Brunswick

Founded at Carlisle, near Hartland, New Brunswick, 1874-75 by the Rev. George W. Orser, who broke away from another group because it wanted him to take offerings, etc. This body is fundamental, Arminian, and does not belong to any ecumenical organization. Individual churches in this body call their own pastor.

Churches: 20 Inclusive Membership: 2,000. Sunday or Sabbath Schools: 15. Total Enrollment: 900. Ordained clergy: 10.

GENERAL ORGANIZATION

Annual Conference meets on first Saturday of July at their conference grounds, Somerville, New Brunswick.

OFFICER

Rev. Philip A. Giverson, Conference Chmn., Bath, New Brunswick. Tel. (506) 375-6673.

PERIODICAL

The Gospel Standard, Box 355, Harland, New Brunswick. Rev. Philip Giverson, Ed.

Reformed Church in America—Ontario Classis

The Ontario Classis is the Canadian branch of the Reformed Church in America which was established in 1628 by earliest Dutch settlers in America as the Reformed Protestant Dutch Church. It is evangelical in theology and Presbyterian in government.

Churches: 18. Inclusive Membership: 5,595.

THE REFORMED EPISCOPAL CHURCH

Sunday or Sabbath Schools: 18. Total Enrollment: 1,588. Ordained clergy: 21.

GENERAL ORGANIZATION

Gen. Sec., Rev. Marion De Velder, 475 Riverside Dr., New York, NY 10027.
Stated Clerk of the Ontario Classis, Rev. C. G. Bons, 194 Clarke St., Woodstock, Ontario. Tel. (519) 537-8935.

PERIODICAL

Pioneer Christian Monthly (m), 4 Undermount Ave., Hamilton, Ontario.

The Reformed Episcopal Church

OFFICERS

Bishop, D. A. G. Rankilor, 4034 Gordon Head Rd., Victoria, British Columbia. Tel. (604) 477-1622.
Sec., Mrs. L. A. Gordon, 1054 Southgate St., Victoria, British Columbia. Tel. (604) 383-5128.
Treas., E. P. Creech, 1249 Palmer Rd., Victoria, British Columbia. Tel. (604) 382-1004.

The Roman Catholic Church in Canada

The largest single body of Christians in Canada, the Roman Catholic Church is under the spiritual leadership of His Holiness the Pope. Catholicism in Canada dates back to 1534, when the first Mass was celebrated on the Gaspé Peninsula, on July 7, by a priest accompanying Jacques Cartier. There seems little doubt that Catholicism had been implanted earlier by fishermen and sailors from Europe. Priests came to Acadia as early as 1604. Traces of a regular colony go back to 1608 when Champlain settled in Quebec. The Recollets (1615), followed by the Jesuits (1625) and the Sulpicians (1657), began the missions among the Indians. The first official Roman document relative to the Canadian missions dates from March 20, 1618. Bishop Francois de Montmorency-Laval, the first Bishop, arrived in Quebec in 1659. The Church developed in the East but not until 1818 did systematic missionary work begin in Western Canada.

Churches: 6,063. Inclusive Membership: 8,759,-625. Sunday or Sabbath Schools: N.R. Total Enrollment: N.R. Ordained clergy: 14,353.

INTERNATIONAL ORGANIZATION

His Holiness the Pope, Bishop of Rome, Vicar of Jesus Christ, Supreme Pontiff of the Catholic Church.
POPE PAUL VI, Giovanni Battista Montini (born 1897; crowned, June 30, 1963).
APOSTOLIC PRO NUNCIO TO CANADA Archbishop Guido Del Mestri, 724 Manor Ave., Ottawa 2, Ontario. Tel. (613) 746-4914.

CANADIAN ORGANIZATION

Canadian Catholic Conference, 90 Parent Ave. Ottawa K1N 7B1, Ontario. Tel. (613) 236-9461. (All offices below are at this address and telephone number unless otherwise stated.)
The Canadian Catholic Conference is an Association of Cardinals, Archbishops, and Bishops of Canada established to assure the progress of the Church and the Coordination of Catholic activities in Canada.

OFFICERS

GENERAL SECRETARIAT OF THE EPISCOPACY
Secrétaire général (French Sector) Mgr. Charles E. Mathieu.
General Secretary (English Sector) Rev. Everett J. MacNeil.
Assistant General Secretary (English Sector), Rev. Bernard A. Prince.
Secrétaire général adjoint (French Sector), Abbé Roland Dufour.

EXECUTIVE COMMITTEE
Pres., Most Rev. William E. Power.
Vice-Pres., S. E. Mgr. Jean-Marie Fortier.
Treas., Most Rev. Francis A. Marrocco.
Councillors, Most Rev. James M. Hayes, S. E. Mgr. Guy Belanger, S. E. Mgr. Henri Légaré.

OFFICERS

Secteur Francais
Bureau du Secrétaire Général, Dir., Mlle Marguerite Cloutier.
Office National de l'Action Sociale, Dir., Abbé Charles E. St. Onge.
Office des Missions, Dir., R. P. Louis de Gonzaque Langevin, P.B.-R.P. Cyril Smith.
Office National du Bien-Être et de la Santé, Dir., Abbé Remi Migneault, 1225 est, boul. St.-Joseph, Montréal 176, Québec. Tel. (514) 274-3658.
Office National du Clergé, Dir., Abbé Yvan Desrochers, 4635 de Lorimier, Montréal, Quebéc. Tel. (514) 276-5355.
Office des Communications Sociales, Dir., Abbé Lucien Labelle, 4635 de Lorimier, Montréal, Québec. Tel. (514) 526-9165.
Office National de L'Education Chrétienne, Dir., Abbé Claude Michaud.
Office National de liturgie, Dir., Pierre Dufresne, 1225 est, boul. St.-Joseph, Montréal 176, Québec. Tel. (514) 277-2133.
Office pour le Dialogue avec les Non-Croyants, Dir., Père Paul Morisset, 1225 est, boul. St.-Joseph, Montréal 176, Québec. Tel. (514) 279-9927.
Office National d'Oecumenisme, Père Irenée Beaubien. 1452 Drummond, Montréal, Québec. Tel. (514) 845-7141.
Services des Relations Publiques, Dir., M. Guy Poisson.
Service des Éditions, Dir., Mlle. Claire Dubé.
English Sector
National Catholic Communications Office, Exec. Dir., Miss B. Brennan, 21 Crenville, Toronto, Ontario. Tel. (416) 929-3125.
National Education Office, Ad Int. Dir., Rev. John Carley, Asst., Rev. Robert Kennedy.
National Liturgical Office, Dir., Rev. Leonard L. Sullivan.
National Office for Ecumenism, Dir., Rev. John Keating, 830 Bathurst, Toronto, Ontario. Tel. (416) 534-2326.
National Office of Religious Education, Co-Directors, Rev. Martin Jeffrey, Rev. Robert Kennedy.
Office for Missions, Directors, Rev. L. DeG. Langevin, Rev. C. W. Smith.
Office of Lay Apostolate, Rev. John Carley.

Office for Social Action/Family Life Bureau, Co-Directors, Rev. Patrick Kierans, Mr. Grant Maxwell, Mr. Bernard Daly.

Social Welfare Bureau, Dir., Rev. R. Murray Tardiff.

Public Relations Service, Dir., Sister Ella Zink.

ARCHDIOCESES AND DIOCESES

The Roman Catholic Church in Canada has 17 Archdioceses, 46 Dioceses, 4 Ukrainian Eparchies and 1 Abbacy. Each of these ecclesiastical jurisdictions appears alphabetically in the following list and contains this information in sequence: Name of incumbent bishop, address of Chancery office (Evêché) or other headquarters, and telephone number.

Cardinals are addressed as "His Eminence" (in French as "Son Eminence") and Archbishops and Bishops as "Most Reverend" (in French as "Son Excellence").

Alexandria, Mgr. Adolphe Proulx. Evêché, 69 rue St-Paul, C. P. 340, Alexandria, Ontario. Tel. (613) 525-1340.

Amos, Mgr. Gaston Hains, Evêché, 450, Principale Nord, Amos, Abitibi-Est, Québec. Tel. (819) 732-3216.

Antigonish, Bishop Mgr. William E. Power. Chancery Office, 155 Main St., Antigonish, Nova Scotia. Tel. (902) 863-4818.

Bathurst, Mgr. Edgar Godin. Evêché, 650 Mont Ste-Marie, C.P. 460, Bathurst, New Brunswick. Tel. (506) 546-3484.

Calgary, Bishop Paul J. O'Byrne. Chancery, P.O. Box 4130, Sta. "C" Calgary 3, Alberta. Tel. (403) 263-3371.

Charlottetown, Bishop F. J. Spence, Chancery Office, North River Rd., P.O. Box 907, Charlottetown, Prince Edward Island. Tel. (902) 892-1357, 894-3730.

Chicoutimi, Mgr. Marius Pare. Evêché: 602 est, rue Racine, C.P. 278, Chicoutimi, Québec. Tel. (418) 543-0783.

Churchill-Baie D'Hudson. Mgr. Omer Robidoux. Evêché, C.P. 10, Churchill, Manitoba, ROB OEO. Tel. (204) 675-2252.

Archdiocese of Edmonton, Archbishop Anthony Jordan. Archdiocesan Office, 10044-113th St., Edmonton, Alberta. Tel. (403) 488-0188.

Eparchy of Edmonton, Bishop Neil N. Savaryn. Bishop's Residence, 6240 Ada Blvd., Edmonton, Alberta. Tel. (403) 479-0381.

Edmundston, Mgr. Fernard Lacroix, Evêché, 48, Rue Queen, C.P. 428, Edmundston, New Brunswick. Tel. (506) 735-5200.

Gaspé Mgr. Gilles Guellet, Evêché, C.P. 440, Gaspé, Québec. Tel. (418) 368-2274.

Grand Falls, Bishop, John M. O'Neill. Bishop's Residence, Church Rd., P.O. Box 278, Grand Falls, Newfoundland. Tel. (709) 2587.

Gravelbourg, Mgr. Aimé Decosse. Evêché C.P. 690, Gravelbourg, Saskatchewan. Tel. (306) 648-2235.

Archidiocèse de Grouard-McLennan, Mgr. Henri Routhier, Chancellerie, C.P. 388 McLennan, Alberta. Tel. (403) 324-3002.

Archdiocese of Halifax, Archbishop James M. Hayes. Archbishop's Residence, 6541 Coburg Rd., P.O. Box 1527, Halifax, Nova Scotia. Tel. (902) 429-9388.

Hamilton, Bishop Joseph F. Ryan. Chancery Office, 700 King St. W., Hamilton 12, Ontario. Tel. (416) 528-7989.

Hauterive, Mgr. Gérard Couturier Evêché, 945, boul. Blanche, C.P. 10, Hauterive, Cte Saguenay, Québec. Tel. (418) 589-5744.

Hearst, Mgr. Jacques Landriault. Administrateur Apostolique Evêché, C.P. 1330, Hearst, Ontario. Tel. (705) 362-4903.

Hull, Mgr. Paul-Émile Charbonneau, Evêché, 119, rue Charillon, Hull, Québec. Tel. (819) 771-8391.

Joliette, Mgr. Réné Audet. Evêché, No. 2, rue St-Charles Borromée, Nord. C.P. 470, Cité de Joliette, Québec. Tel. (514) 753-7596-ext. 24.

Kamloops, Bishop Michael A. Harrington. Bishop's Residence, 635 Tranquille Rd., North Kamloops, British Columbia. Tel. (604) 376-5141.

Archidiocèse de, Keewatin-LePas, Mgr. Paul Dumouchel; Résidence, 108-1st West, C.P. 270, Le Pas, Manitoba R9A 1KY. Tel. (204) 623-3529.

Archdiocese of Kingston, Archbishop J. L. Wilhelm. Archbishop's Residence, 279 Johnson St., P.O. Box 997, Kingston, Ontario. Tel. (613) 546-5521.

Labrador-Schefferville, Mgr. Henri Légaré. Evêché, 303 A.P. Low, C.P. 700, Schefferville, Cté Saguenay, Québec. Tel. (418) 585-2470.

London, Bishop G. Emmett Carter. Chancery Office, 1070 Waterloo St., 520 Richmond St., London 11, Ontario. Tel. (519) 433-0658.

Mackenzie-Fort Smith (T.No.O.), Mgr. Paul Piché. Résidence, Bishop's Residence, Fort Smith, T.N.O. Tel. 872-2537.

Archidiocèse de Moncton, Mgr. Donat Chiasson. Archevêché, C.P. 248, Chartersville, Co. West, Moncton, New Brunswick. Tel. (506) 389-9531.

Mont-Laurier, Mgr. André Ouellette. Evêché, 435, rue de la Madone, C.P. 1290, Mont-Laurier, Québec. Tel. (819) 623-1202.

Archidiocese, de Montréal, Mgr. Paul Grégoire. Arhevêché, 2000 ouest, rue Sherbrooke, Montréal, Québec. Tel. (514) 931-7311.

Moosonee, Mgr. Jules LeGuerrier. Résidence, C.P. 40, Moosonee, Ontario. Tel. (705) 336-2908.

Abbatia Nullius of Muenster, Abbott Ordinary Jerome Weber, OSB. Abbot's Residence, St. Peter's Abbey, Muenster, Saskatchewan. Tel. (306) 682-3373.

Nelson, Bishop W. Emmett Doyle. Bishop's Residence, 813 Ward St., Nelson. British Columbia. Tel. (604) 352-6921.

Nicolet, Mgr. J. Albertus Martin. Evêché, Nicolet, Québec. Tel. (819) 293-4696.

Archidiocese D'Ottawa, Mgr. Joseph-Aurèle Plourde. Archevêché, 145, rue St-Patrice, Ottawa, Ontario K1N 5K1. Tel. (613) 237-4540.

Pembroke, Bishop J. R. Windle. Bishop's Residence, 188 Renfrew St., P.O. Box 7, Pembroke, Ontario. Tel. (613) 732-7933.

Peterborough, Bishop Francis A. Marrocco. Bishop's Residence, 350 Hunter St. W., Box 175, Peterborough, Ontario. Tel. (705) 745-5123.

Prince-Albert, Mgr. Laurent Morin. Evêché, 1415-ouest, 4e Ave., Prince-Albert, Saskatchewan. Tel. (306) 763-2778.

Prince-George, Bishop Fergus J. O'Grady. Bishop's Residence, College Rd., S.S. #2, Prince

THE ROMAN CATHOLIC CHURCH IN CANADA

George, British Columbia. Tel. (604) 964-4755.

Archidiocèse de Québec, Son Eminence le Cardinal Maurice Roy. Archevêché, 2, rue Port Dauphin, C.P. 459, Québec 4, Québec. Tel. (418) 522-3935.

Archdiocese of Regina, Archbishop Michael C. O'Neill. Chancery Office, 3225 13th Ave., Regina, Saskatchewan. Tel. (306) 522-4732.

Archidiocèse de Rimouski, Mgr. Louis, Lévesque. Archevêché, 34 ouest, rue de l'Evêché, C.P. 730, Rimouski, P.O. Tel. (418) 723-3320.

Ste-Anne de la, Pocatière, Mgr. Charles-Henri Lévesque. Evêché, C.P. 430, La Pocatière, Kamouraska, P.O. Tel. (418) 856-1811.

Archidiocèse de Saint-Boniface, Mgr. Maurice Baudoux. Archevêché, 151, ave de la Cathédrale, St-Boniface Manitoba R2H OH6. Tel. (204) 247-9851.

St. Catharines, Bishop Thomas J. McCarthy. Bishop's Residence, 122 Riverdale Ave., St. Catharines, Ontario. Tel. (416) 684-0154.

St. George's, Bishop Richard McGrath. Bishop's Residence, Hammond Dr., Corner Brook, Newfoundland. Tel. 4-5583.

Saint Hyacinthe, Mgr. Albert Sanschagrin. Evêché 1900, Girouard, C.P. 190, Saint-Hyacinthe, Québec. Tel. (514) 773-8581.

Saint-Jean-de-Québec, Mgr. Gérard-Marie Coderre, Evêché, 740 boul. Ste-Foy, C.P. 40, Longueuil, Québec. Tel. (514) 679-1100.

Saint-Jérôme, Mgr. Bernard Hubert, Evêché, 355, rue St-Georges, C.P. 580, Saint-Jérôme, Comte de Terrebonne, Québec. Tel. (514) 432-9741.

Saint John, Bishop J. N. MacNeil. Bishop's Residence, 91 Waterloo St., Saint John, New Brunswick. Tel. (506) 693-4418.

Archdiocese of St. John's, Archbishop Patrick J. Skinner. Archbishop's Residence, P.O. Box 1207, Basilica Residence, Bonaventure Ave. St. John's, Newfoundland. Tel. (709) 722-0337.

Saint-Paul, Mgr. Raymond Roy. Evêché, 4637, 45e Ave., C.P. 339, St-Paul, Alberta, Tel. (403) 645-3277.

Saskatoon, Bishop James P. Mahoney. Bishop's Residence, 1036 College Dr., Saskatoon, Saskatchewan. Tel. (306) 652-8379.

Eparchy of Saskatoon, Bishop Andrew Roborecki. Bishop's Residence, 866 Saskatchewan. Crescent East, Saskatoon, Saskatchewan. Tel. (306) 653-0138.

Sault Ste. Marie, Bishop Alexander Carter Bishop's Residence, 480 McIntyre St., W., P.O. Box 510, North Bay, Ontario. Tel. (709) 472-3970.

Archidiocèse de Sherbrooke, Mgr. Jean-Marie Fortier. Archevêchè, 130, rue de la Cathedrale, C.P. 430, Sherbrooke, Québec. Tel. (819) 569-5176.

Thunder Bay, Bishop Norman Gallagher. Bishop's Residence, 1306 Ridgeway, P.O. Box 113, Thunder Bay, Zone "F" Ontario. Tel. (807) 622-4645.

Timmins, Mgr. Jacques Landriault. Evêché, C.P. 9, Haileybury, Ontario. Tel. (705) 672-3336.

Archidiocese of Toronto, Archbishop P. F. Pocock, Chancery Office, 55 Gould St., Toronto 2, Ontario. Tel. (416) 362-6571.

Eparchy of Toronto, Bishop Isidore Borecky. Bishop's Residence, 61 Glen Edyth Dr., Toronto 7, Ontario. Tel. (416) 924-2381.

Trois-Rivièrès, Mgr. Georges-Léon Péllétier. Evêché, 362, rue Bonaventure, C.P. 879, Trois-Rivièrès, Québec. Tel. (819) 374-2400.

Valleyfield, Mgr. Guy Bélanger. Evêché, 31 rue Fabrique, C.P. 338, Valleyfield, Québec. Tel. (514) 373-8122.

Archdiocese of Vancouver, Archbishop James F. Carney. Chancery Office, 150 Robson St., Vancouver 3, British Columbia. Tel. (604) 683-0281.

Victoria, Bishop Remi J. DeRoo. Bishop's Residence, 740 View St., Victoria, British Columbia. Tel. (604) 388-5571.

Whitehorse (Yukon), Bishop Hubert P. O'Connor, O.M.I. Bishop's Residence, P.O. Box 5119, Whitehorse, Yukon. Tel. (403) 667-2052.

Archdiocese of Winnipeg, Archbishop George Bernard Cardinal Flahiff. Chancery Office 50 Stafford Street, Winnipeg 9, Manitoba. Tel. (204) 474-2361.

Archeparchy of Winnipeg, Archbishop Maxim Hermaniuk. Archbishop's Residence, 235 Scotia St., Winnipeg 17, Manitoba. Tel. (204) 339-7457.

Yarmouth, Mgr. Augustin Emile Burke. Evêché, 53, rue Park, Yarmouth, Nova Scotia. Tel. (902) 742-2237.

Romanian Orthodox Church in America (Canadian Parishes)

The first Romanian Orthodox immigrants in Canada called for Orthodox priests from their native country of Romania. Between 1902-1914, they organized the first Romanian parish communities and built Orthodox churches in different cities and farming regions of western Canada (Alberta, Saskatchewan, Manitoba) as well as in the eastern part (Ontario and Quebec).

In 1929, the Romanian Orthodox parishes from Canada joined with those of the U. S. in a Congress held in Detroit, Mich., and asked the Holy Synod of the Romanian Orthodox Church of Romania to establish a Romanian Orthodox Missionary Episcopate in America (which is the legal title of this body). The first Bishop, Policarp (Morushca), was elected and consecrated by the Holy Synod of the Romanian Orthodox Church and came to the U.S. in 1935. He established his headquarters in Detriot with jurisdiction over all the Romanian Orthodox parishes in the U.S. and Canada.

In 1950, the Romanian Orthodox Church in America (i.e. the Romanian Orthodox Missionary Episcopate in America) was granted administrative autonomy by the Holy Synod of the Romanian Orthodox Church of Romania, and only doctrinal and canonical ties remain with this latter body.

Churches: 18. Inclusive Membership: 15,000. Sunday or Sabbath Schools: 8. Total Enrollment: 373. Ordained clergy: 12.

GENERAL ORGANIZATION

Bishop assisted by the Diocesan Council. Annual Congress for both U.S. and Canada. Canadian Office: St. George's Romanian Orthodox Cathedral, 1960 Tecumeseh Rd., E., Windsor, Ontario.

OFFICERS

Bishop, Rt. Rev. Bishop Victorin.
Chancellor, V. Rev. Archim. Bartholomew V. Anania, 19959 Riopelle St., Detroit, MI 48-203.

PERIODICALS

Credinta—The Faith (m), and Calendarul Credinta (Yearbook of the Episcopate) (a), 19959 Riopelle St., Detroit, MI 48203. V. Rev. Archim. Bartholomew V. Anania and Mr. George Alex, Eds.

The Romanian Orthodox Episcopate of America

Some of the Canadian churches of Romanian origin are under the canonical jurisdiction of the Romanian Orthodox Episcopate of America, chartered in 1929.

Churches: 14. Inclusive Membership: 10,000. Sunday or Sabbath Schools: 10. Total Enrollment: 530. Ordained clergy: 9.

GENERAL ORGANIZATION

Church Congress.

OFFICERS

Vicar to the Bishop: The Very Rev. Archim. Martinian Ivanovici, 421 Victoria Ave., Regina, Saskatchewan. Tel. (306) 523-3501.

PERIODICAL

Solia, Romanian News (m), 11341 Woodward Ave., Detroit, MI 48202.

Russian Orthodox Church in Canada, Patriarchal Parishes of the

Diocese of Canada of the former Exarchate of North and South America of the Russian Orthodox Church. Originally founded in 1897 by the Russian Orthodox Archdiocese in North America.

Churches: 23. Inclusive Membership: 4,500. Sunday or Sabbath Schools: 23. Total Enrollment: N.R. Ordained clergy: 19.

GENERAL ORGANIZATION

General Conference: Meets annually at call from Bishop.

OFFICERS

Administrator: His Excellency the Most Rev. Makary (Svistun), Bishop of Uman, 10630-83rd Ave., Edmonton, Alberta.

The Salvation Army in Canada

An evangelistic organization with a military government, first set up by General William Booth (1829-1912) in England in 1865. Converts from England started Salvation Army work in London, Ontario, in 1882. In 1884, Canada became a separate command which also has included Bermuda since 1933. An act to incorporate the Governing Council of The Salvation Army in Canada received royal assent on May 19, 1909.

Headquarters for Canada and Bermuda: 20 Albert St., Toronto 1, Ontario. Tel. (416) 362-1071.

OFFICERS

Territorial Commander, Commissioner Clarence D. Wiseman.
Chief Sec., Col. Jarl Wahlstrom.
Field Sec., Col. Alfred Simester.
Fin. Sec. Lt. Col. Ernest Falle.
Pub. Relations Sec., Lt. Col. Sidney Mundy.
Editor of War Cry, Lt. Col. Eric Coward.
Information Services and Special Efforts, Sec., Brigadier William Hosty.

PERIODICAL

War Cry, Lt. Col. Eric Coward, Ed.

Seventh-day Adventist Church in Canada

The Seventh-day Adventist Church in Canada is the legal title of the Canadian Union Conference of the Seventh-day Adventist Denomination, General Conference, headquartered in Washington, D. C. The Seventh-day Adventist Church in Canada was organized in 1901 and reorganized in 1932.

Churches: 188. Inclusive Membership: 20,190. Sunday or Sabbath Schools: 219. Total Enrollment: 19,451. Ordained clergy: 137.

GENERAL ORGANIZATION

Headquarters: 1148 King St., E., Oshawa, Ontario. Tel. (416) 723-3409.

OFFICERS

Pres., J. W. Bothe.
Sec.-Treas., C. Klam.

DEPARTMENTS

A.S.I.: J. W. Bothe.
Education: P. W. Manuel.
Lay Activities, Sabbath School, Radio-T.V. and Public Relations: W. E. Juester.
Medical: H. W. Gimbel.
Ministerial: G. E. Knowles.
Public Affairs: D. L. Michael.
Temperance and Y.P.M.V.: R. J. E. Hillock.

PERIODICAL

Canadian Union Messenger (bi-w), Maracle Press, Oshawa, Ontario. C. Klam, Ed.

Ukrainian Greek Orthodox Church of Canada

Toward the end of the 19th century the Ukrainian people began leaving their homeland, and many immigrated to Canada, which has been their homeland for over 75 years. At Saskatoon, in 1918, the Ukrainian pioneers organized this Church. The Ukrainian Greek-Orthodox Church of Canada has grown rapidly in the past 50 years so that today it is the largest Ukrainian Orthodox Church beyond the borders of the Ukraine.

Churches: 288. Inclusive Membership: 140,000. Sunday or Sabbath Schools: N.R. Total Enrollment: N.R. Ordained clergy: 95.

GENERAL ORGANIZATION

General Organization: Sobor (General Council) meets every five years, Presidium meets monthly, Full Consistory, semi-annually.

Headquarters: Consistory of the Ukrainian Greek-Orthodox Church of Canada, 7 St. John's Ave., Winnipeg, Manitoba R2W 1G8. Tel. (204) 586-3093.

OFFICERS

Presidium, Chmn., V. Rev. D. Luchak, 7 St. John's Ave., Winnipeg, Manitoba R2W 1G8.

PERIODICALS

Visnyk (semi-m), 7 St. John's Ave., Winnipeg, Manitoba, R2W 1G8. Rev. S. Jarmus, Ed.

The Herald [English Supplement] (bi-m), 7 St. John's Ave., Winnipeg Manitoba R2W 1G8. Rev. I. Kutash, Ed.

Union of Spiritual Communities of Christ (Orthodox Doukhobors in Canada)

Groups of Canadians of Russian origin living in the western provinces of Canada whose beginnings in Russia are unknown. The name "Doukhobors," or "Spirit Wrestlers," was given in derision by the Russian Orthodox clergy in Russia as far back as 1785. Victims of decades of persecution in Russia, about 7,500 Doukhobors finally arrived in Canada in 1899.

The whole teaching of the Doukhobors is penetrated with the Gospel spirit of love; worshiping God in the spirit they affirm that the outward Church and all that is performed in it and concerns it has no importance for them; the Church is where two or three are gathered together, united in the name of Christ. Their teaching is founded on tradition, which is called among them the "Book of Life," because it lives in their memory and hearts. In this book are recorded sacred songs or chants, partly composed independently, partly formed out of the contents of the Bible, and these are committed to memory by each succeeding generation. Doukhobors observe complete pacifism and non-violence.

The Doukhobors were reorganized in 1938 by their leader, Peter P. Verigin, shortly before his death, into the Union of Spiritual Communities of Christ, commonly called Orthodox Doukhobors. It is headed by a democratically elected Executive Committee which executes the will and protects the interests of the people.

In the present day at least 90 percent of the Doukhobors are law-abiding, pay taxes, and definitely "do not burn or bomb or parade in the nude" as they say a fanatical offshoot called the "Sons of Freedom" does.

Churches: 25. Inclusive Membership: 16,000. Sunday or Sabbath Schools: 8. Total Enrollment: 632. Ordained clergy: None.

GENERAL ORGANIZATION

General Meeting: Annual in January.
Headquarters: USCC Central Office, Box 670, Grand Forks, British Columbia. Tel. (604) 442-3757.

OFFICERS

Honorary and Actg. Chmn. of the Exec. Comm., John J. Verigin, Box 760, Grand Forks, British Columbia.

Sec., Eli A. Popoff, Box 730, Grand Forks, British Columbia.

PERIODICAL

Iskra (bi-w) in Russian with part of Youth Section in English, Box 760, Grand Forks, British Columbia, Peter P. Legebokoff, Ed.

Unitarian-Universalist Association

There is no central Canadian office for the Unitarian-Universalist Association. The headquarters is located at 25 Beacon St., Boston, MA 02108. However, three of the twenty-two districts of the UUA are located partly or wholly in Canada.

Churches: 55. Inclusive Membership: 6,035. Sunday or Sabbath Schools: N.R. Total Enrollment: 3,392. Ordained clergy: 23.

DISTRICTS AND OFFICERS

Pacific Northwest, Mr. D. Rob Stewart, 226A E. 5th St., North Vancouver, British Columbia.

St. Lawrence, Mrs. Helen Tucker, 1524 Douglas Dr., Mississauga, Ontario.

Western Canada, Mr. T. A. Pezarro, 3212 6th St., S.W., Calgary, Alberta.

United Church of Canada

The body resulting from the union, in 1925, of the Methodist Church of Canada, the Presbyterian Church in Canada, and the Congregational churches in Canada. The Canada Conference of the Evangelical United Brethren Church entered the union in 1968.

Churches: 4,442. Inclusive Membership: 1,016,706. Sunday or Sabbath Schools: 3,800. Total Enrollment: 329,857. Ordained clergy: 3,578.

Headquarters: The United Church House, 85 St. Clair Ave., E., Toronto 7, Ontario. Tel. (416) 925-5931.

General Council, meeting every two years. Next meeting, 1974.

OFFICERS

Mod., Rt. Rev. A. B. B. Moore.
Gen. Sec., Rev. George M. Morrison.
Deputy Sec., Rev. Donald G. Ray.
Research Officer, Rev. David R. Stone.
Archivist-Historian, Rev. C. Glenn Lucas.

ORGANIZATIONS

Division of Communication: Sec., Rev. F. G. Brisbin.

Ed., The United Church Observer, Rev. A. C. Forrest.

Assoc. Sec., Rev. Anson C. Moorhouse (Audio Visuals); Rev. Keith Woollard (Broadcasting).

Media Staff, Rev. G. E. Leard, Rev. R. O.

Reid, Rev. R. D. McCalmont, Miss Nancy Edwards.

Director of News Services, Mr. Norman K. Vale.

Committee on Education for Mission and Stewardship: Assoc. Sec., Rev. R. C. Plant; Mission Interpretation and Deputation, Rev. A. G. Smith; Editors, Mission and Stewardship Materials, Miss Nancy E. Hardy, Dr. Nora E. Neilson.

Division of Finance: Sec., Mr. H. L. Arnup. Dept. of the Treasury: Treas., Mr. D. N. Borgal; Asst. Treas., Mr. W. R. Davis.

Dept of Pensions: Sec. Mr. Ralph Wilson; Adm. Asst. Rev. John D. Staples.

Dept. of Stewardship Services: Sec., Rev. H. E. Young; Assoc. Secs., Rev. F. J. Douglas, Rev. W. D. Goodger; Exec. Assoc., Mr. Philip Spence, Mrs. Emily Marquis, Rev. W. H. Tonge.

Division of Ministry, Personnel and Education: Sec., Rev. H. W.. Vaughan.

Assoc. Sec., Rev. R. G. DeMarsh, Rev. J. H. Dean, Rev. O. R. Howard, Mrs. Jean Parker.

Division of Mission in Canada: Sec., Rev. H. M. Bailey.

Deputy Secs., Rev. K. Harriet Christie (Dept. of Christian Development); Rev. W. Clarke MacDonald (Dept. of Church in Society). Assoc. Secs., Rev. P. G. White, Rev. W. R. Adamson, Rev. G. J. Freer, Miss Ferne Graham, Rev. Norman H. MacKenzie, Rev. R. B. Smith, Dr. Robert Rae, Mr. D. G. Smith, Mr. J. D. L. Robertson, Rev. Albion R. Wright.

Division of World Outreach: Sec., Rev. R. E.

OTHER RELIGIOUS BODIES IN CANADA

Webster. Assoc. Secs., Mrs. Mary Birtch, Rev. E. F. Carey, Rev. G. W. Legge.; Adm. Asst., Mr. E. W. Horton.

PERIODICALS

United Church Observer, Toronto, Ontario. Rev. A. C. Forrest, Ed.

United Churchman, Sackville, New Brunswick. Rev. J. Heber Kean, Ed.

Wesleyan Methodist Church of America in Canada

The Canada Conference of the Wesleyan Methodist Church in America (known in the United States as The Wesleyan Church) was organized at Winchester, Ontario in 1889.

GENERAL ORGANIZATION

Central Canada District Conference; Meets annually, Next Conference meeting July, 1973.

Headquarters: 25 Dixon Dr., Trenton, Ontario.

OFFICERS

Pres., Rev. James S. A. Spearman, 27 Dixon Dr., Trenton, Ontario.

Vice-Pres., Rev. Ira M. Taylor, 106 Holland Park Ave., Toronto 10, Ontario.

Sec., Rev. Fred S. Irish, 76 Everett St., Belleville, Ontario.

Treas., Miss Eillen Baker, 374 Glenholme Ave., Toronto 10, Ontario.

PERIODICAL

Wesleyan Advocate. (s-m), Robert W. McIntyre, Ed. Central Canada District News (bi-m).

OTHER RELIGIOUS BODIES IN CANADA

Although a sizable majority of Canadian religious bodies, having most of the Canadian church membership, is accounted for by denominations providing directory materials in the section immediately preceding, a number of important groups have not yet provided directory information.

For the sake of completeness, an alphabetical listing of these religious bodies not yet supplying directory information, together with some fragmentary statistical data, appears below. More complete statistical data for many of these bodies appears in the Table "Canadian Current and Non-Current Statistics" in the Statistical Section of this Yearbook.

The editor of the **Yearbook of American and Canadian Churches** would be grateful for any information concerning significant omissions from this listing of Religious Bodies in Canada as well as for any other information concerning this section.

African Methodist Episcopal Church in Canada. 765 Lawrence Ave., W., Toronto, Ontario. Rev. A. S. Harris.

Apostolic Church of Pentecost, 1612 Adelaide St., E., Saskatoon, Saskatchewan. (130 churches.)

Armenian Evangelical Church in Canada, 34 Glenforest Ave., Toronto, Ontario. Tel. (416) 489-3188.

Buddhist Churches of Canada, 918 Bathurst St., Toronto, Ontario. Tel. (416) 534-4302.

Canadian Reformed Churches, Box 152, Smithville, Ontario.

Christadelphians in Canada, P.O. Box 221, Weston, Ontario.

Christian Reformed Churches in Canada, Council of, Rev. John Van Harmelen, Stated Clerk, R.R. 8, London, Ontario.

Christian Science in Canada, Mr. J. Donald Fulton, 696 Yonge St., Ste. 403, Toronto 285, Ontario. Tel. (416) 922-7473.

Church of God (in Western Canada), 567 Trinity Lane, Moose Jaw, Saskatchewan.

Church of God (Pentecostal), c/o Bramalee Church of God, 600 Balmoral Dr., Bramalee, Ontario.

127

OTHER RELIGIOUS BODIES IN CANADA

Church of the Nazarene, c/o Chairman of the Executive Board, Dr. Herman L. G. Smith, 2236 Capitol Hill Crescent, N.W., Calgary 44, Alberta.

Evangelical Free Church of America, c/o Dr. Arnold Olson, 1515 E. 66th St., Minneapolis, MN 55423. (71 churches.)

Evangelical Mennonite Brethren Conference, c/o Rev. Sam H. Epp. 33573 Lynn Ave., Abbotsford, British Columbia.

Evangelical Mennonite Conference, Box 1268, Steinbach, Manitoba.

Evangelical Mennonite Mission Conference, Box 126, Winnipeg, Manitoba.

Free Methodist Church in Canada, 11 Kingsview Blvd., Weston, Ontario.

Fundamental Baptists of the Maritimes, c/o Rev. Max Balzer, Frederickton, New Brunswick.

Muslims, c/o Islamic Foundation of Toronto, 182 Rhodes Ave., Toronto, Ontario. Tel. (416) 465-2525.

Old German Baptist Brethren in Canada, c/o Elder Amos Baker, Gormley, Ontario.

Orthodox Church in America (Canada Section), c/o The Most Rev. Sylvester, Archbishop of Montreal and Canada, 1175 Champlain St., Montreal, Quebec.

Pentecostal Assemblies of Newfoundland, 444 Water St., St. John, Newfoundland.

Pentecostal Holiness Church of Canada, 4 Hobart Dr., S., Toronto, Ontario. Tel (416) 491-5611.

Reorganized Church of Jesus Christ of Latter Day Saints, P.O. Box 38, Guelph, Ontario.

Sons of Freedom Doukhobors, Krestova, British Columbia.

Standard Church of America (Canadian Section), 243 Perth St., Brockville, Ontario.

United Brethren Churches, c/o Rev. Evan Sider, 29 Priscilla Ave., Toronto, Ontario. Tel. (416) 766-8902.

United Pentecostal Church in Canada, c/o J. O. Moore, Box 801, Picton, Ontario.

5. AGENCIES HAVING ECUMENICAL CONNECTIONS

Following is a listing of major ecumenical agencies with worldwide operations. These agencies are both ecumenical and confessional in nature. For the first time, brief sketches have been added setting forth for each agency the origins, history, and purposes of these groups. The editor of the **Yearbook of American and Canadian Churches** would be grateful for details on any major ecumenical or confessional agencies omitted from this list.

WORLD COUNCIL OF CHURCHES

The World Council of Churches is a fellowship of more than 260 churches of the Protestant, Anglican, Orthodox, and Old Catholic traditions banded together for study, witness, service, and the advancement of unity. It includes in its membership churches in more than 90 countries with various forms of government, and its life reflects the immense richness and variety of Christian faith and practice.

The World Council of Churches came into being after many years of preparation on August 23, 1948, when its First Assembly was held in Amsterdam, Holland.

The basis for World Council membership is: "The World Council of Churches is a fellowship of churches which confess the Lord Jesus Christ as God and Saviour according to the Scriptures and therefore seek to fulfill together their common calling to the glory of the one God, Father, Son, and Holy Spirit."

Membership is open to churches which express their agreement with this basis and satisfy such criteria as the Assembly or Central Committee may prescribe.

The fundamental reorganization of the World Council was approved at the meeting of the Central Committee in Addis Ababa, Ethiopia, in January, 1971. The changes were effective immediately, although the restructuring process will not be completed until the next Assembly, scheduled for 1975.

Headquarters: 150 route de Ferney, 1211 Geneva 20, Switzerland
Office in the U.S.: 475 Riverside Dr., Rm. 439, New York, NY 10027

HONORARY PRESIDENT
Rev. Dr. Willem A. Visser 't Hooft, Switzerland

PRESIDENTS
Dr. (Mrs.) Kiyoko Cho, Japan.
His Holiness, Patriarch German of Serbia, Yugoslavia.
Rt. Rev. Hanns Lilje, Germany.
Rev. Dr. Ernest A. Payne, Great Britain.
Rev. Dr. John Coventry Smith, United States of America.
Rt. Rev. A. H. Zulu, South Africa.

CENTRAL COMMITTEE
Chmn., Dr. M. M. Thomas, India.
Vice-Chairmen: Miss Pauline M. Webb. Great Britain; Metropolitan Meliton, Istanbul.

GENERAL SECRETARIAT
Gen. Sec., Rev. Dr. Philip A. Potter.
Asst. Gen. Sec., Rev. Jens J. Thomsen.
Asst. to the Gen. Sec., Rev. Clément Barbey.
Librarian, Rev. Dr. Ans J. van der Bent.
Reference Librarian and Cataloguer, Mr. Pierre Beffa.
Personnel Dir., Mrs. Moya Burton; Asst. to the Dir., Mr. George Kux.
Ecumenical Institute: Prof. Nikos A. Nissiotis, Dir.; Asst. Dirs., Rev. Alain Blancy, Mr. Gerd von Wahlert, Mr. Rihito Kimura.
Special Study Portfolios: Humanum, Prof. David Jenkins; Biblical, Prof. Hans-Ruedi Weber.

PROGRAM UNIT I—FAITH AND WITNESS
Chairman: Philip A. Potter
Commission on Faith and Order:
  Dir., Rev. Dr. Lukas Vischer.
  Assoc. Dir., Archpriest Vitaly Borovoy.
  Secs.: Rev. Dr. Gerald F. Moede, Dr. Konrad Raiser.
Commission on World Mission and Evangelism:
  Dir., Dr. Emilio Castro.
  Assoc. Dir., Rev. Robbins Strong.
  Secs.: Rev. Henry Daniel; Dr. Gerald C. Hoffman; Rev. Steven G. Mackie; Mr. Sang Jung Park; Miss Machteld van Vredenburch; Dr. Thomas Wieser.
  Editorial Asst. for International Review of Mission, Miss Jean Fraser.

AGENCIES HAVING ECUMENICAL CONNECTIONS

Department on Church and Society:
Exec. Sec., Rev. Paul R. Abrecht.
Sec., Rev. David M. Gill.
Dialogue with Men of Living Faiths and Ideologies:
Dr. Stanley J. Samartha.
Rev. Johan M. Snock.
Christian Medical Commission:
Dir., Mr. James C. McGilvray; Assoc. Dirs., Miss Ruth Nita Barrow; Mrs. Helen Gideon; J. Haken Hellberg, M.D.; Consultant, Eileen Catherine Simmons, M.D.
Agency for Christian Literature Development: 7 St. James's St., London SW 1, England, Dir., Mr. Charles G. Richards.
Theological Education Fund: 13 London Rd., Bromley, Kent, BR1 1DE, England
Dir., Dr. Shoki Coe; Assoc. Dirs.: Rev. James Berquist; Dr. Ivy S.T. Chou; Rev. Aharon Sapsezian; Rev. Desmond Tutu.

PROGRAM UNIT II—JUSTICE AND SERVICE
Chairman: Alan A. Brash.

Commission on Inter-Church Aid, Refugee and World Service:
Dir., Rev. Dr. Alan A. Brash.
Deputy Dir., Rev. Graeme Jackson.
Sec. for Finance and Fund Raising, Mr. Willem Schot.
Sec. for Administration, Mr. Robert Huddleson.
Sec. for Special Development Projects, Mr. Jean Fischer.
Area Secs.: Mr. Kodwo Ankrah and Mr. Fredéric Randriamamonjy, Africa; Rev. Kentaro Buma, Asia; Mr. Canh Nguyen Tang, Indo-China; Rev. Joao de Silva, Latin America; Archpriest Georgios Tsetsis, Middle East; Miss Lois Meyhoffer, Co-secretary for Europe; Rev. Graeme Jackson, Program Planning and Pacific Area.
Project Registration and Analysis, Mrs. Maria Kornelis.
Refugee Service, Mr. Soon Young Hahn; Mrs. Saitzew; Mr. Nils G. Gussing.
Material Aid, Mr. Helmut Reuschle; Emergency Officer, Mr. Stanley Mitton; Personnel and Teams, Mr. Gerhard Hennes; Social Service, Miss Rose Marie Pichal.
Secretary for Migration, Mr. Christopher King.
Ecumenical Church Loan Fund:
Dir., Mr. Bevin Fitzsimons.
Commission of the Churches on International Affairs:
Dir., Dr. Leopoldo J. Niilus; Secs.: Rev. Eduardo Bodipo-Malumba; Rev. Dwain C. Epps; Rev. Dr. Richard M. Fagley (New York).
Commission on the Churches' Participation in Development:
Dir., Dr. C. I. Itty; Secs.: Dr. Roy Neehall; Dr. Reinhild Traitler; Rev. Harvey Perkins.
Advisory Committee on Technical Services:
Dir., Mr. Luiz Carlos Weil. Mr. Mahassen, Mr. de Pury.
Ecumenical Program to Combat Racism:
Dir., Mr. Baldwin Sjollema; Mr. M. S. Nawaz Dawood.

PROGRAM UNIT III—EDUCATION AND COMMUNICATION
Chairman: Werner Simpfendörfer.

Staff Working Group on Renewal:
Exec. Sec., Miss Brigalia Bam; Rev. Rex Davis, editor of RISK; Dr. Ian Fraser, Participation in Change Study; Rev. Archie LeMone, Ecumenical Community Service.
Staff Working Group on Education:
Exec. Sec., Dr. William B. Kennedy; Rev. Leslie Clements, Family Life; Dr. Paulo Freire, special consultant; Scholarships; Rev. Gérson A. Meyer, Education; Rev. Wérner Simpfendörfer, Education; Mr. Ralph Young, Laity Education.
Staff Working Group on Communication:
Exec. Sec., _____. Mr. Martin Conway, Publications; Mrs. Tomoko Evdokimoff, Translation; Mr. John Fulton, Photo Assistant; Miss Frances S. Smith, Press Officer for English Language; Rev. J. J. Bauswein, French-German Press Officer; Mr. John Taylor, Film and Visual Arts; Mrs. Elizabeth Gallin, Assistant to Mr. Taylor; Rev. C. Michael de Vries, Radio/TV; Mr. Stephen Whittle, Information Officer for Inter-Church Aid, Refugee and World Service.
Relations with Regional and National Councils:
Sec., Rev. Victor E. W. Hayward.

FINANCE AND CENTRAL SERVICES

Dir., Mr. Frank Northam; Mr. Andréas Schneider, Deputy Director for Finance, Accounting and EDP Services; Mr. Charles Day, Deputy Director for Administrative Services; Mr. Alan Haigh, Deputy Director for Business Management.
WCC/Roman Catholic Commission on Society, Development and Peace:
Gen. Sec.: Fr. Joseph J. Spae, CIMC; Assoc. Sec., Dr. Roy Neehall; Asst. Sec.: Frère Christophe von Wachter.

New York Office: 475 Riverside Drive, New York, N.Y. 10027.
   Exec. Sec., Rev. Dr. Eugene L. Smith.
   Program Sec., Miss Frances Maeda.
   Assoc. for WCC Studies, Mr. Robert S. Davis.

PERIODICALS

The Ecumenical Review (q), _____.
The Ecumenical Press Service (w), Miss Frances S. Smith, Ed., English edition.
International Review of Mission (q), _____.
Risk (q), Rev. Rex Davis, Ed.
Study Encounter, _____.

THE UNITED STATES CONFERENCE FOR THE WORLD COUNCIL OF CHURCHES

The United States Conference for the World Council of Churches, Inc. is a corporation composed of representatives named by member churches in the United States to the Assembly of the World Council of Churches. There are currently 27 member churches in the U.S. Conference.
   The purposes as stated in the Certificate of Incorporation are:
   "to aid the World Council of Churches and its Central Committee in implementing their policy in the United States of America; to interpret the program of the World Council of Churches to the churches in the United States of America; to represent the American member churches of the World Council of Churches and to secure budgetary support for them; and to perform any and every function and service directly related and appropriate to the foregoing."
   The New York office of the World Council of Churches is maintained jointly by the U.S. Conference and the World Council of Churches. As such, it is the executive arm of both for carrying out of the above purposes.
   The *Ecumenical Courier* is a quarterly publication of the U.S. Conference. It is sent regularly to all who become "Friends of the World Council of Churches."

Headquarters: 475 Riverside Dr., New York, NY 10027.
   Tel. (212) 870-2533
Meets annually. Next meeting, April 30-May 1, 1973. Madison, Wis.

OFFICERS AND STAFF

Chmn., Rev. Dr. John Coventry Smith
Vice-Chmn., Rev. Dr. Marion de Velder
Exec. Sec., Rev. Dr. Eugene L. Smith
Sec. for Program, Miss Frances Maeda
Treas., George W. Young
Consultant: Rev. Dr. Richard M. Fagley: Commission of the Churches on International Affairs

COMMITTEE

Comm. on Interpretation and Support: Chmn., Rev. James W. Kennedy.

PERIODICAL

The Ecumenical Courier (4 issues a year), 475 Riverside Dr., New York, NY 10027.

WORLD COUNCIL OF CHURCHES

Constituent Bodies of the World Council

Argentina
   Iglesia Evangelica Del Rio de la Plata (Evangelical Church of the River Plate)
   Iglesia Evangelica Metodista Argentina

Australasia
   Methodist Church of Australasia
   The United Church in Papua, New Guinea and The Solomon Islands

Australia
   Churches of Christ in Australia
   Church of England in Australia
   Congregational Union of Australia
   Presbyterian Church of Australia

AGENCIES HAVING ECUMENICAL CONNECTIONS

Austria
Alt-Katholische Kirche Oesterreichs (Old Catholic Church of Austria)
Evangelische Kirche A.u.H.B. in Oesterreich (Evangelical Church of the Augsburg and Helvetic Confession)

Belgium
Eglise Chretienne Missionaire Belge (Belgian Christian Missionary Church)
Eglise Evangelique Protestante De Belgique (Evangelical Protestant Church of Belgium)

Brazil
Igreja Episcopal Do Brasil (Episcopal Church of Brazil)
Igreja Metodista Do Brasil (Methodist Church of Brazil)
Igreja Evangelica De Confissao Lutherana Do Brasil (Evangelical Church of Lutheran Confession in Brazil)
The Evangelical Pentecostal Church "Brazil for Christ"

Bulgaria
Bulgarian Orthodox Church (Eglise Orthodoxe de Bulgaria)

Burma
Burma Baptist Convention
Church of the Province of Burma

Cameroon
Eglise Evangelique du Cameroun (Evangelical Church of Cameroon)
Eglise Presbyterienne Camerounaise (Presbyterian Church of Cameroon)
Presbyterian Church in West Cameroon
Union Des Eglises Baptistes du Cameroun (Union of Baptist Churches of Cameroon)

Canada
The Anglican Church of Canada
Canadian Yearly Meeting of the Society of Friends
Christian Church (Disciples of Christ)
The Evangelical Lutheran Church of Canada
The Presbyterian Church in Canada
The United Church of Canada

Central Africa
The Church of the Province of Central Africa

Ceylon
The Anglican Church in Ceylon
Methodist Church, Ceylon

Chile
Iglesia Evangelica Lutherana en Chile (Evangelical-Lutheran Church in Chile)
Iglesia Pentecostal de Chile (Pentecostal Church of Chile)
Mision Iglesia Pentecostal (Pentecostal Mission Church)

China
China Baptist Council
Chung-Hua Chi-Tu Chiao-Hui (Church of Christ in China)
Chung-Hua Sheng Kung Hui (Anglican Church in China)
Hua Pei Kung Li Hui (North China Congregational Church)

Congo (Brazzaville)
Eglise Evangelique du Congo (Evangelical Church of the Congo)

Cyprus
Church of Cyprus

Czechoslovakia
Ceskobratrska Cirkev Evangelicka (Evangelical Church of Czech Brethren)
Ceskoslovenska Cirkev (Czechoslovak Church)
Evangelicka Cirkev A. V. Na Slovensku (Evangelical Church in Slovakia, Augsburg Confession)
Orthodox Church of Czechoslovakia
Ref. Cirkev Na Slovensku (Reformed Christian Church in Slovakia)
Slezka Cirkev Evangelicka A. V. (Evangelical Church of the Augsburg Confession in Silesia)

Denmark
Baptist Union of Denmark
Den Evangelisklutherske Folkekirke I Danmark (Church of Denmark)

East Africa
The Presbyterian Church of East Africa

Egypt
Coptic Evangelical Church—The Synod of the Nile
Coptic Orthodox Church
Greek Orthodox Patriarchate of Alexandria

Ethiopia
Ethiopian Orthodox Church

Finland
Suomen Evankelis—Lutherilainen Kirkko (Evangelical Lutheran Church of Finland)

France
Eglise de la Confession D'Augsbourg D'Alsace et de Lorraine (Evangelical Church of the Augsburg Confession in Alsace and Lorraine)
Eglise Evangelique Lutherienne de France (Evangelical Lutheran Church of France)
Eglise Reformee D'Alsace et de Lorraine (Reformed Church of Alsace and Lorraine)
Eglise Reformee de France (Reformed Church of France)

Gabon
Eglise Evangelique du Gabon (Evangelical Church of Gabon)

Germany
Alkatholische Kirche in Deutschland (Old Catholic Church in Germany)
Evangelische Brueder Unitaet (Moravian Church)
Evangelische Kirche in Deutschland (Evangelical Church in Germany)
Evangelische Kirche in Deutschland:
    Evangelische Kirche in Berlin-Brandenburg
    Evangelische Landeskirche Greitswald
    Evangelische Kirche des Kirchengebietes Goerlitz
    Evangelische Kirche der Kirchenprovinz Sachsen
    Evangelische Kirche von Westfalen
    Evangelische Kirche im Rheinland
    Evangelisch-Lutherische Landeskirche Sachsens*
    Evangelisch-Lutherische Landeskirche Hannovers*
    Evangelisch-Lutherische Kirche in Bayern*
    Evangelisch-Lutherische Kirche in Thueringen*
    Evangelisch-Lutherische Landeskirche Schleswig-Holsteins*
    Evangelisch-Lutherische Landeskirche im Hamburgischen Staate*
    Evangelisch-Lutherische Landeskirche Mecklenburgs*
    Braunschweigische Evangelisch-Lutherische Landeskirche*
    Evangelisch-Lutherische Kirche in Luebeck*
    Evangelisch-Lutherische Landeskirche von Schaumburg-Lippe*
    Evangelische Landeskirche in Wuerttemberg
    Evangelisch-Lutherische Kirche in Oldenburg
    Evangelisch-Lutherische Landeskirche Eutin
    Evangelische Kirche in Hessen und Nassau
    Evangelische Landeskirche von Kurhessen-Waldeck
    Evangelische Landeskirche in Baden
    Vereinigte Protestantische-Evangelisch-Christliche Kirche der Pfalz
    Evangelische Landeskirche Anhalts
    Bremische Evangelische Kirche
    Evangelisch-Reformierte Kirche in Nordwestdeutschland
    Lippische Landeskirche

*This Church is directly a member of the World Council of Churches in accordance with the resolution of the General Synod of the United Evangelical Lutheran Church of Germany, dated January 27, 1949, which recommended that the member churches of the United Evangelical Lutheran Church should make the following declaration to the Council of the Evangelical Church in Germany concerning their relation to the World Council of Churches:

"The Evangelical Church in Germany has made it clear through its constitution that it is a federation (Bund) of confessionally determined churches. Moreover, the conditions of membership of the World Council of Churches have been determined at the Assembly at Amsterdam. Therefore, this Evangelical Lutheran Church declares concerning its membership in the World Council of Churches:
  i) It is represented in the World Council as a church of the Evangelical Lutheran Confession.
  ii) Representatives which it sends to the World Council are to be identified as Evangelical Lutherans.
  iii) Within the limits of the competence of the Evangelical Church of Germany it is represented in the World Council through the intermediary of the Council of the Evangelical Church of Germany."

AGENCIES HAVING ECUMENICAL CONNECTIONS

Vereinigung der Deutschen Mennonitengemeinden (Mennonite Church)

Ghana
Evangelical Presbyterian Church
The Methodist Church, Ghana
Presbyterian Church of Ghana

Greece
Ekklesia tes Ellados (Church of Greece)
Greek Evangelical Church

Hong Kong
The Church of Christ in China, The Hong Kong Council

Hungary
A Magyarorszagi Evangelikus Egyhaz (Lutheran Church of Hungary)
A Magyarorszagi Reformatus Egyhaz (Reformed Church of Hungary)
Magyarorszagi Baptista Egyhaz (Baptist Church of Hungary)

Iceland
Evangelical Lutheran Church of Iceland

India
Church of North India
Church of South India
Federation of Evangelical Lutheran Churches in India
Mar Thoma Syrian Church of Malabar
The Orthodox Syrian Church of the East
The Samavesam of Telugu Baptist Churches

Indonesia
The Church of Nisa in Indonesia
Geredja Geredja Kirsten Djawa di Djawa Tengah (Christian Churches of Mid Java)
Geredja Kalimantan Evangelis (Evangelical Church in Kalimantan)
Geredja Kristen Djawa Wetan (Christian Church of East Java)
Geredja Kristen Indjili Di Irian Barat
Geredja Kristen Indonesia (Indonesian Christian Church)
Geredja Kristen Pasundan (Sundanese Christian Church of West Java)
Geredja Kristen Sulawesi Tengah (Christian Church in Mid-Sulawesi)
Geredja Masehi Indjili di Minahasa (Christian Evangelical Church in Minahasa)
Geredja Masehi Indjili Timor (Protestant Evangelical Church in Timor)
Geredja Protestan di Indonesia (Protestant Church in Indonesia)
Geredja Protestan Maluku (Protestant Church of the Moluccas)
Geredja Toradja (Toradja Church)
Huria Kristen Batak Protestan (Protestant Christian Batak Church)
Karo Batak Protestant Church of Kabandjahe, North Sumatra

Iran
Synod of the Evangelical Church of Iran

Italy
Chiesa Evangelica Metodista D'Italia (Evangelical Methodist Church of Italy)
Chiesa Evangelica Internazionale (The Evangelical International Church)
Chiesa Evangelica Valdese (Waldensian Church)

Jamaica
The Moravian Church in Jamaica
The United Church of Jamaica and Grand Cayman

Japan
Nippon Kirisuot Kyodan (The United Church of Christ in Japan)
Nippon Sei Ko Kai (Anglican-Episcopal Church in Japan)

Jerusalem
Greek Orthodox Patriarchate of Jerusalem

Kenya
Church of the Province of Kenva
The Methodist Church in Kenya

Korea
The Korean Methodist Church
The Presbyterian Church in the Republic of Korea
The Presbyterian Church in Korea

Latin America
Igreja Reformada Latino-Americana

Lebanon
Armenian Apostolic Church
Evangelical Synod of Syria and Lebanon (See under Syria)
Union of the Armenian Evangelical Churches in the Near East

Lesotho
Lesotho Evangelical Church

Liberia
Lutheran Church in Liberia

Madagascar
Church of Christ in Madagascar (former L.M.S. Synod)
Eglise Lutherienne Malgache (Malagasy Lutheran Church)

Malaysia & Singapore
The Methodist Church in Malaysia & Singapore

Mexico
Iglesia Metodista de Mejico (Methodist Church of Mexico)

Netherlands
Algemene Doopsgezinde Societeit (General Mennonite Society)
Evangelisch-Lutherse Kerk (Evangelical-Lutheran Church)
De Gereformeerde Kerken in Nederland (The Reformed Churches in the Netherlands)
Nederlandse Hervormde Kerk (Netherlands Reformed Church)
Oud-Katholieke Kerk Van Nederland (Old Catholic Church of the Netherlands)
Remonstrantse Broederschap (Remonstrant Brotherhood)

New Caledonia
Eglise Evangelique en Nouvelle-Caledonie et aux Iles Loyaute (Evangelical Church in New
Caledonia and the Loyalty Isles)

New Hebrides
Presbyterian Church of the New Hebrides

New Zealand
Associated Churches of Christ in New Zealand
The Baptist Union of New Zealand
Church of the Province of New Zealand (Church of England)
The Congregational Union of New Zealand
The Methodist Church of New Zealand
The Presbyterian Church of New Zealand

Nigeria (see also West Africa)
The Methodist Church, Nigeria
The Presbyterian Church of Nigeria

Norway
Norske Kirke (Church of Norway)

Pakistan (see also under India)
United Presbyterian Church of Pakistan

Philippine Islands
Iglesia Filipina Independiente (Philippine Independent Church)
United Church of Christ in the Philippines
Iglesia Evangelica Metodista en Las Islas Filipinas

Poland
Eglise Autoceph. Orthodox en Pologne (Orthodox Church of Poland)
Kosciol Ewangelicko-Augsburski W Polsce (Evangelical Church of the Augsburg Confession)
Kosciol Polskokatolicki w. P.R.L. (Polish-Catholic Church in Poland)
Old Catholic Mariavite Church

Rumania
Evangelical Synodal Presbyterial Church of the Augsburg Confession in the People's Republic
of Rumania
Biserica Evangelica Dupa Confesiunea Dela Augsburg (Evangelical Church of the Augsburg
Confession)
Biserica Ortodoxa Romana (Rumanian Orthodox Church)
Biserica Reformata D in Romania (Reformed Church of Rumania)

AGENCIES HAVING ECUMENICAL CONNECTIONS

Samoa
Congregational Christian Church in Samoa (former L.M.S. Synod)

Sierre Leone
The Methodist Church, Sierre Leone

South Africa
The Bantu Presbyterian Church of South Africa
Church of the Province of South Africa
Evangelical Lutheran Church in Southern Africa-South Eastern Region
Evangelical Lutheran Church in Southern Africa-Transvaal Region
Methodist Church of South Africa
Moravian Church in South Africa-Eastern Province
Moravian Church in South Africa-Western Cape Province
The Presbyterian Church of Southern Africa
United Congregational Church of South Africa

Spain
Iglesia Evangelica Espanola (Spanish Evangelical Church)

Sweden
Svenska Kyrkan (Church of Sweden)
Svenska Missionsfoerbundet (The Mission Covenant Church of Sweden)

Switzerland
Christkatholische Kirche der Schweiz (Old Catholic Church of Switzerland)
Schweizerischer Evangelischer Kirchenbund—Federation Des Eglises Protestantes de la Suisse
(Swiss Protestant Church Federation)

Syria
Evangelical Synod of Syria and Lebanon
Greek Orthodox Patriarchate of Antioch and all the East
Syrian Orthodox Patriarchate of Antioch and all the East

Tahiti
Eglise Evangelique de Polynesie Francais (Evangelical Church of French Polynesia)

Taiwan
Tai-Oan Ki-Tok Tiu-Lo Kau-Hoe (The Presbyterian Church of Formosa)

Tanzania
Church of the Province of Tanzania
Evangelical Lutheran Church in Tanzania

Thailand
The Church of Christ in Thailand

Togo
Eglise Evangelique du Togo (Evangelical Church of Togo)
(Protestant Methodist Church of Dahomey-Togo) Eglise Protestante Methodiste au Dahomey-
Togo

Trinidad
The Presbyterian Church in Trinidad and Grenada

Turkey
Ecumenical Patriarchate of Constantinople

Uganda
Church of Uganda

United Kingdom and Eire
The Baptist Union of Great Britian and Ireland
Churches of Christ in Great Britain and Ireland
Church of England
Church of Ireland
Church of Scotland
Church in Wales
The Congregational Church in England and Wales
The Congregational Union of Scotland
Episcopal Church in Scotland
The Methodist Church
Methodist Church in Ireland
The Moravian Church in Great Britain and Ireland
Presbyterian Church of England

The Presbyterian Church in Ireland
The Presbyterian Church of Wales
The Salvation Army
Union of Welsh Independents
United Free Church of Scotland

United States of America
African Methodist Episcopal Church
African Methodist Episcopal Zion Church
American Baptist Convention
The American Lutheran Church
Antiochian Orthodox—Christian (Archdiocese of New York and All North America)
The Christian Church (Disciples of Christ)
Christian Methodist Episcopal Church
Church of the Brethren
Church of the East (Assyrian)
The Episcopal Church
Hungarian Reformed Church in America
Lutheran Church in America
The Moravian Church in America (Northern Province)
The Moravian Church in America (Southern Province)
National Baptist Convention of America
National Baptist Convention, U.S.A., Inc.
The Orthodox Church in America
Polish National Catholic Church of America
The Presbyterian Church in the U.S.
Reformed Church in America
The Religious Society of Friends
    Friends Gerneral Conference
    Friends United Meeting
The Romanian Orthodox Episcopate of America
Seventh Day Baptist General Conference
United Church of Christ
The United Methodist Church
The United Presbyterian Church in the United States of America

U.S.S.R.
Armenian Apostolic Church
Estonian Evangelical Lutheran Church
Evangelical Lutheran Church of Latvia
Georgian Orthodox Church
Orthodox Church of Russia
The Union of Evangelical Christian Baptists of USSR

West Africa (see also Nigeria)
The Church of the Province of West Africa

West Indies
Church in the Province of the West Indies
The Methodist Church in the Caribbean and the Americas

Yugoslavia
Reformed Christian Church of Yugoslavia
Serbian Orthodox Church
Slovak Evangelical Church of the Augsburg Confession in Yugoslavia

Zaire (Republic of)
Disciples du Christ au Zaire (Disciples of Christ)
Eglise Evangelique du Zaire (Evangelical Church of Zaire)
The Church of Christ on Earth by the Prophet Simon Kimgangu
Eglise Presbyterienne au Zaire

Zambia
United Church of Zambia

Other Churches
Esti Ev. Lut. Usu Kirik (Estonian Evangelical Lutheran Church)
Latvijas Evangeliska Luteriska Baznica (Latvian Evangelical Lutheran Church)

LIST OF ASSOCIATE MEMBER CHURCHES

Argentina
The United Evangelical Lutheran Church

AGENCIES HAVING ECUMENICAL CONNECTIONS

Bolivia
Iglesia Evangelica Methodista en Bolivia

Cameroon
Eglise Protestante Africaine (African Protestant Church)

Chile
Iglesia Metodista de Chile

Cuba
Iglesia Presbiteriana-Reformada en Cuba (Presbyterian-Reformed Church in Cuba)
Iglesia Metodista en Cuba (Methodist Church in Cuba)

India
Bengal-Orissa-Bihar Baptist Convention

Japan
The Korean Christian Church in Japan

Liberia
The Presbyterian Church

Netherlands Antilles
Union of Protestant Churches in the Netherlands Antilles

Peru
Methodist Church of Peru

Portugal
Igreja Evangelica Presbiteriana de Portugal (Evangelical Presbyterian Church of Portugal)
Igreja Lusitana Catolica Apostolica Evangelica (Lusitanian Church, Portugal)

Spain
Iglesia Espanola Reformada Episcopal (Spanish Reformed Episcopal Church)

Sudan
The Presbyterian Church in the Sudan

Uruguay
Iglesia Evanglica Metodista en el Uruguay

West Africa
The Evangelical Presbyterian Church in Rio Muni

Anglican Consultative Council

The Anglican Consultative Council is the central council for the worldwide Anglican Communion. Its creation was proposed by the Lambeth Conference of Bishops of the Anglican Communion in 1968, and came into being by the end of 1969 with the consent of all the Provinces (or member Churches). Its first meeting was held in Limuru, Kenya, early in 1971.

The membership includes bishops, priests, and lay people. Each Province (or member Church) is represented by two or three members and meetings are held every other year; the Standing Committee meets in the intervening years. Council meetings are held in different parts of the world, and the next meeting is due to take place in Dublin, Ireland, in July, 1973.

True to the Anglican Communion's style of working, the Council has no legislative powers. It fills a liaison role, consulting and recommending, and at times representing the Anglican Communion. Among its functions are "to share information about developments in one or more provinces with the other parts of the Communion and to serve as needed as an instrument of common action"; "to develop as far as possible agreed Anglican policies in the world mission of the Church and to encourage national and regional Churches to engage together in developing and implementing such policies by sharing their resources of manpower, money, and experience to the best advantage of all"; "to encourage and guide Anglican participation in the Ecumenical Movement and the ecumenical organizations."

OFFICERS

Pres., The Archbishop of Canterbury, Most Rev. Arthur Michael Ramsey, Lambeth Palace, London, S.E.1., England.
Chmn., Sir Louis Mbanefo, Onitsha, Nigeria.
Sec. Gen., Rt. Rev. J. W. A. Howe, 21 Chester St., London, S.W.1, England. Tel. 01-235-7461.

AGENCIES HAVING ECUMENICAL CONNECTIONS

Baptist World Alliance

The Baptist World Alliance is a voluntary association of Baptist conventions and unions which was formed at the first world gathering of Baptists in Exeter Hall, London, England, July 11-18, 1905. There have been twelve meetings of the Alliance's Baptist World Congress, the most recent of which was held in Tokyo, Japan, in 1970.

BWA functions as: 1) An agency of communication between Baptists through publications, dissemination of news, film, radio, personal visits, and correspondence; 2) A forum for study and fraternal discussion of doctrines, practice and ways of witness to the world; 3) A channel of cooperation in extending help to each other and those in need; 4) A vigilant force for safeguarding religious liberty and other God-given rights; 5) a sponsor of regional and worldwide gatherings for the furtherance of the gospel.

Headquarters: 1628 16th St., N.W., Washington, DC 20009. Tel. (202) 265-5027. Congress convenes every five years. Next meeting, Stockholm, Sweden, July 8-13, 1975.

OFFICERS

Pres., Dr. V. Carney Hargroves, Philadelphia, PA
Gen. Sec., Dr. Robert S. Denny, 1628 16th St. N.W., Washington, DC 20009.
Associate Secs., Dr. Cyril E. Bryant, Mr. Theo Patnaik, Dr. Carl W. Tiller, 1628 16th St., N.W., Washington, DC 20009; Dr. C. Ronald Goulding, 4 Southampton Row, London, W.C. 1B 4AB England.
Eastern Treas., George Polson, Q.C. Ealing, England.
Western Treas., Dr. Carl W. Tiller, Washington, DC.

Heads of Eastern Orthodox Churches

The term "Eastern Orthodox Churches" relates to three main groups: 1) The Orthodox, composed of sixteen bodies listed below, which recognize each other and are recognized by the Ecumenical Patriarch of Constantinople, who is considered the keeper of the "canons" of Orthodoxy. 2) The Oriental Orthodox, commonly referred to as Monophysite (e.g., Copts; Ethiopian, Armenian, Syrian Orthodox, Syrian Malabar (India); and the Nestorians, known as the Armenian Church of the East). 3) Churches which have authentic Orthodox roots and adhere to Orthodox doctrine, but which are temporarily estranged.

Ecumenical Patriarchate: His All-Holiness Demetrios I, Archbishop of Constantinople, and Ecumenical Patriarch, Phanar, Istanbul, Turkey.
Patriarchate of Alexandria: Nicolaos V, Patriarch of Alexandria and All Egypt, Greek Orthodox Patriarchate, Alexandria, Egypt.
Patriarchate of Antioch: His Holiness Elia, Patriarch of Antioch, Damascus, Syria.
Patriarchate of Jerusalem: His Holiness Benediktos, Patriarch of Jerusalem, Jerusalem, Israel.
Patriarchate of Russia: His Holiness Pimen, Patriarch of Moscow and All Russia, 5 Tchisty Pereulok, Moscow 34, U.S.S.R.
Patriarchate of Serbia: His Holiness German, Patriarch of the Serbian and Macedonian Orthodox Church, Belgrade, Yugoslavia.
Patriarchate of Romania: His Holiness Justinian, Patriarch of Romania, Bucharest, Romania.
Patriarchate of Bulgaria: His Holiness Maxime, Patriarch of Bulgaria, Sofia, Bulgaria.
Church of Greece: His Beatitude Hieronymos, Archbishop of Athens and Primate of All Greece, Athens, Greece.
Church of Cyprus: Most Rev. Archbishop Makarios III, Archbishop of Cyprus, Nicosia, Cyprus.
Church of Sinai: The Archbishop-Abbot Gregory, Mt. Sinai, Arabia.
Church of Georgia: Vacant
Church of Albania: Most Rev. Archbishop Damian, Archbishop of Albania, Tirane, Albania.
Church of Finland: Most Rev. Archbishop Paavali, Archbishop of Karelia and All Finland, Kupio, Finland.
Church of Poland: His Beatitude Vasili, Metropolitan of Warsaw and All Poland, Warsaw, Poland.
Church of Czechoslovakia: His Beatitude Dorotej, Metropolitan of Prague and All Czechoslovakia, V. Jame 6, Prague, Czechoslovakia.

Ecumenical Satellite Commission

Instituted on July 6, 1970, this commission has ten members, five appointed by the World Association for Christian Communication and five by international Catholic organizations concerned with press, cinema, radio and television. The sponsoring bodies are: The World Association for Christian Communication (WACC), United Kingdom; L'Union Catholique Internationale de la Presse (UCIP), France; L'Office Catholique International du Cinéma (OCIC), France; and The International Catholic Association for Radio and Television (Unda), United Kingdom.

AGENCIES HAVING ECUMENICAL CONNECTIONS

ECUSAT has the following objectives: information for the churches; representation at meetings of international organizations; action for the use of satellites in conformity with the Christian conscience.

Hèadquarters: 7 St. James's St., London S.W. 1, England. Tel. 01-839 5776.

OFFICERS

Pres., M. l'Abbé Lucien Labelle, 4635 rue de Lorimier, Montreal-34, Quebec, Canada; Sec. Gen., Rev. E. H. Robertson, United Kingdom.
Commission Members: Dr. Sigurd Aske, Norway; Mr. Roger Bourgeon, France; Mr. Alva Clarke, Caribbean; Fr Emmanuel Flipo, France; Mr. Christopher Kolade, Nigeria; Dr. Konrad Kraemer, W. Germany; Fr. Tomy Luiz, India; Abbé Lucien Labelle, Canada; Dr. Allen E. Throop, United States; Rev. Albert van den Heuvel, Netherlands.
Commission Consultants: Mr. Jean d'Arcy, France; Dr. William Kennedy, United States; Mr. Edward J. Roth, United States; Dr. Abe G. Thiessen, United States.

Friends World Committee for Consultation
AMERICAN SECTION AND FELLOWSHIP COUNCIL, INC.

The Friends World Committee for Consultation (FWCC) was formed in 1937. There has been an American Section as well as a European Section from the early days. Since 1954, the American Section of the FWCC and the American Friends Fellowship Council, which was formed in 1936, have existed under the official name Friends World Committee for Consultation, American Section and Fellowship Council, and the programs of the two groups have been merged. The purposes of the American Section can be summarized as follows:

1) To encourage and strengthen the spiritual life within the Society of Friends through such measures as the promotion of intervisitation, study, conferences, and a wide sharing of experience on the deepest spiritual level.
2) To help Friends to gain a better understanding of the worldwide character of the Society of Friends and its vocation in the world today.
3) To promote consultation amongst Friends of all cultures, countries, and languages. The Committee seeks to bring the different groups of Friends into intimate touch with one another on the basis of their common Quaker heritage, with a view to sharing experience and coming to some measure of agreement in regard to their attitude to modern world problems.
4) To promote understanding between Friends of all countries and members of other branches of the Christian Church and members of other religious faiths, and to interpret the specific Quaker message to those who seek for further religious experience.
5) To keep under review the Quaker contribution in world affairs and to facilitate both the examination and presentation of Quaker thinking and concern.

Headquarters: 152-A N. 15th St., Philadelphia, PA 19102. Tel. (215) 563-0757.
Sec., Herbert M. Hadley.

Midwest Office: 203 South East St., Plainfield, IN 46168. Tel. (317) 839-6317.
Assoc. Sec., Robert J. Rumsey.

International Association of Women Ministers

This organization was founded in 1919 and was formerly known as the American Association of Women Ministers. Membership is open to women who are licensed or ordained by Evangelical bodies. The IAWM exists to promote equal ecclesiastical rights for women in the church and to encourage young women to enter the ministry.

OFFICERS

Pres., Pauline Thames, 5458 No. Michigan Ave., Indianapolis, IN 46208.
Gen. Sec., Constance Bradshaw, Box 406, Montello, WI 53949.
Rec. Sec., Carrie George, 1652 Detroit Ave., Atlanta, GA 30314.
Treas., Mary Hoffman Ryan, 1464 W. 101 St., Cleveland, OH 44102.

PERIODICAL

The Woman's Pulpit (q), 212 Elm St., Cloverport, KY 40111. Rev. Marietta Mansfield, Ed.

Lambeth Conference of Bishops of the Anglican Communion

The Lambeth Conference consists of all the diocesan bishops (and sometimes also the assistant bishops) of the Anglican Communion, and is called together by the personal invitation of the Archbishop of Canterbury.
The first Lambeth Conference was held in 1867 at the request of the bishops in Canada and the United States, and it became a recurring event at ten-year intervals.

AGENCIES HAVING ECUMENICAL CONNECTIONS

The Anglican Communion has no central legislative body, but a practice of consultation and acknowledged interdependence assures its identity as a worldwide family of autonomous Churches and Provinces in communion with the See of Canterbury. The main instrument of consultation has been the Lambeth Conference.

After the Lambeth Conference of 1958, a full-time officer, who became known as the Anglican Executive Officer, was appointed "to collect and disseminate information, keep open lines of communication, and make contact when necessary with responsible authority." The next Lambeth Conference in 1968 proposed the setting up of an Anglican Consultative Council, which, with the consent of all the Provinces (or member Churches), came into being at the end of 1969. The appointment of Secretary General of the Council replaced that of Anglican Executive Officer.

Pres., The Archbishop of Canterbury, Most Rev. Arthur Michael Ramsey, Lambeth Palace, London, S.E.1., England.

Lutheran World Federation

The Lutheran World Federation is the successor to an earlier world organization of Lutheran churches named the Lutheran World Convention and organized in Eisenach, Germany, in 1923. World War II inflicted such tremendous damage upon the spiritual and welfare activities of Lutheran and other churches in western Europe and elsewhere in the world that it was felt necessary to establish a more functional organization. Thus, the Lutheran World Federation was organized on July 1, 1947, at Lund, Sweden, and plunged immediately into programs of emergency relief, interchurch aid, and studies. Currently it functions between assemblies through major departments of Studies, Church Cooperation, and World Service. The 1972 membership consists of 83 member churches from all parts of the world with constituencies exceeding 53 million persons.

The LWF is incorporated under Swiss law and has its headquarters in Geneva. Its constitution stipulates that "the Lutheran World Federation shall be a free association of Lutheran Churches. It shall act as their agent in such matters as they assign to it. It shall not exercise churchly functions on its own authority, nor shall it have power to legislate for the Churches belonging to it or to limit the autonomy of any Member Church.

"In accord with the preceding paragraphs, the Lutheran World Federation shall:

(a) Further a united witness before the world to the Gospel of Jesus Christ as the power of God for salvation.

(b) Cultivate unity of faith and confession among the Lutheran Churches of the world.

(c) Develop fellowship and cooperation in study among Lutherans.

(d) Foster Lutheran interest in, concern for, and participation in ecumenical movements.

(e) Support Lutheran Churches and groups as they endeavor to meet the spiritual needs of other Lutherans and to extend the Gospel.

(f) Provide a channel for Lutheran Churches and groups to help meet physical needs."

Headquarters: 150 Route de Ferney, 1211 Geneva 20, Switzerland
Meets every six years. Next meeting in 1976.

OFFICERS

Pres., Prof. Mikko E. Juva, Evangelical Lutheran Church of Finland, Valskarinkatu 7, Helsinki 26, Finland.
Vice Presidents: Rev. Soritua A. E. Nababan, Batak Protestant Christian Church, Djakarta, Indonesia; Rev. Dr. Robert J. Marshall, Lutheran Church in America, New York, NY; Rev. Juan Cobrdra, United Evangelical Lutheran Church, Buenos Aires, Argentina.
Treas., Dr. Rudolf Weeber, Vice-Pres., Evangelischer Oberkirchenart Stuttgart, Postfach 97, 7, 1, Stuttgart, Germany.
Gen. Sec., Dr. Andre Appel, Geneva.
Gen. Sec., U.S. National Committee, Dr. Carl H. Mau, Jr., 315 Park Ave. So., New York, NY 10010. Tel. (212) 677-3950.

PERIODICALS

Lutheran World; Lutherische Rundschau (German Ed.), Geneva.

Mennonite World Conference

The first Conferenec was held in Basel, Switzerland, in 1925 under the leadership of Christian Neff, elder of the Weierhof, Palatinate, Germany. All of the major Mennonite church bodies around the world participate in the program of the World Conference and these bodies represent approximately 400,000 baptized members. The MWC does not legislate for the member churches; it convenes basically for inspiration and discussion. Each of the participating Mennonite church bodies retains its autonomy. The Mennonite World Conference meets every five years.

OFFICERS

Pres. and Chmn., Exec. Committee,, Erland Waltner, 3003 Benham Ave., Elkhart, IN 46514. Tel. (219) 523-1385.
Exec. Sec., Cornelius J. Dyck, 3003 Benham Ave., Elkhart, IN 46514.

AGENCIES HAVING ECUMENICAL CONNECTIONS

Pentecostal World Conference

The Pentecostal World Conference was organized in 1947 at Zurich, Switzerland, where Pentecostal leaders met in conference seeking ways to help bring about greater understanding and cooperation among their churches.

Formed and continuing as a nonlegislative body, the conference provides a forum for exchanging ideas, sharing information, and participating in fellowship together.

The main event of the organization is the triennial worldwide convention. Past conventions have been in Zurich, Switzerland; Paris, France; London, England; Stockholm, Sweden; Toronto, Canada; Jerusalem, Israel; Helsinki, Finland; Rio de Janerio, Brazil; and Dallas, Texas. The next convention will be in Seoul, Korea, September 18-23, 1973.

Between conventions in the World Conference Advisory Committee supervises the work of the conference and plans the next convention. The 22-man committee is elected at each Pentecostal World Conference convention and has members from around the world.

Conference every three years. Next Meeting: Seoul, Korea, September 18-23, 1973.

OFFICERS

Chmn., Dr. Thomas F. Zimmerman, 1445 Boonville Ave., Springfield, MO 65802.
Sec., Rev. P. S. Brewster, The City Temple, Cowbridge Rd., Cardiff, Wales, Gr. Britain.
Arrangements Comm. Chmn., Dr. Yonggi Cho, 10th Pentecostal World Conference, C.P.O. Box 6172, Seoul, Korea.

ADVISORY COMMITTEE

Members in addition to the officers: Australia, Rev. Ralph Read; Brazil, Rev. Paulo L. Macaloa and Rev. A. P. Vasconcelos; Canada, Rev. Robert W. Taitinger; Finland, Rev. Veikko Manninen; France, Rev. Andre Nicolle; Germany, Rev. Erwin Lorenz; Indonesia, Rev. Ho Lukas Senduk; Japan, Rev. Kiyoma Yumiyama; Java, Rev. Paul Tehupuring; Korea, Rev. Yung Chul Han; Mexico, Rev. Alejandro Portugal; Peru, Rev. Lucas Munoz; Philippines, Rev. Veronico Suan; Sweden, Rev. Lewi Pethrus; Trinidad, W. I., Rev. Pat Ryan; U.S.A., Dr. Howard P. Courtney, Bishop S. M. Crouch, and Bishop J. Floyd Williams.

PERIODICAL

World Pentecost, (q), P. S. Brewster, Ed., The City Temple, Cowbridge Rd., Cardiff, Wales, Gr. Britain.

United Bible Societies

The United Bible Societies is a world fellowship of over 50 national Bible Societies which, through its national, regional, and global organization, coordinates the efforts of Bible Societies and their staff in over 100 countries, and serves another 50.

The UBS was founded in 1946 to facilitate consultation and mutual support between its then 16 member Societies, thus helping them to carry out the translation, production, distribution, and encouragement of effective use of the Scriptures with ever-increasing efficiency and devotion. In fulfilling this purpose the UBS has evolved over the years, and is now a single partnership of Societies—some old-established, some very recently formed—responsible corporately through national and regional representation in the operation of a World Service Budget (now totaling some $8 million annually), for planning, policy-making, financing, and carrying out the worldwide work.

The UBS has functional subcommittees (on translation, production, distribution, promotion, World Service Budget, etc.) and a team of technical consultants in these same matters, some located at the two World Service Centres (at present in London and New York) but most working in the four Regions of Africa, Americas, Asia-Pacific, and Europe. The UBS organizes training institutes and publishes technical helps for translators; coordinates and advises on the most efficient and economical production of the Scriptures; makes known and stimulates new methods of Scripture distribution, especially by church members, for whom training courses are organized; occasionally engages in special studies leading to practical developments (e.g. on the use of the Bible in evangelism and Scriptures for new literates); represents Bible Society interests at world and regional interdenominational conferences and committees; and when necessary coordinates arrangements to provide Scriptures in emergency situations.

Headquarters: 101 Queen Victoria St., London EC4P 4EP, England
Council and Assembly meeting at least once every ten years.

OFFICERS

Pres., Most Rev. Dr. F. D. Coggan, Archbishop of York.
Gen. Sec., The Rev. H. Ulrich Fick.

United Bible Societies Bulletin (q); The Bible translator (q): Technical Papers (1 & 3), P. Elling-worth, Ed.; Practical Papers (2 & 4), W. D. Reyburn, Ed.

World Alliance of Reformed Churches
(Presbyterian and Congregational)

The World Alliance of Reformed Churches (Presbyterian and Congregational) was formed in 1970 at Nairobi, Kenya, with the union of the former World Alliance of Reformed Churches and the former International Congregational Council. Both organizations were composed of member churches whose origins lie mainly in the Reformation with which the names of Calvin and Zwingli are linked.

Member churches constituent to WARC number 127 in some 75 different countries with a total estimated 55 million people as members.

The constitution provides that *ordinarily* once in five years delegates from member churches will meet in General Council (Assembly). Only this Assembly has the authority to make and administer policies and plans, and to speak as the Alliance. Between Assemblies, the Executive Committee exercises general oversight of the Alliance work; it meets annually.

The Executive Committee consists of the president, three vice-presidents, department heads, and fifteen members. WARC headquarters are in the ecumenical center in Geneva, Switzerland, and its staff members maintain close contact with departments and agencies of the World Council of Churches and with the executives of other world confessional organizations.

Regional needs and growing membership in all parts of the world have produced area organizations within the Alliance. Two areas are fully organized: Europe and North America; an informal consultative group is at work in Latin America. The major object of such area organizations is to provide means of cooperation, fellowship, and study in specific regions of the world.

THE ALLIANCE

OFFICERS

Pres., Dr. William P. Thompson, U.S.A.
Vice Presidents: The Rev. Victor Rakotoarimanana, Madagascar; The Rev. John Huxtable, England; Mrs. Shanti R. Solomon, India.
Gen. Sec., The Rev. Edmond Perret, 150 route de Ferney, Geneva, Switzerland.
North American Sec., The Rev. Dr. James I. McCord, Princeton Theological Seminary, Princeton, NJ 08540.
Gen. Treas., Mr. Jean Francois Rochette, 11, Corraterie, 1204 Geneva, Switzerland.

THE NORTH AMERICAN AREA

OFFICERS

Chmn., Dr. Hubert Morrow, Bethel College, McKenzie, TN 38201. (Cumberland Presbyterian.)
Past Chmn., Bishop Dezso Abraham, 331 Kirkland Pl., Perth Amboy, NJ 08861. (Hungarian Reformed Church.)
North American Sec., Pres. James I. McCord, Princeton Theological Seminary, Princeton, NJ 08540. (United Presbyterian Church in the U.S.A.)
Rec. Clk., The Rev. William I. Klempa, 129 Mt. Pleasant Rd., Toronto 5, Ontario, Canada. (Presbyterian Church in Canada.)
Treas., Rev. Dr. James A. Millard, Jr., 341 Ponce de Leon Ave., N.E., Atlanta, GA 30308. (Presbyterian Church in the United States.)
Dir. of Information, The Rev. Frank H. Heinze, Witherspoon Bldg., Philadelphia, PA 19107. (United Presbyterian Church in the U.S.A.)

World Alliance of Young Men's Christian Associations

The World Alliance of YMCAs was constituted at the First World Conference of Young Men's Christian Associations, held in Paris in 1855. Geneva, Switzerland, was designated as its headquarters, and in the early years the work was largely undertaken by lay and honorary officers, using the professional assistance of the staff of some National Movements. In 1878 a permanent office was acquired and the first General Secretary, with related staff, was appointed.

The World Alliance is basically a confederation, its members being the National YMCAs around the world. At present 66 National YMCA Movements maintain membership in the Alliance, and, in addition to these, the World Alliance cooperates with YMCAs in 17 other countries where National Movements have not yet been organized. Thus the World Alliance provides the coordination and service functions for National Movements which National Movements in turn provide for the Member Associations in their several countries.

The basis of the World Alliance, popularly known as the Paris Basis, because it was at the 1855 Conference in Paris that it was formulated, is as follows:

AGENCIES HAVING ECUMENICAL CONNECTIONS

"The Young Men's Christian Associations seek to unite those young men who, regarding Jesus Christ as their God and Saviour according to the Holy Scriptures, desire to be His disciples in their faith and in their life, and to associate their efforts for the extension of His Kingdom amongst young men."

The World Alliance is governed by a World Council of YMCAs, which meets at four-year intervals. An Executive Committee and Standing Committees on Intermovement Cooperation, Programme and Leadership, Finance, and Work with Refugees and Migrants, meet at regular intervals between World Councils and carry the responsibility for the ongoing work.

It helps to coordinate intermovement cooperation, particularly to extend the Movement into new fields and to develop new programs. It represents the World Movements at the United Nations and its agencies. It cooperates with other world Christian bodies, notably the World YWCA, the World Council of Churches, the Catholic Church and its international youth organizations, and the World Student Christian Federation.

Headquarters: 37 Quai Wilson, 1201 Geneva, Switzerland. Tel. (022) 32-31-00

OFFICERS

Pres., David M. Robinson, U.K.
Sec. Gen., Fredrik Franklin, 37 Quai Wilson, 1201 Geneva, Switzerland.

World Association for Christian Communication

The World Association for Christian Communication is an international organization of agencies and individuals who are concerned with the use of communications media as instruments for the development of a just society, and who wish to assist Christian agencies to make more effective use of the media in proclaiming the Christian gospel in its relevance to all aspects of life.

The WACC was formed in Oslo, Norway, in June, 1968, by the union of the Coordinating Committee for Christian Broadcasting and the World Association for Christian Broadcasting. Although these predecessor organizations were concerned primarily with broadcasting, WACC is interested in all media of communication, and seeks to work closely with literature, film, and other specialized groups in serving the needs of both Christian agencies and persons engaged in communication. It is flexible as an organization and is prepared to modify its structure, procedures, and program in response to the communication needs of the Christian community.

Headquarters: 7 St. James's St., London SW 1, England. Tel. 01-839-5776

OFFICERS

Pres., Rev. Dr. Frederick R. Wilson (U.S.A.).
1st Vice-Pres., Dr. J. Ozinga (Netherlands).
Pres. Emeritus, Rt. Rev. Dr. F. Birkeli (Norway).
Vice-Presidents: E. V. Badejo (Africa); Mr. Mathew S. Ogawa (Asia-Pacific); Bishop A. Samuel (Middle East); Dr. Roy Neehall (Latin America-Caribbean); William F. Fore (North America).
Sec. Rev. W. D. Kennedy-Bell (U.K.)
Treas., Kirchenrat Robert Geisendörfer (Germany).

EXECUTIVE COMMITTEE

Rev. Dr. Frederick R. Wilson (U.S.A.); Mr. John Kamau (Kenya); Rev. W. D. Kennedy-Bell (U.K.); Rev. Albert Isteero (Lebanon); Kirchenrat Robert Geisendörfer (Germany); Mr. Mathew S. Ogawa (Japan); Mr. Rolando Zapata (Mexico).

STAFF

Exec. Dir., Dr. Philip A. Johnson (London).
Assoc. Dirs., Rev. E. H. Robertson (London); Dr. A. J. van Dulst (London).
Adm. Asst., Miss Lesley Walmsley (London).
European Chmn., Mr. Robert Geisendörfer (Munich).
Sec., European Office, Miss Murri Selle (Munich).
Co-ordinator, Pacific, Rev. J. William Matthews.

World Convention of Churches of Christ

The World Convention of Churches of Christ was organized in 1930 in Washington, D.C. It normally meets every five years and is an international confessional grouping including churches and work in 34 countries of the world. It uses the name "Churches of Christ" because it is the name used by many of its churches in various parts of the world.

This organization, according to its constitution, "may in no way interfere with the independence of the churches or assume the administrative functions of existing ongoing organizations among us." It exists "in order more fully to show the essential oneness of the churches in the Lord Jesus

Christ; impart inspiration to the world brotherhood; cultivate the spirit of fellowship; provide unity among the churches; and to cooperate with Christians everywhere toward the unity of the Church upon the basis of the New Testament."

Headquarters: Room 448, 475 Riverside Dr., New York, NY 10027. Tel. (212) 870-2751.

Next Convention: Mexico City, July, 1974.

OFFICERS

Pres., Dr. J. Daniel Joyce, Enid, OK.
First Vice-Pres., Rev. Daniel Lopez de Lara, Mexico City, Mexico.
Gen. Sec., Dr. Allan W. Lee, New York, NY.

World Council of Synagogues (Conservative)

The World Council of Synagogues (Conservative) was organized in 1957 as an alliance of Conservative synagogues and synagogue organizations throughout the world. Its purpose is to extend fellowship and mutual aid to each other and to foster the growth and development of Conservative Judaism.

OFFICERS

Pres., Morris Speizman, 3080 Broadway, New York, NY 10027. Tel. (212) 749-8000.
Dir., Morris Laub, 3080 Broadway, New York, NY 10027. Tel. (212) 749-8000.

World Methodist Council

The World Methodist Council is an association of 54 different Methodist, or Methodist-related, groups at work in 87 countries of the world. According to its constitution, "it does not seek to legislate for them nor to invade their autonomy. Rather it exists to serve them and to give unity to their witness and enterprise."

Although the name World Methodist Council was adopted in 1951 at Oxford, England, the Council dates from 1881, when the first Ecumenical Methodist Conference met in London, England. As the Ecumenical Methodist Conference, this world organization convened at ensuing ten-year intervals with the exception of the 1941 Conference, which because of World War II was not held until 1947. Since 1951, meetings have been held every five years.

The membership of the Council is composed of autonomous churches or such units of international church organizations as have attained a significant degree of autonomy.

The World Methodist Council seeks: to deepen the fellowship of the Methodist peoples over the barriers of race, nationality, color, and language; to foster Methodist participation in the ecumenical movement and to promote the unity of Methodist witness and service in that movement; to advance unity of theological and moral standards in the Methodist churches of the world; to suggest priorities in Methodist activity; to promote the most effective use of Methodist resources in the Christian mission throughout the world; to encourage evangelism in every land; to promote Christian education and the church's care for youth; to uphold and relieve persecuted or needy Christian minorities; to provide a means of consultation and cooperation between world Methodism and the other world communions of the Christian Church; to study union and reunion proposals which affect Methodist member churches and to offer advice and help as needed; to arrange the exchange of preachers through a committee appointed for that purpose.

OFFICERS

Gen. Sec., Dr. Lee F. Tuttle, Lake Junaluska, NC 28745; Tel. (704) 456-9432; Geneva Secretary, Dr. Hugh B. Sherlock, 150 Route de Ferney, 1211 Geneva 20, Switzerland; Tel. 33-34-00.

World Student Christian Federation

The World Student Christian Federation was founded in 1895 by a group of Student Christian Movement leaders, John R. Mott prominent among them. WSCF now has movements in about 80 countries with constituency at all levels of education: high schools, higher education, and the academic community generally. For many years WSCF published the quarterly *Student World,* which has been replaced by Federation Books, available from its Geneva office.

The Federation played a significant role in promoting ecumenism among Christian denominations and therefore in creating the World Council of Churches in 1948.

At the Helsinki, Finland, General Assembly in 1968, a decision was made to regionalize the WSCF. Therefore, six regional groups have developed their own programs for implementing the vocation of Christian community and in furthering programs working toward a just world. A growing awareness on the part of the educational community of the need for radical social change has influenced the WSCF in the areas of leadership training for young Christians, study conferences, campus ministry conferences, and experimental programs in education.

The General Assembly meets every four years; the next meeting will be in Ethiopia in 1973. WSCF is supported by national movements, senior friends, and the churches.

Headquarters: Case Postale, 391, 1211 Geneva 2, Switzerland.
North American Office: 235 E. 49th St., New York, NY 10017.

OFFICERS

Gen. Sec., Risto Lehtonen.
Chmn., Richard Shaull.
North American Sec., Rev. Placide Bazoche.

World Union for Progressive Judaism

The World Union for Progressive Judaism was established in London, England, in 1926, by representatives of Liberal, Progressive, and Reform congregational associations and individual synagogues from six nations. The movement has grown, and today the World Union stimulates the development of a worldwide movement and its congregations in 25 countries. The membership of these congregations totals approximately 1.1 million Jewish men, women, and children.

The World Union operates a secondary school in Haifa, Israel, a college for training rabbis in London, and a teacher training school for the French-speaking world in Paris. It extends organizational and financial assistance to new congregations in many countries, assigns and employs rabbis wherever Jews are in search of their religious heritage, operates religious and social youth programs in Israel and Europe, publishes prayer books and other texts in many languages, holds biennial conferences for Jewish leaders and scholars from all corners of the world.

Office: 838 Fifth Ave., New York, NY 10021. Tel. (212) 249-0100.

OFFICERS

Pres., Rabbi Dr. Maurice N. Eisendrath.
Exec. Dir., Rabbi Richard G. Hirsch.

World Young Women's Christian Association

The World YWCA was founded in 1894 by four of the existing National YWCAs: the Associations of Great Britain, Norway, Sweden, and the United States. During the first years of its history the world movement, reflecting the patterns of its national affiliates, was primarily made up of members of various Protestant denominations. However, as the work spread around the world, Roman Catholic and Orthodox Christians joined the Association, and the World YWCA became consciously ecumenical. Today it includes large numbers of women from all confessions and serves many women and girls of many faiths. The latest World YWCA constitution was adopted in 1955 and expressed the functions of the World Association as follows:

"The World YWCA provides a channel for the sharing of resources and the exchange of experience among its affiliated associations.

It helps its affiliated associations with the development of their leadership and programme.

It surveys new fields and promotes work to meet the needs therein.

It acts in cooperation with world voluntary movements and with intergovernmental organizations in matters of common concern.

It works for international understanding for improved social and economic conditions and for basic human rights for all people.

In times of emergency it undertakes and sponsors international humanitarian, welfare, and relief work, in accordance with Christian principles, irrespective of religious, social, political, national or racial differences."

The YWCA is now at work in 80 countries with programs including a variety of educational activities, vocational training programs for women and girls, hostels, rural projects, and programs of study and action in relation to social and economic issues. A wide network of sharing of financial resources and personnel between Associations and of financial aid from other sources forms the World YWCA program of development aid. The World YWCA also carries on refugee services in cooperation with other ecumenical bodies and with its own member associations.

The World YWCA has a legislative Assembly which brings together representatives of its national affiliates every four years and an Executive Committee made up of twenty members from all parts of the world which meets annually. An international staff works at the headquarters in Geneva.

Headquarters: 37 Quai Wilson, 1201 Geneva, Switzerland. Tel. (022) 32-31-00.

OFFICERS

Pres., Mrs. A. Tsouderow-Athanassiou.
Gen. Sec., Miss Elizabeth Palmer.

World's Christian Endeavor Union

Christian Endeavor is a movement composed of committed followers of Jesus Christ, organized in groups called societies or grades, for the purpose of: leading young people (also children and adults) to accept Jesus Christ as Saviour and Lord; bringing them into the life of the church; sustaining and training them for the service of Christ and his cause; releasing them through all channels of human activity in the service of God and man.

Christian Endeavor societies are generally sponsored by a local church, which determines theology, program, activities, and relationships. In most countries it is a graded program including organizational pattern and materials for various age groups.

The first society was organized February 2, 1881, in Portland, Maine. The idea spread rapidly, and by 1895 Christian Endeavor had become a worldwide movement and the World's Christian Endeavor Union was organized in Boston, Mass. As the movement spread to other lands, many national unions were formed. Presently, Christian Endeavor operates in 76 nations and islands and is used by 83 different Christian groups; there are approximately 2 million members world wide. The World's Union is composed of two areas for the effective promotion of the work—Area I (the Americas, Caribbean, Pacific Region, and Asia) and Area II (Europe, Africa, India, Pakistan, and the Near East). World conventions are held quadrennially and Area conferences in the intervening years. The union is incorporated and is governed by a Council which meets every four years, a Board of Trustees which meets annually, and an Executive Committee which meets on call. There are no full-time paid employees. Most of the work is carried on by volunteer service.

Headquarters: 1221 East Broad St., Columbus, OH 43216. Tel. (614) 253-8541.
London Office: "Sunnydene," 23 Leamington Rd., Ryton-on-Dunsmore, Coventry CV8 3FL, England.
Next convention: Essen, Germany, July 24-28, 1974.

OFFICERS

Pres., Dr. Clyde W. Meadows.
Treas., Phyllis I. Rike.
Gen. Sec., Rev. Charles W. Barner.
Area II. Gen. Sec., William J. Sharpe.

6. UNITED STATES REGIONAL AND LOCAL ECUMENICAL AGENCIES

Christians and Christian churches relate to each other through ecumenical agencies in many and varied ways at different regional and local levels. Some agencies have single purpose programs such as ministry to drug addicts, or to persons released from prison, or to senior citizens. Other agencies are broad and inclusive. Some serve an extensive geography, such as Appalachia, whereas others are neighborhood-oriented "cluster parishes." Many agencies bring together church people (ministerial associations, local units of Church Women United, etc.), while others provide for cooperation of congregations, judicatory units, or church agencies. "Council of Churches" is still a standard designation for organization of churches in relation to each other, but new terms have come into use such as "conference of churches," "area church board," "area coalition," "ecumenical ministry," "cooperative ministry," and "interchurch agencies."

If a composite list of all local and regional ecumenical instrumentalities were compiled it would number into many thousands; however, no such compilation exists at this time. The **Yearbook** listing which follows includes the more standard regional and local ecumenical expressions, including a number that serve on an interstate basis. Interstate agencies are listed first. There are other ecumenical agencies, but accurate information has not been available concerning them. More information concerning local ecumenical developments within a state is usually available from the state ecumenical agency.

After the interstate agencies this section lists states, arranged alphabetically, with the state-wide ecumenical agencies listed first; then follow metropolitan, city, or area agencies with paid staff, listed alphabetically by name of agency. This is followed by an alphabetical listing of councils or other local agencies with voluntary leadership. If the voluntary agency is a council, the term "council" is not repeated in the name.

For councils or agencies with paid staff, the name, address, and telephone number of the agency are given and the names of all professional staff are listed. When the name of the city is omitted from an address, the city is the same as the headquarters of the organization. For councils or agencies with voluntary leadership, the name and address of the president is given, if the information was available.

Information concerning changes in staff, officers, mailing addresses, and program emphases for those agencies listed here can be secured from the Commission on Regional and Local Ecumenism, National Council of Churches, 475 Riverside Dr., New York, NY 10027, or it may be secured from the executive or the president of the agency.

Listing includes information available through September, 1972, by the Commission on Regional and Local Ecumenism.,

† Indicates that information is repeated from the previous **Yearbook** listing.

* Designates part-time staff.

REGIONAL

Agropolitan Ministries
P.O. Box 145, Merom, IN 47861
Tel. (812) 356-4681

Exec. Dir., Rev. Keith L. Inskeep

An ecumenical service center for churches of southern Indiana and Illinois supported by four denominations, the Indiana Council of Churches, and the Illinois Conference of Churches. Schedules retreats and workshops.

Association for Christian Training & Service
500 North Roan St., Johnson City, TN 37601

Coordinator, Rev. William A. Jones, Jr.

ACTS was organized to assist congregations and communions in the southern region to understand and fulfill their mission in the region.

The Commission on Religion in Appalachia, Inc.
864 Weisgarber Rd, N.W., Knoxville, TN 37919
Tel. (615) 584-6133

Exec. Dir., Rev. Max E. Glen
Asst. Dir., Rev. John B. McBride
Adm. Asst., Miss Lenore A. Mullarney

Chm., The Rt. Rev. William E. Sanders
Treas., Dr. D. M. Aldridge

A 13-state regional ecumenical agency composed of 17 communions (national mission boards and judicatories); 10 state councils of churches; The Council ot the Southern Mountains, Inc.; Division of Christian Life and Mission, National Council of Churches; National Catholic Rural Life Conference; Lutheran Council in the USA; and Christian Associates of Southwest Pennsylvania.

CONTACT Teleministry, Inc.
900 S. Arlington Ave., Rm. 125, Harrisburg 17109
Tel. (717) 652-3410.

Exec. Dir., Rev. Robert E. Larson, Jr.

Pres., Rev. Emerson S. Colaw, 1345 Grace Ave., Cincinnati, OH 45208
Treas., Mr. Samuel H. Meares, P.O. Box N, Greensboro, NC 27402

Major Activities: Development of telephone counseling/crisis intervention centers; assistance to local CONTACT centers; coordination of telephone ministries; maintainence of ties with Life Line International; liaison with other telephone hotlines; development of training programs, materials, and other aids for teleministry centers.

The Ecumenical Center of Renewal and Planning
P.O. Box 88377, Indianapolis, IN 46208
Tel. (317) 924-1331

Dir., Rev. Donald W. Zimmerman

A regional center for renewal and planning with emphasis on the nonmetropolitan areas. Workshops, consultations, seminars; action research projects; situation analysis and evaluation; quarterly packet and occasional papers.

Great Plains Inter-Religious Commission
Chm., Msgr. George Weber

Purpose of this Commission is to focus attention on needs and to assist the people living in the Great Plains region to meet their religious, economic, and educational needs. Specific need task forces formed as necessary.

IMPACT
110 Maryland Ave., N.E., Washington, DC 20002
Tel. (202) 504-8636.

National Director, Rev. Robert Odean

An interfaith legislative information and action network. Design of information flow: education and perspective development; progress and status reports; action alerts with recommendations for immediate response; network organizations with specific response objectives.

National Farm Worker Ministry
1411 W. Olympic Blvd., Suite 511, Los Angeles, CA 90015
Tel. (213) 386-8130

Dir., Rev. Wayne C. Hartmire
Assoc. Dir., Mr. David Hernandez, P. O. Box 3, Dayton, OH 45402
Tel. (513) 222-6747

Continuing the National Migrant Ministry. Related to the National Council of the Churches of Christ in the U.S.A.

Tri-State Inter-Faith Development Enterprise, Inc.
1201 Hughitt Ave., Superior, WI 54880

Exec. Dir., Rev. Karl Aho

TIDE is a catalyst in helping to create a community which is responsive to human need and conducive to development in the Upper Great Lakes region by identifying and interpreting the religious, moral, spiritual, and human implications of the economic, social, and cultural conditions of the Upper Great Lakes region.

ALABAMA

No state council at present

ALASKA

Alaska Conference of Churches
(Send mail to President)

Pres., Mr. Amos J. Alter, P.O. Box 1581 Fairbanks 99707

Treas., Mrs. Gordon E. Green, Box 1912, Anchorage 99501

Major Activities: Christian Education; Worship, Evangelism & Communication; Christian Social Relations

Voluntary Leadership
Greater Anchorage, Mr. Harold Gallwas, P.O. Box 3-3798, 99501
Fairbanks, Pres., Rev. David Crockett, 3500 College Road, 99701

ARIZONA

Arizona Ecumenical Council
10 E. Roanoke, Suite 23, Phoenix 85004
Tel. (602) 264-6724

Exec. Dir., Rev. David M. Reed

Pres., Rev. Richard K. Smith, 10 E. Roanoke, Suite 31, 85004
Treas., Mr. Keith Turley, Box 21666, 85036

Major Activities: Interfaith Cooperation; Special Ministries; Church Women United; Farm Labor Ministry; Local Ecumenical Communication and Cooperation

Maricopa Ecumenical Council
10 E. Roanoke, Phoenix 85004
Tel. (602) 264-6724

Exec. Dir., Rev. Leon Glenn

Pres., Rev. Donal Rowland, 717 E. Southern Ave. 85040
Treas., Mr. Norman J. Baker, 1606 E. Bethany Home Rd. 85016

Major Activities: Communication between local churches

Tucson Ecumenical Council
715 N. Park Ave., Tucson 85719
Tel. (602) 325-7973

Exec. Dir., Rev. Frank R. Williams
Admin. Sec., Mrs. Elsie Robinson

Pres., Rev. John Martin, 715 N. Park Ave., 85719
Treas., Mr. Andrew Lauver, 1217 N. Bedford Pl. 85715

Major Activities: Worship; Education; Social Outreach

ARKANSAS

Arkansas Council of Churches
715 W. 22nd St., P. O. Box 6011, Little Rock 72206
Tel. (501) 375-1553

Adm.-Coordinator, Mrs. Frances Wood
Pres., Mr. S. H. Allman, 201 Pecan, Hot Springs
Treas., Mr. Warren K. Bass, 923 Pyramid Life Bldg., Little Rock 72201

Major Activities: Christian Life & Mission; Christian Education; Christian Unity; Public Relations; Church Women United

CALIFORNIA

Northern California Ecumenical Council
83 McAllister St., San Francisco 94102
Tel. (415) 861-4726

Exec. Dir., Rev. Lynn Hodges
Asst. to Exec. Dir., Rev. Dane Packard
Sec., Miss Janet Verkuyl
Exec. Dir. of JSAC, Rev. Robert Davidson
Dir. United Camps, Rev. Scott Nelson

Pres., Dr. David Held, 83 McAllister St.
Treas., Mr. Gordon Johnson, 900 Hearst Bldg. 94103

Major Activities: Legislation; Migrant Ministries; State Park Ministries; Urban Work; United Camps

Council of Churches in Southern California
1716 N. Wilton Pl., Los Angeles 90028
Tel. (213) 465-5171

Adm. Dir., Rev. Priscilla A. Chaplin

Pres., Dr. Fred P. Register, 466 E. Walnut St., Pasadena 91101
Treas., Mr. Douglas Chalmers, 3411 Finley St., Newport Beach 92660

Major Activities: Church Women United; Faith and Order Studies; Local Councils; Church Planning Task Force; Radio, TV and Films; Legislative Issues Studies; Church World Service; Ecology Studies and Action

Interreligious Council of Southern California
P. O. Box 75968, Los Angeles 90010

Pres., Rabbi Alfred Wolf
Treas., Father Royale M. Vadakin

The Council provides an opportunity at the interfaith level to deal with issues which affect the total religious community; to share common concern for the problems of the community, the nation, and the world; to voice this concern when by common consent the members feel that moral leadership is needed by the people of the community; to earn the respect of the community as leaders by understanding and respect shown toward each other.

Greater Bakersfield Council of Churches
500 Truxtun Ave., Bakersfield 93301
Tel. (805) 325-8794

*Ofc. Sec., Mrs. Frances Hall

Pres., Mrs. Jean Rivers, Rt. 1, Box 564-C 93308

Treas., Mr. John King, 1625 Los Robles 93306
Major Activities: Public Relations; Christian Education; Nursing Home Ministry; CWS Participation

Berkeley Area Council of Churches
2340 Durant Ave., Berkeley 94704
Tel. (415) 841-0881

Exec. Dirs., Mr. & Mrs. Arthur Farey

Pres., Ms. Louise Stoltenberg, 2340 Durant Ave. 94704
Treas., Mr. Dudley Mark Bonds, 2340 Durant Ave. 94704

Major Activities: Ecumenical Community of Commitment; Round Table; News Notes

Council of Churches of Central Contra Costa County
404 Gregory Lane, Pleasant Hill 94523
Tel. (415) 689-4363

*Exec. Dir., Rev. Roland Smith
*Chaplain, Rev. Keith Spooner
*Chaplain, Rev. Leonard Gilmour
*Chaplain, Rev. Ralph West
*Chaplain, Mr. Stephen Ott

Pres., Rev. Orville Shick, 222 W. El Pintado Rd., Danville 94526
Treas., Mr. Frank Patty, 234 Vallecito Ct., Walnut Creek 94596

Major Activities: Institutional Ministries; Social Education and Action; Christian Education; Campus Ministry

Fresno Metropolitan Ministry
P.O. Box 2452, Fresno 93723

Exec. Dir., Rev. Arthur Gafke

Pres., Mrs. Ruth E. Albright, P.O. Box 2452 93723
Treas., Mrs. Lester Leas, 1206 W. Dayton 93705

Major Activities: Television; Forum for Public Concerns; Training Programs; Responsible Government

Glendale Council of Christian Churches
P.O. Box 189, Glendale 91209
(Send mail to President)

Pres., Dr. Carl Kniseley, P.O. Box 189 91209
Treas., Rev. Luther L. Bartron, 1609 Santa Rosa 91208

Major Activities: Christian Education; Church Women United; Public Relations; Social Action; Spiritual Welfare; Ministers' Fellowship; Youth

Harbor Council of Churches
(Send mail to President)

Pres., Mrs. Stanley Mumford, 583 W. 19th St., Costa Mesa 92627

Major Activities: Serving Newport Beach & Costa Mesa areas

Long Beach Area Council of Churches
1542 E. 7th St., Long Beach 90813
Tel. (213) 436-3350

Exec. Dir., Rev. Don E. Lindblom
*Inner City Coordinator, Rev. Fred Newkirk
Project Dir., Hoffman House, Mrs. Elizabeth Moore

Pres., Mrs. Thomas T. Sato, 2895 Easy Ave. 90810
Treas., Mr. Will Henderson, 1150 New York St. 90813

Major Activities: Weekday Christian Education; Hoffman House; Pastoral Counseling Center HELP NOW; Interchurch Relations; Community Action; Witness; Communications

The Los Angeles Council of Churches
1718 N. Wilton Place, Hollywood 90028
Tel. (213) 466-3531

Exec. Dir., Rev. Horace N. Mays
Exec. Dir. Child Care & Development, Rev. Robert Wright
Exec. Dir. Protestant Community Services, Miss Evelyn Knight

Pres., Rev. Randall C. Phillips, 711 S. Plymouth 90005
Treas., Mr. Homer Price, 1345 S. Burlington Ave. 90006

Major Activities: Business & Finance; United Church Men; Church Women United; Public Relations; Christian Education; Church World Service; Interreligious Council; Public Affairs; Arrangements

The Social Service Bureau of Oakland, Inc.
534—22nd St., Oakland 94612
Tel. (415) 832-8542

Exec. Dir., Rev. Roger Boyvey
Senior Action Project Dir., Rev. Leslie L. Sauer
Senior Aide Program Dir., Rev. Nathaniel Linzie, Sr.
Project Read Dir., Mrs. Christian Houston
Areawide Model Project on Aging Dir., Miss Billi Joyce Purnell
Halfway House & Creative Living Center Dir., Rev. Charles McLain
Manager, Oak Center Better Housing, Max Levy
Pres., V. Hap Smith, 1520 Lakeside Dr., Oakland 94612
Treas., Dr. Robert L. Winslow, 2538 Telegraph Ave. 94612

Major Activities: Senior Action Project; Senior Aide Program; Project Read; Areawide Model Project on Aging; Halfway House & Creative Living Center Development

The Ecumenical Council of the Pasadena Area Churches
541 East Colorado Blvd., Pasadena 91101
Tel. (213) 795-5148

Exec. Sec., Rev. Charles B. Milburn

Pres., Rev. William H. Goddard, 75 North Marengo Ave. 91101
Treas., Rev. Albert W. Langley, 2540 E. Orange Grove Blvd. 91107

Major Activities: Friendly Visitation; Student Ministry; Housing Department; Community Worship; Peace Commission; Christian Unity

† Peninsula Council of Churches
139 Primrose Rd., Burlingame 94010
Tel. (415) 344-2204

*Exec. Sec., Mr. J. P. Baxter
*Chaplain, Rev. Ralph Benson
Assoc. Exec. Sec. for Foster Homes, Rev. Robert Paulus

Pres., Rev. Carl Stocking, Howard & El Camino Real 94010
Treas., Mr. Alfred H. Harris, 2515 Alameda de las Pulgas, San Mateo 94403

Major Activities: Institutional Ministry; Foster Homes

Pomona Valley Council of Churches
1753 North Park Ave., Pomona 91768
Tel. (714) 622-3806

Exec. Dir., Rev. G. Merrill Lenox
Pres., Rev. James W. Angell
Treas., Mr. Harlan P. Goodrich

Major Activities: Christian Education; Housing for Low Income Families; Pastoral Counseling; Broadcasting Ministry; Evangelism

Church Service Bureau
Sacramento 95816
Tel. (916) 456-6484

Coordinator-Mass Media Dept., Rev. John T. Wylie, 5010-15th Ave. 95820
Pres., Msgr. Richard Dwyer, 10497 Coloma Rd., Rancho Cordova 95670
Treas., Dr. Kimball Salmon, 1641—11th Ave. 95818

Major Activities: Mass Media; Youth Chaplaincy

San Diego County Ecumenical Conference
1875 2nd Ave., San Diego 92101
Tel. (714) 232-6385

Exec. Dir., Rev. Mel Harter

Dir. Audio-Visual Aids, Mrs. Dallas Stewart
Admin. Asst., Mrs. Kenton C. Lint
Pres., Rev. Ralph B. Johnson, 1875 2nd Ave. 92101
Treas., Rev. Heber Pitman, 1875 2nd Ave. 92101

Major Activities: Social Concerns; Special Ministries; Publicity & Proclamation: Education & Youth; Ecumenical Relations; Church Women United

San Francisco Council of Churches
942 Market St., Room 502, San Francisco 94102
Tel. (415) 982-4161

Acting Exec. Dir. & Dir. of Social Services, Rev. John F. Duffy, Jr.

Pres., Rev. Douglas L. Siden, 83 McAllister St. 94102
Treas., Mr. Robert D. Lintner, 2087 33rd Ave. 94116

Major Activities: Legislation; Community Organization; Leadership Development

The Santa Clara County Council of Churches
Box 4430, San Jose 95126
Tel. (408) 297-2660

Exec. Dir., Rev. R. Kenneth Bell
Dir. Friendly Visiting, Mrs. Carol Hoyt

Pres., Rev. Dodds B. Bunch, 1525 Bittern, Sunnyvale 94087
Treas., Mr. Robert F. Lundy, 16456 Englewood Ave., Los Gatos 95030

Major Activities: Social Services; Migrant-Urban Ministry; Christian Unity; Church World Service; Public Relations

Santa Monica—Westside Council of Churches
1008—11th Street, Santa Monica 90403
Tel. (213) 394-1518

Exec. Sec., Rev. Maurice D. Fulkerson

*Coordinator of Visitation Ministries, Mrs. Helen Wallace

Pres., Rev. Fred M. Judson, Trinity Baptist Church, 1015 California Ave. 90403
Treas., Mr. Lester Green, 529 California Ave. 90403

Major Activities: Visitation Ministries; Ecumenical Relations; Key 73; Interchurch Study of Consultation on Church Union; Social Concerns; Chaplain Services

Whittier Area Council of Churches
6227 S. Greenleaf Ave., Whittier 90601
Tel. (213) 693-7973

*Exec. Sec., Rev. S. J. Russell Ensign

Pres., Rev. Hans Holborn, 10005 Cole Rd. 90603
Treas., T. Elbert Nicholson, 11303 E. Indiana St. 90601

Major Activities: Life and Work; Christian Education; Missions; Business and Finance

Voluntary Leadership
Chico Area: Pres., Rev. Robert Scott, 1st & Broadway 95926
Eden: Pres., Rev. Marvin H. Olson, 100 Hacienda Ave., San Lorenzo 94580
Humboldt: Pres., Mrs. Marie Giampaolo, 1737 H. St., Eureka 95501
Lodi: Pres., Mr. Clarence Hirning, 510 Ribler St. 95240
Modesto: Pres., Mr. Norman N. Glick, P.O. Box 3998, 95352
Peninsula: Pres., Rev. John Worthington, 6410 Palos Verdes Dr. S., Portugese Bend 90274
Porterville: Pres., Mrs. Inez Cobb, Box 293 93258
Richmond: Pres., Jun W. Jue, 5838 McBryde Ave. 94805
St. Helena: Pres., Rev. Robert F. Hansen, 1520 Hillview Ave. 94574
San Pedro: Pres., Rev. Ronald Fleming, 1491 W. Ofarrell St. 90731
Santa Ana—Tustin: Pres., Rev. Francis Cook, 1810 Westwood Ave. 92706
Santa Barbara: United Churches of: 2101 State St. 93105
Siskiyou: Pres., Rev. Carl Schwarzenberg, Box 565, Mt. Shasta 96067

COLORADO

† Colorado Council of Churches
1313 Clarkson St., Denver 80218
Tel. (303) 292-0296

Admin. Ofc., Mrs. Lena W. Riedel
Dir. Church Community Service, Rev. W. Spencer Wren
Dir. Commission on Service Ministries, Rev. James L. Selmser
*Dir. Communications, Dr. William H. Mackintosh
Dir. Colorado CROP, Mr. Frank L. Weaver
Moderator, Rev. Harold A. Malmborg, P.O. Box 18253, Denver 80218
Treas., Mr. J. L. Boettner, 622 High St. 80218

Major Activities: Service Ministries, Church Community Service; Communications; Social Concerns; Educational Ministries; Ecumenical Relations; CROP

Pikes Peak Association of Churches
709 N. Nevada Ave., Rm. 205A, Colorado Springs 80902
Tel. (303) 633-3624

*Sec., Mrs. Becky Gose

Pres., Rev. Dennis V. Tyler, 611 E. Espanola 80907
Treas., Mr. Claude H. Sullivan, Jr., 1904 Carlton Ave. 80909

Major Activities: Christian Education; Church Extension; Church World Service; Communications; Evangelism; FISH

Pueblo Inter Faith Association of Churches
403 W. Ninth St., Pueblo 81003
Tel. (303) 543-5604

Exec. Sec., Mr. Leslie M. Haynes

Pres., Rev. Bernard Tuttle, 5 Tulane 81005
Treas., Mr. Harry Deitchler, 201 Colorado Ave. 81004

Major Activities: Audio Visual; Ecumenism; Evangelism; Transient Ministry

Voluntary Leadership
Boulder: Pres., Rev. Wallace Ford, 950 28th St. 80302
Fort Collins: Pres., Dr. Willard Schmehl, 2001 Orchard Pl. 80521
Loveland: Pres., Rev. Arthur W. Miller, P. O. Box 56, 80537

CONNECTICUT

Connecticut Council of Churches
60 Lorraine St., Hartford 06105
Tel. (203) 236-4281

Gen. Sec., Rev. Dwight Kintner
Program Dir. Social Issues, Mrs. Mary Ambler
Program Dir. Communications, Mr. Ivor Hugh
Field Chaplain, Rev. Albert Dalton
Spec. Education, Miss Ethelyn Nichols
Admin. Sec., Mrs. Pearl Eisenberg

Pres., Rev. Nicholas Titus
Treas., Mr. Robert Ahlness, 45 Castle Rd., Manchester 06040

Major Activities: Ministry to Persons of Special Need; Ministry to Seasonal Farm Workers; Cooperative Broadcast Ministry; Social Issues, Chaplaincy

Council of Churches of Greater Bridgeport, Inc.
3030 Park Ave., Bridgeport 06604 Tel. (203) 374-9471

Exec. Dir., Rev. Roger W. Floyd
Assoc. Dir., Rev. Frank Denton
*Hospital Chaplain, Rev. Paul Beavers

Pres., Mr. Miller Wachs, 852 Wilcoxon Ave., Stratford 06497
Treas., Mr. George Lindquist, Redding Rd., Westport 06880

Major Activities: Jail Chaplaincy; Hospital Chaplaincy; Regional Welfare Task Force; Leadership Training; Ecumenical Worship and Programming; Nursing Home Ministry

Center City Churches of Hartford
170 Main St., Hartford 06106
Tel. (203) 527-3658

Administrator, Rev. David S. King

The Greater Hartford Council of Churches
30 High St., P. O. Box 1290, Hartford 06101
Tel. (213) 246-6838

Exec. Dir., Rev. David D. Mellon
Dir. Pastoral Care & Training and Anna M.
Fulling Chaplain, Rev. E. Wendell Stephan,
Hartford Hospital 06115
Dir. Social Service, William A. Kennedy
Dir. Dept. of Aging, Douglas A. Beals
Dir. Pastoral Counseling Center, Rev. William
J. Boone, 120 Sigourney St., Hartford 06105
Dir. Retired Sr. Volunteer Program, Mrs.
Rosemary R. Nixon
Dir. Metropolitan Outreach Project, Rev.
George H. Wells, Jr.
Community Organizer, Mrs. Laurrine Blakeney
Dir. Cooperative Broadcast Ministry, Ivor T.
Hugh

Pres., Rev. J. Ralph Shotwell, 457 Main St.
06103
Treas., Mr. Arthur E. Erickson, Jr., 691 Waterville Rd. 06001

Major Activities: Social Services; Chaplaincy;
Aging; Legislative Action; Cooperative
Broadcast Ministry; Metropolitan Outreach
Project; Retired Senior Volunteer Program

New Britain Area Conference of Churches, Inc.
53 Franklin Square, New Britain 06053
Tel. (203) 229-3751

Exec. Dir., Rev. Mark Rohrbaugh
*Chaplain, Rev. C. Ernest Harman

Pres., Mr. George Martin, 560 Lincoln St.
06052
Treas., Mr. John Ronalter, 22 Eton Pl. 06053

Major Activities: Education; Church and Community; Christian Unity; Special Ministries

† New Haven Council of Churches
158 Davenport Ave., New Haven 06519
Tel. (203) 562-9849

Exec. Sec., ———
Ofc. Sec., Miss Mollie Volk

Major Activities: Task Forces as Needed

Stamford-Darien Council of Churches and Synagogues, Inc.
58 Church St., Stamford 06906 Tel. (203)
348-2800

Exec. Dir., Rev. Grover Wilson
*Hospital Chaplain, Rev. Claude Peters
*Program Coordinator, Mrs. B. H. Leather

Pres., Rev. Gabe Campbell, Lathan Park 06906
Treas., Mr. Arthur Hutchinson, 409 Strawberry
Hill Ave. 06906

Major Activities: Radio Ministry; Prisoner &
Parolee Rehabilitation; Public Religion;
Counseling, Hospital Chaplaincy; Systems
Change

Waterbury Area Council of Churches
24 Central Ave., Waterbury 06702
Tel. (203) 756-7831

Exec. Coordinator, Mrs. Virginia B. Tillson
*Hosptial Chaplain, Rev. William A. Sexton
Community Organizer: Mrs. Deborah M.
Wright
Community Organizer, Mr. Robert J. Hickson
Pres., Rev. Michael S. Kendall, 16 Church St.
06702
Treas., Mrs. Mildred Paris, 16 Willard St.
06702

Major Activities: Christian Education; Urban
Ministry; Hospital Chaplaincy; Welfare Reform; Prison Reform

Voluntary Leadership
Bristol: Pres., Rev. Aubrey L. Murphy, 127
Pilgrim Rd. 06010
East Hartford: Pres., Rev. G. Uno Ludmark,
1120 Silver Ln. 06810
Granby Area: Pres., Rev. Alan H. Buttaro,
Church, East Granby 06026
Jewett City Area: Pres., Mr. Fred Olson,
Voluntown 06348
Killingly-Brooklyn: Pres., Mr. Clinton Debolt,
Day St., Danielson 06239
Manchester: Pres., Mr. Robert Loomis, 343
Porter St. 06040
Mid-State Region: Pres., Rev. Arthur J. Larson,
300 Washington St., Middletown 06457
Naugatuck: Pres., Mr. William G. Leuchars,
124 Concord St. 06770
New London: Pres., Rev. Kilworth Maybury,
76 Federal St. 06320
Norwich Area: Pres., Mr. H. Dexter Hyland,
Jr., RFD #1, North Franklin 06254
Stratford Federation: Pres., Rev. Arthur Ted-
castle, 2600 Main St. 06497
Suffield: Pres., Rev. William V. Dorn, 65 S.
Grand St., West Suffield 06093
West Haven: Pres., Mr. Carleton C. Byers,
161 Main St. 06516
Wethersfield: Pres., Mr. Gerald Stevens, 37
Dale Rd. 06109
Winsted Area: Pres., Mr. Franklin Batson,
Riverton 06065

DELAWARE

Delmarva Ecumenical Agency, Inc.
1213 Delaware Ave., Wilmington 19806
Tel. (302) 655-6151

Exec. Dir., Rev. Donald E. Leiter

Chrm., Rev. Howell O. Wilkins, 1213 Delaware
Ave. 19806
Treas., Mr. Arthur Gregory, 2 Blackberry Ln.
19807

Major Activities: Migrant Ministry; Ocean City
Beach Ministries; Rehoboth-Bethany Beach
Ministries; Audio-Visual Library; Pacem In
Terris; RAP & CERT

DISTRICT OF COLUMBIA

The Council of Churches of Greater Washington
1239 Vermont Ave., N.W., Washington 20005
Tel. (202) 638-1077

Exec. Dir., Rev. B. Cortez Tipton
Assoc. Exec. Dir. for Administration & Church Development, Rev. Robert T. Jones
Dir. Inner City Ministry, Rev. Ernest R. Gibson
Dir. Suburban Ministry, Rev. David J. Robb
Assoc. Dir Inner City Ministry, Rev. Rodney L. Young
Dir. Church Women United, Miss Peggy Eckel
Pres., Rev. Arnold F. Keller, Jr., 212 E. Capitol St., N.W. 20002
Treas., Mr. Samuel L. Foggie, 3940 Minnesota Ave., N.E. 20019

Major Activities: Development of Group and Community Ministries; Church Development and Redevelopment; Liaison with Public Agencies; Theological Education and Training; Special Projects: Audio-Visual Library; Neighborhood Youth Corps; Hope Valley Camp; Pastoral Care

FLORIDA

Florida Council of Churches
710 E. Colonial Dr., Ste. 200, Orlando 32803
Tel. (305) 422-7077

Exec. Sec., Rev. Wliliam M. Belk
Ofc. Admin., Mrs. Ann K. Johnson

Pres., Rev. Canon Theodore R. Gibson, Box 33006, Miami 33133
Treas., Mr. Gary Bruce Cheatum, 3312 Young St., Winter Park 32789

Major Activities: New Church Development Workshop; Growth Group Work & Organizational Development; United Clothing Appeal; Campus Ministry; Ecumenical Dialogues; Church Planning & Strategy; Legislative Seminar

Metropolitan Fellowship of Churches of Southeast Florida, Inc.
36 N.E. 1st St., Room 1008, Miami 33132
Tel. (305) 358-0964

Pres., Rev. J. Lloyd Knox, 1800 S.W. 15th St. 33145.
Treas., Mr. George P. Harth, 4150 N.W. 7th Ave. 33127

Major Activities: Christian Social Concerns; Radio-TV; Evangelism; Church and Synagogue Directory for Dade County

Cooperating Churches of Greater St. Petersburg
2529—34th St. S., St. Petersburg 33711
Tel. (813) 866-1664

Admin., Mrs. Robert L. Culpepper

Pres., Rev. H. McNeal Harris, 912 Third Ave. N. 33705
Treas., Mrs. Edith Sanford, 4719—7th Ave. N. 33713

Major Activities: Christian Education; Television; Community Agencies; Ecumenical Services; Key 73; Criminal Justice

Voluntary Leadership
Jacksonville Alliance of Churches: Pres., Mr. Theo. W. Glocker, Jr., 417 Florida Title Bldg., Jacksonville 32202

Orange County: Pres., Rev. John M. Fletcher, 2113 E. South St., Orlando 32803

GEORGIA

Georgia Interchurch Association
159 Forrest Ave., N.E., Atlanta 30303
Tel. (404) 659-0935

Exec. Sec., Rev. Jackson P. Braddy
Pres., Mr. John J. Deifell, 159 Forrest Ave., N.E. 30303

Treas., Dr. Harry V. Richardson, 1165 Tuckawanna Dr., S.W. 30311

Major Activities: Church World Service; Research & Survey; Public Relations

Christian Council of Metropolitan Atlanta
167 Walton St., N.W., Atlanta 30303
Tel. (404) 523-7533; 524-1167

Exec. Dir., Dr. Harmon D. Moore

Pres., Mr. Charles M. Watt, Jr.
Treas., Mr. Henry L. Hills

Major Activities: Adventures in Understanding; Aging; Airport Chaplaincy; Alcohol and Drug Abuse; Christian Emergency Help Center; Communications and Interpretation; Evangelism; Housing; Legislation and Criminal Justice; Mental Health; Today's Family and Its Changing Role

Voluntary Leadership
Rome Area: Pres., Rev. Robert C. Pooley, Jr., Box 1301, 30162

HAWAII

Hawaii Council of Churches
200 N. Vineyard Blvd., Room 403, Honolulu 96817
Tel. (808) 521-2666

Exec. Dir., Rev. Stanley E. Kain
Waikiki Minister, Rev. Howard D. Corry
*Program Asst., Rev. Ronald C. Kurtz
*Program Asst., Mrs. Pat Mumford

Pres., Rev. William E. Phifer, Jr., 200 N. Vineyard Blvd. 96817
Treas., Mr. James Hirano, 200 N. Vineyard Blvd. 96817

Major Activities: Ministry to World & Community; Waikiki Ministry; Education & Training; Legislative Concerns; Human Services Coalition; Religious Educators Ecumenical Fellowship; United Campus Ministry

IDAHO

Idaho Council of Churches
P.O. Box 2188, Boise 83701
Tel. (208) 343-1058

Pres., Rev. John D. Metzler, Sr.

Major Activities: Ecumenical Camping Program; Cooperative Efforts; Social Responsibility; Church World Service; Agricultural Concerns; Clergy Training & Lay Education

ILLINOIS

Illinois Conference of Churches
416 S. 7th St., Springfield 62701
Tel. (217) 544-3423

Exec. Sec., Rev. Charles E. F. Howe
Assoc. Exec. Sec., Mrs. Irene E. Sanders
Assoc. Sec., Rev. Charles E. F. Howe
Assoc. Sec., Rev. Blaine Ramsey, Jr.
Field Dir. CROP, Rev. Lowell H. Brown
Assoc. Field Dir. CROP, Rev. John R. Burke
Pres., Rev. Gerald K. Johnson, 53 W. Jackson
Blvd., Chicago 60604
Treas., Rev. William W. Roth, 320 S. College
62701
Major Activities: Poverty & Race; Migrant &
Farm Worker Ministry; Chaplaincy in Institu-
tions; Legislative Concerns; Research & Plan-
ning; Peace Ministries; Key 73

† Bloomington-Normal Area Council of Churches
808 E. Walnut St., Bloomington 61701
(Address all mail to Secretary)

*Sec., Mr. Noble Thomas, 808 E. Walnut St.
61701
Pres. pro tem., Rev. Samuel Buck, 706 S. Allin
61701
Treas., Mr. John E. Clark, 303 S. Vale 61701

Major Activities: Christian Education; Christian
Life & Witness; Interchurch Interests; Public
Relations; Church Women United

The Church Federation of Greater Chicago
116 S. Michigan Ave., Room 300, Chicago 60603
Tel. (312) 372-2427

Interim Exec. Dir., Rev. Daniel A. Barrett
Exec. Producer, Radio & TV, Rev. Daniel A.
Barrett
Producer, Mr. Jan Sheehan
Controller, Mr. William Richard
Admin. Assist., Miss Eunice J. Barbknecht

Pres., Dr. K. Everett Munson
Treas., Mr. George Sisler

Major Activities: Radio & Television; Interfaith
Development; Social Welfare; Christian Education

Elgin Federation of Christian Churches
256 E. Chicago, Elgin 60120
Tel. (312) 869-0051

Ofc. Sec., Mrs. Albert Elvin

Chairman, Rev. Noah M. Inbooy, Jr., 616 Lake
St. 60201
Co-Chairman, Rev. Walter F. Somerville, 1421
Oak Ave. 60201
Treas., Mr. Carl B. Davis, 1317-A Pitner 60201
Major Activities: Task Forces on Education,
Housing, Environment, New Forms of Church
Life, Literacy, Friendly Vistor

Evanston Ecumenical Action Council
P.O. Box 1414, Evanston 60204
Tel. (312) 869-4950

Chairman, Rev. Walter F. Somerville
Treas., Mr. Carl E. Davis

Major Activities: Task Forces on Education,
Housing, Communications, Literacy, New
Forms of Church Life, Church Women United

† Council of Hyde Park & Kenwood Churches & Synagogues
1400 E. 53rd St., Chicago 60615
Tel. (312) 324-5300

*Exec. Sec., Mr. Claud L. Shaw
Pres., Rev. Paul F. Rosemeyer, 1012 E. 47th
St. 60653
Treas., Mr. Joseph B. Field, 1400 E. 53rd St.
60615

Oak Park-River Forest Council of Churches
324 N. Oak Park Ave., Oak Park 60302

Ofc. Sec., Mrs. Robert A. Schimek

Pres., Mr. John W. McCracken, 324 N. Oak
Park Ave. 60302

Major Activities: Church Women United; Community Affairs; Ecumenical Affairs; Youth;
Education

† United Protestant Council of Park Forest
10 Hemlock, Park Forest 60466
Tel. (312) 747-0500

*Admin. Sec., Mrs. Alex Hughes

Pres., Mr. August J. Gartner, 131 Berry 60466
Treas., Mr. Jack Jacobs, 134 Iroquois 60466

Major Activities: Lenten & Thanksgiving Program; Youth

† Metropolitan Peoria Council of Churches

(Send mail to President)

Pres., Mr. Don Houk, 301 S. W. Adams 61601
Treas., Mr. Neil Clifton, 909 Comm. Bank Bldg.
61602

Major Activities: Church Relations; Christian
Education; Personnel; Public Relations;
Finance; Youth; Nominating; Planning;
Urban Work

River Forest: see Oak Park-River Forest

Protestant Community Services
304 N. Church St., Rockford 61101
Tel. (815) 965-8769

Exec. Dir., Mr. Ralph R. Schroeder

Pres., Mr. Fred Thompson, 304 N. Church St.
61101
Treas., Mr. Ed Fieser, 304 N. Church St. 61101

Major Activities: Church Relations; Finance;
Forest Hall Committee; Nominating; Executive; Home Health Aid Service; Home De-
livered Meals

Churches United of Scott County, Iowa & Rock Island County, Illinois
639—38th St., Rock Island 61202
Tel. (309) 786-6494

Exec. Dir., _____
Dir. Urban Ministry, Rev. Clarence M. Savoy

Pres., Rev. Philip L. Nelson, 639—38th St. 61202

Treas., Mr. Robert E. Carlson, 639—38th St. 61201

Major Activities: Criminal Justice; Urban Ministry; Migrant Ministry; Communications; Low Cost Housing; Education

Springfield Area Council of Churches
322½ South 6th St., Springfield 62701
Tel. (217) 528-8449

Ofc. Sec., Mrs. S. R. Virco
Chaplain, Rev. John Cavitt

Pres., Rev. Fred Telecky, 2309 W. Iles 62704
Treas.. Mr. Leslie F. Ryburn, 932 S. Cleveland 62704

Major Activities: Christian Education; Christian Community Relations; Christian World Relations; Interchurch Activities; Ministry to Institutions; Youth

† Waukegan Area Council of Churches
704 Grand Ave., Waukegan 60085
Tel. (312) 662-2916

Ofc. Sec., Mrs. Kenneth Marqui

Pres., Rev. Gehl Devore, 128 N. Utica St. 60085
Treas., Mrs. Edward Warship, Shiloh Baptist Church, 837 S. Utica St. 60085

Major Activities: Community Relations; Evangelism; Finance; Public Relations; Religious Education; Youth; Church Women United

Voluntary Leadership
Adams: Pres., Mr. Dale Danley, Mendon 62351
Argenta: Pres., Mr. William Newman 62501
Atwood: Pres., Mr. Howard E. Black 61913
Belleville: Pres., Mr. Robert B. O. Neal, 701 Southgate 62223
Blue Mound Inter-Church Council: Pres., Chet Minks 62513
Carlinville: Pres., Mrs. Esther Shirley, 404 E. 2nd S., 62626
Dekalb County Association: Pres., Mr. John A. Rey, 836 S. 1st., 60115
Delavan: Pres., Rev. Floyd R. Stradley 61734
Dixon Church Council: Pres., Mr. Charles Fleming, 1208 Institute Blvd. 61021
Downers Grove: Pres., Dr. Edgar Cook, 1048 Curtis 60515
Farmington: Pres., Mr. Hubert Schuman, 432 E. Pearl St. 61531
Forest Park: Pres., Rev. R. W. Roth, 622 Nannah St. 60130
Freeport Area Church Cooperative: Pres., Dr. William Pfautz, 216 E. Stephenson St. 61032
Fulton County: Pres., Mrs. Howard Rock, Rt. 1, Cuba 61427
Galesburg: Pres., Mr. O. L. Baumgartner, 107 E. Main St. 61401
Knoxville: Pres., Mr. Orval Gates, 210 W. South St. 61448
Lexington: Pres., Mr. Charles Loible, R. R. #2 61753
Naperville: Pres., Rev. A. Wayne Myers, 25 E. Benton 60540
Paris: Pres., Mr. Chester P. Sutton, Sr., 114 E. Washington St. 61944
Polo: Pres., Mrs. Irene Fierheller, 204 N. Cherry St. 61064

Proviso: Pres., Mr. Joseph H. Nelson, 213 Augusta St., Maywood 60153
Rushville: Pres., Mrs. Margaret Street, 903 E. Lafayette 62681
Sterling Rock: Pres., Mr. Andy Hodges, 805 W. 8th St., Sterling 61081
Stronghurst: Pres., Mr. Lee ¦Carlson 61480
Virginia: Pres., Mr. W. Wayne Briggs, Rt. 3, Box 152, 62691
Will County: Pres., Rev. Alvin R. Abbott, Clara & Larkin Ave., Joliet 60435

INDIANA

Indiana Council of Churches
1100 W. 42nd St. Indianapolis 46208
Tel. (317) 923-3674

Exec. Sec., Dr. Grover L. Hartman
Admin. Assist., Mrs. Lillian R. King
Assoc. Exec. Sec., Rev. Walter F. Horlander
Dir. of CROP, Rev. Gerald L. Wilson
Dir. of Literacy, Rev. Rebecca Frankford
Dir. of Migrant and Hispanic Ministries, Mr. Al Martinez
*Coordinator Selective Service & Volunteer Programs & Vietnam Veterans, Mr. James Leachman

Pres., Mr. Ernest E. Ittner, Jr., 3960 E. 77th St. 46240
Treas., Rev. George F. Cox, 1100 W. 42nd St. 46208

Major Activities: Ecumenical Teaching Ministry Congress; Legislation; Migrant Ministries; CROP; Literacy Education; World Missions Interpretation to College Campuses

Indiana Interreligious Commission on Human Equality
1100 W. 42nd St., Indianapolis 46208
Tel. (317) 924-4426

Exec. Dir., Mr. Thomas J. Weber
Staff, Kenneth Wilson, Douglas Stoehr
Pres., Dr. John Fox
Treas., Mr. Marion McPherson

Major Activities: Project Equality; Project Commitment; Project Spark

† Anderson Association of Churches, Inc.
28 W. 12th St., YMCA Bldg., Anderson 46015
Tel. (317) 642-1156

Ofc. Sec., Mrs. Phyllis Swallow

Pres., Judge Carl T. Smith, 1015 E. 6th St. 46012
Treas., Mr. Patrick Cunningham, 1022 Chase St. 46016

Major Activities: Church Women United; Christian Nuture; Outreach; Youth; Weekday Religious Education; Ministerial Association Work; Finance; Radio-TV

† Calumet United Ministries
575 Washington St., Gary 46402
Tel. (219) 886-1586

Exec. Dir., Rev. Harold Lundgren

Major Activities: Chaplaincy; Community Concerns, C.W.S.; Ecumenical Affairs; Interdenomination & Community Agencies; Leadership Development; Migrant Ministry; Missionary Education; Public Relations; Social Welfare

Delaware County Council of Churches
300 W. Main St., Muncie 47305
Tel. (317) 288-0601

Exec. Sec., Mrs. Elisabeth Battle

Pres., Mr. Arthur Duerson, 1807 E. Hines St. 47303

Treas., Mr. David Hoover, 2 Elizabeth Dr. 47304

Major Activities: Migrant Ministry; Christian Education; Youth Program on Hunger

Elkhart County Council of Churches
431 S. 3rd St., Elkhart 46514
Tel. (219) 294-3263

Ofc. Sec., _____

Pres., Rev. Paul Koepke, 431 S. 3rd St. 46514

Treas., Mr. Don Stauffer, 431 S. 3rd St. 46514

Major Activities: Witness; Nurture; General Services

Evansville Area Council of Churches, Inc.
203 N.W. 5th St., YMCA Bldg., Evansville 47708
Tel. (812) 425-3524

Admin., Rev. Francis I. Frellick

Assoc., Christian Education, Ms Delbert Hill

Dir. Communications Ministries, Ms Bobbie Hoy

Pres., Dr. Richard E. Hamilton, 203 N.W. 5th St. 47708

Treas., Mr. Melvin Wimpelberg, 203 N.W. 5th St. 47708

Major Activities: Christian Education; Mass Media Ministries; Ecumenical Relations; Community Responsibility & Service; Public Relations; Interpretation; Church Women United

The Associated Churches of Fort Wayne & Allen County, Inc.
6430 U.S. Highway 24 W., Fort Wayne 46804
Tel. (219) 432-1521

Exec. Dir., Rev. J. Frank Lansing

Campus Minister, Rev. Daniel D. Motto

Ofc. Sec., Mrs. Virginia M. Drummond

Pres., Mr. Melvin Lew, 228 W. Crown Ln. 46807

Treas., Mr. Robert E. Lee, 227 S. Seminole Circle 46807

Major Activities: Weekday Religious Education; Radio & TV; Community Ministry; Race Relations; Christian Education; Interfaith Activities

The Church Federation of Greater Indianapolis, Inc.
1100 W. 42nd St., Indianapolis 46208
Tel. (317) 926-5371

Exec. Dir., _____.

Program Assoc., Mr. Paul E. McClure

Communications Assoc., Rev. Thomas R. Stratton

*Financial Affairs, Mr. Donald Trout

*Business Consultant, Mr. Cassius M. Fenton

*TV Consultant, Rev. Alfred R. Edyvean

Chaplains, Rev. C. T. Boyd, Rev. Wilbur L. Harvey, Rev. Harrison C. Neal, Rev. Frank

O. Carlson, *Rev. Joshua R. Cutler, *Rev. Robert S. Medcalf, *Rev. Stacy R. Shields.

Pres., Mrs. Beauford Norris

Treas., Mr. Richard I. Blankenbaker

Major Activities: Congregational Concerns; Communications; Special Ministries; Urban Affairs

Housing Opportunities Multiplied Ecumenically, Inc. (H.O.M.E.)
2360 N. Central, Indianapolis 46205
Tel. (317) 923-5318

Exec. Dir., Rev. L. Richard Hudson

Pres., Mr. George Maley, 1828 N. Meridian 46202

Treas., Mr. John Barnard, 307 E. McCarty 46225

Major Activities: Housing and Related Services

Weekday Religious Education of Indianapolis & Marion Co.
3544 Central Ave., Indianapolis 46205
Exec. Dir., Dr. William A. Hulick

Pres., Mr. James R. Johnston, 4564 Carrollton Ave. 46205

Treas., Mr. Robert McFarling, 2849 W. 30th 46222

Major Activities: Curriculum; Housing; Public Relations

Greater Kokomo Association of Churches
311 W. Lincoln Rd., Kokomo 46901
Tel. (317) 457-2521

Exec. Advisor, Mr. John R. Brown

Pres., Rev. Ronald P. Anjard

Major Activities: Christian Education; Life & Work; Missions & Services; Research & Planning; Church Women United; Ministerial Association

Monroe County United Ministries
828 Thirteenth Ct., P. O. Box 863, Bloomington 47401
Tel. (812) 339-3429; 339-1516

Minister-Director, Rev. Paul F. Crafton

Chm., Dean Berkley

Major Activities: Communications; Community Concerns; Christian Center; Federal Credit Union; Volunteer Service; Housing Opportunities; Ecumenical Commission

Downtown Neighborhood Council
222 E. Spring St., New Albany 47150
Tel. (812) 944-1297 or 944-4694

Dir., Rev. George P. Beury

Assoc. Dir., Mr. William Hunter

Ofc. Mgr., Mrs. Marian Casey

Pre-School Educ. Dir., Mrs. Jo Davis

Chm., Mrs. Maxine Lorch, Crestview Dr. 47150

Treas., Mr. Joe Bosier, 1330 Miller Ln. 47150

Major Activities: Youth Ministries; Black Heritage Classes; Community Forum; Denominational Camping; CONTACT-RAP Crisis Teleministry; Housing & Job Information

United Religious Community of St. Joseph County
319 S. Main St., South Bend 46601
Tel. (219) 282-2397

Exec. Sec., Rev. John E. Gaus

Assoc. Exec. Sec., Rev. Arthur F. Gouthro, S.A.

Admin. Asst., Mrs. John E. Byers

Major Activities: Juvenile Justice; Communications; Racial Problems; Education; Prayer & Ecumenical Services; Housing Authority

Greater Terre Haute Church Federation
630 Ohio St., Terre Haute 47801

Tel. (812) 232-2361

Coordinator, Rev. John J. Drag

Pres., Mr. James N. Hollis, 127 Madison Blvd. 47803

Treas. Mr. Dennis E. Ehm, 1816 S. 32nd St. 47807

Voluntary Leadership
Carroll County: Pres., Rev. Richard Recher, Box 23, Camden 46917

Cass County: Pres., Rev. Donald Ruhl, 17 E. Main St., Logansport 46947

Columbus Ecumenical Assembly: Pres., Mr. Charles E. Van Naytu, 2615 Sycamore 47201

Crawford County: Pres., Mr. Nolan Atz, Milltown 47145

Culver: Pres., Rev. John Krueger, C.U.M.M.C., Grace United Church of Christ 46511

East Noble: Pres., Mr. Wade Siler, 224 E. Diamond St., Kendallville 46755

Fulton County: Pres., Mr. Joe Behney, Akron 46910

Harrison County: Pres., Rev. Paul T. Byrns, R.R. 1, Corydon 47112

Hendricks County: Pres., Mr. Churchel Swarm, 333 N. East St., Plainfield 46168

Huntington Association: Pres., Mr. Edgar H. Casey, Box 447, Andrews 46702

Jefferson County: Pres., Mr. Phil Sherman, 714 W. Main St., Madison 47250

Kosciusko County: Pres., Mr. Edmond P. Whitby, R.R. #7, Warsaw 46580

Lafayette: Pres., Rev. William M. Blessing, Trinity United Methodist Church, 314 N. 6th St. 47901

Madison County: Pres., Rev. Gene Smith, YMCA Bldg., Anderson 46016

Marion Area: Pres., Mr. Ralph Aldrich, (Marion Area Churches Cooperating in Mission) 46952

Miami County: Pres., Mr. Kermit Burrous, Mexico 46958

Mt. Vernon: Pres., Rev. Carl Middleton, Mt. Pleasant General Baptist Church, Rte. #3 47620

Newton County: Pres. Mr. J. D. Hancock, Morocco 47963

Steuben County: Pres., Mr. Cecil Lepley, R.R. 1, Pleasant Lake 46779

Washington: Pres., Mr. Marion Barber, R.R. 3 47501

Wayne County: Pres., Mr. Fred Reeve, 930 National Rd. W., Richmond 47374

Whitley County: Pres., Rev. Harold Oechsle, Trinity United Methodist Church, Chauncey at Jackson Sts., Columbia City 46725

IOWA

Iowa Council of Churches
317 E. 5th St., Des Moines 50309

Tel. (515) 244-2253

Exec. Sec., Rev. Paul H. King

Assoc. Sec., Rev. Gerald D. Brown

Assoc. Sec., Rev. Harold E. Butz

Pres., Rev. Harry E. Coulter

Treas., Mr. James G. Friesz

Major Activities: Quest for Justice; Small Church; Continuing Education; Communications; Social Services; Legislative Education

Churches United—Cedar Rapids Metropolitan Area
1026 3rd Ave. S.E., Cedar Rapids 52403

Tel. (319) 366-7163

Exec. Asst., Mrs. Harry R. Mullin

Pres., Mr. Richard Steninger, 2939 Bever Ave. S.E. 52403

Treas., Mr. F. Eugene Bender, 1015 MNB Bldg. 52401

Major Activities: Key 73; Week of Prayer for Christian Unity; Christian Education; Central Food Bank Program; "Each One-Teach One"; CROP

Des Moines Area Council of Churches
317 E. 5th St., Des Moines 50309

Tel. (515) 288-9561

Exec. Minister, Rev. John E. Donovan

Pres., Rev. Robert W. Rae

Treas., Lorin Hansen

Major Activities: Evangelism; Education; Social Concerns; Mission; Worship, Use of Resources

† Fort Dodge Council of Churches
c/o Mrs. R. A. Borgstrom, 1053 N. 23rd St., Fort Dodge 50501

Tel. (515) 573-4517

Pres., Father Paul Roder, Corpus Christi

Treas., Mrs. R. A. Borgstrom

Major Activities: Christian Education; Community Relations; Interchurch: Youth Ministries, Music

Voluntary Leadership
Black Hawk: Pres., Mrs. John Hockaday, 623 Orange Grove, Waterloo 50701

Burlington: Pres., Rev. G. A. Saathoff, 115 S. Central 52601

Clinton: Pres., Mr. Melvin A. Erickson, 1109 N. 12th St. 52732

Dubuque: Pres., Mr. Gent Wittenberg, 2670 New Haven 52001

English Valleys Interchurch; Pres., Mr. Harold Seitzinger, R. R., Wellman 52355

Fort Madison: Pres., Rev. Sherburne Ray, 507 Avenue C 52627

Greene County: Pres., Mr. Don Benson, Rt. 1, Box 24, Jefferson 50129

Iowa City: Pres., Rev. Robert Welsch, 217 Iowa Ave. 52240

Jefferson County: Pres., Mr. Henry McCleary, Packwood 52580

Keokuk County: Pres., Mr. Kenneth Matthews, 2323 Aeroway 52632

Madison County: Pres., Mrs. Keith Anderson, 1105½ Avenue F, Fort Madison 52627

Marion County: Pres., Mr. Herman Nollen, 1420 W. 2nd St., Pella 50219

Ottumwa: Pres., Dr. Barry O. Barnes, 2305 N. Court 52501

Perry: Pres., Rev. Mark Wetteland, 1625 Evelyn St. 50220

Rock Rapids: Pres., Mr. Charles Telford, 101 S. 10th 51246

Sioux City: Pres., Mr. Ralph Parsons, 3811 Forest View, 51109

Washington: Pres., Mr. Robert Gillesby, Washington 52353

KANSAS

Kansas Council of Churches
4125 Gage Center Dr., Topeka 66604
Tel. (913) 272-2512

Exec. Dir., Rev. Oscar W. Olsen

Pres., Rev. Joseph Bogle, 6000 E. Harry, Wichita 67218

Treas., Mr. Duane Tietze, 5701 W. 16th 66604

Major Activities: Training Laboratories, Legislative Affairs; Upgrading Human Life; Institutional Ministry; Parish Planning; Faith & Order

† Hutchinson Council of Churches
800 N. Main, Hutchinson 67501
Tel. (316) 663-4828

*Exec. Dir., Rev. Marion O. Wheaton

Pres. Rev. George Van Hook, 518 S. Maple 67501

Treas., Mr. Houston Gordon, 225 E. 6th 67501

Cross-Lines Cooperative Council
902 Southwest Blvd., Kansas City 66103
Tel. (913) HE 2-5497

Exec. Dir., Rev. Donald C. Bakely
Program Dir., Mr. M. Myron Dice
Staff Assistants: Arlene Hernon, Beth Seberger, Gail Asel

Pres., Rev. Don Anderson
Treas., Mr. Floyd E. Henderson

Major Activities: Community Action Program; Education; Housing; Legislation; Social Services; Team Ministries; Volunteer Services

Topeka Council of Churches
110 E. 7th, Topeka 66603
Tel. (913) 357-1493

Exec. Dir., Fr. Thomas E. Punzo
Ofc. Sec. Mgr., Mrs. Margaret D. Hughes

Pres., Rev. Robert A. Langston, Jr.
Treas., Rev. David M. Bryan

Major Activities: Finance and Administration; Social Concerns; Special Ministry; Education and Communication; Worship

Wichita Council of Churches
607 N. Broadway, Wichita 67214
Tel. (316) 264-9303

Exec. Minister, Rev. Leonard S. Cowan
*Dir. Weekday Church School, Mrs. Harry Duke
*Dir. Indian Center, Mrs. Robert McKenzie
*Dir. UNICOMM, Rev. Arnold Regier
Pres., Rev. W. G. Williams, 601 N. Water 67203
Treas., Mr. W. Glea Rittgers, Wichita State Bank, Box 634 67201

Major Activities: Weekday Church School;

UNICOMM (United Interfaith Commission on Mass Media); Indian Center; CROP; Community Service; Chaplaincy

Voluntary Leadership
Fredonia: Pres., Mr. Floyd Prichard, 1509 Washington 66736

Great Bend: Pres., Rev. Ralph Nelson, Box 581, 67530

Jackson County Association of Churches: Pres., Mr. Floyd Nowlin, 400 W. 4th, Holton 66436

Salina Area: Pres., Mr. Rudolph Barta, 714 Highland 67411

Sedgewick: Pres., Rev. Richard Vail, Box 63 67135

Wamego: Pres., Rev. Stacy Ollar Jr., First United Methodist Church, 6th & Lincoln 66547

Winfield: Pres., Rev. Karl O. Magnusson, R.R. #4, 67156

KENTUCKY

Kentucky Council of Churches
1500 West Main St., Lexington 40505
Tel. (606) 255-4402

Exec. Dir., Rev. John S. Chambers

Pres., Dr. Albert Sweazy, Box 7172 40502

Major Activities: Migrant Work; Institutional Ministry; Faith and Order; Christian Vocation; Thru-the-Week Christian Education

Louisville Area Interchurch Organization for Service
520 W. Magnolia, Louisville 40208
Tel. (502) 637-2591 or 637-2745

Coordinator, Rev. Thomas H. Quigley
Chm., Rev. C. Wm. Schiphorst, 8515 Cheltenhem Circle 40222
Treas., Rev. David J. Cull, 318 W. Kentucky 40203

Major Activities: Interdenominational Mission Planning; Interfaith Counseling Service; Campus Ministry; Radio-TV

Northern Kentucky Interfaith Commission, Inc.
118 W. 6th St., Covington 41011
Tel. (606) 581-2237

Sec.-Prog. Coordinator, Miss Mary Pons

Pres., Msgr. Donald F. Hellmann, 118 W. 6th St. 41011

Treas., Rev. Dwayne Daehler, 118 W. 6th St. 41011

Major Activities: Community Summer Programs; Emergency Aid for the Needy; Education & Religious Programs; Campus Ministry; Implementation of National & State Programs

LOUISIANA

Louisiana Interfaith Conference
333 East Chimes St., Baton Rouge 70802
Tel. (504) 342-4998

Exec. Dir., Rev. Lewis L. Wilkins

Pres., Rt. Rev. Iveson B. Noland, P. O. Box 50850, New Orleans 70150

Treas., Mr. James A. Morgan, LNB Bldg, Ste. 940, Baton Rouge 70801

Major Activities: Correction Reform; Building Trust Among Communions' Decision-Makers

Greater New Orleans Federation of Churches
330 St. Charles Ave., New Orleans 70130
Tel. (504) 524-0246

Exec. Dir., Rev. David E. Mason
Admin. Sec., Mrs. Charles Hodapp
Pres., Mrs. Fred Landis, 1473 Nashville Ave. 70115
Treas., Mr. M. H. VanManen, 4623 S. Derbigny 70125

Major Activities: Radio-TV; Youth; Christian World Fellowship; Senior Citizens; Chaplaincies; Evangelism

MAINE

† Maine Office for Religious Cooperation
(in process of formation)

Voluntary Leadership
Biddeford: Pres., Rev. Paul K. Weiner, Saco 04072
Brunswick Area: Pres., Rev. Gerald W. Beals, 11 Thomas St., Topsham 04086
Farmington: Pres., Mr. Richard B. Day, Box 208 04938
North Cumberland: Pres., Mr. Stanford Brown, R.R. 3, Cumberland 04021
Oakland: Pres., Rev. Edith L. Morton, 155 High St. 04963
Waterville: Pres., Mrs. Frank Pitman, 30 Roosevelt Ave. 04901

MARYLAND

Maryland Churches United
(Send mail to President)
Pres., Rev. Royden B. Kohler, 5607 Talbott Pl., Baltimore 21207

Presently working as a non-staff ecumenical agency

Columbia Cooperative Ministry
Interfaith Center, Wilde Lake Village Green, Columbia 21044
Tel. (301) 730-7566

Coordinator-Enabler, Rev. Gerald Goethe
Pres., Rev. William M. Deutschmann, Div. American Missions, Urban Life Center, Ste. 603, American Cities Bldg., Columbia 21044
Treas., Mr. Frank T. Butehorn, 10201 Wesleigh Dr., Simpsonville 21150

Major Activities: Counseling; Christian Education; Women's Center; Evangelism; Communications; Housing Concerns

Voluntary Leadership
Washington County: Pres., Rev. Laverne E. Rohrbaugh, 712 Church St., Hagerstown 21740

MASSACHUSETTS

Massachusetts Council of Churches
14 Beacon St., Boston 02108
Tel. (617) 523-2771

Gen. Secy., —————
Assoc. Sec., Rev. Leslie H. Johnson
Dir. Communications, Rev. T. C. Whitehouse
Dir. Social Relations, Rev. James A. Nash
Dir Pastoral Ministries, Rev. J. Albert Dalton
Pres., Rev. Gene E. Bartlett, 848 Beacon St., Newton Centre 02159
Treas., Mr. Richard R. Higgins, Rm. 301, 211 Congress St. 02110

Major Activities: Communications; Social Relations; Pastoral Services; Christian Unity

Massachusetts Commission on Christian Unity
818 Middle St., Fall River 02722
Exec. Sec., Rev. Reginald Theriault

Attleboro Area Council of Churches, Inc.
505 N. Main St., Attleboro 02703
Tel. (617) 222-2933

Exec. Sec., Rev. Robert C. Ryder
Admin. Sec., Mrs. Franklyn E. Holbrook
*Chaplain, Rev. John M. Bowmar
Pres., Mr. Ralph Perry, 151 West St. 02703
Treas., Mr. Willard Olmsted, 30 Warren Rd. 02703

Major Activities: Christian Education; Radio-TV; Men's and Women's Departments; Institutional Ministry; Christian Social Action; Christian Unity

† Council of Churches of Greater Brockton
320 Main St., Brockton 02401
Tel. (617) 588-0797

Pres., Mr. William Thurberg, 79 Bonney St. 02402
Treas., Mr. Matthew Nicoll, 28 Troy St. 02401

Major Activities: Christian Education; Ecumenical Worship; Hospital Chaplaincy; Ministers Union; Radio-TV

† The Cape Cod Council of Churches, Inc.
298 Main St., Hyannis 02601
Tel. (617) 775-5073

Exec. Sec., Rev. David S. Grogan
*Chaplain, House of Correction & Jail, Rev. Richard L. Payne
*Chaplain, Cape Cod Hospital, Rev. John R. Smith
*Chaplain, Pocasset Hospital, Rev. John H. Thomas
Pres., Mr. Harmon W. Smith, 42 Lakefield Rd., S. Yarmouth 02664
Treas., Mr. Neil B. Donovan, 52 Country Club Dr., S. Yarmouth 02664

Major Activities: Stewardship & Finance; Pastoral Services; Study & Planning; Social Concerns; Communications; Christian Education

Greater Fall River Council of Churches, Inc.
618 Rock St., Fall River 02720
Tel. (617) 673-4670

Exec. Sec., Mrs. Everett W. Broadhurst
Pres., Rev. Edward VanderHey, 178 Pine St. 02720
Treas., Miss Helene Sunderland, 3555 N. Main St. 02720

Major Activities: Task Forces as Needed

Greater Lawrence Council of Churches
403 Lowell St., Lawrence 01841
Tel. (617) 686-4012
*Office Sec., Mrs. Alice B. Moore
*Chaplains, Rev. Vincent E. Taber, Rev. Lester J. Moore
*Weekday School Dir., Rev. Vincent E. Taber
Pres., Mr. Rene J. Morissette, 1 Presidential Lane, Methuen 01844
Treas., Mr. Leslie H. Thomson, 120 Green St., North Andover 01845
Major Activities: Audio-Visual; Ecumenical; Institutional Ministry; Religious Education; Social Action; Weekday Religious Education

The Greater Lynn Council of Churches, Inc.
405 Broadway, Lynn 01904
Tel. (617) 598-0515
*Exec. Dir., Rev. Gerald G. Wyrwas
Pres., Rev. N. Zane Knoy, 35 Range Rd., Nahant 01908
Treas., Mr. William A. Goodrich, Jr., 8 Berkshire Rd., Peabody 01960
Major Activities: Christian Education; Christian Life; Christian Mission; Pastoral Services; Social Concerns

† Montachusett Council of Churches
820 Main St., Fitchburg 01420
Tel (617) 345-6473
*Exec. Sec., Miss Elizabeth V. Brooks
Pres., Rev. Everett Page, 1469 Main St. 01420
Treas., Mr. H. Leonard Allen, 411 North St. 01420
Major Activities: Chaplaincy, Juvenile Court and Hospital; Ecumenical Affairs

Inter-Church Council of Greater New Bedford, Inc.
412 County St., New Bedford 02740
Tel. (617) 993-6242
Exec. Sec., Rev. Sydney Adams
Ofc. Sec., Mrs. Florence L. Hilton
Pres., J. Richard Early, 231 Green St., Fairhaven 02719
Treas., Mr. Leroy F. Anderson, 5 Middle St., S. Dartmouth 02748
Major Activities: Chaplaincy; Community Relations; Radio-TV; Religious Education; Research & Planning; Social Issues

Pittsfield Area Council of Churches
27 East St., Pittsfield 01201
Tel. (413) 447-7351
Ofc. Sec., Miss Grace L. Wheeler
Pres., Rev. Carrol A. Turner, 11 Grove St. 01201
Treas., Mr. James S. Krege, 87 Mountain Dr. 01201
Major Activities: Community Worship; Evangelism; Religious Education; Social Action; Friendly Town; Publicity

† Rockland Area Council of Churches
78 Hingham St., Rockland 02370
Tel. (617) 878-5025

*Exec. Sec. Mr. Robert Bowles
Pres., Mrs. Edwin Nash, 96 North St., North Hanover 02339
Treas., Mr. Walter Pulsiffer, III, 511 Washington St., Abington 02351
Major Activities: Social Action; United Worship; University Life; Youth

† Somerset-Swansea Council of Churches
2073 Riverside Ave., Somerset 02726
Tel. (617) 672-5459
Exec. Sec., Mr. Harry A. Johnson
Pres., Mrs. Myles Dewey, 370 Dillon Lane, Swansea 02777
Treas., Mrs. Eleanor Yerzley, 585 Old Fall River Rd., Swansea 02777
Major Activities: Social Action

† South Shore Council of Churches
1354 Hancock St., Quincy 02169
Tel. (617) 773-1360
Exec. Sec., _____
Pres., Dr. James R. Cameron, 64 Davis St., Wollaston 02170
Treas., Mrs. Penuel E. Sullivan, 1354 Hancock St. 02169
Major Activities: Chaplaincy; Radio; Church Women United

† Council of Churches of Greater Springfield
152 Sumner Ave., Springfield 01108
Tel. (413) 733-2149
Exec. Dir., Rev. Emerson Wesley Smith
Assoc. Exec. Dir., Rev. Donald G. Whitney
Brightwood-Riverview Minister, Rev. Fernando R. Malave
Pres., Mr. Howard K. Rodenhizer, 35 Paulding Rd., Ludlow 01056
Treas., Mr. Cahill A. Tolman, 52 Wexford St. 01118
Major Activities: Public Relations; Hospital Chaplaincy; Urban Ministry; Counseling; Christian Education; Ecumenical Affairs; Christian Social Relations; Pastoral Service

† Taunton Area Council of Churches
P.O. Box 908, Taunton 02780
*Sec., Mrs. Leslie H. Phillips
Pres., Mr. Fred W. Woodcock, 758 Prospect St., N. Dighton 02715
Treas., Mr. Charles Gelette, 583 S. Main St., Raynham 02767
Major Activities: Civic Relations; Evangelism; Institutional Ministry; Radio; Women; Youth

Worcester Area Council of Churches
63 Wachusett St., Worcester 01609
Tel. (617) 757-8385
Exec. Dir., Rev. Edgar H. S. Chandler
Dir. Pastoral Counseling Center, Dr. Rutherford E. Everest
Dir. Public Relations, Mrs. E. Andrew Harvie
Pres., Van M. Aroian
Fin. Chm, James C. Gray
Major Activities: Pastoral Counseling; Church Women; Christian Education; Evangelism; Social Action; Radio & TV

Voluntary Leadership

Allston-Brighton: Pres., Rev. Joseph B. Laurentis, Brooks & Bigelow, Brighton 02135

Amesbury: Pres., Mr. Leslie J. Hartman, 13 Essex St. 01913

Amherst: Pres., Mr. Martin Sevoyian, 167 Montague Rd., N. Amherst 01059

Andover: Pres., Rev. J. Edson Pike, 29 Central St. 01810

Arlington: Pres., Rev. Halsey Andrews, 31 Hopkins Rd. 02174

Barre: Pres., Rev. George Upham, Broad St. 01005

Bedford: Pres., Mrs. Lester Stacey, Jr., Books St., Carlisle 01741

Belmont: Pres., Mr. Frank H. Durgin, 151 Lexington St. 02178

Cambridge: Pres., Rev. Wells B. Grogan, 11 Garden St. 02138

Cape Ann: Pres., Rev. Edmund W. Nutting, 1st Congregational Church, Rockport 01966

Duxbury: Pres., Rev. Stephen Turrell, Washington St. 02332

Framingham Area: Pres., Rev. Harvey L. Ammerman, 125 Adgell Rd. 01704

Groton: Pres., Mr. Richard Bissell, Kemp St., West Groton 01472

Haverhill: Pres., Rev. Arthur Petenaud, 818 Amesbury Rd. 01830

Holyoke: Pres., Rev. Edward Johnston, 605 South St. 01041

Hyde Park: Pres., Mr. Arthur King, Hyde Park YMCA 02136

Jamaica: Pres., Mr. William D. Coutts, 58 Seaverns Ave., Jamaica Plain 02130

Lexington: Pres., Rev. Kenneth Peterson, First Baptist Church, Massachusetts Ave. 02173

Littleton: Pres., Mr. Robert Temple, Bullsley Rd. 01460

Lowell: Pres., Rev. Victor Scalise, 222 Liberty St. 01850

Malden: Pres., Mr. James H. Dulong, 38 Main St. 02148

Martha's Vineyard: Pres., Mr. Edward K. Simpton, Edgartown 02539

Maynard Stowe: Pres., Mr. Fred S. Wilson, Jr., 244 Mossman Rd., N. Sudbury 01776

Medford: Pres., Rev. Robert Durkee, 160 High St. 02155

Melrose: Pres., Rev. Paul D. Huss, 179 Green St. 02176

Middlesex: Pres., Mr. David Dayton, 49 Taylor Rd., Acton 01720

Milford Area: Pres., Mr. M. Russell Denett, 178 Dutcher St., Hopedale 01747

Nantucket: Pres., Rev. Fred D. Bennett, 6th & Center St. 02554

Natick: Pres., Rev. William B. Lawson, 39 E. Central St. 01760

Needham: Pres., Mrs. Richard F. Roberts, 157 Melrose Ave. 02192

Newburyport: Pres., Dr. Prescott E. Tulloch, 4 Roosevelt Pl. 01950

North Berkshire: Pres., Rev. William Carlsen, 7 School St., Williamstown 01267

Northampton: Pres., Mr. Gordon Hill, 234 Crescent 01060

Norwood: Pres., Mr. Paul B. Williams, 100 High Plain St., Walpole 02081

Salem: Pres., Rev. Forrest R. Gilmore, 13 Manning St. 01970

Saugus: Pres., Rev. Forrest Gordon Clark, 83 Chestnut St. 01906

Sharon Interfaith Council: Pres., Rabbi Shamai Kanter, Box 377 02067

Somerville: Pres., Rev. Quinton Ivy, 14 Chapel St., West Somerville 02144

South Shore Federation: Pres., Rev. Ernest B. Johnson, 74 Commerical St., Braintree 02184

Stoneham: Pres., Mr. Clyde Severance, 1 Tremont St. 02180

Walpole: Pres., Rev. Robert P. Noble, Jr., Union Congregational Church, Rhoades Ave., East Walpole 02032

Waltham: Pres., Mr. Howard Strum, 89 Marlboro Rd. 02154

Westboro: Pres., Rev. F. Robert Brown, 18 Forbes St. 01581

Western Hampden: Pres., Mr. Ward B. Carlstrom, Vine St., Westfield 01085

Westport: Pres., Mr. Thomas D. Pacheco, 1094 Main Rd. 02790

West Roxbury: Pres., —————.

Weymouth: Pres., Rev. Harold Sheppard, 47 Beal St. 02170

Wilmington: Pres., —————.

Winchendon: Pres., Mr. Robert L. Slavin, 11 Locust St. 01475

MICHIGAN

Michigan Council of Churches
205 West Saginaw, P.O. Box 206, Lansing 48901
Tel. (517) 485-4395

Exec. Dir., —————.
Assoc. Dir., Rev. Arthur E. Crouch, Jr.
Dir. Migrant Ministry, —————.
Dir. Peace Education Program, Mrs. Marion Anderson
Dir. Radio-TV Dept., Rev. Edward Willingham
Pres., Rev. Eric White
Treas., Mr. Robert Fisher

Major Activities: Migrant Ministry; Peace Education Program; Radio-TV; CROP

Michigan Community Organization Council

Chm., Mr. Joseph Samples, Jr., 18636 Wildemere, Detroit 48221
Treas., Rev. William H. Daniels, 7305 Curtis Ave., Detroit 48221

Major Activities: Developing Strategies for Empowerment of the Poor in the Region; Communication with National IFCO Board; Screening, Project Evaluation

Battle Creek Area Council of Churches
72 E. Michigan Ave., Battle Creek 49017
Tel. (616) 963-2280

*Exec. Sec., Rev. Arthur H. Ryan

Pres., Mr. Gordon L. Howard, 536 Glendale Ave. 49017
Treas., Mr. Dale K. Holmes, 100 Starlight 49015

Major Activities: Ministry to Underprivileged Children; Ecumenical Services; Religion & Arts Exposition; Non-Profit Housing Sponsor; Chaplaincy Services

Berrien County Council of Churches
505 Pleasant St., Room 319, St. Joseph 49085
Tel. (616) 983-6535

Exec. Dir., Rev. Arnold R. Bolin
Admin. Asst., Mrs. Edward O'Keefe
*Dir. Migrant Center, Mrs. Vernon Hiler
*Dir. Camp Warren, Mr. John Sonneman
Pres., Rev. Robert Trenery, 29 N. 3rd St., Niles 49120
Treas., Mr. Robert Kibler, 742 Ansley 49085
Major Activities: Migrant Hospitality Center; Camp Warren; Hospital Chaplaincy and Pastoral Care; Ecumenical Experience and Planning; Information and Referral; Berrien Homes (Low Income Housing)

Metropolitan Detroit Council of the Churches of Christ
600 Francis Palms Bldg., 2111 Woodward Ave., Detroit 48201
Tel. (313) 962-0340

Exec. Dir., Dr. Robert L. Kincheloe
Dir. Communications, Rev. Edward B. Willingham, Jr.
Dir. Mission, Dr. John B. Forsyth
*Dir. Ecumenical worship, Mr. Harold F. Koch
*Dir. Finance and Development, Rev. Hale Thornberry
Dir. Social Service and Family Life, Rev. Raymond B. Cover
Dir. Interfaith Housing, Dr. John B. Forsyth
*Exec. Sec., Church Women United, Mrs. A. L. Spafford
Fin. Asst., Mrs. Helen G. Jobbitt
Admin. Sec., Miss Louise Scott
*Dir. Educational Service, Mrs. Constance Pipok
*Dir. Interfaith Action Council, Dr. John B. Forsyth
Exec. Dir. Protestant Community Services, Mr. James Cox
Pres., Mr. Robert R. Baumgartner, 2421 Second 48226
Treas., Mr. John B. Watkins. 211 W. Fort St. 48226
Major Activities: Area Interchurch Organizations; Chaplains Fellowship; Chaplaincy Service; Church Music; Church Social Service; Church Women United; Communication; Ecumenical Worship; Education Services; Faith & Order; Family Life; Information; Protestant Community Services; Mission; Public Affairs; Radio & TV; Pastors' Union

Greater Flint Council of Churches
900 Chippewa St., Flint 48503
Tel. (313) 238-0477

Office Administrator, Miss Elayne A. Pownall
Pres., Rev. James R. Breckenridge
Treas., Mr. Earl Graves, Jr.
Major Activities: Christian Education; Christian Missions; Christian Unity; Church in Society

Interfaith Metropolitan Agency for Planning
900 Chippewa St., Flint 48503
Tel. (313) 238-0477
Dir., _____
Interim Executive Coordinator, Gerald Nechal
Chm., Rev. James B. Bettendorf
Treas., James B. Jones

An agency for interfaith activity and involvement in the life of the Greater Flint community. Action arms: area councils; communications; coordination of mission; ecumenical education; life and theology; pastoral services; policy review and planning; situation and crisis.

Grand Rapids Area Center for Ecumenism
141 Federal Square Bldg., Grand Rapids 49502
Tel. (616) 458-1716

Exec. Dir., Dr. Russell H. McConnell
Assoc. Exec. Dir. for Ecumenism, Rt. Rev. Msgr. Charles W. Popell
Pastoral Care Consultant, Rev. Marvin C. Hueller
Coordinator of Migrant Ministry, Mrs. Phyllis Gifford
Pres., Dr. Donald G. Lester
Treas., _____
Major Activities: Ministry to Institutions; Music; Public Relations; Public Witness and Radio-TV; Research and Planning; Faith and Order; Christian Education and Christian Life and Work

Jackson County Council of Churches
407 S. Mechanic St., Jackson 49201
Tel. (517) 782-6660

Chaplain-Dir., Rev. Carl J. Benes
Pres., Rev. Ed Dahringer, 100 Main St., P.O. Box 86, Parma 49269
Treas., Mr. Douglass Bennett, 309 S. Bowen, Jackson 49203
Major Activities: Chaplaincy; Radio & TV; Education; Social Concerns; Worship Services at Rest Homes and Juvenile Homes

Lansing Area Council of Churches
205 West Saginaw, Box 206, Lansing 48901
Tel. (517) 372-2333

Exec. Dir., Rev. William H. Work
Pres., Dr. Floyd D. Barrows
Treas., Mr. Howard J. Root, 103 East Greenfield Rd. 48917
Major Activities: Week of Prayer; Key 73; Radio Hours; Chaplaincies; Continuing Education; Poverty

Muskegon County Council of Churches
Jefferson and Hume, Muskegon Heights 49444
Tel. (616) 733-0012

*Exec. Dir., Mr. H. A. Kruizenga
*Sec., Mrs. Elaine Van Donkelaar
Pres., Mr. David Couch, 1848 Antisdale Rd. 49441
Treas., Mr. Duane Buchan, 1840 Eloise 49444
Major Activities: Martin Luther King Fund; Radio; Ecumenical Seminars; Youth; Audio-Visual

Saginaw Religious Coalition
107 S. Washington Ave., Saginaw 48607
Pres., Mr. Norman D. Osborne

Washtenaw County Council of Churches
437 S. Fourth Ave., Ann Arbor 48104
Tel. (313) 761-0930

*Exec. Dir., Rev. Howard F. Gebhart
Dir. Social Services, Mr. Donald Haugen

Pres., Rev. Emmett L. Green, 216 Beakes St. 48104

Treas., Mr. Albert M. Voltmer, 437 S. Fourth Ave. 48104

Major Activities: Christian Education; Social Service (Advocacy and Direct Relief); Radio; Ecumenical Services

Voluntary Leadership

Adrian Area: Pres., Dr. Ed. R. Pickering, 337 S. Madison St. 49221

Cass City: Pres., Mrs. Mary Rexin, RFD 48726

Dundee: Pres., _____, 631 Pearl St. 48131

Grand Traverse Area: Pres., Dr. Milton J. Hagelberg, 1410 Orchard Dr. S. 49684

Monroe: Pres., Mrs. William Farner, 2111 S. Custer 48161

Ottawa: Pres., Mr. Herman Lang, Coopersville 49404

South Haven District: Pres., Mr. George Minert, 701 Center St. 49090

Tri-Cities: Pres., Rev. Albert G. Parker, 1st Presbyterian Church, Grand Haven 49417

MINNESOTA

Minnesota Council of Churches
122 W. Franklin Ave., Minneapolis 55404
Tel. (612) 332-2571

Exec. Dir., Dr. Alton M. Motter

Assoc. Exec. Dir. Church & Community Development, Research & Planning, Rev. George K. Tjaden

Coordinator, Indian Work, Mr. E. G. Holstein

Social Worker Aide, Indian Work, Mrs. Henry Green Crow

Coordinator & Consultant, Indian Work in Northern Minnesota, Mr. Donald Bibeau

Dir. Audio-Visual Services, Mrs. John D. Hale

Coordinator-Dir. Educational Ministries, Mr. Gerald C. Fahrenholz

Coordinator, Joint Religious Legis. Comm., Mr. Patrick Marx

Assoc. Dir. Business Admin., Mr. E. Charles Fowlston

Pres., Mrs. Louise C. Hoistad, 2265 Edgcumbe Rd., St. Paul 55116

Treas., Mr. Andrew W. Hobart, 3100 W. Lake St. 55404

Major Activities: Christian Education; Christian Social Relations; Ecumenical Relations; Church and Community Development; Communications; Indian Work; Research and Planning; Administration

Arrowhead Council of Churches
1015 E. 11th St., Duluth 55805
Tel. (218) 727-5021

*Exec. Dir., Mrs. A. Dean Headley

Pres., Rev. Wm. Brice, 830 E. 1st 55805

Treas., Mr. H. Wittmore Gooch, 2725 E. 1st 55812

Major Activities: Christian Education; Interchurch Evangelism; Twin Ports Ministry; Community Concerns

Greater Minneapolis Council of Churches
122 W. Franklin Ave., Minneapolis 55404
Tel. (612) 339-3048

Exec. Dir., Rev. David E. Witheridge

Dir. Coordinator of Educational Ministries, Mr. Gerald C. Fahrenholz

Adult Court Chaplain, Rev. Leo B. Vetvick

Juvenile Court Chaplain, Rev. Henry W. Taxis

Minneapolis Workhouse Chaplain, Rev. Bill P. Russell

Youth Counselor, Rev. Clyston Holman, Jr.

Pres., Mrs. Leroy E. Hood

Treas., Mr. John C. Anderson

Major Activities: Chaplaincy Services; Church Women United; Educational Ministries; Ecumenical Relations; Social Ministries

St. Paul Area Council of Churches
1671 Summit Ave., St. Paul 55105
Tel. (612) 646-8805

Exec. Dir., Rev. C. Arthur Scott

Dir. Education, Mr. Gerald Fahrenholz

Juvenile Court Chaplain, Rev. John Gilmore

Dir. Indian Work, Mrs. Betty Green Crow

Dir. Women's Work, Mrs. C. W. Hautzenrader

Dir. of Kinship, Mr. Verdell D. Schramm

Institutional Chaplain, Rev. Robert E. Thomas

Dir. Indian Work, Mrs. Sheila White Eagle

Pres., Dr. George E. Whetstone

Treas., Roy O. Overmann

Major Activities: Religious Services and Counseling for Prisoners at Detention and Corrections Authority Institutions; Delinquency Prevention Counseling; Kinship Program for Youth; Educational Development; Ecumenical Encounters and Activities

Voluntary Leadership

Fillmore County: Pres., Mr. Moppy Anderson, Preston 55965

Minnesota Valley: Pres., Dr. Robert C. Wright, 224 Crocus Pl., Mankato 56001

New Ulm: Pres., Dr. Ronald Albright, 1121 Summit Ave. 56073

Rochester Area: Pres., Mr. Richard Husband, 1820 26th St. N.W. 55901

MISSISSIPPI

No state ecumenical agency at present.

Delta Ministry
P.O. Box 457, Greenville 38701

Dir., Mr. Owen H. Brooks

Assoc. Dir., Rev. Harry Bowie

Chm., Earl Lucas, Mound Bayou

A related movement of the National Council of Churches.

MISSOURI

Missouri Council of Churches
420 B Madison St., P.O. Box 839, Jefferson City 65101
Tel. (314) 636-3169

Exec. Dir., Rev. Walter B. Price

Assoc. Exec. Dir. & Dir. of Church Planning, Rev. Raymond A. Schondelmeyer

Pres., Dr. Charles C. Hoskinson

Treas., Rev. Charles A. McEowen

Major Activities: Christian Life and Mission; Christian Education; Christian Unity; Overseas Ministries; Communication; Legislative Affairs

Missouri Delta Ecumenical Ministry
Box 524, Hayti 63851
Tel. (314) 359-1718
Exec. Dir., Richard I. Male
Chm., Rev. Wallace G. Ellinger, 220 South Sprigg, Cape Girardeau 63701
Treas., Richard F. Spitzer, Jr., Box 167, Parma 63870

Major Activities: Community Economic Development; Pemiscot Organization for Welfare Recipients; Community Mental Health; Volunteers & Counterparts; Senior Citizens; FISH

Interchurch Coordinating Council of West Central Missouri
Union State Bank Bldg., P. O. Box 211, Clinton 64735
Tel. (816) 855-5976
Exec. Dir., Rev. John C. Bush
Moderator, Rev. Eugene Moll, 707 Parkview, Butler 64730
Treas., Rev. D. Joseph Snider, Montrose 64770

Major Activities: An enabler or catalyst by which needs are examined and met, such as counseling, ecology, health issues, rural action, hunger, lake ministries, interseminary project, land reclamation, housing, church planning.

Metropolitan Inter-Church Agency
3501 Campbell, Kansas City 64109
Tel. (816) 756-1422
Exec. Dir., Rev. James O. Leffingwell
Assoc. Dir., Rev. Simon P. Montgomery
Pres., Mr. James Owens
Treas., Rev. Lee Soxman

Major Activities: Task Forces on Chaplaincy, Church Development, Communications; Education Training; Faith & Order; Human Justice Task Forces on Welfare, Ecumenical Witness for Peace, Police & Community Relations, Hunger Hike

Midland Empire Regional Ministry
303 N. 7th St., St. Joseph 64501
Tel. (816) 232-2082
Exec. Sec., Miss Nancy E. Sandehn
Adm. Sec., Mrs. Samuel E. Crowley

Chairman, Rev. Bruce Urich
Treas., Sr. Irene Holz

Major Activities: Task forces as appointed to function in four general program areas: Media and Promotion; Dialogue and Education; Worship; and Mission

Springfield Area Council of Churches
Box 3686, Glenstone Station, Springfield 65804
Tel. (417) 862-3586
Exec. Dir., Rev. Dorsey E. Levell

Pres., Dr. Frank Maple, 1211 S. Glenstone 65804

Major Activities: Crosslines-Volunteer Program;

Housing; Low Income Jobs; Legislation; Weekly TV Program; Ecumenical Witness

Voluntary Leadership
Andrew County: Pres., Mr. John Anno, Amazonia 64421
Bulter Association of Churches: Pres., Mr. Ira Wilson, RFD 4 64730
Carondelet Ecumenical Council: Pres., Rev. E. W. Gearhart, 701 Dover Pl., St. Louis 63111
Clay County: Pres., Mrs. Arthur Kincaid, 726 W. Mississippi, Liberty 64068
Creighton: Pres., Mrs. Elsie Birch 64739
Columbia: Pres., Mr. George Keepers, Box 1115, Columbia 65201
Montgomery County: Pres., Mr. George K. Fisher 63361
Osage County: Pres., Mr. Arthur Schwinkler, Morrison 65061
Sarcoxie Alliance: Pres., Rev. Ralph Sipes, Sarcoxie 64862
St. Charles County: Pres., Mr. Merle E. Porter, St. Charles Presbyterian Church, Gamble & Sibley Streets 63301

MONTANA

Montana Council of Churches
1511 Poly Dr., Billings 59102
Tel. (406) 252-5138
*Exec. Dir., Mr. Cecil E. Gubser
Pres., Rev. Jack Hart, 311 Power, Helena 59601
Treas., Mrs. Mervyn Johnson, 2108 Pryor Lane, 59102

Major Activities: Christian Education Leadership Training; Leadership Training in Church Camping Programs; Organizing Churches to Serve New Communities; Merging Small Congregations; Lobbying; Newsletter

NEBRASKA

Interchurch Ministries of Nebraska
215 S. 15th, Room 303, Lincoln 68508
Tel. (402) 432-3391
Exec. Sec., Rev. Robert W. Jeambey
Admin. Asst., Mrs. Edith L. Svoboda
Pres., Mr. John Newman, Farmers State Bank Bldg., Aurora 68818
Treas., Mr. William Fager, 700 S. 51st 68510

Major Activities: Omaha Metro; Perimeter Study & Comity Conference; Nebraska Indian Project; Ministers' Convocation; Camp and Conference Study; Key 73 & Good News

Lincoln Fellowship of Churches
215 S. 15th, Room 303, Lincoln 68508
Tel. (402) 432-3391
Exec. Sec., Rev. Robert W. Jeambey
Admin. Asst., Mrs. Edith L. Svoboda
Pres., Rev. Warren Swartz, 7140 Vine 68505
Treas., Mr. Stan Maly, Jr., 2005 Ryons 68503

Major Activities: Religious Education; Sector and Local Mission; Ecumenical; Troubled Youth; Mass Media; Parish and Community Services

† **Omaha Metropolitan Association of Churches, Inc.**
124 South 24th St., Suite 203, Omaha 68102
Tel. (402) 341-0246

Exec. Sec., Dr. Ernest E. Smith
Pres., Mr. J. D. Anderson, 8271 Indiana Hills Dr. 68114
Treas., Mr. Ralph W. Shaw, 3621 N. 79th St. 69134

Voluntary Leadership
Hastings: Pres., Dr. Elmer E. Glenn, 1114 North Denver St. 68901
Nemaha County: Pres., Mr. Gayle Hecht, R.R., Dubois 68345

NEVADA

Nevada Council of Churches
(no current information)

NEW HAMPSHIRE

New Hampshire Council of Churches
24 Warren St. (P. O. Box 63), Concord 03301
Tel. (603) 224-1352

Exec. Sec., Rev. Frank H. Gross
Local Councils Consultant, Rev. Samuel N. McCain
Ministry to Older People Consultant, Mr. Earl N. Taraldsen
Ministry to the Poor Consultant, Rev. H. Marshall Budd
Pres., Rev. Charles Broadbent, P. O. Box 486, 03301
Treas., Mr. Richard N. Edmunds, P. O. Box 136, 03301
Major Activities: Evangelism & Mission; Town & Country Ministry; Christian & Higher Education; Institutional Ministry; Social Action; Women's Work

† **Greater Manchester Federation of Churches**

111 North St., Manchester 03104
Tel. (603) 624-9382

*Exec. Sec., Mrs. William Elmes
Pres., Rev. G. Edward Bingham, 650 Varney St. 03102
Treas., Mr. Ralph Farmer, 1226 Chestnut St. 03104

Major Activities: Church Women United; Church Men; Radio & TV; Ministry to Public Institutions; COCU

Voluntary Leadership
Cheshire: Pres., Rev. Ben Andrew, United Church of Christ, Keene 03431
Colebrook: Pres., Mr. Donald Dickson, Park St. 03576
Concord: Pres., Mr. Edward G. Robinson, 77 N. Main St. 03301
Lisbon Inter-Church Council: Pres., Mrs. Harold Foster, 55 Landaff Rd. 03585
Milford-Amherst: Pres., Mrs. Barbara Watts, Foster Rd. 03055

Nashua Area: Pres., Mrs. Robert B. Burns, Jr., 6-A Abbott St. 03060
White Mountain: Pres., Mr. Paul Faringer, 21 Alpine St., Gorham 03581

NEW JERSEY

New Jersey Council of Churches
116 North Oraton Parkway, East Orange 07017
Tel. (201) 675-8600

Gen. Sec., Rev. Paul L. Stagg
Office Mgr., Miss Dorothy Stewart
Dir. Dept of Radio & Television, Mr. James Roberts, 110 South Munn Ave. 07017
Dir. Dept of Research & Church Development, Rev. Jean Paul Richter
Dir. of Social Concerns, Rev. Philip Kunz
Pres., Dr. Homer J. Tucker
Treas., Mr. Leslie Hoyle

Major Activities: Task Forces to Meet Emerging Needs

Bergen County Council of Churches
165 Burton Ave., Hasbrouck Heights 07604
Tel. (201) 288-3784

Exec. Dir., Dr. Stanley I. Stuber
Office Sec., Mrs. A. E. Vander Vliet
Pres., Mrs. William Beattie, 918 Phyllis Lane, Oradell 07649
Treas., Mr. George Theuret, 188 Central Ave., Bogota 07603

Major Activities: Task Forces for Charter Reform Study; Family Life Education; Market Place Ministry; Ministries for & with Youth; Services to the Aging; United Campus Ministry; Boy Scouts; Girl Scouts; Evaluation and Planning

Council of Churches of Greater Camden
Box 1103, Merchantville 08109
Tel. (609) 665-1919

*Exec. Sec., Dr. Samuel A. Jeanes
Pres., Rev. Robert E. DuBois, Haddon Heights 08033
Treas., Merrill N. O'Brien, Audubon 08106

Major Activities: Radio & TV; Hospital Chaplaincy; United Services; Good Friday Breakfast; Mayors' Prayer Breakfast; Public Affairs

Council of Churches of Cherry Hill
Box 163, Cherry Hill 08034
(Send mail attention President)

Hunterdon Fellowship of Churches
(Send mail to President)

Pres., Rev. Norman Hansen, R.D. #1, Pittstown 08867

Major Activities: Audio-Visual Aids; Bible Agent; Children's Work; Evangelism; Leadership Training; Social Action

† **Jersey City Council of Churches**
654 Bergen Ave., Jersey City 07304
Tel. (201) 432-1355

Co-Chairmen, Steering Committee, Rev. David C. Pierson, Rev. Louis S. Bell

Office Sec., Mrs. E. G. Schabert

Major Activities: Training Programs; Recruitment System; Information & Public Relations

† Morris County Council of Churches
(Send mail to President)

Pres., Rev. John L. Phaler, Jr., 190 Diamond Spring Rd., Denveille 07834. Tel. (201) 627-1041

Treas., Mr. Warren Apgar, 122 Oak St., Dover 07801

Major Activities: Audio-Visual; Library; Chaplaincy; Christian Education; Broadcasting & Public Relations; Social Concerns

New Brunswick Area Council of Churches
2 High St., New Brunswick 08901

*Exec. Sec., Rev. Jarvis S. Morris

Pres., Rev. Henry Hilderbrand, 3 Llewellyn Pl. 08901

Treas., Mr. V. K. Coffill, Jr., 134 Norris Ave., Metuchen 08840

Major Activities: Chaplaincy; Church World Service; UNICEF; Ecumenical Services of Worship; Transient Aid Program; Flood Relief

Metropolitan Ecumenical Ministry
969 McCarter Highway, Newark 07102
Tel. (201) 623-9224

Exec. Dir., Rev. Horace H. Hunt

Dir. Puerto Rican Ministry, Rev. Alfonso A. Roman

Associate in Social Welfare, Miss Edith C. List

Pres., Mr. Augustus F. Frick, 109 Inwood Ave, Upper Montclair 07043

Treas., Mr. Lawrence Belcher, Jr.

Major Activities: Urban Crisis; Education; Health; Welfare; Counsel to Churches

† Passaic-Clifton Council of Churches
145 Paulison Ave., Passaic 07055
Tel. (201) 779-7521

Exec. Sec., Rev. Donald Steinl

Pres., Rev. Msgr. Frank J. Rodimer, 145 Paulison Ave. 07055

Treas., Mr. Richard J. O'Brien

† Greater Paterson Council of Churches
128 War St., YMCA Bldg., Paterson 07505
Tel. (201) 523-7119

*Exec. Sec., Mrs. Charles White

Pres., Rev. Paul E. Spiecker, 452 Lafayette Ave., Hawthorne 07506

Treas., Mr. Charles Kara, 22 3rd Ave., Hawthorne 07506

Major Activities: Youth; Scouting; Social Actions; Interfaith Relations; Narcotics; Evangelism; Interchurch Activities; Ministry in Public Institutions; Spanish Work

† Sussex County Council of Churches and Cooperative Parish
P. O. Box 397, Newton 07860
Tel. (201) 383-2030

*Clerk, Mrs. Joanna A. van der Haeghen

Pres., Rev. John D. Kennety, P. O. Box 345, Vernon 07462

Treas., Mrs. Joanna A. van der Haeghen

Major Activities: Task Forces for Chaplaincy & Specialized Ministries, Communications, Education, Social Concern & Community Planning

Council of Churches of Greater Trenton
1235 Greenwood Ave., Trenton 08609
Tel. (609) 396-9166

Interim Exec. Dir., Victor Downing

Adm. Asst., Mrs. Evelyn Newman

Chaplain, Trenton State College, Rev. Gary Lee Starrett

Chaplain, Rider College, William Spencer

Pres., Rev. Roger H. Berg

Treas., Peter S. Heberling

Major Activities: Metropolitan Missions; Ecumenical Ministries; Chaplaincy Services

United Trenton Ministry
910 Stuyvesant Ave., Trenton 08618
Coordinator, Rev. Harry B. Zane

Major Activities: An ecumenical effort sponsored by the Presbytery of New Brunswick and the Southern New Jersey Methodist Conference

Voluntary Leadership

Allentown: Pres., Rev. L. R Applegate, Box 183, 08501

Atlantic City: Pres., Rev. F. Schwartz, Community Church, Ventor & Victoria 08406

Belleville: Pres., Rev. Frederick Long, 393 Washington Ave. 07109

Camden Metro Council: Pres., Rev. Sam Appel, 900 Point St. 08102

Freehold Area: Pres., Rev. James T. Memmott, 118 W. Main St. 07728

Hackensack: Pres., Mr. Sidney H. Palmer, 187 Krone Pl. 07601

Irvington: Pres., Mrs. Lillian E. Eilau, 19 Orange Pl. 07111

Metuchen-Edison Clergy Assoc.: Pres., Fr. Richard A. Bower, St. Luke's Episcopal Church, 17 Oak Ave., Metuchen 08840

Montclair: Pres., Miss Rita Hogan, 480 Valley Rd. 07043

Moorestown: Pres., Rev. Fred Tennie, 217 Cedar St. 08057

Paulsboro Area: Pres., Mr. Charles Heister, 124 S. Market St., Gibbstown 08027

Plainfield: Pres., Mr. R. R. Opt, 7 Valley Rd., Watchun 07060

Rahway: Pres., Mr. B. V. Smith, YMCA, 1564 Irving St. 07065

Red Bank: Pres., Rev. Harold Hornberger, 145 Wallace St. 07701

Sommerville: Pres., Rev. Wayne N. Nadley, 130 W. High St. 08876

South Amboy: Pres., Mr. H. G. Semoneit, 357 Portia St. 08879

South Orange: Pres., Rev. Edgar G. Thomas, 152 Academy St. 07079

Summit: Pres., Mr. Andrew R. Skinnell, 2 Glen Oaks Ave. 07901

Tri-Community: Pres., Mr. William Francisco, 85 Beech Ave., Berkeley Hts. 07922

NEW MEXICO

New Mexico Inter-Church Agency
525 San Pedro NE, Albuquerque 87108
Tel. (505) 255-1509

Exec. Sec., Rev. Harry V. Summers
Pres., Bishop Alsie H. Carleton, 1201 First National Bank Bldg. East 87108
Treas., Mr. Robert J. Guerin, 9520 Snow Heights Blvd. N.E. 87112

Major Activities: Home Education Livelihood Program; United Adoption Agency; Day Care Center; Encino House; Police Chaplaincy; Storehouse; Knowplace Coffee House

NEW YORK

New York State Council of Churches, Inc.
3049 E. Genesee St., Syracuse 13224
Tel. (315) 446-6151

Exec. Dir., Rev. Kenneth A. Roadarmel
Assoc. Exec. Dir., Educational Dev. & Adm., Rev. Robert E. Breth
Assoc. Exec. Dir., Social Order, Rev. Robert T. Cobb
Assoc. Exec. Dir., Endowment Development, Rev. Charles H. Schmitz
Assoc. Exec. Dir., Planning & Church Development, Rev. Stanley E. Skinner
Assoc. Exec. Dir., Planning & Research, Rev. Arthur C. Tennies
Pres. (acting), Rt. Rev. Charles B. Persell, Jr., 68 E. Swan St., Albany 12210
Treas., Mr. Donald R. Waful, 2005 W. Genesee St., Syracuse 13219

Major Activities: Legislation; Chaplaincy in State Institutions; Migrant and Poverty; Regional Planning; Research and Planning; Educational Development

Broome Council of Churches, Inc.
42 Chenango St., Room 203, Binghamton 13901
Tel. (607) 724-9130

Exec. Dir., Rev. Louis F. Kirlin
Hospital & Jail Chaplain, Rev. Lavere A. Dodson
Campus Minister, Rev. Kenneth R. Carder
Pres., Mr. Gordon Goodyear, 4 Kirkwood Ave. 13901
Treas., Mr. Leland R. Post, 71 Helen St. 13905

Major Activities: Campus Christian Life; Christian Education; Radio & TV; Urban Services; Chaplaincy to Hospital & Jails; Christian Life & Work

Buffalo Area Council of Churches
1272 Delaware Ave., Buffalo 14209
Tel. (716) 882-4793

Exec. Dir., Rev. Carl F. Burke
Dir. Campus Ministry, Rev. Rodney G. Snedeker
Dir. Chaplains, Rev. C. Charles Bachmann
Dir. Church Supply Agency, Mr. Otis Leslie
Dir. Housing Foundation, Mr. Armand Sieper
Dir. Radio-TV, Mrs. Marilyn G. Stahlka
Dir. Social Service Dept., Rev. J. Samuel Williams

Admin. Sec., Church Women United, Mrs. Thorvald M. Stein
Pres., Mr. Fred H. White, Room 400, Statler Hilton 14202
Treas., Mr. George Henderson, 1 Summit Ave. 14214

Major Activities: Radio-TV; Housing; Social Services; Campus Ministry; Hospital Chaplains

Capital Area Council of Churches, Inc.
810 Madison Ave., Albany 12208
Tel. (518) 489-8441

Exec. Dir., Rev. Vladimir E. Hartman
Campus Ministers, Rev. Harvey Bates, Rev. J. Andy Smith III
Exec. Dir. Religious Broadcasting Commission, Mr. Charles H. Saile
Pres., Rev. Louis C. Brewer
Treas., Mr. John F. McColl, 20 Glendale Ave., Elsemere 12054

Major Activities: Church Women United; Campus Ministry; Christian Education; Community Worship; Faith & Order; Hospital Ministry; Ecumenical Comm. on Continuing Education for Clergy; International Affairs; Interfaith Clergy Association; Religious Broadcasting; Young Adults; Social Education & Action

Christians United in Mission
40 North Main Ave., Albany 12203
Tel. (518) 438-5178

Coordinator, Mr. Joseph A. Powers

Major Activities: A four-county regional ecumenical organization

Council of Churches of Chemung County, Inc.
330 West Church St., Elmira 14901

Adm. Asst., Mrs. Frances S. Lewis
Pres., Mr. Ralph E. Fudge, 819 West Second St., Elmira 14905
Treas., Mr. D. E. Foote, 123 Sunset Dr., Horseheads 14845

Major Activities: Campus Ministry; Retarded Children Released Time; Ministry in Hospitals and Homes

The Cortland County Council of Churches, Inc.
97 N. Main St., Cortland 13045
Tel. (607) 753-0754

*Sec., Mrs. Marguerite K. Walrad
Pres., Mrs. Marian Higgins, 41 Burgett Dr., Homer 13077
Treas., Mr. Wesley D. Stisser, Jr., 226 McLean Rd. 13045

Major Activities: Christian Education; Radio; Campus Ministry; Church World Service; UNICEF; Institutional Visitation; Alcoholism and Drug Programs

Dutchess Interfaith Council
75 Market Place, Poughkeepsie 12601
Tel. (914) 471-7333

Acting Exec. Dir., Mrs. Martha Miller
Pres., Rev. Ernest R. Falardeau

Treas., Mr. Walter W. Wagner

Major Activities: Included in the purposes are: To deepen the spiritual forces of the community; to focus attention and energies of the religious communities on urgent community problems; to combat community deterioration

Genesee County Council of Churches
306 E. Main St., Batavia 14020
Tel. (716) 343-9002

*Exec. Sec., Mrs. Pearl Hyatt

Pres., Rev. Fremont L. Chapman, 306 E. Main St. 14020

Treas., Mr. Burton Sackett, 306 E. Main St. 14020

Major Activities: Youth; Ecumenical Service; Radio; Chaplaincy Services; Housing Project

Genesee Ecumenical Ministries
130 E. Main St., Rochester 14604
Tel. (716) 232-6530

Exec. Dir., Rev. Henry Atwell

Dir. Black Church Ministries, Rev. Marvin Chandler

Pres., Rev. Robert M. Wainwright, East Ave. at Vick Park B. 14607

Treas., Mr. Raymond R. Beardsley, 32 Kurt Rd., Pittsford 14534

Major Activities: Judicial Process Commission; Hanover Houses Ministry; Pastoral Counseling; Audio-Visual; Church Women United

Area Congregations Together (A.C.T.)
206 N. Cayuga St., Ithaca 14850
Tel. (706) 272-2367

*Exec. Dir., Percy L. Dunn

Pres., Mrs. Joan Loehr, 102 Willard Way 14850

Treas., Mrs. Ruth Stewart, 9 Miller Rd. E. 14850

Major Activities: Food for Needy Families; Clothing for Lower Income Persons; Religious Education

The Long Island Council of Churches
249 Merrick Road, P. O. Box 105, Rockville Centre 11570
Tel. (516) 536-8707

Exec. Dir., Rev. Clayton L. Williams

Assoc. Exec. Dir., Rev. Jack H. Alford, 318 Roanoke Ave., Riverhead 11901. Tel. (516) 727-2210

Pres., Rev. Trevor A. Hausske, 131 Middle Rd., Sayville 11782

Treas., Mr. Edmund L. Roel, 9 Hillcrest Ln., Woodbury 11797

Major Activities: Ministry in Institutions; Ministry in Higher Education; Planning; Pastoral Counseling; Communications; Social Ministries; Church Women United; White House Task Force on Aging; Migrant Ministries

Council of Churches of the Mohawk Valley Area, Inc.
1644 Genesee St., Utica 13502
Tel. (315) 733-4661

Exec. Dir., Dr. Alan B. Peabody

Adm. Sec., Mrs. Olga Long

Pres., Mr. Elliott R. Hughes, Crow Hill Rd., Clinton 13323

Treas.,———

Major Activities: Christian Education; Social Action; Urban Ministry; Ecumenical Relations; Ministry in Higher Education; Church Women United; Radio and TV

The Mount Vernon, New York Council of Churches, Inc.
E. Lincoln & N. Columbus Aves., Mount Vernon 10553
Tel. (914) 667-1860

*Sec., Mrs. Eugene S. Fiske

Pres., Rev. William H. Edwards

Treas., Mr. Fred Gates

Major Activities: School of Christian Education; Drama; Hospital Chaplaincy Program; Pulpit Exchange Sunday; Easter Dawn Service

† The New Rochelle Council of Churches
381 Fifth Ave., New Rochelle 10801

Pres., Mr. Arthur L. Pulley

Treas., Mr. John Carling, 32 Ellenton Ave. 10801

Major Activities: Christian Education (Weekday Released Time School, Youth); Christian Life & Work; Christian Social Concerns; Family Chaplaincy; Church Women United; Public Relations & Publicity

The Council of Churches of the City of New York
475 Riverside Dr., Ste. 456, New York 10027
Tel. (212) 749-1214

Exec. Dir., Rev. Dan M. Potter

Program Dir, Rev. Franklin D. Graham

Controller, Mr. George W. Waller

Exec. Sec. Church Planning & Research, Rev. Leland Gartrell

Dir. Ofc. of Development, Mr. Cecil R. Simms, Jr.

*Pastoral Care to Institutions & Agencies, Dir. of Program for Chaplain's Aid, Rev. Norman Quick

Exec. Sec. Public Relations,———

Exec. Sec. Radio & TV, Rev. Reuben Gums

Program Dir. of Radio & TV, Mr. Ted Bair

Exec. Dir. Housing & Development Corporation, Mr. Enoch Williams

Youth Services, Miss Doris Waters

*Chaplain, Protestant Chapel, Kennedy Airport, Rev. Marlin Bowman

Pres., Mr. George M. Duff, Jr., 475 Riverside Dr., Ste. 456, 10027

Treas., Mr. Harry F. Reiss, Jr., 475 Riverside Dr., Ste. 456, 10027

Major Activities: Christian Education; Church Planning & Research; Radio & TV; Church Women United; Housing Development Corporation; Youth Services; Specialized Ministries; Pastoral Care; Protestant Chapel, Kennedy International Airport; Public Relations

Bronx Division of the Council of Churches of the City of New York
1808 Grand Concourse, Bronx 10457
Tel. (212) 299-3156

Exec. Sec.,———

Dir. of Christian Education,——

Pres., Rev. John Kellman, 3759 White Plains Rd. 10467

Treas., Mr. Ray Levie, 60 W. 190th St. 10461

Major Activities: Christian Social Relations; Protestant Chapel; Church Planning & Research; Pastoral Care; Spanish Work; Radio-TV; Christian Education

Brooklyn Division of the Council of Churches of the City of New York
66 Court St., Ste. 700, Brooklyn 11201
Tel. (212) 625-5851

Exec. Sec., Rev. Charles H. Straut, Jr.

Pres., Rev. V. Simpson Turner

Treas., Mr. Sydney Allan

Major Activities: Church Community Associations; Church Women United; Protestant Consultant, Brooklyn Family Court; Pastoral Care to Institutions; Christian Education; Protestant Chaplains at Boy Scout Camps; Cooperative Ministry; Federation of Protestant Men; Church Planning; Christian Relations

Manhattan Division of the Council of Churches of the City of New York
475 Riverside Dr., Ste. 456, New York 10027
Tel. (212) 749-1214

Program Dir., Rev. Bernard Holliday

Pres., Rev. F. Herbert Skeete

Treas., Miss Evelyn Harris

Major Activities: Summer Satellite Center Project; Family Offense Term court; Family Institute; Wall Street Ministry; Release Time Education; Drug Abuse Education & Prevention; Day Care Center Development

Staten Island Division of the Council of Churches of the City of New York
P. O. Box 89, Staten Island 10314
Tel. (212) 761-6782

Ofc. Mgr., Mrs. Marjorie R. Bergendale

Pres., Rev. Austin H. Armistead, 582 Delafield Ave. 10310

Treas., Mr. Charles A. Saderholm, 94 Russell St. 10308

Major Activities: Support; Christian Education; Parish Services; Civic Affairs; Community Action

The Niagara Council of Churches
122 Jefferson Ave., Niagara Falls 14303
Tel. (716) 285-7505

*Adm. Sec., Mrs. Robert Ketcham

Pres., Rev. Pierre Tangent, 554 Main St., Niagara Falls 14301

Treas., Mr. John Pfisterer, 727 The Circle, Lewiston 14092

Major Activities: Christian Education; Evangelism and Mission; Services to Tourists; Referral Services; Institutional Ministries; Cooperation with Other Ecumenical Agencies

† Queens Federation of Churches, Inc.
86-17 105th St., Richmond Hill 11418
Tel. (212) 847-6764

Exec. Sec., Dr. Grant F. Anderson

Pres., Rev. C. Leonard Miller, 114-05 170th St., St. Albans 11434

Treas., Mr. Dwain M. Smith, 136 Dawson Lane, Jericho 11753

Major Activities: Laymen's Retreat; Research & Planning; Church Women United; Family Court Work, Social Action; Christian Education; Blood Bank; Scouting

Rochester: see Genesee Ecumenical Ministries

The Inter-Faith Community of Schenectady
271 State St., Schenectady 12305
Tel. (518) 370-2150

Pres., Rev. Thomas Orr, Jr., 2533 Balltown Rd. 12309

Treas., Mr. Lloyd Rivest, 2275 Berkley Ave. 12309

Major Activities: Community Housing; Drug Control; Joint Youth Facilities and Programs; Prison Services; Racial Concerns

Metropolitan Church Board of the Syracuse Area, Inc.
3049 E. Genesee St., Syracuse 13224
Tel. (315) 446-3750

Exec. Dir., Rev. Robert E. Grimm

Assoc. Dir., Church Community Relations, Rev. John P. McCrea

Assoc. Dir., Community Mission & Services, Rev. Rodger Reed

Assoc. Dir., Ecumenical Education, Mrs. O. Allen Thompson

Pres., Rev. Warren G. Odom, 3049 E. Genesee St. 13224

Treas., Mr. Harry W. Homan, 140 E. Ononodaga St. 13202

Major Activities: Community Services; Cooperative Education; Community Mission; Ecumenical Education; Special Ministries; Communication

†Tioga County Council of Churches
17 Lake St., Owego 13827
Tel. (607) MU 7-2520

Exec. Sec., Miss Pauline Kishpaugh

Pres., Rev. Arthur Chauncey, R.D. 1, Owego 13827

Treas., Mrs. Lewis Hockman, Box 304, Newark Valley 13811

Major Activities: Adult Work; Children's Work; Leadership Education; Social Concerns; Weekday Christian Education; Youth

† Troy Area Council of Churches
520 Pawling Ave., Troy 12180
Tel. (518) 272-0612

*Exec. Sec., Rev. Charles J. Warner

Pres., Mr. Douglas L. Bartow, 1 Sunset Lane 12182

Treas., Mr. Adolph F. Duerschner, 15 Euclid Ave. 12180

Major Activities: Christian Education; Social Education and Action; Legislative; Faith & Order; Evangelism

United Urban Ministry
1st & Congress Sts., Troy 12180
Tel. (518) 273-4788
Exec. Dir. & Dir. of Community Development, Dr. Thomas Bickman
Dir. Training & Communications, Mr. David Raycroft
Dir. Community Organization, Rev. John Lyons
Major Activities: Community Development; Community Education; Community Organizations

Yonkers Council of Churches
111 N. Broadway, Yonkers 10701
Tel. (914) 965-5695
*Ofc. Coordinator, Mr. John F. Koolstra
Pres., Rev. William E. Palmer, Bryn Mawr Presbyterian Church, Lockwood Ave. 10701
Treas., Mr. Jack George, 20 Grosbeak Rd. 10701
Major Activities: Chaplaincy Program; Seminars

Voluntary Leadership
Addison: Pres., Mr. Carlton Ford, Painted Post 14870
Amsterdam Area: Pres., Mr. Mark C. T. Andreae, 55 Coolidge Rd. 12010
Arcade: Pres., Rev. Kenneth Snyder, 212 Main St. 14009
Bainbridge: Pres., Mr. Charles A. Haase, 56 E. Main St. 13733
Bellevue: Pres., Rev. Roland Kelly, 2146 Broadway, Schenectady 12306
Brockport: Pres., Mr. John C. Crandall, 3907 Lake Rd. 14420
Bronx: Pres., Rev. Henry H. Hobbs, 2547 E. Tremont Ave. 10461
Brunswick: Pres., Mr. Kenneth W. Clickner, Box 175, RFD # 3, Troy 12180
Byron-Bergen: Pres., Mrs. Adrian Fodge, 29 S. Lake St., Bergen 14416
Caledonia: Pres., Mr. Charles Russ, Caledonia 14423
Canandaigua: Pres., Rev. Richard Bowen, 3361 Middle Cheshire Rd. 14424
Clinton County: Pres., Mr. Roger Wilson, Mooers 12958
Cooperstown: Pres., Rev. Robert Herst, 27 Church St. 13326
Corning: Pres., Mr. Graham D. Wightman, 2 Flower Ave. 14830
Cuba: Pres., Mr. Frederick G. Pugh, 97 W. Main St. 14727
Delhi: Pres., Mr. Sheldon Merritt, 4 Cuddebeck Ave., Delhi 13753
Dundee Area: Pres., Rev. David Geer, 9 Harpending Ave. 14837
Dunkirk: Pres., Mr. Lyndon F. Wise, P. O. Box 271, 14048
East Aurora: Pres., Mr. H. V. Ackerman, 812 Lawrence Ave. 14952
Edmeston: Pres., Mrs. Jacob Williams, W. Burlington 13482
Geneva: Pres., Rev. Thomas Hansen, 520 S. Main St. 14456
Glens Falls Area: Pres., Mr. Grant Cole, Ridge Rd. 12801
Gloversville: Pres., Mrs. Catherine Costello, 97 —6th Ave. 12078
Granville Area: Pres., Mr. Earle Wood 12832

Greene: Pres., Mrs. Helen Treyz, 15 Washington St. 13778
Greenville Area: Pres., Rev. Richard Clark 12083
Hamburg Assoc.: Pres., Rev. George C. Ruof, 261 E. Main St. 14075
Hannibal: Pres., Rev. Orval McBride 13074
Honeoye Falls: Pres., Rev. Arthur C. Guild, Box 568 14472
Hoosic Valley: Pres., Mr. Paul Wiley, R.D., Johnsonville 12094
Hudson Falls: Pres., Rev. Marshall Dodd, 29 North St. 12839
Jefferson County: Pres., Mr. J. Leslie Hanson, 247 Paddock St., Watertown 13601
Kingston: Pres., Mr. Harold Van Allen, Box 703, Uptown /Station 12402
Livonia Area: Pres., Mrs. Robert Mallory, Hemlock 14466
Lowville: Pres., Dr. J. R. Schlieder, Lowville 13367
Milford: Pres., Mr. Morris Leidkie, Milford 13807
Moriah: Pres., Mr. Harold Babcock, Moriah 12960
Norwich: Pres., Mr. Edwin Vantine, 55 W. Main St. 13815
Nunda: Pres., Mr. Mark Wiseman, Warsaw Central School 14569
Olean: Pres., Mr. Walter M. Babcock, 438 4th Ave. 14760
Oneida: Pres., Rev. Robert Washer, 82 E. 8th St., Oneida Castle 13421
Ontario: Pres., Mr. Dan Stroba, Knickerbocker St. 14519
Oswego City: Pres.,———, 3 Jacqueline Ct., Utica 13502
Penn-Yan Area: Pres., Mr. Elmer Willard, 306 Clinton St. 14527
Portchester: Pres., Rev. John Sanborn, St. Paul's Lutheran Church, King St. & Comly Ave. 10573
Pulaski: Pres., Mr. Carlton Rounds, R.D. 13142
St. Lawrence County: Pres., Mr. Charles H. Jones, 101 Rowley St., Gouverneur 13642
Saranac Lake Interchurch Council: Pres., Rev. Peter O. Hill, St. Lukes Episcopal Church, Saranac Lake 12983
Schuyler County: Pres., Mr. Liston Coon, Watkins Glen 14891
Seneca-Rural: Pres., Mrs. Rufus Blodgett, Rushville 14544
Shenendehowa Area: Pres., Rev. Robert J. De Young, Elnora 12065
Sherburne Community: Pres., Mrs. Richard Hill, Sherburne 13460
Sullivan County: Pres., Mr. Robert T. Many, Grahamsville 12470
Trumansburg Area: Pres., Rev. Charles F. Schwartz, Alpine 14805
Twin Cities: Pres., Mrs. John Tyo, Shortsville 14548
Walworth Area: Pres., Mr. Michael Rudovitz, 310 Kittering Rd., Macedon 14502
Warwick Valley: Pres., Mr. Herbert D. Couser, 46 S. Main St., Florida 10921
Webster: Pres., Mrs. Walter Harrison, 1486 Creek St., Rochester 14625
Windsor: Pres., Mr. William Boyce, Windsor 13865
Wolcott Area: Pres., Rev. H. Wesley Bacon 15 Draper St. 14590

NORTH CAROLINA

North Carolina Council of Churches
Box 6637, College Station, Durham 27708
Tel. (919) 688-3819

Exec. Dir., Rev. Samuel S. Wiley
Dir. Social Ministries, Rev. S. Collins Kilburn, 740 Nash Dr., Raleigh 27608. Tel. (919) 828-6501
Dir. Migrant Project, Mr. William H. Shipes, 723 W. Johnson St., Raleigh 27603. Tel. (919) 828-0303
Pres., Rev. James H. Lightborne, Jr., P. O. Box 2410, Burlington 27215
Treas., Mr. John R. B. Hawes, Jr., 306 Argonne Dr. 27704

Major Activities: Christian Social Ministries; Christian Nurture; Christian Unity; Public Relations; Radio, TV and Audio-Visuals; Church Women United

The Robeson County Church and Community Center
705 So. Willow St., Lumberton 28358
Tel. (919) 738-5204

Dir., Rev. Robert L. Mangum
Assoc. Dir., Miss Mary Cameron
Counselor-Caseworker, Mrs. Matilda Locklear Hocker
Chm., Mr. Adolph Dial
Treas., Mr. Howard Cooper

Major Activities: Emergency Aid; Referral; Pastoral Counseling; Mobilization of Volunteers for Service; Information and Research; Creation of New Services; Dialogue

NORTH DAKOTA

North Dakota Conference of Churches
202 1/2 N. 3rd St., Bismarck 58501
Tel. (701) 255-0604

Exec. Dir., Rev. J. Winfred Stoerker
Pres., Dr. James Cottrell, Jamestown College, Jamestown 58401
Treas., Rev. Glenn J. Fruth, Box 797, Cando 58324

Major Activities: Religion in the Public Schools; Religious Legislation; Urban-Rural Youth Exchange; Regional Activities; Ecumenical Relations; Leisure Ministry

Voluntary Leadership

Benson County: Pres., Mr. Harry Hetler, Esmond 58332
Bismarck: Pres., Rev. Charles Hill, 722 N. 4th St. 58501
Burke County: Pres., Mrs. Howard Corey, Bowbells 58721
Dickey County: Pres., Mrs. Ralph Hollan, Guelph 58447
La Moure County: Pres., Mr. Alvin Hanneld, Kulm 58456
Minot: Pres., Rev. Allen E. Schauer, 700 6th St. S.W. 58701
Sargent County: Pres., Mr. Henry Hassenbrock, Cogswell 58017
Towner County: Pres., Mrs. Glenn Barrett, Egeland 58331
Wells County: Pres., Mr. Adolph Pepple, Cathay 58422

OHIO

Ohio Council of Churches, Inc.
89 E. Wilson Bridge Road, Columbus 43085
Tel. (614) 885-9590

Exec. Dir., Rev. Carlton N. Weber
Assoc. Dir., Rev. Henry Gerner
Dir. Institutional Ministries, Rev. Harold A. Lindberg
Dir. Ecumenical Commission on Church & Government, Rev. Robert Graetz
Admin. Sec., Education, Mrs. Estalla Worth
Admin. Sec., Church Women United, Mrs. George Johnson
Pres., Bishop Francis E. Kearns, 1226 Market St., Canton 44714
Treas., Mr. Robert Newlon, 42 East Gay St. 43215

Major Activities: Church & Community; Church in Witness; Education; Institutional Ministries; Church Women United; Ecumenical Commission on Church & Government

Council of Churches of Greater Akron
282 West Bowery St., Akron 44307
Tel. (216) 535-2654

Exec. Dir., Rev. James P. Ebbers
Chaplain, University of Akron, Rev. Barrie F. Bodden
Pres., Mr. Oliver W. Durrant, 4493 Larkspur Ln. 44313

Major Activities: Ecumenical Relations; Campus Ministry; Urban Ministry; Pastoral Care; Issue-Oriented Task Force Development

Greater Akron Intergroup Ministry
282 West Bowery St., Akron 44307
Tel. (216) 762-6435

Dir., Rev. James H. Klink
Educational Coordinator, Ms Alice Y. Murray
Consultant, Rev. James J. Gardiner, S.A.
Black Church Consultant, Rev. Howard B. Washington

Major Activities: Urban Crisis Concerns; Organizational Development Concerns; Supportive Ministry Concerns; Resource Center

† Alliance Area Council of Churches
470 E. Broadway, Alliance 44601
Tel. (216) 823-2025

Exec. Sec., Rev. D. Andrew Howey
Pres., Mr. M. Dale Allison, 513 E. Main St. 44601
Treas., Mrs. Ruth Sheehan, First National Bank 46601

Major Activities: Christian Education; Community Relations & Service; Public Meetings & Evangelism

Canton: see Central Stark County

Council of Christian Communions of Greater Cincinnati
1836 Fairmont Ave., Cincinnati 45214
Tel. (513) 251-4666

Exec. Dir., Rev. Tecumseh X. Graham
Chaplain, Juvenile Court, Rev. Ray Lindley
Dir. Protestant Big Sister Program, Miss Carol Allen

*Sec., Weekday & Audio-Visual, Mrs. Peggy Ball
Dir. Christian Education & Communications, Rev. James Egbert
Pres., Rev. Robert C. Brock, 8130 Clough Pike 45244
Treas., Mr. Herbert A. Vogt, 128 W. Nixon 45220

Major Activities: Christian Unity; Communications; Chaplaincy; Religious Education; Trust Property

Metropolitan Area Religious Coalition of Cincinnati (MARCC)
632 Vine St., Rm. 920, Cincinnati 45202
Tel. (513) 721-4843

Exec. Dir., Rev. C. Joseph Sprague
Assoc. Dir., Mr. Edgar S. Lotspeich, III
Staff Sec., Mrs. Larry E. Dalton
Research Assoc., Rev. Malcolm Grad
Pres., Bernard L. Rosenberg, 105 E. 4th St. 45202
Treas., Rev. Carl K. Moeddel, 29 E. 8th St. 45202

Major Activities: Health Care; Cable TV; Voter Registration; Local Housing; Public Relations; Police/Community Relations

† Clark County Council of Churches
135 N. Limestone St., Springfield 45502
Tel. (513) 325-9872

*Exec. Sec., Rev. Fahy G. Mullaney
*Sec., Mrs. Donald Gibler
Pres., Rev. William E. Richardson, 909 West Grand Ave. 45506
Treas., Mrs. Donald Gibler, 135 N. Limestone St. 45502

Council of Churches of Greater Cleveland
2230 Euclid Ave., Cleveland 44115
Tel. (216) 621-5925

Exec. Dir., Dr. Donald G. Jacobs
Dir. Public Witness, Rev. Donald Stockford
Dir. Metropolitan Affairs, Mr. Hilbert Perry
Pres., Mr. John W. Gergen, 13607 Ellwood Ave. 44135
Treas., Mr. Ernest P. Scott, 3294 Hyde Park Ave. 44118

Major Activities: Public Witness; Metropolitan Affairs; Ecumenical Education

Metropolitan Area Church Board
209 S. High St., Columbus 43215
Tel. (614) 228-4637

Exec. Dir., Rev. John T. Frazer
Dir. of Mission, Rev. Richard Trelease
Dir. of Communications, Rev. Don Pendell
Chairman, Mr. Edward H. Laylin, 50 W. Broad St. 43215
Treas., Mr. Lowell S. Rinehart, 246 N. High St. 43215

Major Activities: Area Councils; Coummunications; Coordination of Mission; Ecumenical Education; Faith & Order; Pastoral Services; Policy Development & Design; Situation & Crisis; Review & Evaluation

Darke County Council of Churches
525 1/2 South Broadway, Rm. 309, Greenville 45331

Tel. (513) 548-3291
Pres., Rev. John McRoberts, 3652 North Dr. 45331
Treas., Mr. Harold James, 342 W. Water St. 45331

Major Activities: Weekday Religious Education; Youth; Social Action; Church Women United; CROP; Migrant Ministry

Metropolitan Churches United
212 Belmonte Park E., P. O. Box #3, Dayton 45402
Tel. (513) 222-8654

Exec. Dir., Rev. Robert E. Kolze
*Radio-TV Coordinator, Mrs. Paul Shank
*Hospital Notification Service, Mrs. Emma Montgomery
*Chaplain, Dr. W. R. Grunewald
Pres., Mr. Nicholas E. Davis, 111 Aberdeen Ave. 45419
Treas., Mr. James Rempe, 817 Britton Dr., Kettering 45429

Major Activities: Communications; Services to the Churches & Community; Social Action & Legislation

Licking County Council of Churches
29 N. 4th St., Newark 43055

Exec. Sec., Rev. George C. Vance

Mahoning Valley Association of Churches
631 Wick Ave., Youngstown 44502
Tel. (216) 744-8946

Exec. Dir., Rev. Norman M. Parr
University Chaplain, Rev. Richard D. Speicher
Hospital Chaplains, Rev. Carl Beighley, Rev. D. West Richards
Social Workers, Mrs. Florence Deeter, Mrs. Ronald Smart
Pres., Mrs. David E. Jones, 2309 Selma Ave.
Treas., Mr. Paul Fayman, 42 Venloe Dr., Poland

Major Activities: United Campus Ministry; Communications; Christian Education; Ecumenism; Social Action

† Council of Churches of Christ of Greater Mansfield
(Send mail to Secretary)
Pres., Dr. William C. Childress, 38 Lexington Ave., Mansfield 44907
Sec., Mrs. Howard Perathaner, 1000 Lexington Ave., Mansfield 44907

Major Activities: Task Forces as Needed

The Council of Churches of Central Stark County
405 2nd St., N. W., Canton 44702
Tel. (216) 455-5143

*Exec. Dir., Rev. William J. Hodder
Pres., Dr. Ralph K. Ramsayer, Cleve-Tusc Bldg. 44702
Treas., Mr. John Mani, 301 E. Tuscarawas 44702

Major Activities: Christian Education; Citywide Activities; United Church Action; Youth; Church School for Retarded Children; Counseling Service

Toledo Area Council of Churches
2138 Madison Ave., Toledo 43624
Tel. (419) 242-7401

Exec. Dir., Rev. Leonard E. Klippen
Program Asst., Mrs. Margaret Hoepfl
Exec. Dir., Toledo Metropolitan Mission, Rev. Claude Kilgore
Exec. Dir. Toledo Campus Ministry, Rev. Roger E. Ridgway
Exec. Dir. Ecumenical Communications of Northwest Ohio, Rev. Gene G. Phlegar
Pres., Dr. Richard N. Lower
Treas., Mr. Jason D. Lindower, 3866, S. Beverly Hills Dr. 43614

Major Activities: Campus Ministry; Communications; Education; Governmental Relations; Interfaith Relations; Toledo Metropolitan Mission; Social Services

Tuscarawas County Council for Church and Community
120 First Drive S. E., New Philadelphia 44663
Tel. (216) 343-6012

Exec. Dir., Rev. John H. Visser
Pres., Rev. Howard Fox, Box 22, Strasburg 44680
Treas., Mr. Max Dapoz, 1048 Kelly St. N.W., New Philadelphia 44663

Major Activities: Poverty and Welfare Services; Mental Health/Family Life Services; Delinquency/Rehabilitation Program; Initation and Promotion of Community Services; Lay Training; Dialogue and Communication

Youngstown: see Mahoning Valley

Voluntary Leadership
Clinton County: Pres., Rev. Randall Griffith, 162 N. Walnut St., Wilmington 45177
Cochocton County: Pres., Dr. Lester F. Cott, 1700 N.E. Main 43812
Delaware County Interchurch Council: Pres., Mrs. Eugene White, 184 W. Heffner St., Delaware 43015
Edgerton: Pres., Mr. Donald Gruver, Edgerton 43517
Elyria: Pres., Mr. Lewis Szanyi, Jr., 603 Lodi St. 44035
Granville: Pres., Rev. A. Gary Angleberger, 123 S. Pearl St. 43023
Green County Association: Pres., Mr. Carston Reynolds, Church of God, Xenia 45385
Hamilton Federation of Churches: Pres., Rev. Lester Dresch, Front St. 45012
Hancock: Pres., Mr. Tell Thompson, 1620 E. Sandusky St., Findlay 45840
Hillsboro: Pres., Rev. Paul Jones, 142 S. High St. 45133
Hollansburg: Pres., Mr. William Moore, R.R. #1, New Paris 45347
Middletown Area: Pres., Rev. Joseph C. Harvey, McGee & McKnight Dr. 45042
Muskingum County: Pres., Mr. Carl Funk, 1251 Marwood Dr., Zanesville 43701
Newton Falls: Pres., Mrs. Charles Smith, R.D. #1, Box 25, 44444
Richland County: Pres., Mr. Marshall Moore, 295 Westgate Dr., Mansfield 44906
Sandusky: Pres., Rev. Larry Miracle, Christian Church, Clyde 43410

Scioto County: Pres., Mr. Forrest J. Newman, 1543 6th St., Portsmouth 45662
Tiffin County: Pres., Rev. H. Joe Grimm, 125 Hall St. 44883
Troy: Pres., Mr. Herman Conine, 138 Littlejohn Rd. 45373

OKLAHOMA

Oklahoma Conference of Churches
2915 Classen Blvd., Oklahoma City 73106
Tel. (405) 521-1439

Exec. Dir., Rev. Earl N. Kragnes
Dir. Indian Cooperative Ministry, Rev. Robert Pinezaddleby
Dir. CROP, John E. Thomas, Sr.
Pres., Rev. H. Ray Baker, Midwest City
Treas., Mr. J. W. Smith, Oklahoma City

Major Activities: Task Committees, such as Mission Concerns (Research, Implementation, Coordination); Religion and Public Education; CROP; Indian Cooperative Ministry

† Council of Churches of Enid
1111 W. Broadway, Enid 73701
Tel. (405) 233-1214

Pres., Rev. Lloyd Lambert, 1111 W. Broadway 73701
Treas., Mr. Paul Fossett, 701 W. Maine 73701

Major Activities: Faith & Order; Christian Education; Life & Work; Community Service

Tulsa Metropolitan Ministry
222 East Fifth St., Tulsa 74103
Tel. (918) 582-3147

Exec. Minister, Rev. Donald O. Newby
Assoc. Exec. Minister, Miss Dorothy G. Berry
Dir. Promotion & Development, Mrs. Mary Bobb
Dir. Youth Services, Rev. J. Richard Galusha
*Dir Youth Ministry, Rev. Clement Graham
Pres., Mr. Ross Cockrell, 222 East Fifth St. 74103
Treas., Mr. Francis Campbell, 222 East Fifth St. 74103

Major Activities: Task Forces, such as Friends of Day Care, Youth Services, Institute on Urban Ministries; Tulsa Ministries Foundation; Church Planning & New Ministries; Tulsa Jr. College Ministry; Tulsa Youth Ministry

OREGON

Oregon Council of Churches
0245 S.W. Bancroft St., Portland 97201
Tel. (503) 221-1054

Exec. Dir., Rev. Richard N. Hughes
Assoc. Dir., _____
Dir. Interfaith Broadcasting Comm., Rev. Eric L. Robinson
Pres., Mr. William H. Boland, Standard Plaza Bldg. 97204
Treas., Rev. Vernon P. Jaeger, 0245 S.W. Bancroft St. 97201

Major Activities: Christian Education (Camps, Conferences, Children's Work, Family Life,

Religion & Public Education); Communications; Pastoral Services; Social Action & Legislation; Migrant Ministry

Greater Portland Council of Churches
0245 S.W. Bancroft St., Portland 97201
Tel. (503) 221-1054

Exec. Dir., Rev. Richard N. Hughes
Assoc. Dir., Rev. Rodney I. Page
CUE Director, Mr. Stephen V. Schneider
Pres., Rev. Bertram F. Griffin
Treas., Mr. James L. Sampson

Major Activities: Church Community Action; Center for Urban Encounter; Metropolitan Ministries; Public Relations; FISH; Communications; Church Women United

Voluntary Leadership
Central Oregon Council: Pres., Rev. Ray Ferguson, 1336 W. Glacier, Redmond 97756
Coos Bay: Pres., Dr. James L. Layport, 1290 W. Thompson Rd. 97420
Corvallis: Pres., Mr. Paul E. Hyde, 221 N. 10th St., Corvallis 97330
Hood River Area: Pres., Rev. Paul A. Chell, Rt. 4, Box 988, 97031
Lincoln: Pres., Mr. Lloyd Drake, 331 N.E. 6th, Newport 97365
McMinnville Association: Pres., Rev. Bernard Turner, 1st & Cowls 97128
Milton: Pres., Mr. Bud Owens, Rt. 2, Box 41 97862
Pendleton: Pres., Mr. Ernest Cristler, Rt. 1, Mt. Hebron 97801
Springfield Fellowship: Pres., Mr. Robert F. Kugler, 2215 Rocklyn, Eugene 97401
West Tuality: Pres., Dr. Levering Reynolds, Pacific University, Forest Grove 97116

PENNSYLVANIA

The Pennsylvania Council of Churches
900 S. Arlington Ave., Harrisburg 17109
Tel. (717) 545-4761

Exec. Dir., Rev. John B. Ketcham
Special Asst. to Exec., Rev. Charles C. Frazier
Exec. Dir. for Social Relations, Rev. Paul D. Gehris
Pres., Rev. Horace S. Sills
Treas. Mr. Omni Kangas, 900 S. Arlington Ave. 17109

Major Activities: Ecumenical Relations; Church & Public Education; Institutional Ministry; Migrant Ministry; Social Relations; Park Ministry

Allentown: see Lehigh County Conference

Ecumenical Conference of Greater Altoona
1108—15th St., Altoona 16601

Pres., Ms Patricia Gildea
Treas., Ms Eileen Becker

Major Activities: Youth Counseling Program; Literature Sharing Project; Interfaith Library; Coffee House; Church Unity Octave; Teacher Development Workshops

Federation of Churches of Armstrong County
P.O. Box 10, Worthington 16262

*Campus Missioner, Mr. Terry Thomas
*Adm. Asst., Mrs. Betty Kutsch
*Ofc. Sec., Mrs. Ann Frederick
Pres., Rev. Charles R. Stadler

Major Activities: Higher Education; Continuing Education; Parks and Recreation; Mass Media; Economic Development; Hospital and Institutions; Youth

Christians United in Beaver County
682 Third Street, Rm. 6, Beaver 15009
Tel. (412) 774-1446

*Exec. Sec., Mr. John F. Johnston
*Ofc. Sec., Mrs. Lysle P. Shaffer
*Chaplains, Rev. Charles H. A. Woods, Rev. William J. Green
Pres., Rev. James N. Frank, 2100 Mercer Rd., New Brighton 15066
Treas., Mr. Charles H. Kennedy, Kennedy Place, New Brighton 15066

Major Activities: Christian Education; Evangelism; Radio; Social Action; Church Women United; Ecumenism

Greater Bethlehem Area Council of Churches
520 E. Broad St., Bethlehem 18018
Tel. (215) 867-8671

Exec. Dir., Dr. Edwin H. Frey
Pres., Mrs. Voris Latshaw, 275 Buckingham Dr. 18017
Treas., Mr. Glenn Koplin, 2941 Avon Rd. 18017

Major Activities: Church Women United; Ministerial Association; Christian Education; Christian Life & Work; Spiritual Ministry

† Easton Area Council of Churches
330 Ferry St., Easton 18042
Tel. (215) 258-4955

Sec., Mrs. Anthony Fretzo
Pres., Mr. Paul E. Myers, 342 Nulton Ave. 18042
Treas., Mr. John Hugh Price, 215 W. Lafayette St.

Major Activities: Worship & Evangelism; Pastoral Services; Christian Education; Migrant Ministry; Church Women United; United Church Men; United Church Youth

Christian Associates of Metropolitan Erie
235 W. 6th St., Erie 16507
Tel. (814) 454-2411

Exec. Dir., Rev. Gordon P. Irvine
Program Dir., Mr. Nicholaus Rybak
Pres., Mr. Anthony Onisko, 4314 Link St. 16509
Treas., Mr. Robert Arentson, 403 Ardmore Ave. 16505

Major Activities: Coordinate Urban Ministries; Non-Profit Housing; Training Events; Human Relations

The Erie County Council of Churches
235 West Sixth St., Erie 16507
Tel. (814) 454-2411

Exec. Dir., Rev. Macklyn E. Lindstrom
Institutional Chaplain, Rev. Eugene Wm. Mace
Pres., Rev. Levi J. Ziegler, 1011 W. 38th St. 16508
Treas., Mr. Paul C. Baker, 3326 Eliot Rd. 16508

Major Activities: Hamot Hospital Chaplaincy; Clinical Pastoral Education Program; Ministry to Migrants; Christian Ministry to Exceptional Persons; Radio & TV Ministry

† **Greater Greensburg Council of Churches**
510 Mace St., Greensburg 15601
Tel. (412) 834-1454

Exec. Sec., Mrs. James Porter
Pres., Rev. Braynard Kurkowski, 4th & Maclay Sts. 17110
Treas., Miss M. Elizabeth Balmer, 1502 Verbeke St. 17103

Major Activities: Communications; Community Relations; Religious Unity; Institutional Ministries

Council of Churches of Greater Harrisburg
900 S. Arlington Ave., Harrisburg 17109
Tel. (717) 652-2771

Exec. Minister, Rev. Charles E. Dorsey
*Admin. Asst., Mrs. Mildred Mason
Pres., Mrs. James Evans, 2301 Oakwood Rd. 17104
Treas., Miss M. Elizabeth Balmer, 1502 Verbeke St. 17103

Major Activities: Institutional Ministries; Community Relations; Religious Unity; Communications; Task Force on Peace

Council of the Churches of Christ in Greater Johnstown
309 Lincoln St., Johnstown 15901
Tel. (814) 535-1804

*Exec. Sec., Mrs. Charles E. Kimmel
Pres., Rev. Robert G. Whisler, 105 Sheridan St. 15906
Treas., Mr. J. Heil Custer, 1176 Krissay St. 15904

Major Activities: Christian Communications; Christian Education; Christian Life and Work; Christian Missions

Lancaster County Council of Churches
447 E. King St., Lancaster 17602
Tel. (717) 393-1541

Exec. Sec., Rev. Richard E. Grant
Hospital Chaplain, Rev. Myron E. Ebersole
Dir. Christian Social Ministry, Rev. John A. Blackwell
Dir. Horizon House, Mr. Victor P. Salansky
*Migrant Chaplain, Rev. Bienvenido Valentin
*Coordinator, Shared Holiday, Mrs. Charles Crosson
Pres., Mr. Melvin J. Evans, 713 Barrcrest Ln. 17603
Treas., Mr. Fred W. Slaugh, 410 Ruby St. 17603

Major Activities: Hospital Chaplaincy, Christian Social Ministry; Residential Ministry to Youthful Offenders; Migrant Ministry; Prison Ministry; Housing

Lebanon County Council of Churches
P.O. Box 654, Lebanon 17042
Tel. (717) 272-5555

*Exec. Sec., Rev. Clarence D. Ulrich
Pres., Mr. Guy Forry, 1320 E. Cumberland St. 17402
Treas., Mr. Fred Schoener, 740 Hanover St. 17042

Major Activities: School of Religious Education; Chaplaincy; Boy Scout Chaplaincy Program; Men's Fellowship Breakfast; United Ecumenical Rally; Coordinate Radio, TV & Ministry to "Homes"

Lehigh County Conference of Churches
36 South Sixth St., Allentown 18101
Tel. (215) 433-6421

Exec. Sec., Rev. George S. Wilson
Pres., Mr. Herbert D. Nash, 990 Little Lehigh Dr., Emmaus 18049
Treas., Mr. William Speer, First National Bank, 7th & Hamilton Sts. 18101

Major Activities: Experimental Youth Ministry; Chaplaincy Program; Migrant Ministry; Social Concerns and Action

† **Lehighton-Weissport Area Council of Churches**
645 Mahoning St., Lehighton 18235
Tel. (215) 377-3666

Exec. Sec., Miss Myrtle A. McDaniel
Pres., Rev. Jerome A. Wenner, 225 Iron St. 18235
Treas., Miss Alice R. Heintzelman, 223 N. 3rd St. 18235

Major Activities: Christian Education; Life & Work; Missions; Spiritual Life

United Churches of Lycoming County
143 W. Fourth St., Rm. 217, Williamsport 17701
Tel. (717) 322-1110

*Exec. Sec., Mr. Robert D. Smink
Pres., Mr. Victor J. Michael, 1100 High St. 17701
Treas., Mr. John E. Schultz, 2725 Newberry St. 17701

Major Activities: Radio Ministry; Services to Institutions; Counseling Service; Evangelism; United Christian Youth; Social Action

Northeastern Pennsylvania Congregations in Christian Mission
550 Madison Ave., Scranton 18510
Tel. (717) 347-4730

Ofc. Mgr., Mrs. Paul A. Knorr
Pres., Mrs. Joseph H. Young, 811 Olive St. 18510
Treas., Mr. Harold M. Thorpe, 19 Lakeside Dr., Clarks Summit 18411

Major Activities: Chaplaincy; Communications; Human Affairs; Special Ministry to Housing Projects

Metropolitan Christian Council of Philadelphia
1211 Chestnut St., Philadelphia 19107
Tel. (215) 563-7854

Exec. Dir., Rev. Rufus Cornelsen
Asst. Dir., Rev. Robert A. Gallagher
Dir. Planning & Strategy, Rev. R. Cotton Fife
Assoc. for Information & Planning, Alice Mann
Assoc. for Information & Communications, Barbara Johnson
Pres., Bishop Robert L. Dewitt, 202 W. Rittenhouse Square 19103
Chm., Rev. Frank H. Stroup, 2200 Locust St. 19103

Major Activities: Task Forces as Needed

South Hills Village Ministry in the Mall
201 South Hills Village, Pittsburgh 15241
Tel. (412) 833-6177

Dir., Rev. Lyndon E. Whybrew
*Detached Youth Worker, Mr. Charles Eric Levy
*Admin. Asst., Mrs. Margie Haroff
Exec. Sec., Mrs. Hazen Totton
Pres., Mrs. Walter Wiest, 366 Parkway Dr. 15228
Treas., Mr. Jerome Sherman, 159 Inglewood Dr. 15228

Major Activities: Referral Counseling; Family Center; Youth; Elderly; Information Booth; FOCUS (Focus on Community Understanding and Services)

University and City Ministries
4401 Fifth Ave., Pittsburgh 15213
Tel. (412) 682-2751

Exec., Dr. Samuel Gibson
Urban Action Asst., Mr. Jerry Lockwood

Major Activities: Community of Reconciliation; Youth Ministries; Center for Creative Work with Children; Urban Action; University Ministry and Academic Concerns; Church and Society Institute; Draft Information Center; Youth Learning Center

† Greater Reading Council of Churches
631 Washington St., Reading 19601
Tel. (215) 375-6108

Exec. Sec., Dr. Mervin A. Heller
*Ofc. Sec., Mrs. Herbert B. Browne
Pres., Mr. John W. Davis, 836 Woodward Dr. 19601
Treas., Mr. Raymond P. Dunkelberger, 726 Weiser St. 19601

Major Activities: Leadership Education; Evangelism; Public Relations; Weekday School; Social Action; Church Women United; Institutional Ministry; Migrant Ministry; Ecumenical Relations

Scranton: see Northeastern Pennsylvania

Christian Associates of the Shenango Valley
240 N. Hermitage Rd., Sharon 16146
Tel. (412) 347-5021

*Sec., Mrs. Arthur Langford
*Hospital Chaplain, Rev. Adam E. Simon
Pres., Mrs. Frank Douds, 438 W. State St. 16146
Treas., Mr. David J. Cole, 2638 Hill Rd., R.D. 1, Sharpsville 16150

Major Activities: Chaplaincy; Christian Education for the Mentally Retarded; School of Religion; Campground Services

Christian Associates of Southwest Pennsylvania
401 Wood St., Pittsburgh 15222
Tel. (412) 281-1515

Exec. Dir., Rev. W. Lee Hicks
Spec. Asst., Rev. G. Mason Cochran
Dir. of Planning, Rev. Bruce H. Swenson
Dir. of Communications, Rev. Harry G. Souders
Asst. Dir. of Communications, Mr. Edward W. Eckman
Asst. Radio/TV Prod., Rev. Roy T. Lloyd
Dir. of Spec. Ministries, Rev. G. V. McCausland
Dir. of Project Equality, Mr. Arthur B. Pisula
*Asst. Dir. City Court, Rev. Leroy Walker, Jr.
*Asst.-City Court, Mrs. Lois Hayford
*Asst.-City Court, Mr. Raymond Page
Admin. Asst., Mrs. Sue Parmenter
Pres., Rev. William B. Grove, Centre & South Aiken 15232
Treas., Mr. Harry R. Edelman III, Seven Parkway Center 15220

Major Activities: Communications; Planning; Project Equality; Counseling and Referral; Specialized Ministries

† Uniontown Area Council of Churches
115 Lawn Ave., Uniontown 15401
Tel. (412) 438-8019

Ofc. Sec., Miss Thelma Dannels
Pres., Dr. Eugene F. Hilton, Buttermilk Lane, Hopwood 15445
Treas., Mr. Rolla M. Varndell, 93 Lawn Ave. 15401

Major Activities: Christian Missions; Spiritual Life; Christian Social Concern; Christian Education

Wyoming Valley Council of Churches
35 S. Franklin St., Wilkes-Barre 18701
Tel. (717) 825-8543

Admin., Miss Anita J. Ambrose
Bookstore Mgr., Mrs. H. Owen Roberts
Pres., Rev. Robert D. Yost, 163 N. Pioneer Ave., Shavertown 18708
Treas., Mr. James Evans

Major Activities: Social Concerns; Migrant Program; Radio-TV; Christian Education; Evangelism & Spiritual Life; Ecumenical Interpretations

York County Council of Churches
145 South Duke St., York 17403
Tel. (717) 854-9504

Exec. Sec., Rev. Harold B. Statler
Pres., Rev. Thomas R. Jones, 2401 Wyndhurst Court 17404
Treas., Mr. Laurence B. McCullough, 639 Linden Ave. 17404

Major Activities: Educational Development; Community Witness; Ecumenical Concerns; Special Ministries; Cluster Projects

Voluntary Leadership

Annville: Pres., Mr. Wethington, 316 Ridge Rd. 17003
Bedford: Pres., Hon. Percy G. Foor, 139 W. Main St., Everett 15537
Bellefonte: Pres., Mr. Nelson W. Billett, 116 E. Lamb St. 16823
Bradford: Pres., Mr. A. E. Wilmarth, 440 Congress St. 16701
Carbondale: Pres., Mr. David A. Howarth, 10 High St. 18407
Carlisle: Pres., Rev. Newton L. Poling, 221 Walnut St. 17013
Chester: Pres., Rev. Alpha Finch, 203 Media Parkway 19013
Corry Area: Pres., Mr. Edwin Cole, 159 W. Columbus Ave. 16407
Huntingdon: Pres., Mr. John Day, 1012 Washington St. 16652
Indiana: Pres., Rev. Delbert Jolley, Church & 7th St. 15701
Lansdowne: Pres., Mrs. William E. Green, 121 Elder Ave., Yeadon 19051
Latrobe Area: Pres., Rev. J. Gordon Bechtel, 428 Main St. 15650
Lewisburg: Pres., Mr. Herbert Bendt, 319 Market St. 17837
Lock Haven: Pres., Miss Mary M. Bryerton, 403 W. Main St. 17745
Lower Bucks County: Pres., Rev. John Itzen, Sexton Land & Levittown Pkwy. 19105
Montour: Pres., Mr. Harold H. Fullmer, 61 Beaver Pl., Danville 17821
Newton Area: Pres., Mr. Robert H. Davis, 251 N. State St. 18940
North Lehigh: Pres., Rev. George W. Bickel, 232 Franklin St., Weissport 18235
Schuylkill Haven & Vicinity: Pres., Rev. William C. Butts, 444 Hess St. 17972
Shippensburg: Pres., Mr. Elmer J. Gruver, R.D. #3 17257
Warwick Association: Pres., Mr. Elmer C. Allwine, 442 S. Spruce St., Lititz 17543
Washington: Pres., Rev. A. C. Young, 675 McKinley Ave. 15301
Waynesboro: Pres., Mr. H. L. Berkey, 125 Garfield St. 17268
Wilkinsburg: Pres., Mr. L. H. Defibough, 1601 Penn Ave., Apt. 205, Pittsburgh 15221
Windber Area: Pres., Mr. Donald Berkey, 631 Horner St. 15963

PUERTO RICO

† **Evangelical Council of Puerto Rico**
P.O. Box 1788, Hato Rey 00919

Exec. Sec., Rev. Antonio Rivera Rodriguez
Medical Center Chaplain, Rev. Salvador Bernart
Institutional Chaplain, Rev. Juan Sanchez Padilla
University Work Dir., ―――――
Pres., Rev. Luis A. Orengo, United Church of Christ, Box 8771, Santurce 09910
Treas., Narciso Olmedo, Ponce de Leon Ave. 1906, Santurce 09909

Major Activities: Chaplaincy; Evangelism; Higher Education; Christian Social Action; Religious Education; Parochial Schools; Radio & TV

RHODE ISLAND

Rhode Island State Council of Churches
2 Stimson Ave., Providence 02906
Tel. (401) 861-1700

Gen. Sec., Rev. James M. Webb
Dir. Urban Division, Rev. Thomas W. Olcott
*Assoc. Dir. Communications, Rev. Richard D. Fischer
*Assoc. Dir. Communications, Rev. Ernest E. Ryden
Admin. Asst., Mrs. Ruth Barker
Pres., Mr. Walter Coupe, Chepachet Hill Rd., Chepachet 02814
Treas., Mr. Seth Gifford, 810 Hospital Trust Bldg. 02903

Major Activities: Urban Ministries; Radio-TV; Chaplaincy; Social Action; Legislative Liaison; Faith & Order; Research & Strategy; Church World Service; Migrant Ministry

Voluntary Leadership

Newport: Pres., Mr. E. Paul Grimm, Bel Air —Old Beach Rd. 02840
South Kingston: Pres., Dr. Frank Woods, 1314 Kingstown Rd. 02881

SOUTH CAROLINA

Christian Action Council
907 Richland St., Rm. 301, Columbia 29201
Tel. (803) 254-1679

Exec. Dir., Rev. Howard G. McClain
Pres., Dr. Joseph T. Stukes, 907 Richland St. 29201

Major Activities: Citizenship; Community Services; Continuing Education; Interchurch and Public Relations

SOUTH DAKOTA

The Association of Christian Churches
P.O. Box 1304, Huron 57350

Exec. Dir., Rev. Wesley C. Hunter
Pres., Rev. John I. Murray
Treas., Mr. Melvin Schoen

Major Activities: Church and Community Relations; Ecumenical Committee on Veterans' Affairs; Churchmen's Seminar in Social Concerns; Indian Ministry; Continuing Education; Institutional Chaplaincies; Legislative Information Services

Voluntary Leadership

Rapid City: Pres., Rev. Dan Leighton, 1012 Soo San Dr. 57701

TENNESSEE

†**Tennessee Council of Churches**
1108—17th Ave. S., Nashville 37212
Tel. (615) 256-1424

Exec. Sec., Rev. Tom Baker, Jr.
Pres., Brigadier Luther M. Smith, P.O. Box 236, 37202
Treas., Mr. Jules U. Durham, 3700 Central Ave. 37205

Major Activities: Christian Education; Christian Life & Work; Christian Missions; Public Relations

Voluntary Leadership
Bristol: Pres., Mr. L. R. Driver, 1706 Windsor Ave. 37620
Greene County: Pres., Mr. Herbert Silvers, Box 679, Greenville 37743
Rogersville: Pres., Mr. William Blevins, 305 Watterson St. 37857

TEXAS

Texas Conference of Churches

2704 Rio Grande #9, Austin 78705
Tel. (512) 478-7491

Exec. Dir., Mr. Roy J. Cates
Assoc. Dir., Rev. Fr. George H. Sallaway
Assoc. Dir., Rev. Robert Navarro
Pres., Rev. William J. Fogleman, 5203 Montrose, Houston 77006
Treas., Mr. Albert J. Maloney, City National Bank, 832 Congress Ave. 78701

Major Activities: Faith and Order; Christian Education; Migrant Ministry; Public Relations; Self-Development; Christian-Jewish Relations

Austin Area Conference of Churches
1110 Guadalupe, Austin 78701
Tel. (512) 472-7627

*Jail Chaplain, Rev. Arthur R. Anderson
*Ofc. Sec., Mrs. C. D. Burnette
Pres., Dr. Marvin Griffin, 1010 E. 10th 78702
Treas., Mr. Marvin A. McCoy, 4010 Ave. G 78751

Major Activities: Church & Society; Cooperative Ministries; Education; Jail Chaplaincy; Scouting; Hospital Ministry

Greater Dallas Council of Churches
901 Ross Ave., Dallas 75202
Tel. (214) 748-5235

Exec. Dir., Rev. Louis A. Saunders
Assoc. Exec. Dir., Rev. E. Ray Goodwin
Chaplain Supervisor (Hospitals), Rev. Herman Cook
Chaplain, County Jail, Rev. Asa E. Hunt III
Dir. Block Partnership, Don Johnson
Dir. Pastoral Counseling and Education Center, Dr. C. Kenneth Pepper
Dir. North Texas Christian Communications Commission, Mr. Frank L. Gregg
Pres., Robert L. Oetting
Treas., Robert B. Cullum

Major Activities: Communications and Community Relations; Pastoral Services (Counseling Center, Hospital Chaplaincy, Jail Chaplaincy, Scouting Chaplaincy); Urban Concerns (Block Partnership, Hunger, Ethnic Relations, Joint Action for Mission); Ecumenical Relations

El Paso County Conference of Churches
415 E. Yandell, Ste. 307, El Paso 79902
Tel. (915) 532-9490

*Exec. Sec., Mrs. Frank Smith
Pres., Rev. John W. Ellison, 810 N. Campbell 79902
Treas., Mr. Phil Holmberg, 808 Cincinnati 79902

Ft. Worth Area Council of Churches
703 Medical Arts Bldg., Ft. Worth 76102
Tel. (817) 335-3437

Admin. Asst., Mrs. Arch Sink
Exec. Dir. Block Partnership, Mr. Joe Gonzales
Dir. Community Parish Program, Mr. Barney R. McLaughlin
Chaplain, Rev. James Ellison
Dir. N. Texas Christian Communications, Mr. Frank Gregg
Pres., Dr. Jack Hardwick, 2501 Ridgmar Plaza 76116
Treas., Mr. Robert McClean, P.O. Box 748 76101

Major Activities: Block Partnership; Peace Task Force; FISH; Summer Recreation Program; United Christian Leadership School

Houston Metropolitan Ministries
900 Lovett Blvd., Houston 77006
Tel. (713) 522-3955

Exec. Dir., Rev. Clifton Kirkpatrick
Dir. Senior Volunteer Activities, Mrs. June S. Holly
Dir. RSVP, Mrs. Versia Shelton
Dir. FGP, Miss Dana Merrell
Manager, Oxford Place, Mrs. Mary Brown
Area Dir., Mr. Winston John
Dir. MASPI, Mr. Marcos Urbina
Chaplain, Referrals, Fr. James H. Murray, Jr.
Area Dir., Mr. David Ortiz
Financial Development Officer, Mr. Robert L. Rosenstiel
Pres., Rev. Frank Schulman, 1900 Bergin Dr. 77027
Treas., Mrs. Thyrza Beall, 140 Radney 77024

Major Activities: Social Services; Programs for the Elderly; Educational Programs; Jail Chaplaincy; Non-Profit Housing; Coalitions for Social Change; Network Action Training Center; Interfaith Planning Agency

† Council of Churches of Metropolitan San Antonio
301 Broadway, San Antonio 78205
Tel. (512) 226-7264

Exec. Dir., Rev. D. Don Baugh
Urban Minister & Chaplain, Rev. Christian H. Kehl
Pres., Mr. Nelson T. Meckel, 4018 Pawnridge Dr. 78229
Treas. Mr. E. Douglas Boyden, P.O. Box 12372 78212

Major Activities: Communications; Evangelism; Worship; Social Relations; Education; World Fellowship; Interfaith

Voluntary Leadership
Amarillo Area: Pres., Mr. Franklin A. Jeffers, 3900 Doris 79109
Midland: Pres., Mr. Lyle L. Livingston, 3517 Seaboard 79701

UTAH

Utah Council of Churches
232 University St., Salt Lake City 84102
Tel. (801) 582-4357
*Admin. Sec., Mrs. John M. Wade
*Admin. of Leadership Training Commission,
Mrs. William Youngblood
Pres., Rev. Walter Aman, #17, 1112 E. 27th
South 84106
Treas., Mrs. Helen Tyler, 565 Catherine St.
84116
Major Activities: Ministry at Intermountain
Indian School; Prison Chaplaincy; Leadership
Training; Social Action; Communication;
Higher Education

Voluntary Leadership
Salt Lake Metro Division: Pres., Rev. Frank R.
Brougher, 1915 S. Orchard Dr., Bountiful
84010

VERMONT

**Vermont Ecumenical Council and Bible
Society**
P.O. Box 593, 300 Flynn Ave., Burlington 05401
Tel. (802) 864-7723
Exec. Minister, Rev. Howard O. Stearns
Pres., Rev. Russell Ellis, Rock Point School
05403
Treas., Mr. Leslie MacKenzie, 37 Catherine St.
05403
Major Activities; Community Ministries; Public
Witness; Election Law Reform Task Force;
Ministry to Institutions; Religious Education;
Research and Planning

Voluntary Leadership
Burlington: Pres., Mr. David Cooper, R.D. #3,
Waybury Rd., Winooski 05404
Orleans County: Pres., Rev. J. M. Finley
Brown, Glover St., Barton 05822
Windham County: Pres., Rev. Carroll Newquist,
20 Elliott St., Brattleboro 05301

VIRGINIA

Virginia Council of Churches, Inc.
2321, Westwood Ave., Richmond 23230
Tel. (703) 353-5587
Exec. Sec., Rev. Myron S. Miller
Assoc. Exec. Sec., Rev. Carl L. Howard
*Dir. Weekday Religious Education, Miss
Evelyn Langford
Pres., Rev. Charles L. Evans, 1500 N. Lom-
bardy St. 23220
Treas., Mr. Russell Rowlett, 2321 Westwood
Ave. 23230
Major Activities: Educational Development;
Church and Society; Direct Ministries; Ecu-
menical Affairs; Communications

Voluntary Leadership
For information concerning local councils of
churches and councils of weekday and religious
education, write to the Executive Secretary of
the Virginia Council of Churches, listed above.

WASHINGTON

Washington State Council of Churches
2005 Fifth Ave., Rm. 210, Seattle 98121
Tel. (206) 624-5286
Acting Gen. Sec., Rev. Loren A. Arnett
*Consultant, Rev. Everett J. Jensen
Dir. of Mobilization of Resources, Mrs. Betty
Jacobson
Pres., Rev. John Lockerby, 1551 10th Ave. E.,
Seattle 98102
Treas., The Hon. Tracy Owen, 5717 N.E. 182nd,
Seattle 98155
Major Activities: Legislation; Poverty Relief
Coordination; Congregational Renewal; De-
nominational Staff Coordination

Church Council of Greater Seattle
314 Fairview Ave. N., Seattle 98109
Tel. (206) 624-2595
Pres.-Dir., Rev. William B. Cate
Exec. Admin., Mrs. Earl Kinnear
*Coordinating Chaplain, Rev. George McCleave
Pres., Rev. William B. Cate, 314 Fairview Ave.
N. 98109
Treas., Mr. Fred O. Paulsell, Jr., 3036 Cascadia
S. 98144
Major Activities: Racial Justice; Religious
Peace Action Coalition; Black Church Ecu-
menical Ministries; Neighbor in Need Food
Banks; Citizen Feed Back; Pastoral Ministry

Spokane Christian Coalition
310 Peyton Building, Spokane 99201
Tel. (509) MA4-5156
Acting Administrator, Mrs. Nadeene E. Coun-
tryman
Pres., Mr. Lester A. Smith, 510 Mohawk Bldg.
99201
Treas., Mr. Frank Storey, 214 E. 13th 99202
Major Activities: Task Force on Social Minis-
tries

**Associated Ministries of Tacoma-Pierce
County**
2520 Sixth Ave., Tacoma 98406
Tel. (206) 383-3056
Metropolitan Minister, Rev. Bruce E. Foreman
Pres., Rev. Rodney Case, 315 S. "K" 98405
Treas., Mrs. William Detering, 523—129th St.
98445
Major Activities: Hospital Chaplaincy Program;
Tacoma Seamen's Center; Food First Pro-
gram; FISH; Key 73; Peace Action Network;
Regional Ecumenical Staff Development

Voluntary Leadership
Everett Snohomish County: Pres., Rev. Ivan C.
Cleveland, 2624 Rockefeller, Everett 98201
Grays Harbor: Pres., Rev. J. B. Brandt, Box
901, Aberdeen 98520
Lewis County: Pres., Mrs. Harriet Flagg, 2353
19th St., Chehalis 98532
Tri-City Area: Pres., Mr. Harold Harty, 811
Birch, Richland 99352

Vancouver: Pres., Rev. Milton S. Hunt, Box 5
98660
Wenatchee: Pres., Mr. Jay Eller, Box 338
98801
Yakima: Pres., Dr. William Ritchey, Wesley
United Methodist Church, 14 N. 48th Ave.
98902

WEST VIRGINIA

West Virginia Council of Churches
612 Virginia St. E., Charleston 25301
Tel. (304) 344-3141

Exec. Sec., Rev. John F. Price
*Assoc. Exec. Sec., Rev. Stewart B. Lawrence
*Chaplain, Pipestem State Park, Rev. William
Eason
Pres., Rev. Samuel Marshall, 1341 Juliana St.,
Parkersburg 26101
Treas., Mr. Shelby Sturm, Box 390, St. Albans
25177

Major Activities: Christian Education; Radio-
TV; Leisure Ministry; Migrant Ministry;
Human Rights; Welfare Reform; Ecumenical
Events

Greater Fairmont Council of Churches
216 Monroe St., P.O. Box 108, Fairmont 26554
Tel. (304) 363-8408 or 366-4988

*Exec. Sec., Mrs. Evelyn L. Maring
Pres., Rev. Ezra Dunnavant, 1118 Sunset Dr.
26554
Treas., Mr. David Brown, 433-½ Walnut Ave.,
Apt. 3 26544

Major Activities: Education; Mass Media; Social Concerns; Special Services; Youth;
Church Women United

The Greater Wheeling Council of Church-
es
110 Methodist Bldg., Wheeling 26003
Tel. (304) 232-5315

Exec. Sec., Mrs. Emily Cook
*Hospital Notification Sec., Miss Helen Mohle
Pres., Rev. Andrew Slade, 3806 Jacob St. 26003
Treas., Mr. Ralph Porter, 110 Methodist Bldg.
26003

Major Activities: Christian Education; Evangelism; Vespers; Radio; Television; Institutional Ministry

Voluntary Leadership
Barbour County: Pres., Mr. Delmar Nestor,
Walnut St., Philippi 26416
Braxton County: Pres., Mr. C. W. Moats,
Heaters 26627
Doddridge County: Pres., Mrs. Gladys Bland,
Blandville 26328
Gilmer County: Pres., Mr. Ralph Wagner
Glenville 26351
Harrison County: Pres., Mr. Maurice Creak,
RFD 1, Box 39, Bridgeport 26330
Jackson County: Pres., Mr. Carl Dolan, Kenna
25248
Lewis County: Pres., Mr. Charles R. Hall,
Horner 26272
Marshall County: Pres., Mrs. Thomas G. Wil-
son, 32 9th St., McMechen 26040

Mason County: Pres., Rev. Landis Absten, RFD
#3, Leon 25123
Monongal County: Pres., Dr. Earl Core, 460
Brockway Ave., Morgantown 26505
Preston County: Pres., Mrs. June F. Thomas,
102 Aurora St., Terra Alta 26764
Roane County: Pres., Mr. Gene Ashley, Amma
25005
Randolph County: Pres., Mr. Homer F. Riggle-
man, Beverly 26253
Upshur County: Pres., Mr. Guy Foster, Rt. 2,
Box 427, Buckhannon 26201
Wirt County: Pres., Mr. W. G. Monroe,
RFD #1, Palestine 26160

WISCONSIN

Wisconsin Council of Churches
818 W. Badger Rd., Ste. 201, Madison 53713

Exec. Dir., Rev. Willis J. Merriman
Asst. to the Exec., Kenneth Scholen
Adm. Sec., Mrs. Phyllis Brinkham
Dir. Ofc. of Pastoral Services, Rev. G. Lloyd
Rediger, 615 N. Sherman Ave., Madison
53704. Tel. (608) 249-7151
*Dir. Pastoral Care, Rev. John R. Thomas
(address of Pastoral Services)
Dir. Wisconsin-Milwaukee Religious Broadcast-
ing Ministry, Rev. Robert P. Seater, 1933
W. Wisconsin Ave., Milwaukee 53233. Tel.
(414) 342-4664
Pres., Rev. Frank K. Efird
Treas., Mr. Arnold G. Gehner

Major Activities: Christian Unity; Church and
Society; Education; Camps and Conferences;
Draft Counseling; Religion and Leisure;
Indian Ministry; Migrant Ministry; Pastoral
Services; Pastoral Care; Broadcasting Minis-
try

Christian Youth Council
1715—52nd St., Kenosha 53140
Tel. (414) 652-9543

Exec. Dir., Mr. Carroll K. Rikli
Youth Coordinator, Mr. Steve Mills
Physical Supv., Mr. Jeff McDorman
*Christian Education, Mrs. Paul Mitchell
Arts & Crafts, Mrs. Carroll Rikli
*Youth Supv., Mr. William Thompkins
Pres., Mr. James Seymour

Major Activities: Christian Education; Leisure
Time Ministry; Radio-Communication Task
Force; Institutional Ministries; Ecumenical
Committee

Madison Area Community of Churches,
Inc.
142 W. Johnson St., Madison 53703
Tel. (608) 255-0528

Exec. Sec., Mrs. Sally Lavik
Pres., Rev. Paul Z. Hoornsta, 116 W. Washington Ave. 53703
Treas., Mr. Bernard Stumbras, 13 S. Black-
hawk Ave. 53705

Major Activities: Social Action; Education;
Communications; Worship & Celebration;
Ministry in Institutions

Greater Milwaukee Conference on Religion & Urban Affairs
704 W. Wisconsin Ave., Rm. 407-E, Milwaukee 53233
Tel. (414) 276-9050

Exec. Dir., Rev. John D. Fischer
Admin. Asst., Mrs. Barbara Robinson
*Education Task Force, Mr. John Gilligan
Aging Task Force, Sister Margaret Shekleton
*Consultant in Communications, Rev. Robert Seater
Dir. Alternative Service Program, Mr. Joseph Schuman
Housing Task Force, Mr. John Severson
Chairman, Rev. Roy F. Alberswerth
Treas., Rev. Carl R. Simon

Major Activities: Task Forces on Housing, Education, Aging, Environment, Communication & Training

Racine Office of Urban Concern, Inc.
1235 Villa St., Racine 53403

Exec. Dir., Rev. Jack M. Murtaugh
Assoc. Dir., Mrs. Jean Mandli
Research & Development Dir., Rev. William Williams
Dir for Project Acceptance, Mr. John Jude
Staff Aid for Project Acceptance, Mr. William Wilson & Mr. Joe Castro, Jr.

Major Activities: Research; Community Development; Special Projects (Project Acceptance, Emergency Needs, Addiction); Institutional; Communication.

Racine Urban Ministry
815 Silver St., Racine 53404
Tel. (414) 637-1341

Exec. Dir., Rev. Eugene L. Boutilier
Pres., Mr. A. Clifford Holmes, 204 White Sand Ln. 53402
Treas., Mr. C. Oliver Strom, 2800 Bate St. 53403

Major Activities: Day Care Centers; Community Development; Farm Labor & Spanish-speaking Organizing; Welfare Reform; Mission Education; Women's Movement Support

Voluntary Leadership
Appleton: Pres., Mr. Everett Bethe, 819 E. Frances 54911
Brown County: Pres., _____, P.O. Box 651, Green Bay 54305
Grant County: Pres., Rev. Myrtle Baker, Boxcobel 53805
Lancaster: Pres., Mrs. Donald E. Vesperman, Rt. 1, Box 197, 53813
Sheboygan County: Pres., Mr. Gordon Johnson, 1627 Washington Ave. 53081

WYOMING
Coalition of Denominational Executives
Chm., Rt. Rev. David T. Thornberry, P.O. Box 1007, Laramie 82070

7. CANADIAN REGIONAL AND LOCAL ECUMENICAL AGENCIES

Most of the organizations listed below are councils of churches in which churches participate officially, whether at the parish or judicatory level.

There are two provincial bodies and one inter-provincial. The others operate at either the city, metropolitan area, or county level. Parish clusters within urban areas are not included.

Canadian local ecumenical bodies operate without paid staff, with the exception of two which have part-time staff. In most cases the name and address of the president or chairman is listed. As these offices change from year to year, some of this information may be out of date by the time the **Yearbook of American and Canadian Churches** is published. However, a letter to the address listed will be forwarded. Up-to-date information may be secured from the Canadian Council of Churches, 40 St. Clair Ave., E., Toronto 7, Ontario.

ALBERTA

Alberta Inter-Faith Community Action Committee
Pres., Dr. Nelson Mercer, Central United Church, 7th Ave. and 1st St., W., Calgary, Alberta.

Calgary Inter-Faith Community Action Committee
Pres., Pastor J. R. Jacobson, 210-18 Ave., S.W., Calgary, Alberta T25 OC1; Exec. Dir., Rev. P. B. O'Byrne, 210-18th Ave., S.W., Calgary, Alberta T25 OC1.

Calgary Council of Churches
Pres., Rev. Andrew Wood, 117-7th Ave., S.W., Calgary, Alberta.

Edmonton & District Council of Churches
Pres., Rev. Howard McIlveen, 6708-99th Ave., Edmonton, Alberta.

Sherwood Park Inter-Faith Committee
Pres., Fr. B. O'Brien, 256 Fir St., Sherwood Park, Alberta.

ATLANTIC PROVINCES

Atlantic Ecumenical Council
Pres., Rt. Rev. H. L. Nutter, 808 Brunswick St., Frederickton, New Brunswick.

BRITISH COLUMBIA

Vancouver & District Council of Churches
Pres., Mrs. G. M. Ledingham, 4756 W. 7th Ave., Vancouver, British Columbia.

Victoria Council of Churches
Pres., Rev. Msgr. M. O'Connell, 740 View St., Victoria, British Columbia.

MANITOBA

Manitoba Inter-Faith Council
Chmn., Rev. Dr. A. Grant Smith, 95 Houde Dr., St. Norbert, Manitoba.

Winnipeg Area Church Council
Pres., Rev. A. Gaspar, Jr., 364 Lanark St., Winnipeg, Manitoba R3N 1L4.

NOVA SCOTIA

Amherst Lay Inter-Faith Committee
Sec., Mrs. Alex M. Cameron, 9 Haliburton St., Amherst, Nova Scotia.

Halifax-Dartmouth Council of Churches
Pres., Mr. John Godwin, Q.C., 1749 Connaught Ave., Halifax, Nova Scotia.

Industrial Cape Breton Council of Churches
Pres., Rev. Francis J. Abbass, Box 123, Sydney, Nova Scotia.

Queen's County N.S. Association of Churches
Chmn., Rev. Alton Alexander, P.O. Box 3, Milton, Nova Scotia.

Wolfeville Inter-Church Council
Pres., Mrs. Doreen Tillatson, Wolfeville, Nova Scotia.

ONTARIO

Christian Council of the Capital Area (Ottawa)
Pres., Rev. J. W. Beaudeau, Box 615, Kanata, Ontario KOA 2CO.

Glengarry-Prescott Christian Council
Sec., Rev. G. Charette, Hawkesbury, Ontario.

Kitchener-Waterloo Council of Churches
Pres., Rev. T. R. Schaffer, 54 Benton St., Kitchener, Ontario.

London Inter-Church Council
Pres., Rev. David Rees, 889 Adelaide St., Kitchener, Ontario.

Oshawa Church Council
Pres., Rev. William Piercy, 165 Gregorian St., Oshawa, Ontario (Mail to: P.O. Box 243, Oshawa, Ontario).

Stratford & District Council of Churches
Pres., Rev. J. Ferguson, 46 Church St., Stratford, Ontario.

PRINCE EDWARD ISLAND

Summerside Council of Churches
Pres., Rev. Hugh Farquhar, 151 Belmont St., Summerside, Prince Edward Island.

QUÉBEC

Groupe de Travail des Églises de Montréal /Joint Working Group of the Montreal Churches
Pres., Père Stéphane Valiquette, S.J., 1444 rue Drummond, Montreal 107, Quebec.

SASKATCHEWAN

Saskatoon Council of Churches
Pres., Dean R. A. Wood, 816 Spadina Crescent, E., Saskatoon, Saskatchewan; Staff Sec. (part-time), Mrs. A. C. Cox, 816 Spadina Cresent, E., Saskatoon, Saskatchewan.

8. THEOLOGICAL SEMINARIES IN THE UNITED STATES

The following list of theological seminaries also includes certain departments of colleges and universities in which ministerial training is given. This list has been checked with the *Education Directory* published by the U. S. Office of Education, and with other directories. The compilation is fairly complete for Protestant and Jewish institutions and for the larger Roman Catholic seminaries.

The listings follow this order: Institution, affiliation, location, head, telephone number.

Academy of the New Church (Theol. Sch.), Gen. Ch. of the New Jerusalem, 2815 Huntingdon Pike, Bryn Athyn, PA 19009, Erik Sandstrom. Tel. (215) WI 7-4200.

American Baptist Seminary of the West, Amer. Bapt., C. Adrian Heaton. Berkeley Campus, 2606 Dwight Way, Berkeley, CA 94704. Tel. (415) 841-1905. Covina Campus, 1300 E. Covina Hills Rd., Covina, CA 91722. Tel. (213) 332-4034.

American Baptist Theol. Sem. and College of the Bible, Natl. Bapt., U.S.A., Inc., So. Bapt. Conv., 1800 White's Creek Pike, Nashville, TN 37207, Charles Emerson Boddie. Tel. (615) 262-3433.

Anderson College School of Theology, Ch. of God, Anderson, IN 46011, Gene W. Newberry. Tel. (317) 644-0951.

Andover Newton Theol. Sch., Amer. Bapt., U. Ch. of Christ, 210 Herrick Rd., Newton Centre, MA 02159, Roy Pearson. Tel. (617) 332-1100.

Aquinas Institute of Theology, Cath., 2570 Asbury St., Dubuque, IA 52001, Cletus Wessels. Tel. (319) 583-6406.

Asbury Theol. Sem., interdenom., Wilmore, KY 40390, Frank Bateman Stanger. Tel. (606) 858-3581.

Ashland Theol. Sem., Breth. Ch., Ashland, OH 44805, Glenn L. Clayton. Tel. (419) 324-4561.

Atlanta Christian College, CC/CC, 2605 Ben Hill Rd., East Point, GA 30344, James C. Redmon. Tel. (404) 761-8861.

Auburn Theol. Sem. (in assoc. with Union Theol. Sem.), U. Presb. Ch. USA, 3041 Broadway, New York, NY 10027, Robert W. Lynn. Tel. (212) 662-7100.

Austin Presbyterian Theol. Sem., Presb. US, 100 E. 27th St., Austin, TX 78705, Prescott H. Williams, Jr. Tel. (512) 472-6736.

Azusa Pacific College, interdenom., Highway 66 at Citrus Ave., Azusa, CA 91702, Cornelius P. Haggard. Tel. (213) 334-4991.

Bangor Theol. Sem., U. Ch. of Christ, 300 Union St., Bangor, ME 04401, Frederick W. Whittaker. Tel. (207) 942-6781.

Baptist Missionary Association Theol. Sem., Bapt. Missionary Assoc. of Amer., P. O. Box 1797, Jacksonville, TX 75766, Philip R. Bryan, Act'g. Tel. (214) 586-2501.

Barrington College, interdenom., Barrington, RI 02806, Charles E. Hummel. Tel. (401) 246-1200.

Berkeley Divinity Sch. at Yale, Epis., New Haven, CT 06510, J. C. Michael Allen. Tel. (203) 436-3636.

Berkshire Christian College, Adv. Christian Ch., Lenox, MA 01240, Vincent Taber. Tel. (413) 637-0838.

Bethany Bible College, Assem. of God, 800 Bethany Dr., Santa Cruz, CA 95060, Cordas C. Burnett. Tel. (408) 438-3800.

Bethany Lutheran Theol. Sem., Evang. Luth. Synod, 734 Marsh St., Mankato, MN 56001, M. H. Otto. Tel. (507) 388-2977.

Bethany Theol. Sem., Ch. of Breth., Butterfield and Meyers Rd., Oak Brook, IL 60521, Paul M. Robinson. Tel. (312) 629-2400.

Bethel Theol. Sem., Bapt. Gen. Conf., St. Paul, MN 55112, Carl H. Lundquist. Tel. (612) 633-6880.

Beulah Heights Bible College, Pentecostal, 892-906 Berne St., SE, Atlanta, GA 30316, James B. Keiller. Tel. (404) 627-2681.

Biola College, interdenom., 13800 Biola Ave., La Mirada, CA 90638, J. Richard Chase. Tel. (213) 941-3224.

Bishop College, Div. of Religion and Philosophy, Bapt. Missionary and Educational Convention of Texas; Am. Bapt. Conv.; Bapt. Gen. Conv., Texas; 3837 Simpson Stuart Rd., Dallas, TX 75241, John D. Mangram. Tel. (214) 376-4311.

Bloomfield College, U. Presb. Ch. USA, Bloomfield, NJ 07003, Merle F. Allshouse. Tel. (201) 748-9000.

Boston University (Sch. of Theol.), U. Meth., 745 Commonwealth Ave., Boston, MA 02215, J. Robert Nelson. Tel. (617) 353-3051.

Brite Divinity Sch., Texas Christian University, Christian Ch. (Disc.), Fort Worth, TX 76129, William E. Tucker. Tel. (817) 926-2461.

California Lutheran Bible School, Luth., Los Angeles, CA 90006, Maynard A. Force. Tel. (213) 385-1804.

Calvary Bible College, interdenom., 1111 W. 39th St., Kansas City, MO 64111, Roger J. Andrus. Tel. (816) PL 3-4511.

Calvin Theol. Sem., Christian Ref., Grand Rapids, MI 49506, J. H. Kromminga. Tel. (616) 949-4000.

Catholic Theological Union, Cath., 5401 S. Cornell Ave., Chicago, IL 60615, Paul Bechtold. Tel. (312) 272-2700.

Catholic University of America (Theol. College), 401 Michigan Ave., N.E., Washington, DC 20017, Edward J. Frazer. Tel. (202) 529-4113.

Central Baptist Theol. Sem. in Indiana, Natl. Bapt., U.S.A., Natl. Bapt. of Amer., Prog. Natl. Bapt., 1519-41 Martindale Ave., Indianapolis, IN 46202, F. Benjamin Davis. Tel. (317) 636-6622.

Central Baptist Theol. Sem., Amer. Bapt., Kansas City, KS 66102, Paul T. Losh. Tel. (913) 371-5313.

Central Bible College, Assem. of God, 3000

N. Grant Ave., Springfield, MO 65802, Philip Crouch. Tel. (417) 833-2551.

Central Wesleyan College, Wesleyan Ch., College St., Central, SC 29630, Claude R. Rickman. Tel. (803) 639-2453.

Chicago Theol. Sem., U. Ch. of Christ, 5757 University Ave., Chicago, IL 60637, Thomas C. Campbell. Tel. (312) 752-5757.

Christ the King Sem. of St. Bonaventure University, Cath., St. Bonaventure, NY 14778, Juvenal Lalor. Tel. (716) 372-4545.

Christian Theol. Sem., Christian Ch. (Disc.), Indianapolis, IN 46208, Beauford A. Norris. Tel. (317) 924-1331.

Church Divinity Sch. of the Pacific, Epis., 2451 Ridge Rd., Berkeley, CA 94709, Frederick H. Borsch. Tel. (415) 848-3282.

Cincinnati Bible Seminary, CC/CC, 2700 Glenway Ave., Cincinnati, OH 45204, Harvey C. Bream, Jr. Tel. (513) 471-4800.

Colgate Rochester Divinity School/Bexley Hall /Crozer Theological Seminary, interdenom., Rochester, NY 14620, Arthur R. McKay. Tel. (716) 271-1320.

College of the Immaculate Conception (Dominican House of Studies), Cath., 487 Michigan Ave., N.E., Washington, DC 20017, F. M. Jelly. Tel. (202) 529-5300.

Columbia Bible College, interdenom., P.O. Box 3122, Columbia, SC 29203, J. Robertson McQuilkin. Tel. (803) 754-4100.

Columbia Theol. Sem., Presb. US, Decatur, GA 30031, C. Benton Kline. Tel. (404) 378-8821.

Concordia Sem., Luth. Ch.—Mo. Synod, St. Louis (Clayton), MO 63105, John H. Tietjen. Tel. (314) 721-5934.

Concordia Theol. Sem., Luth. Ch.—Mo. Synod, Springfield, IL 62702, Richard J. Schultz. Tel. (217) 544-7401.

Conservative Bapt. Theol. Sem., Cons. Bapt., P. O. Box 10,000, University Park Sta., Denver, CO 80210, Vernon C. Grounds. Tel. (303) 761-2482.

Covenant Theol. Sem., Ref. Presb., 12330 Conway Rd., St. Louis, MO 63141, Robert G. Rayburn. Tel. (314) 434-4044.

Dallas Theol. Sem., undenom., 3909 Swiss Ave., Dallas, TX 75204, John F. Walvoord. Tel. (214) 824-3094.

Detroit Bible College, interdenom., 17370 Meyers Rd., Detroit, MI 48235, Wendell G. Johnston. Tel. (313) 864-8400.

Disciples Divinity House, Univ. of Chicago, Chr. Ch. (Disc.), 1156 E. 57th St., Chicago, IL 60637, W. B. Blakemore. Tel. (312) 643-4411.

Divinity Sch. of the Protestant Episcopal Church in Philadelphia, The, Epis., 4205 Spruce St., Philadelphia, PA 19104, Edward G. Harris. Tel. (215) 386-7475.

Dominican Pontifical Faculty of Theo., Cath., 487 Michigan Ave., N. E., Washington, DC 20017, John M. Donahue. Tel. (202) 529-5300.

Drew University (Theol. School), U. Meth., Madison, NJ 07940, James M. Ault. Tel. (201) 377-3000.

Dubuque, Univ. of (Theol. Sem.), U. Presb. Ch. USA, 2570 Asbury Rd., Dubuque, IA 52001, Walter F. Peterson. Tel. (319) 557-2222.

Duke University (Divinity Sch.), U. Meth., Durham, NC 27706, Thomas A. Langford. Tel. (919) 684-4041.

Earlham School of Religion, Friends (Quakers), Richmond, IN 47374, Wilmer A. Cooper. Tel. (317) 962-2588.

Eastern Baptist Theol. Sem., Amer. Bapt., City Line and Lancaster Ave., Philadelphia, PA 19151, J. Lester Harnish. Tel. (215) TR 7-4200.

Eastern Mennonite College, Menn. Ch., Harrisonburg, VA 22801, Myron S. Augsburger. Tel. (703) 433-2771.

Eden Theol. Sem., U. Ch. of Christ, 475 E. Lockwood Ave., St. Louis, MO 63119, Robert T. Fauth. Tel. (314) 961-3627.

Emmanuel School of Religion, CC/CC, Milligan College, TN 37682, Fred P. Thompson, Jr. Tel. (615) 928-1165.

Emory University (The Candler Sch. of Theol.), U. Meth., Atlanta, GA 30322, James T. Laney. Tel. (404) 377-2411.

Episcopal Theol. Sch., Epis., Cambridge, MA 02138, Harvey H. Guthrie, Jr. Tel. (617) 868-3450.

Episcopal Theol. Sem. of the Southwest, Epis., P. O. Box 2247, Austin, TX 78767, Lawrence L. Brown. Tel. (512) 472-4133.

Erskine Theol. Sem., Assoc. Ref. Presb., P. O. Box 207, Due West, SC 29639, L. M. Allison. Tel. (803) 379-8885.

Evangelical Congregational Sch. of Theol., Evangel. Congreg. Ch., 121 S. College St., Myerstown, PA 17067, Harold H. Scanlin. Tel. (717) 866-5775.

Evangelical Sem. of Puerto Rico, interdenom., Box C., Rio Piedras, PR 00928, George V. Pixley. Tel. (809) 766-6078.

Evangelical Theol. Sem., Inc., Evang. Bapt., 2302-2400 E. Ash St., Goldsboro, NC 27530, William Howard Carter. Tel. (919) 735-0831.

Evangelical Theol. Sem., U. Meth. 329, E. School Ave., Naperville, IL 60540, Wayne K. Clymer. Tel. (312) 355-8500.

Fort Wayne Bible College, Missionary Ch., 1025 W. Rudisill Blvd., Fort Wayne, IN 46807, Timothy M. Warner. Tel. (219) 456-2111.

Franciscan Sch. of Theol. Cath., 1712 Euclid Ave., Berkeley, CA 94709, Kenan B. Osborne. Tel. (415) 848-5232.

Fuller Theol. Sem., undenom., 135 N. Oakland Ave., Pasadena, CA 91101, David A. Hubbard. Tel. (213) 449-1745.

Garrett Theol. Sem., U. Meth., 2121 Sheridan Rd., Evanston, IL 60201, Merlyn W. Northfelt. Tel. (312) 869-2511.

General Theol. Sem., Epis., 175 Ninth Ave., New York, NY 10011, Stephen F. Bayne, Jr. Tel. (212) 243-5150.

George Mercer, Jr., Memorial Sch. of Theol., Epis., Garden City, NY 11530, Robert F. Capon. Tel. (516) 248-4807.

Golden Gate Bapt. Theol. Sem., S. Bapt., Seminary Dr., Mill Valley, CA 94941, Harold K. Graves. Tel. (415) 388-8080.

Gordon-Conwell Theological Seminary, interdenom., South Hamilton, MA 01982, Harold John Ockenga. Tel. (617) 468-7111.

Goshen Biblical Sem., Menn., 3003 Benham Ave., Elkhart, IN 46514, John Howard Yoder. Tel. (219) 523-1385.

Grace Bible Institute, interdenom., 1515 S. 10th St., Omaha, NE 68108, Robert W. Benton. Tel. (402) 342-3377.

Grace Theol. Sem. and Grace College, Natl. Fellowship of Breth. Churches, Winona Lake, IN 46590, Herman A. Hoyt. Tel. (219) 267-8191.

Graduate Theol. Union, nondenom., 2465 Le Conte Ave., Berkeley, CA 94709, Claude Welch. Tel. (415) 841-9811.

Greenville College, Free Meth., 315 E. College Ave., Greenville, IL 62246, Orley Herron. Tel. (618) 664-1840.

Hamma Sch. of Theol., Wittenberg Univ., Luth. Ch. in Amer., Springfield, OH 45501, Frederick K. Wentz. Tel. (513) 327-6121.

Hartford Seminary Foundation, The, interdenom., Hartford, CT 06105, James N. Gettemy. Tel. (203) 232-4451.

Harvard Divinity School, undenom., 45 Francis Ave., Cambridge, MA 02138, Krister Stendahl. Tel. (617) 495-5761.

Hebrew Union College—Jewish Inst. of Religion, Jewish, 3101 Clifton Ave., Cincinnati, OH 45220; 40 W. 68th St., New York, NY 10023, Tel. (212) 873-0200; 3077 University Avenue, Los Angeles, CA 90007; 13 King David St., Jerusalem, Israel, Alfred Gottschalk.

Hellenic College, (Holy Cross Sch. of Theol.), Greek Orthodox, 50 Goddard Ave., Brookline MA 02146, Bishop Iakovos Garmatis, actg. Tel. (617) 731-3500.

Holy Trinity Orthodox Seminary, Russian Orthodox, Jordanville, NY 13361, Archbishop Averky Tauscheff. Tel. (315) 858-1332.

Howard University (Sch. of Religion), interdenom., 2601 Sixth St., N.W., Washington, DC 20001, Samuel L. Gandy. Tel. (202) 636-7277.

Huntington College, School of Christian Ministries, U. B. in Christ, Huntington, IN 46750, Paul R. Fetters. Tel. (219) 356-6000.

Iliff School of Theol., The, U. Meth., 2201 S. University Blvd., Denver, CO 80210, Smith Jameson Jones, Jr. Tel. (303) 744-1287.

Immaculate Conception Monastery, Cath., 223 E. 14th St., Hastings, NE 68901, Neil Emon. Tel. (402) 463-3188.

Immaculate Conception Sem., Cath., Conception, MO 64433, David J. Clements. Tel. (816) 944-2211.

Immaculate Conception Sem., Cath., Darlington (Ramsey P. O.), NJ 07446, William F. Hogan. Tel. (201) 327-0300.

Interdenominational Theol. Center, 671 Beckwith St., S.W., Atlanta, GA 30314, Oswald P. Bronson. Tel. (404) 522-1772.

Jewish Theol. Sem. of America, Jewish, 3080 Broadway, New York, NY 10027, Gerson D. Cohen. Tel. (212) RI 9-8000.

Johnson Bible College, Christian Ch., Kimberlin Hts. Sta., Knoxville, TN 37920, David L. Eubanks. Tel. (615) 573-4517.

Kentucky Christian College, Churches of Christ, College and Landsdown, Grayson, KY 41143, J. Lowell Lusby. Tel. (606) 474-6613.

Lakeland College, U. Ch. of Christ, P. O. Box 359, Sheboygan, WI 53081, John B. Morland. Tel. (414) 565-2011.

Lancaster Theol. Sem. of the U. Ch. of Christ, Lancaster, PA 17603, James D. Glasse. Tel. (717) 393-0654.

Lexington Theol. Sem. (formerly College of the Bible, The), Chr. Ch. (Disc.), 631 S. Limestone, Lexington, KY 40508, W. A. Welsh. Tel. (606) 252-0361.

Lincoln Christian College, CC/CC, Box 178, Lincoln, IL 62656, Leon H. Appel. Tel. (217) 732-3168.

Loma Linda University, Seventh-day Adv., Loma Linda Campus, Loma Linda, CA 92354, Tel. (714) 796-7311; La Sierra Campus, Riverside, CA 92505, Tel. (714) 785-2000; David J. Bieber.

Louisville Presbyterian Theol. Sem., Presb. US, U. Presb. Ch. USA, 1044 Alta Vista Rd., Louisville, KY 40205, Albert Curry Winn. Tel. (502) 895-3411.

Luther Theol. Sem., Amer. Luth. Ch., 2375 Como Ave. W., St. Paul, MN 55108, Alvin N. Rogness. Tel. (612) 646-4323.

Lutheran Bible Institute of America, Luth., Minneapolis, MN 55422, Bernt C. Opsal. Tel. (612) 545-0461.

Lutheran Brethren Schools (Hillcrest Lutheran Academy), Ch. of the Luth. Breth., Fergus Falls, MN 56537, J. H. Levang. Tel. (218) 736-7055.

Lutheran Sch. of Theol. at Chicago, Luth. Ch. in Amer., 1100 E. 55th St., Chicago, IL 60615, Walter F. Wolbrecht. Tel. (312) 667-3500.

Lutheran Theol. Sem., Luth. Ch. in Amer., Gettysburg, PA 17325, Donald R. Heiges. Tel. (717) 334-6286.

Lutheran Theol. Sem., Amer. Luth., 2199 E. Main St., Columbus, OH 43209, F. W. Meuser. Tel. (614) 236-6407.

Lutheran Theol. Sem. at Philadelphia, Luth. Ch. in Amer., Mt. Airy, Philadelphia, PA 19119, John D. Newpher. Tel. (215) CH 2-3555.

Lutheran Theol. Southern Sem., Luth. Ch. in Amer., Columbia, SC 29203, Hugh George Anderson. Tel. (803) 256-0758.

Malone College, Friends (Quakers), 515 25th St., N.W., Canton, OH 44709, Lon D. Randall. Tel. (216) 454-3011.

Manhattan Christian College, Christian Churches, 14th and Anderson Sts., Manhattan, KS 66502, W. F. Lown. Tel. (913) 539-3571.

Marion College (Div. of Religion and Philosophy), Wesleyan Ch., 40th and So. Washington, Marion, IN 46952, R. Duane Thompson. Tel. (317) 674-6901.

Mary Immaculate Sem. and College, Cath., Box 27, Northampton, PA 18067, Robert P. Maloney. Tel. (215) 262-7866.

Maryknoll Seminary (Cath. For. Miss. Soc. of Amer., Inc.), Cath., Maryknoll, NY 10545, Thomas H. Keefe. Tel. (914) 941-7590.

McCormick Theol. Sem., U. Presb. Ch. USA, 800 W. Belden Ave., Chicago, IL 60614, Marshal L. Scott. Tel. (312) 549-3700.

Meadville/Lombard Theol, Sch., Unit. Univ., 5701 Woodlawn Ave., Chicago, IL 60637, Malcolm R. Sutherland, Jr. Tel. (312) 753-3195.

Memphis Theol. Sem., Cumb. Presb., 168 E. Parkway S., Memphis, TN 38104, W. T. Ingram, Jr. Tel. (901) 458-8232.

Mennonite Biblical Sem., Gen. Conf. Menn., 3003 Benham Ave., Elkhart, IN 46514, Erland Waltner. Tel. (219) 523-1385.

Mennonite Brethren Biblical Sem., Menn. Breth. Ch. in N.A., 4824 E. Butler at Chestnut Ave. Fresno, CA 93727, H. H. Dick. Tel. (209) 251-8628.

Meth. Theol. Sch. in Ohio, U. Meth., Box 630, Delaware, OH 43015, John W. Dickhaut. Tel. (614) 363-1146.

Midwestern Bapt. Theol. Sem., S. Bapt., 5001 N. Oak Trafficway, Kansas City, MO 64118, Millard J. Berquist. Tel. (816) 453-4600.

Minnesota Bible College, Ch. of Christ, 920 Mayowood Rd., S.W., Rochester, MN 55901, Galen E. Skinner. Tel. (507) 288-4563.

Moody Bible Institute, interdenom., 820 N. La Salle St., Chicago, IL 60610, George Sweeting. Tel. (312) 329-4000.

Moravian Theol. Sem., Morav., Bethlehem, PA 18018, William W. Matz. Tel. (215) 865-0741.

Moreau Sem. (Holy Cross Fathers), Cath., Notre Dame, IN 46556, James E. Kelly. Tel. (219) 283-7735.

Morehouse School of Religion, Amer. Bapt. Conv. (affiliated with Interdenom. Theol. Center), 645 Beckwith St., S.W., Atlanta, GA 30314, C. S. Hamilton. Tel. (404) 681-2800.

Morris College, S. C. Bapt. Educational and Missionary Convention, Sumter, SC 29150, H. E. Hardin. Tel. (803) 773-3461.

Mt. Angel Sem., Cath., St. Benedict, OR 97373, Elden Curtiss. Tel. (503) 845-2221.

Mt. St. Alphonsus Sem., Cath., Esopus, NY 12429, James F. Kerins. Tel. (914) 384-6550.

Mt. St. Mary's Sem., Cath., Emmitsburg, MD 21727, Harry J. Flynn. Tel. (301) 447-6122.

Mt. St. Mary's Sem. of the West, Cath., 5440 Moeller Ave., Norwood, OH 45212, J. Raymond Favret. Tel. (513) 731-2630.

Multnomah School of the Bible, interdenom., 8435 N.E. Glisan St., Portland, OR 97220, Willard M. Aldrich. Tel. (503) 255-0332.

Nashotah House (Theol. Sem.), Epis., Nashotah, WI 53058, Donald J. Parsons. Tel. (414) 646-3371.

Nazarene Theol. Sem., Nazarene, 1700 E. Meyer Blvd., Kansas City, MO 64131, William M. Greathouse. Tel. (816) 333-6254.

Ner Israel Rabbinical College, Jewish, Mt. Wilson Lane, Baltimore, MD 21208, Jacob I. Ruderman. Tel. (301) 484-7200.

New Brunswick Theol. Sem., Ref. Amer., 17 Seminary Pl., New Brunswick, NJ 08901. Tel. (201) 247-5241.

New Orleans Baptist Theol. Sem., S. Bapt., New Orleans, LA 70126, Grady C. Cothen. Tel. (504) 282-4455.

New York Theol. Sem., interdenom., 235 E. 49th St., NY 10017, George W. Webber. Tel. (212) 355-4434.

North American Baptist Sem., N. Amer. Bapt. Gen. Conf., 1605 S. Euclid Ave., Sioux Falls, SD 57105, David J. Draewell. Tel. (605) 336-6588.

North Park Theol. Sem., Evang. Cov. Ch., 5125 N. Spaulding Ave., Chicago, IL 60625, Lloyd H. Ahlem. Tel. (312) JU 3-2700.

Northeastern Collegiate Bible Institute, interdenom., Essex Fells, NJ 07021, Charles W. Anderson. Tel. (201) 226-1074.

Northern Bapt. Theol. Sem., Amer. Bapt., 100 W. Butterfield Rd., Oak Brook, IL 60521, Bryan F. Archibald. Tel. (312) 629-4100.

Northwest College, Assem. of God, 11102 N.E. 53rd St., Kirkland, WA 90833, D. V. Hurst. Tel. (206) VA 2-8266.

Northwest Nazarene College, Ch. of Nazarene, Nampa, ID 83651, John E. Riley. Tel. (208) 467-8011.

Northwestern College, Ind. Bapt., Roseville, MN 55113, William B. Berntsen. Tel. (612) 646-4840.

Northwestern Lutheran Theol. Sem., Luth. Ch. in Amer., St. Paul, MN 55108, C. H. Zeidler. Tel. (612) 645-6434.

Notre Dame Sem., Cath., 2901 S. Carrollton Ave., New Orleans, LA 70118, Alexander O. Sigur. Tel. (504) 866-7426.

Oakland City College, Gen. Bapt., Oakland City, IN 47660, Bernard A. Loposer. Tel. (812) 749-4781.

Oblate College of the Southwest (Theol. Sem.), Cath., 285 Oblate Dr., San Antonio, TX 78216, Patrick Guidon. Tel. (512) 341-1366.

Olivet Nazarene College (Div. of Religion and Philosophy), Nazarene, Kankakee, IL 60901, J. Ottis Sayes. Tel. (815) 939-5264.

Ozark Bible College, CC/CC, 1111 North Main St., Joplin, MO 64801, Don Earl Boatman.

Pacific Christian College, CC/CC, 4835 East Anaheim St., Long Beach, CA 90804, Medford .H. Jones. Tel. (213) 434-9991.

Pacific Lutheran Theol. Sem., Luth. Ch. in Amer., 2770 Marin Ave., Berkeley, CA 94708, Charles M. Cooper. Tel. (415) 524-5264.

Pacific Sch. of Religion, interdenom., Berkeley, CA 94709, Davie Napier. Tel. (415) 848-0528.

Pasadena College (Div. of Graduate Studies), Nazarene, Pasadena, CA 91104, L. Paul Gresham. Tel. (213) 798-0541.

Perkins Sch. of Theol. (Southern Methodist Univ.), U. Meth., Dallas, TX 75222, Joseph D. Quillian, Jr. Tel. (214) 692-2138.

Philadelphia College of Bible, interdenom., 1800 Arch St., Philadelphia, PA 19103, Douglas B. MacCorkle. Tel. (215) 564-4820.

Philadelphia Divinity School, The, Epis., 4205 Spruce St., Philadelphia, PA 19104, Edward G. Harris. Tel. (215) 386-7475.

Phillips University, The Graduate Seminary, Chr. Churches (Disc.), Enid, OK 73701, J. Daniel Joyce. Tel. (405) 237-4433.

Pittsburgh Theol. Sem., U. Presb. Ch USA, Pittsburgh, PA 15206, William H. Kadel. Tel. (412) 362-5610.

Pontifical College Josephinum, Cath., Worthington, OH 43085, Thomas P. Campbell. Tel. (614) 885-6263.

Princeton Theol. Sem., U. Presb. Ch. USA, Princeton, NJ 08540, James I. McCord. Tel. (609) 921-8300.

Protestant Episcopal Theol. Sem. in Virginia, Epis., Alexandria, VA 22304, G. Cecil Woods, Jr. Tel. (703) 370-6600.

Rabbi Isaac Elchanan Theol. Sem. (affil. of Yeshiva Univ.), Orth. Jewish 2540 Amsterdam Ave., New York, NY 10033, Zevulun Charlop. Tel. (212) 568-8400.

Reconstructionist Rabbinical College, Jewish, 2308 North Broad St., Philadelphia, PA 19132, Ira Eisenstein. Tel. (215) 333-8121.

Reformed Presbyterian Theol. Sem., Ref. Presb. Ch. in N. A., 7418 Penn Ave., Pittsburgh, PA 15208, S. Bruce Willson. Tel. (412) 731-8690.

St. Bernard's Sem., Cath., 2260 Lake Ave., Rochester, NY 14612, J. P. Brennan. Tel. (716) 254-1020.

St. Charles Borromeo Sem., Cath., Overbrook, Philadelphia, PA 19151, Thomas J. Welsh. Tel. (215) TE 9-3760.

St. Charles Sem., Cath., Carthagena Station, Celina, OH 45822, Robert Siebeneck. Tel. (419) 925-4531.

St. Columban's Major Sem., Cath., 1200 Brush Hill Rd., Milton, MA 02186 Donald M. Wodarz, actg. Tel. (617) 333-0688.

St. Francis School of Pastoral Ministry, Cath., 3257 S. Lake Dr., Milwaukee, WI 53207, William N. Schuit. Tel. (414) 744-1730.

St. Francis Sem. (Formerly, Our Lady of Loretto Sem.), Cath., Loretto, PA 15940, Michael Scanlan. Tel. (814) 472-7670.

St. John Vianney Sem., Cath., East Aurora, NY 14052, James F. Chambers. Tel. (716) 652-8900.

St. John's Sem., Cath., Brighton, MA 02135, Robert J. Banks. Tel. (617) 254-2610.

St. John's Sem. College, Cath., Camarillo, CA 93010, Theodore Wiesner. Tel. (805) 482-2755.

St. John's University, School of Divinity, Cath., Collegeville, MN 56321, Alfred H. Deutsch. Tel. (612) 363-7761.

St. Joseph's Abbey, Cath., Spencer, MA 01562, Thomas Keating. Tel. (617) 885-3901.

St. Joseph's Sem., Cath., 201 Seminary Ave., (Dunwoodie), Yonkers, NY 10704, Edward J. Montano. Tel. (914) 968-6200.

St. Leo Abbey, Cath., St. Leo, FL 33574, Fidelis J. Dunlap. Tel. (904) 588-2881.

St. Louis Roman Cath. Theol. Sem. (Kenrick Sem.), Cath., 7800 Kenrick Rd., St. Louis,

MO 63119, Anthony J. Falanga. Tel. (314) 961-4320.

St. Mary-of-the-Lake Sem., Cath., Mundelein, IL 60060, John R. Gorman. Tel. (312) 566-6401.

St. Mary Sem., Cath., 1227 Ansel Rd., Cleveland, OH 44108, Michael J. Murphy. Tel. (216) 721-9595.

St. Mary's Sem., Cath., 9845 Memorial Dr., Houston, TX 77024, Warren F. Dicharry. Tel. (713) 686-4345.

St. Mary's Sem. and Univ., Cath., 5400 Roland Ave., Baltimore, MD 21210, William J. Lee. Tel. (301) 323-3200.

St. Meinrad School of Theology, Cath., St. Meinrad, IN 47577, Daniel Buechlein. Tel. (812) 357-6522.

St. Michael's Pontifical Inst. of Philosophy and Letters (Gonzaga Univ.), Cath., Spokane, WA 99202, Patrick B. O'Leary. Tel. (509) 328-4220.

St. Patrick's Sem. Cath., Middlefield Rd., Menlo Park, CA 94025, Melvin L. Farrell. Tel. (415) 325-5621.

St. Paul Bible College, Chr. and Miss. All., Bible College, MN 55375, Francis Grubbs. Tel. (612) 446-1411.

Saint Paul Sch. of Theol., U. Meth., 5123 Truman Rd., Kansas City, MO 64127, Don W. Holter. Tel. (816) 483-9600.

St. Paul Sem., Cath., 2260 Summit Ave., St. Paul, MN 55105, William Baumgaertner. Tel. (612) 698-0323.

St. Paul's College, Cath., 3015 Fourth St., N.E., Washington, DC 20017, Wilfred Dewan. (202) 832-6262.

St. Thomas Sem., Cath., Denver, CO 80210, Francis H. Agnew. Tel. (303) 722-4687.

St. Tikhon's Theol. Sem., Russian Orth., South Canaan, PA 18459, Archbishop Kiprian. Tel. (717) 937-4411.

St. Vincent Sem., Cath., Latrobe, PA 15650, Demetrius R. Dumm. Tel. (412) 539-9761.

St. Vladimir's Orth. Theol. Sem., Eastern Orth., 575 Scarsdale Rd., Crestwood, Tuckahoe, NY 10707, Most Rev. Metropolitan Ireney. Tel. (914) 961-8313.

SS. Cyril and Methodius Sem., Cath., Orchard Lake, MI 48034, Walter J. Ziemba. Tel. (313) 682-1885.

San Francisco Theol. Sem., U. Presb. Ch. USA, San Anselmo, CA 94960, Arnold B. Come. Tel. (415) 453-2280.

San Jose Bible College, CC/CC, 790 South 12th St., San Jose, CA 95108, Woodrow Phillips. Tel. (408) 293-9058.

Savonarola Theol. Sem., Pol. Natl. Cath., 1031 Cedar Ave., Scranton, PA 18505, Thaddeus F. Zielinski. Tel. (717) 343-0100.

Sch. of Divinity, St. Louis Univ. (formerly St. Mary's Coll.), Cath., 220 N. Spring Ave., St. Louis, MO 63108, William J. Sullivan. Tel. (314) 535-3300.

Sch. of Theol. at Claremont, U. Meth., Christian Ch. (Disc.), Epis., Claremont, CA 91711, Gordon E. Michalson. Tel. (714) 626-3521.

Seabury-Western Theol. Sem., Epis., 2122 Sheridan Rd., Evanston, IL 60201, Armen D. Jorjorian. Tel. (312) 328-9300.

Sem. of Our Lady of Angels, Cath., P. O. Box 1865, Albany, NY 12201, James D. Collins. Tel. (518) 767-2216.

Sem. of St. Thomas the Apostle, Cath., Kenmore, WA 98028, Edward J. Hogan. Tel. (206) 827-5611.

Seventh-day Adventist Theol. Sem., Andrews Univ., Seventh-day Adv., Berrien Springs, MI 49104, W. G. C. Murdoch. Tel. (616) 471-7771.

Seventh Day Bapt. Center for Minsterial Education, Seventh Day Bapt. Gen. Conf., 510 Watchung Ave., Box 868, Plainfield, NJ 07061, Rex E. Zwiebel. Tel. (201) 755-0812.

Shaw University (Shaw Divinity Sch.), Natl. Bapt., Raleigh, NC 27602, James Z. Alexander. Tel. (919) 755-4980.

Simpson College, Christian and Missionary All., 801 Silver Ave., San Francisco, CA 94134, Mark W. Lee. Tel. (415) 334-7400.

Southeastern Baptist Theol. Sem., S. Bapt., Wake Forest, NC 27587, Olin T. Binkley. Tel. (919) 556-3101.

Southeastern Bible College, interdenom., 1401 S. 29th St., Birmingham, AL 35205, vacant. Tel. (205) 322-0514.

Southern Baptist Theol. Sem., S. Bapt., Louisville, KY 40206, Duke K. McCall. Tel. (502) 897-4011.

Southern California College, Assem. of God, 2525 Newport Blvd., Costa Mesa, CA 92626, Emil A. Balliet. Tel. (714) 545-1178.

Southwestern Assemblies of God College, Assem. of God, 1200 Sycamore, Waxahachie, TX 75165, Blake Farmer. Tel. (214) 937-2110.

Southwestern Baptist Theol. Sem., S. Bapt., Fort Worth, TX 76122, Robert E. Naylor. Tel. (918) 923-1794.

Starr King Sch. for the Ministry, Unit., Berkeley, CA 94709, Robert C. Kimball. Tel. (415) 845-6232.

Swedenborg Sch. of Religion (formerly New Church Theol. Sch.), Genl. Conv. The Swedenborgian Ch., Newton, MA 02158, Edwin G. Capon. Tel. (617) 244-0504.

Theol. Sem. of the Ref. Epis. Ch., Ref. Epis., 25 S. 43rd St., Philadelphia, PA 19104, Fred Carl Kuehner. Tel. (215) BA 2-5158.

Toccoa Falls Institute, Christian and Missionary All., Toccoa, GA 30577, Julian A. Bandy. Tel. (404) 886-6831.

Trevecca Nazarene College (Relig. Dept.), Nazarene, 333 Murfreesboro Rd., Nashville, TN 37210, William J. Strickland. Tel. (615) 244-6000.

Trinity College & Trinity Evangel. Divinity Sch. Evangel. Free Ch. of Amer., 2045 Half Day Rd., Deerfield, IL 60015, Harry L. Evans. Tel. (312) 945-6700.

Union Theol. Sem., undenom., Broadway and 120 St., New York, NY 10027, J. Brooke Mosley. Tel. (212) 662-7100.

Union Theol. Sem. in Va., Presb. US, 3401 Brook Rd., Richmond, VA 23227, Fred R.

Stair, Jr. Tel. (703) 355-0671.

United Theol. Sem., U. Meth., 1810 Harvard Blvd., Dayton, OH 45406, John R. Knecht. Tel. (513) 278-5817.

United Theol. Sem. of the Twin Cities, U. Ch. of Christ, 3000 Fifth St., N.W., New Brighton, MN 55112, Dayton D. Hultgren. Tel. (612) 633-4311.

University of Chicago (Divinity Sch.)., interdenom., Swift Hall, Chicago, IL 60637, Joseph M. Kitagawa. Tel. (312) 753-4031.

University of the South (Sch. of Theol.), Epis., Sewanee, TN 37375, Stiles B. Lines. Tel. (615) 598-5235.

Vanderbilt University (Divinity Sch.), interdenom., Nashville, TN 37240, Walter J. Harrelson. Tel. (615) 322-2776.

Virginia Union University (Sch. of Theol.), Amer. Bapt., Richmond, VA 23227, Allix B. James. Tel. (703) 359-9331.

Walla Walla College (Sch. of Theol.) Seventh-day Adv., College Pl., WA 99324, Gordon S. Balharrie. Tel. (509) 527-2195.

Wartburg Theol. Sem., Amer. Luth., 333 Wartburg Pl., Dubuque, IA 52001, William H. Weiblen. Tel. (319) 582-7211.

Wesley Theol. Sem., U. Meth., 4400 Massachusetts Ave., N.W., Washington, DC 20016, John L. Knight. Tel. (202) 363-2171.

Western Baptist Bible College, 5000 Deer Park Dr., S.E. Salem, OR 97302, Fred R. Brock, Jr. Tel. (503) 581-8600.

Western Baptist Bible College, Mo. Missionary Bapt. State Conv., 2119 Tracy Ave., Kansas City, MO 64108, William M. Singleton.

Western Conservative Baptist Sem., Cons. Bapt., 5511 S.E. Hawthorne Blvd., Portland, OR 97215, Earl D. Radmacher. Tel. (503) 236-2175.

Western Theol. Sem., Ref. Ch. in Amer., Holland, MI 49423, Lester J. Kuyper. Tel. (616) 392-8555.

Westminster Theol. Sem., Presb., Chestnut Hill, Philadelphia, PA 19118, Edmund P. Clowney. Tel. (215) 887-5511.

Weston College School of Theol., Cath., 3 Phillips Pl., Cambridge, MA 02138, Robert P. White. Tel. (617) 492-1960.

Whitefriars Hall, Cath., 1600 Webster St., N.E., Washington, DC 20017, Eugene F. Kilkenny. Tel. (202) 526-1221.

Winebrenner Theol. Sem., Churches of God in N.A., 701 E. Melrose Ave., Findlay, OH 45840, W. T. Jackson, actg. Tel. (419) 422-4824.

Wisconsin Lutheran Sem., Luth. (Wis.), 11831 N. Seminary Dr., 65 W, Mequon, WI 53092, Carl Lawrenz. Tel. (414) 242-2330.

Woodstock College, Cath., Room 240, 475 Riverside Dr., New York, NY 10027, Christopher F. Mooney. Tel. (212) 866-8500.

Yale University (Divinity Sch.), undenom., New Haven, CT 06510, Colin W. Williams. Tel. (203) 436-2494.

Yeshiva Torah Vodaath and Mesivta, Jewish, 425 E. 9th St., Brooklyn, NY 11218, G. Schorr. Tel. (212) 633-8000.

9. CANADIAN THEOLOGICAL SEMINARIES AND FACULTIES, AND BIBLE SCHOOLS

The following list has been developed by direct correspondence with the institutions involved and is, therefore, a current and hopefully comprehensive list of the major Canadian theological seminaries and faculties, and Bible schools. The editor of the **Yearbook** would be grateful for knowledge of any significant omissions from this compilation.

Listings are alphabetical by name of institution and generally have the following order: Institution, affiliation, location, head, telephone number.

Acadia Divinity College, Un. Bapt. Conv. of the Atlantic Provinces, Wolfville, Nova Scotia, Abner J. Langley. Tel. (902) 542-2885.

Alberta Bible College, CC/CC, 599 Northmount Dr., N.W., Calgary, Alberta T2K 3J6, Boyd L. Lammiman. Tel. (403) 282-2294.

Alberta Bible Institute, Ch. of God (And.), 4704 55th St., Camrose, Alberta T4V 2B6, Gordon A. Schieck. Tel. (404) 672-2174.

Aldersgate College, Free Meth. Ch., Box 460, Moose Jaw, Saskatchewan S6H 4P1 George E. Leasor. Tel. (306) 692-1816.

Atlantic Baptist College, Un. Bapt. Conv. of the Atlantic Provinces, Moncton, New Brunswick, Stuart E. Murray. Tel. (506) 382-7550.

Atlantic School of Theology, ecumenical (Ang. Ch. of Canada, Cath., Un. Ch. of Canada), Halifax, Nova Scotia, Lloyd J. Robertson. Tel (902) 423-6801.

Berea Bible Institute, Pent. Assem. of Canada, 1711 Henri-Bourassa, E. Montreal 359, Quebec, R. G. Bergeron.

Berean Bible College, interdenom., 460 31st Ave., N. W. Calgary, Alberta T2M 2P4, C. Hutchinson. Tel. (403) 277-5616.

Bethany Bible Institute, Box 160, Hepburn, Saskatchewan SOK 1Z0, C. Braun. Tel. (306) 947-2175.

Bishop's University, interdenom., Lennoxville, Quebec, D. M. Healy. Tel. (819) 569-9551.

Briercrest Bible Institute, interdenom., Caronport, Saskatchewan SOH OSO, Henry Hildebrand. Tel. (306) 756-2321.

Burrard Inlet Bible Institute, undenom., 1155 Barnet Hwy., Port Moody, British Columbia, R. Wesley Affleck. Tel. (604) 936-7535.

Camrose Lutheran College, Ev. Luth. Ch. in Canada, Camrose, Alberta, T4V 0E5, K. Glen Johnson. Tel. (403) 672-3381.

Canadian Mennonite Bible College, 600 Shaftesbury Blvd., Winnipeg, Manitoba R3P OM4, Henry Poettcker. Tel. (204) 888-6781.

Canadian Nazarene College, Ch. of the Nazarene, 1301 Lee Blvd., Winnipeg, Manitoba R3T 2P7, A. E. Airhart. Tel. (204) 269-2120.

Canadian Theological College, Chr. and Miss. All., 4400-4th Ave., Regina, Saskatchewan S4T OH8, David Rambo. Tel. (306) 569-0635.

Central Baptist Seminary, Fell. of Evan. Bapt. Churches in Canada, 95 Jonesville Cres. Toronto 16, Ontario, D. A. Loveday. Tel. (416) 752-1976.

Central Pentecostal College, Pent. Assem. of Canada, 1303 Jackson Ave., Saskatoon, Saskatchewan S7B 2H9, Alvin C. Schindel. Tel. (306) 374-6655.

Centre for Christian Studies, Ang. Ch. of Canada, Un. Ch. of Canada, 77 Charles St., W., Toronto 181, Ontario, Miss Marion G. Niven. Tel. (416) 923-1168.

College of Emmanuel and St. Chad, Ang. Ch. of Canada, Saskatoon, Saskatchewan S7N OW6, J. D. F. Beattie. Tel. (306) 343-3030.

Columbia Bible Institute, Menn. Br. and Un. Menn., 2940 Clearbrook Rd., Clearbrook, British Columbia, P. R. Toews. Tel. (604) 853-3358.

Covenant Bible College, Ev. Cov. Ch. of Canada, 245-21st St., Prince Albert, Saskatchewan S6J 1L9, W. B. Anderson. Tel. (306) 763-2764.

Eastern Pentecostal Bible College, Pent. Assem. of Canada, 49 Argyle St., Peterborough, Ontario, C. Herbert Bronsdon. Tel. (705) 745-7450.

Elim Christian Education Centre, Manitoba Conf. of Menn., Ev. Menn. Missions Conf., Box 120 Altona, Manitoba ROG OBO, George A. Neufeld. Tel. (204) 324-5464.

Emmanuel Bible College, Miss. Ch., 100 Fergus Ave., Kitchener, Ontario, vacant. Tel. (519) 1662.

Emmanuel College (see under **Toronto School of Theology**).

Foothills Bible Institute, Pent. Holiness, R.R. 1, Site 4, Box 2, Winfield, Alberta TOC 2XO, Walter Gamble. Tel. (403) 682-2405.

Full Gospel Bible Institute, Apost. Ch. of Pent., Box 579, Eston, Saskatchewan SOL 1AO, G. S. McLean. Tel. (306) 962-3314.

Hillcrest Christian College, Ev. Ch., 2801-13th Ave., S.E., Medicine Hat, Alberta, G. W. Epp. Tel. (403) 527-2770.

Huron College, Ang. Ch. of Canada, Faculty of Theology, London 72, Ontario, J. G. Morden.

Ignatius College, Cath., Guelph, Ontario, John E. Le Sarge. Tel. (519) 824-1250.

Institute for Christian Studies, nondenom., 229 College St., Toronto 2B, Ontario, John A. Olthuis. Tel. (416) 923-3921.

Knox College (see under **Toronto School of Theology**).

Lutheran Theological Seminary, Ev. Luth. Ch. of Canada, Luth. Ch. in Am., Saskatoon, Saskatchewan, William Hordern. Tel. (306) 343-8204.

Maritime Christian College, CC/CC, 223 Kent St., Charlottetown, Prince Edward Island, Kenneth T. Morris.

McMaster Divinity College, Bapt. Conv. of Ontario and Quebec, Hamilton 16, Ontario, Ivan C. Morgan. Tel. (416) 4971.

191

CANADIAN THEOLOGICAL SEMINARIES

Mennonite Brethren Bible College, Menn. Br., 77 Henderson Hwy., Winnipeg, Manitoba R2L 1L1 John Regehr, actg. Tel. (204) 667-9560.

Montreal Diocesan Theological College, Ang. Ch. of Canada, 3473 University St., Montreal 112, Quebec. Monroe Peaston. Tel. (514) 849-3004.

Mountain View Bible College, Miss. Ch., Box 190, Didsbury, Alberta, TOM OWO, J. William Cox. Tel. (403) 335-3566.

Nipawin Bible Institute, interdenom., Box 1986, Nipawin, Saskatchewan, Jacob G. Wiebe. Tel. (306) 862-5098.

North American Baptist College, N. Amer. Bapt. Gen. Conf., 23rd Ave. and 115th St., R.R. #3, South Edmonton, Alberta T6H 4N7, Joseph Sonnenberg. Tel. (403) 399-5571.

Northwest Baptist Theological College, B. C. Reg. Bapt,. 3358 S. E. Marine Dr., Vancouver 16, British Columbia, H. G. Anderson. Tel. (604) 433-1013.

Northwest Bible College, Pent. Assem. of Canada, 11605-107th Ave., Edmonton, Alberta, J. C. Cooke.

Ontario Bible College, nondenom., 16 Spadina Rd., Toronto, Ontario, S. L. Boehmer. Tel. (416) 924-7167.

Peace River Bible Institute, Box 99, Sexsmith, Alberta TOH 300, C. W. Johnson. Tel. (403) 568-3962.

Prairie Bible Institute, nondenom,. Three Hills, Alberta TOM 2AO, L. E. Maxwell. Tel. (403) 443-5511.

Presbyterian College, 3495 University St., Montreal 112, Quebec, C. Ritchie Bell, actg. Tel. (514) 288-5256.

Queen's Theological College, Un. Ch. of Can., Kingston, Ontario.

Regent College, interdenom., 5990 Iona Dr., Vancouver, British Columbia, J. M. Houston. Tel. (604) 224-3245.

Regis College (see under **Toronto School of Theology**).

Salvation Army Training College, Salv. Army, 2130 Bayview Ave., Toronto 317, Ontario, Edward Reed. Tel. (416) 481-6133.

St. Andrews College, Un. Ch. of Canada, Saskatoon, Saskatchewan.

St. Augustine Seminary (see under **Toronto School of Theology**).

St. John's College, Faculty of Theology, Ang. Ch. of Canada, Winnipeg, Manitoba R3T 2M5, J. R. Brown. Tel. (204) 474-8529.

St. Joseph's Catholic College, Cath., Edmonton, Alberta T6G 2J5, J. B. Courtney. Tel (403) 433-1569.

St. Mark's College, Cath., 5935 Iona Dr., Vancouver 8, British Columbia, R. W. Finn. Tel. (604) 224-3311.

St. Michael's College, Faculty of Theology (see under **Toronto School of Theology**).

St. Stephen's College, Un. Ch. of Canada, Edmonton, Alberta T6G 2J6, George M. Tuttle. Tel. (403) 439-4381.

Steinbach Bible Institute, Menn., Box 1420, Steinbach, Manitoba ROA 2AO, Harvey Plett. Tel. (204) 326-6451.

Swift Current Bible Institute, Menn., Box 1268, Swift Current, Saskatchewan S9H OLO, Walter Franz. Tel (306) 773-5440.

Toronto Baptist Seminary, Bapt., 337 Jarvis St., Toronto 2, Ontario, G. A. Adams. Tel. (416) 925-3263.

Toronto School of Theology (A federation of seven theological colleges: three Roman Catholic, two Anglican, one Presbyterian, and one United Church of Canada. Affiliated with the University of Toronto. McMaster Divinity College is an associate member), C. Douglas Day. Tel. (416) 928-4039.

Emmanuel College, Un. Ch. of Canada, 75 Queen's Park Crescent, Toronto 181, Ontario, William O. Fennell. Tel. (416) 928-3811.

Knox College, Presb. Ch. in Canada, 59 St. George St., Toronto, Ontario, J. Stanley Glen. Tel. (416) 923-7809.

Regis College, Cath., 3425 Bayview Ave., Willowdale 433, Ontario, Gerald W. Tait. Tel (416) 225-8823.

St. Augustine Seminary, Cath., 2661 Kingston Rd., Scarborough 713, Ontario, John A. O' Mara. Tel. (416) 261-7207.

St. Michael's College, Faculty of Theology, Cath., 50 St. Joseph St., Toronto 181, Ontario, J. M. Kelly. Tel. (416) 921-3151.

Trinity College, Faculty of Divinity, Ang. Ch. of Canada, Hoskin Ave., Toronto 181, Ontario. Tel. (416) 928-2011.

Wycliffe College, Ang. Ch. of Canada, Hoskin Ave., Toronto 181, Ontario, Leslie Hunt. Tel. (416) 923-8596.

Trinity College (see under **Toronto School of Theology**).

United Theological College, Un. Ch. of Can., 3473 University St., Montreal 112, Quebec.

Universite de Moncton, undenom., Moncton, Nouveau-Brunswick, M. Adelard Savoie. Tel. (506) 858-4000.

Universite de Montreal, Faculte de theologie, Cath., CP. 6128, Montréal 101, Québec, Richard Brosseau. Tél. (514) 343-7160.

Universite de Sherbrooke, Faculte de theologie, Cath., Cité Universitaire, Boulevarde de L' Université, Sherbrooke, Québec.

Universite Laval, Faculte de theologie, Cath., Québec 10e, Québec, Roland Beaudet. Tél. (418) 656-7823.

University of Windsor, Department of Theology, 40 Huron Lane, Windsor 11, Ontario.

University of Winnipeg, Faculty of Theology, Un. Ch. of Can., Winnipeg, Manitoba R3B 2E9, G. E. Taylor. Tel. (204) 786-7811.

Vancouver Bible Institute, Bapt. Gen. Conf., 15100-66 A. Ave., Surrey, British Columbia, Walter R. Anderson. Tel. (604) 596-7105.

Vancouver School of Theology, ecumen., 6000 Iona Dr., Vancouver 8, British Columbia, James P. Martin. Tel (604) 228-9031.

Waterloo Lutheran Seminary, Luth. Ch. in Am., Waterloo, Ontario, Delton J. Gleve. Tel. (519) 884-1970.

Western Pentecostal Bible College, Pent. Assem. of Can., 3451 St. Mary's Ave., North Vancouver, British Columbia, L. Thomas Holdcroft. Tel. (604) 988-2410.

Winkler Bible Institute, Menn. Breth., Box 950, Winkler, Manitoba ROG 2X0, H. R. Baerg. Tel. (204) 325-4242.

Winnipeg Bible College, Otterburne, Manitoba ROA 1GO, Kenneth G. Hanna. Tel. (204) 284-2923.

Wycliffe College (see under **Toronto School of Theology**).

10. CHURCH-CONTROLLED AND CHURCH-RELATED ACCREDITED COLLEGES AND UNIVERSITIES IN THE UNITED STATES

The following alphabetical listing of church-controlled and church-related colleges and universities is derived mainly from the *Education Directory*, 1971-1972, Part 3, "Higher Education," published by the Office of Education, U. S. Department of Health, Education and Welfare, although other sources were used as well.

The listing below does not include junior colleges, teachers' colleges, and other professional schools.

Of the 633 colleges and universities listed below, approximately 80 per cent were identified as church-controlled in reports to the U. S. Office of Education. The remaining 20 per cent did not report church control but have been identified as church-related in varying degrees.

A tabulation in the *Education Directory*, 1971-1972, cited above, indicates that in 1971-1972 there were 2,626 institutions of higher learning in the United States, including outlying parts. Of these, 1,152 were public and 1,474 private. Of the 1,474 institutions of higher education identified as private, 671 were organized independent of a religious group, 489 were Protestant, 280 Catholic, and 34 other (including Orthodox, interdenominational, Jewish, Latter-day Saints, Unitarian-Universalist), the *Education Directory* notes.

Abbreviations for nationally recognized regional Accrediting Associations are as follows:

MS	Middle States Association of Colleges and Secondary Schools.
NC	North Central Association of Colleges and Secondary Schools.
NE	New England Association of Colleges and Secondary Schools.
NW	Northwest Association of Secondary and Higher Schools.
S	Southern Association of Colleges and Schools.
West	Western Association of Schools and Colleges.

Other abbreviations are as follows:

C	Co-educational
M	Men
W	Women
Co-Ord.	Coordinate

Each item in the listing below has the following order: Name of institution, address, telephone number, head of institution, nature of student body, accrediting, denominational relationship, enrollment.

Abilene Christian College, Abilene, TX 79601, Tel. (915) 677-1911. John C. Stevens, C S, Ch. of Christ, 3,210.

Academy of the New Church, Byrn Athyn, PA 19009, Tel. (215) 947-4200. Willard D. Pendelton, C MS, Ch. of New Jerusalem, 131.

Adrian College, Adrian, MI 49221, Tel. (313) 265-5161. John H. Dawson, C NC, Un. Meth., 1,562.

Agnes Scott College, Decatur, GA 30030, Tel. (404) 373-2571. Wallace M. Alston, W S, Presb. U.S., 694.

Alaska Methodist University, Anchorage, AK 99504. Tel. (907) 272-4401. William E. Davis, actg. C NW, Un. Meth., 749.

Albertus Magnus College, New Haven, CT 06511, Tel. (203) 777-6631. Francis H. Horn, W NE. Cath., 549.

Albion College, Albion, MI 49224, Tel. (517) 629-5511. Bernard T. Lomas, C NC, Un. Meth., 1,826.

Albright College, Reading, PA 19604, Tel. (215) 374-2226. Arthur L. Schultz, C MS, Un. Meth., 1,535.

Albuquerque, University of, Albuquerque, NM 87120, Tel. (505) 243-9461. Francis A. Kleinhenz, C NC, Cath., 1,563.

Alderson-Broaddus College, Philippi, WV 26416, Tel. (304) 457-1700. Richard E. Shearer, C NC, Am. Bapt., 1,024.

Allegheny College, Meadville, PA 16335, Tel. (814) 724-3100. Lawrence L. Pelletier, C MS, Un. Meth., 1,804.

Allentown College of Saint Francis de Sales, Center Valley, PA 18034, Tel. (215) 282-1100. J. Stuart Dooling, C MS, Cath., 545

Alma College, Alma, MI 48801, Tel. (517) 463-2141. Robert D. Swanson, C NC, U. Presb. U.S.A., 1,282.

Alvernia College, Reading, PA 19607, Tel. (215) 777-5411. Sr. M. Victorine, W MS, Cath., 282.

Alverno College, Milwaukee, WI 53215, Tel. (414) 671-5400. Sr. M. Joel Read, W NC, Cath., 890.

American University, The, Washington, DC 20016, Tel. (202) 686-2000. George H. Williams, C MS, Un. Meth., 15,324.

Anderson College, Anderson, IN 46011, Tel. (317) 644-0951. Robert H. Reardon, C NC, Ch. of God, (And.), 1,893.

Andrews University, Berrien Springs, MI 49104, Tel. (616) 471-7771. Richard Hammill, C NC, S.D.A., 2,061.

Anna Maria College for Women, Paxton, MA 01612, Tel. (617) 757-4586. Sr. Irene Marie Socquet, W NE, Cath., 615.

Annhurst College, R. R. 2, Woodstock, CT 06281, Tel. (203) 928-7773. Sr. Cecile Comtois, W NE, Cath., 456.

Aquinas College, Grand Rapids, MI 49506, Tel. (616) 459-8281. Norbert J. Hruby, C NC, Cath., 1,413.

Arkansas College, Batesville, AR 72501, Tel. (501) 793-2282. R. W. Wygle, C NC, Presb. U.S., 362.

Ashland College, Ashland, OH 44805, Tel. (419) 324-4561. Glenn L. Clayton, C NC, Ch. Breth. (Prog.), 2,976.

Assumption College, Worcester, MA 01609, Tel. (617) 752-5615. Wilfred J. DuFault C NE, Cath., 1,578.

Athenaeum of Ohio, Norwood, OH 45212, Tel. (513) 731-2630. James R. Fauret M NC, Cath. 290.

Athens College, Athens, AL 35611, Tel. (205) 232-1802. Sidney E. Sandridge, C S, Un. Meth., 1,077.

Atlantic Christian College, Wilson, NC 27893, Tel. (919) 237-3161. Arthur D. Wenger, C S, Christian Church (Disc.), 1,747.

Atlantic Union College, South Lancaster, MA 01561, Tel. (617) 365-4561. William G. Nelson, C NE, S.D.A., 708.

Augsburg College, Minneapolis, MN 55404, Tel. (612) 332-5181. Oscar A. Anderson, C NC, Am. Luth., 1,697.

Augustana College, Rock Island, IL 61201, Tel. (309) 794-7000. Clarence W. Sorensen, C NC, Luth. in Am., 2,124.

Augustana College, Sioux Falls, SD 57102, Tel. (605) 336-0770. Charles L. Balcer, C NC, Am. Luth., 2,178.

Aurora College, Aurora, IL 60507, Tel. (312) 892-6431. James E. Crimi, C NC, Adv. Chr. Ch., 1,261.

Austin College, Sherman, TX 75090, Tel. (214) 892-9101. John Dean Moseley, C S, Presb. U.S., 1,102.

Avila College, Kansas City, MO 64145, Tel. (816) 942-3204. Sr. Olive Louise Dallavis, C NC, Cath., 596.

Baker University, Baldwin City, KS 66006, Tel. (913) 594-6451. James E. Doty, C NC, Un. Meth., 848.

Baldwin-Wallace College, Berea, OH 44017, Tel. (216) 243-5000. Alfred B. Bonds, Jr., C NC, Un. Meth., 3,135.

Baptist College at Charleston, Charleston, SC 29411, Tel. (803) 553-5110. John A. Hamrick, C S, So. Bapt., 1,839.

Barat College, Lake Forest, IL 60045, Tel. (312) 234-3000. Sr. Margaret Burke, W NC, Cath., 518.

Barber-Scotia College, Concord, NC 28025, Tel. (704) 786-5171. William C. Brown, interim, C S, Presb., U.S., 537.

Bard College, Annandale-on-Hudson, NY 12504, Tel. (914) 758-6072. Reamer Kline, C MS, Epis., 712.

Barry College, Miami, FL 33161, Tel. (305) 758-3392. Sr. M. Dorothy Browne, C S, Cath., 1,260

Bates College, Lewiston, ME 04240, Tel. (207) 784-1545 Thomas H. Reynolds, C NE, Am. Bapt., 1,157.

Baylor University, Waco, TX 76703, Tel. (817)

755-1611. Abner V. McCall, C S, So. Bapt., 6,440.

Beaver College, Glenside, PA 19038, Tel. (215) 884-3500. Edward D. Gates, W MS, U. Presb. U.S.A., 768.

Belhaven College, Jackson, MS 39202, Tel. (601) 352-0013. Howard J. Cleland, C S, Presb. U.S., 594.

Bellarmine College, Louisville, KY 40205, Tel. (502) 452-8011. Alfred F. Horrigan, C S, Cath., 1,612.

Belmont Abbey College, Belmont, NC 28012, Tel. (704) 825-3711. John P. Bradley, M S, Cath., 679.

Belmont College, Nashville, TN 37203, Tel. (615) 291-7001. Herbert C. Gabhart, C S, So. Bapt., 921.

Beloit College, Beloit, WI 53511, Tel. (608) 365-3391. Miller Upton, C NC, U. Ch. of Christ., 1,782.

Benedict College, Columbia, SC 29204, Tel. (803) 779-4930. Benjamin F. Payton, C S, Am. Bapt., 1,340.

Benedictine College, Atchison, KS 66002. Tel. (913) 367-6110. Sr. M. Noel Walter, C NC, Cath., 1,228.

Bennett College, Greensboro, NC 27420, Tel. (919) 275-9791. Isaac H. Miller, Jr., W. S. Un. Meth., 572.

Bethany College, Bethany, WV 26032, Tel. (304) 829-7000. Perry E. Gresham, C NC, Christian Church (Disc.), 1,089.

Bethany College, Lindsborg, KS 67456, Tel. (913) 227-3312. Arvin Hahn, C NC, Luth. in Am., 670.

Bethany-Nazarene College, Bethany, OK 73008, Tel. (405) 789-6400. Roy H. Cantrell, C NC, Naz., 1,720.

Bethel College, McKenzie, TN 38201, Tel. (901) 352-2557. James E. McKee, C S, Cumb. Presb. 544.

Bethel College, North Newton, KS 67117, Tel. (316) 283-2500. Harold J. Schultz, C NC, Menn., 466.

Bethel College, Mishawaka, IN 46544, Tel. (219) 259-8511. Ray P. Pannabecker, C NC, Interdenom., 490.

Bethel College and Seminary, St. Paul, MN 55108, Tel. (612) 646-4501. Carl H. Lundquist, C NC, Bapt. Gen'l Conf., 1,107.

Bethune-Cookman College, Daytona Beach, FL 32015, Tel. (904) 255-1401. Richard V. Moore, C S, Un. Meth., 1,065.

Birmingham-Southern College, Birmingham, AL 35204, Tel. (205) 328-5250. Charles D. Hounshell, C S, Un. Meth., 1,040.

Biscayne College, Miami, FL 33054, Tel. (305) 625-1561. John H. McDonnell, M S, Cath., 450.

Bishop College, Dallas, TX 75241, Tel. (214) 376-4311. M. K. Curry, Jr., C S, Am. Bapt., 1,623.

Blackburn College, Carlinville, IL 62626, Tel. (217) 854-3231. Glenn L. McConagha C NC, U. Presb. U.S.A., 589.

Bloomfield College, Bloomfield, NJ 07003, Tel. (201) 748-9000. Merle F. Allshouse, C MS, U. Presb. U.S.A., 1,619.

Blue Mountain College, Blue Mountain, MS 38610, Tel. (601) 685-5711. E. Harold Fisher, W S, So. Bapt., 279.

Bluffton College, Bluffton, OH 45817, Tel. (419) 358-8015. Robert S. Kreider, C NC, Menn., 728.

Borromeo Seminary of Ohio, Wickliffe, OH 44092, Tel. (216) 943-3888. Robert C. Wolff, M NC, Cath., 178.

Boston College, Chestnut Hill, MA 02167, Tel. (617) 969-0100. W. Seavey Joyce, C NE, Cath., 10,956.

Boston University, Boston, MA 02215, Tel. (617) 353-2200. John R. Silber, C NE, Un. Meth., 25,124.

Brescia College, Owensboro, KY 42301, Tel. (502) 685-3131. Sr. Joan Marie Lechner, C S, Cath., 1,017.

Briar Cliff College, Sioux City, IA 51104, Tel. (712) 252-4631. Sr. Mary Jordan Dahm, C NC, Cath., 1,131.

Bridgewater College, Bridgewater, VA 22812, Tel. (703) 828-2051. Wayne F. Geisert, C. S, Ch. Breth., 849.

Brigham Young University, Provo, UT 84601, Tel. (801) 374-1211. Dallin H. Oakes, C NW, L.D.S., 26,626.

Bucknell University, Lewisburg, PA 17837, Tel. (717) 523-1271. Charles H. Watts, II, C MS, Am. Bapt., 2,933.

Buena Vista College, Storm Lake, IA 50588, Tel. (712) 749-2351. W. Q. Halverson, C NC, U. Presb. U.S.A., 948.

Butler University, Indianapolis, IN 46208, Tel. (317) 923-3451. Alexander E. Jones, C NC, Christian Church (Disc.), 4,403.

Cabrini College, Radnor, PA 19087, Tel. (215) 687-2100. Sr. Regina Casey, C MS, Cath., 405.

Caldwell College, Caldwell, NJ 07006, Tel. (201) 226-4424. Sr. Ann John, W MS, Cath., 859.

California Baptist College, 8432 Magnolia Ave., Riverside, CA 92504, Tel. (714) 689-5771. James R. Staples, C. West, So. Bapt., 690.

California Lutheran College, Thousand Oaks, CA 91360, Tel. (805) 492-2411. Maurice H. Knutson, actg. C West, Am. Luth. and Luth. Ch. in Am., 1,195.

Calvin College, Grand Rapids, MI 49506, Tel. (616) 949-4000. William Spoelhof, C NC, Christ. Ref., 3,437.

Campbell College, Buies Creek, NC 27506, Tel. (919) 893-4111. Norman A. Wiggins, C S, So. Bapt., 2,207.

Campbellsville College, Campbellsville, KY 42718, Tel. (502) 465-8158. W. R. Davenport, C S, So. Bapt., 914.

Canisius College, Buffalo, NY 14208, Tel. (716) 883-7000. James M. Demske, C MS, Cath., 3,912.

Capital University, Columbus, OH 43209, Tel. (614) 236-6011. Thomas H. Langevin, C NC, Am. Luth., 2,045.

Cardinal Cushing College, Brookline, MA 02146, Tel. (617) 734-8950. John Mulvehill, W NE, Cath., 390.

Cardinal Glennon College, St. Louis, MO 63119, Tel. (314) 644-0266. Ignatius M. Melito, M NC, Cath., 188.

Cardinal Stritch College, Milwaukee, WI 53217, Tel. (414) 352-5400. Sr. Mary Aquin, C NC, Cath., 662.

Carleton College, Northfield, MN 55057, Tel. (507) 645-4431. Howard R. Swearer, C NC, U. Ch. of Christ, 1,521.

Carlow College, Pittsburgh, PA 15213. Tel. (412) 683-4800. Sr. Jane Scully, W MS, Cath., 1,006.

Carroll College, Helena, MT 59601, Tel. (406) 442-3450. Joseph D. Harrington, C NW Cath., 1,054.

Carroll College, Waukesha, WI 53186, Tel. (414) 547-1211. Robert V. Cramer, C NC, U. Presb. U.S.A., 1,250.

Carson-Newman College, Jefferson City, TN 37760, Tel. (615) 475-9061. John A. Fincher, C S, So. Bapt., 1,686.

Carthage College, Kenosha, WI 53140, Tel. (414) 551-8501. Harold H. Lentz, C NC, Luth. in Am., 1,849.

Catawba College, Salisbury, NC 28144, Tel. (704) 636-5311. Martin L. Shotzberger, C S, U. Ch. of Christ, 1,099.

Catholic University of America, Washington, DC 20017, Tel. (202) 529-6000. Clarence C. Walton, C MS, Cath., 6,112.

Catholic University of Puerto Rico, Ponce, PR 00731, Tel. (809) 842-4150. Francisco J. Carreras, C MS, Cath., 7,140.

Cedar Crest College, Allentown, PA 18104, Tel. (215) 437-4471. Pauline Tompkins, W MS, U. Ch. of Christ, 795.

Centenary College, Shreveport, LA 71104, Tel. (318) 861-2431. John H. Allen, C S, Un. Meth., 932.

Centenary College for Women, Hackettstown, NJ 07840, Tel (201) 852-1400. Edward W. Seay, W MS, Un. Meth., 640.

Central Methodist College, Fayette, MO 65248, Tel. (816) 248-3223. Harold P. Hamilton, C NC, Un. Meth., 804.

Central University of Iowa, Pella, IA 50219, Tel. (515) 628-4151. Kenneth J. Weller, C NC, Ref. in Am., 1,226.

Centre College of Kentucky, Danville, KY 40422, Tel. (606) 236-5211. Thomas A. Spragens, C S, Presb. U.S. & U. Presb. U.S.A., 774.

Chaminade College of Honolulu, 3140 Walalae Ave., Honolulu, HI 96816, Tel. (808) 732-1471. Robert C. Maguire, C West, Cath., 1,480.

Chapman College, Orange, CA 92666, Tel. (714) 633-8821. Donald C. Kleckner, C West, Christian Church (Disc.), 4,501.

Chestnut Hill College, Philadelphia, PA 19118, Tel. (215) 247-4212. Sr. Mary Xavier, W MS, Cath., 1,120.

Christian Brothers College, Memphis, TN 38104, Tel. (901) 278-0100. Bro. Malcolm O'Sullivan, C S, Cath., 960.

Church College of Hawaii, Box 1153, Laie,

Oahu, HI 96762, Tel. (808) 293-9211. Stephen L. Brower, C West, L.D.S., 1,307.

Claflin College, Orangeburg, SC 29115, Tel. (803) 534-2710. H. V. Manning, C S, Un. Meth., 775.

Clark College, Atlanta, GA 30314, Vivian W. Henderson, C S, Un. Meth., 1,085.

Clarke College, Dubuque, IA 52001, Tel. (319) 588-6300. Robert J. Giroux, W NC, Cath., 802.

Coe College, Cedar Rapids, IA 52402, Tel. (319) 364-1511. Leo L. Nussbaum, C NC, U. Presb. U.S.A., 1,108.

Colby College, Waterville, ME 04901, Tel. (207) 873-1131. Robert E. L. Strider, II, C NE, Am. Bapt. 1,562.

College of Emporia, Emporia, KS 66801, Tel. (316) 342-3670. Ronald A. Ebberts, C NC, U. Presb. U.S.A., 858.

College of Great Falls, Great Falls, MT 59401, Tel. (406) 761-8210. E. Milton Grassell, C NW, Cath., 1,165.

College of Idaho, Caldwell, ID 83605, Tel. (208) 459-5011. Warren B. Knox, C NW, U. Presb. U.S.A., 1,119.

College Misericordia, Dallas, PA 18612, Tel. (717) 675-2181. Sr. Miriam T. O'Donnell, W MS, Cath., 941.

College of Mt. St. Joseph-on-the Ohio, Mt. St. Joseph, OH 45051, Tel. (513) 244-4200. Sr. Adele Clifford, W NC, Cath., 906.

College of Mt. St. Vincent, Riverdale, NY 10471, Tel. (212) 549-8000. Sr. Mary David Barry, W MS, Cath., 958.

College of New Rochelle, New Rochelle, NY 10801, Tel. (914) 632-5300. Joseph P. McMurray, W MS, Cath., 1,168.

College of Notre Dame, Belmont, CA 94002, Tel. (415) 593-7674. Sr. Catherine Julie Cunningham, C West, Cath., 1,486.

College of Notre Dame of Md., Baltimore, MD 21210, Tel. (301) 435-0100. Sr. Kathleen Feeley, Co. Ord. MS, Cath., 947.

College of Our Lady of the Elms, Chicopee, MA 01013, Tel. (413) 598-8351. Thomas F. Devine, W NE, Cath., 566.

College of the Sacred Heart, Santurce, PR 00914, Tel. (809) 724-7800. Rafael Enrique Garcia Bottari, W MS, Cath., 797.

College of St. Benedict, St. Joseph, MN 56374, Tel. (612) 363-7711. Stanley J. Idzerda, Co. Ord. NC, Cath., 736.

College of St. Catherine, St. Paul, MN 55116, Tel. (612) 698-5571. Sr. Alberta Huber, W NC, Cath., 1,339.

College of St. Elizabeth, Convent Sta., NJ 07961, Tel. (201) 539-1600. Sr. Elizabeth Ann Maloney, W MS, Cath., 761.

College of St. Francis, Joliet, IL 60435, Tel. (815) 726-7311. Francis J. Kerins, C NC, Cath., 806.

College of St. Mary, Omaha, NB 68124, Tel. (402) 393-8800. Sr. M. Angelica Costello, W NC, Cath., 517.

College of St. Rose, Albany, NY 12203, Tel.

(518) 438-3567. Alphonse R. Miele, C MS, Cath., 1,446.

College of St. Scholastica, Duluth, MN 55811, Tel. (218) 728-3631, Sr. Francis X. Shea, C NC, Cath., 817.

College of St. Teresa, Winona, MN 55987, Tel. (507) 452-9302. Sr. M. Joyce Rowland, W NC, Cath., 1,047.

College of St. Thomas, St. Paul, MN 55101, Tel. (612) 647-5000. Terrence J. Murphy, M NC, Cath., 2,430.

College of Santa Fe, Santa Fe, NM 87501, Tel. (505) 982-6011. Br. Cyprian Luke Roney, C NC, Cath., 1,258.

College of Steubenville, Steubenville, OH 43952, Tel. (614) 283-3771. Kevin R. Keelan, C NC, Cath., 1,380.

College of the Holy Cross, Worcester, MA 01610, Tel. (617) 793-2011. John E. Brooks, M NE, Cath., 2,478.

College of the Holy Names, Oakland, CA 94619, Tel. (415) 436-0111. Sr. Mary Ambrose Devereux, C West, Cath., 860.

College of the Ozarks, Clarksville, AR 72830, Tel. (501) 754-2788. Don E. Davis, C NC, U. Presb. U.S.A., 600.

College of Wooster, Wooster, OH 44691, Tel. (216) 264-1234. J. Garber Drushal, C NC, U. Presb. U.S.A., 1,685.

Columbia College, Columbia, SC 29203, Tel. (803) 754-1100. R. Wright Spears, W S, Un. Meth., 892.

Columbia Union College, Takoma Park, MD 20012, Tel. (301) 589-2135. George H. Akers, C MS, S.D.A., 914.

Concordia College at Moorhead, Moorhead, MN 56560, Tel. (218) 299-4321. Joseph L. Knutson, C NC, Am. Luth., 2,360.

Concordia College at St. Paul, St. Paul, MN 55104, Tel. (612) 646-6157. Harvey A. Stegemoeller, C NC, Luth. (Mo.), 810.

Concordia Senior College, Ft. Wayne, IN 46825, Tel. (219) 748-7105. Martin J. Neeb, M NC, Luth. (Mo.), 407.

Cornell College, Mt. Vernon, IA 52314, Tel. (319) 895-8811. Samuel Enoch Stumpf, C NC, Un. Meth., 938.

Corpus Christi, University of, Corpus Christi, TX 78411, Tel. (512) 991-6810. Kenneth A. Maroney, C S, So. Bapt., 611.

Creighton University, Omaha, NB 68131, Tel. (402) 536-2700. Joseph J. Labaj, C NC, Cath., 4,129.

Culver-Stockton College, Canton, MO 63435, Tel. (314) 288-5221. Fred Helsabeck, C NC, Christian Church (Disc.), 782.

Cumberland College, Williamsburg, KY 40769, Tel. (606) 549-2200. James M. Boswell, C S, So. Bapt., 1,857.

Dakota Wesleyan University, Mitchell, SD 57301, Tel. (605) 996-6511. Donald E. Messer, C NC, Un. Meth., 609.

Dallas Baptist College, Dallas, TX 75211, Tel. (214) 331-8311. Charles P. Pitts, C S, So. Bapt., 1,451.

Dallas, University of, Irving, TX 75060, Tel.

(214) 253-1123. Donald A. Cowan, C S, Cath., 1,359.

Dana College, Blair, NB 68008, Tel. (402) 426-4101. Earl R. Mezoff C NC, Am. Luth., 962.

David Lipscomb College, Nashville, TN 37203, Tel. (615) 269-5661. Athens Clay Pullias, C S, Ch. of Christ, 2,237.

Davidson College, Davidson, NC 28036, Tel. (704) 892-8021. Samuel R. Spencer, Jr., M S, Presb. U.S., 1,053.

Davis and Elkins College, Elkins, WV 26241, Tel. (304) 636-1900. Gordon Hermanson, C NC, U. Presb. U.S.A. Presby. U.S., 747.

Dayton, University of, Dayton, OH 45409, Tel. (513) 229-2111. Raymond A. Roesch, C NC, Cath., 9,120.

Defiance College, Defiance, OH 43512, Tel. (419) 784-4010. W. Noel Johnston, C NC, U. Ch. of Christ, 1,137.

Denison University, Granville, OH 43023, Tel. (614) 582-9181. Joel P. Smith, C NC, Am. Bapt., 2,170.

Denver, University of, Denver, CO 80210, Tel. (303) 753-1964. M. B. Mitchell, C NC, Un. Meth., 9,350.

DePaul University, Chicago, IL 60604, Tel. (312) 939-3525. John R. Cortelyou, C NC, Cath., 9,194.

DePauw University, Greencastle, IN 46135, Tel. (317) 653-9721. William E. Kerstetter, C NC, Un. Meth., 2,370.

Detroit, University of, Detroit, MI 48221, Tel. (313) 342-1000. Malcolm Carron, C NC, Cath., 9,638.

Dickinson College, Carlisle, PA 17013, Tel. (717) 243-5121. Howard L. Rubendall, C MS, Un. Meth., 1,642.

Dillard University, New Orleans, LA 70122, Tel. (504) 943-8861. Broadus N. Butler, C S, U. Ch. of Christ, Un. Meth., 968.

Divine Word College, Epworth, IA 52045, Tel. (319) 876-3362. Harold W. Rigney, M NC, Cath., 129.

Doane College, Crete, NB 68333, Tel. (402) 826-2161. Philip Heckman, C NC, U. Ch. of Christ, 721.

Dominican College, Houston, TX 77021, Tel. (713) 747-2700, Vacant, W S, Cath., 381.

Dominican College, Racine, WI 53402, Tel. (414) 639-7100. Thomas C. Stevens, C NC, Cath., 828.

Dominican College of San Rafael, San Rafael, CA 94901, Tel. (415) 453-1047. Sr. M. Samuel Conlan, C West, Cath., 717.

Don Bosco College, Newton, NJ 07860, Tel. (201) 383-3900. Joseph S. Bajorek, M MS, Cath., 116.

Dordt College, Sioux Center, IA 51250, Tel. (712) 722-3771, Bernard J. Haan, C NC, Christ. Ref. Ch., 932.

Drake University, Des Moines, IA 50311, Tel. (515) 271-2011, Vacant, C NC, Christian Church (Disc.), 7,606.

Drew University, Madison, NJ 07940, Tel. (201)

377-3000. Robert F. Oxnam, C MS, Un. Meth., 1,556.

Dropsie University, The, Philadelphia, PA 19132, Tel. (215) 229-0110. Abraham I. Katsh, C MS, Jewish, 155.

Drury College, Springfield, MO 65802, Tel. (417) 865-8731. William E. Everheart, C NC, U. Ch. of Christ, 2,390.

Dubuque, University of, Dubuque, IA 52001, Tel. (319) 557-2121. Walter F. Peterson, C NC, U. Presb. U.S.A., 1,245.

Duke University, Durham, NC 27706, Tel. (919) 684-8111. Terry Sanford, C S, Un. Meth., 8,061.

Dunbarton College of Holy Cross, Washington, DC 20008, Tel. (202) 362-1501. Paul G. Buchanan, W MS, Cath., 388.

Duns Scotus College, Southfield, MI 48075, Tel. (313) 444-4388. Corman J. Mullen, M NC, Cath., 255.

Duquesne University, Pittsburgh, PA 15219, Tel. (412) 434-6064. Henry J. McAnulty, C MS, Cath., 8,080.

D'Youville College, Buffalo, NY 14201, Tel. (714) 884-8100. Sr. Mary Charlotte Barton, C MS, Cath., 1,187.

Earlham College, Richmond, IN 47374, Tel. (317) 962-6561. Landrum R. Bolling, C NC, Friends, 1,972.

East Texas Baptist College, Marshall, TX 75670, Tel. (214) 935-7963. Howard C. Bennett, C S, So. Bapt., 756.

Eastern Baptist College, St. Davids, PA 19087, Tel. (215) 688-3300. J. Lester Harnish, C MS, Am. Bapt., 554.

Eastern Mennonite College, Harrisonburg, VA 22801, Tel. (703) 434-7331. Myron S. Augsburger, C S, Menn., 995.

Eastern Nazarene College, Wollaston, MA 02170, Tel. (617) 773-6350. Leslie Parrott, C NE, Nazarene, 851.

Edgecliff College, Cincinnati, OH 45206, Tel. (513) 961-3770. Sr. M. Jane Kirchner, C NC, Cath., 821.

Edgewood College, Madison, WI 53711, Tel. (608) 257-4861. Sr. Mary Cecilia Carey, C NC, Cath., 577.

Elizabethtown College, Elizabethtown, PA 17022, Tel. (717) 367-1151. Morley J. Mays, C MS, Ch. Breth., 1,707.

Elmhurst College, Elmhurst, IL 60126, Tel. (312) 279-4100. Ivan Frick, C NC, U. Ch. of Christ, 2,896.

Elon College, Elon College, NC 27244, Tel. (919) 584-9711. James Earl Danieley, C S, U. Ch. of Christ, 1,715.

Emmanuel College, Boston, MA 02115, Tel. (617) 277-9340. Sr. Marie Barry, W NE, Cath., 1,449.

Emory and Henry College, Emory, VA 24327, Tel. (703) 944-3121. Vacant, C S, Un. Meth., 826.

Emory University, Atlanta, GA 30322, Tel. (404) 377-2411. Sanford S. Atwood, C S, Un. Meth., 5,126.

Erskine College, Due West, SC 29639, Tel.

(803) 379-2131. Joseph Wightman, C S, Asso. Ref. Presb., 772.

Eureka College, Eureka, IL 61530, Tel. (309) 467-3721. Ira W. Langston, C NC, Christian Church (Disc.), 541.

Evangel College, Springfield, MO 65802, Tel. (417) 865-2811. J. Robert Ashcroft, C NC, Assem. of God., 1,120.

Evansville, University of, Evansville, IN 47701, Tel. (812) 477-6241, Wallace B. Graves, C NC, Un. Meth., 5,373.

Fairfield University, Fairfield, CT 06430, Tel. (203) 255-1011. William C. McInnes, C NE, Cath., 3,612.

Findlay College, Findlay, OH 45840, Tel. (419) 422-8313. Ivan E. Frick, C NC, Ch. of God, Gen. Eldership, 1,258.

Fisk University, Nashville, TN 37203, Tel. (615) 244-3580. James R. Lawson, C S, U. Ch. of Christ, 1,326.

Florida Memorial College, Miami, FL 33054. Tel. (305) 625-4141. R. W. Puryear, C S, Am. Bapt., 777.

Florida Presbyterian College, St. Petersburg, FL 33733, Tel. (813) 867-1166. Billy O. Wireman, C S, Presb. U.S., U. Presb. U.S.A., 1,050.

Florida Southern College, Lakeland, FL 33802, Tel. (813) 683-5521. Charles T. Thrift, Jr., C S, Un. Meth., 1,468.

Fontbonne College, St. Louis, MO 63105, Tel. (314) 862-3456. Sr. Roberta Schmidt, W NC, Cath., 778.

Fordham University, New York, NY 10458, Tel. (212) 933-2233. Michael P. Walsh, C MS, Cath., 12,591.

Fort Wright College of the Holy Names, Spokane, WA 99204. Tel. (509) 328-2970. Sr. Monica Schmidt, W NW, Cath., 465.

Franklin College of Indiana, Franklin, IN 46131, Tel. (317) 736-8441. Wesley N. Haines, C NC, Am. Bapt., 779.

Franklin & Marshall College, Lancaster, PA 17604, Tel. (717) 393-3621. Keith Spalding, C MS, U. Ch. of Christ, 2,797.

Friends University, Wichita, KS 67213, Tel. (316) 263-9131. Roy F. Ray, C NC, Friends, 1,005.

Furman University, Greenville, SC 29613, Tel. (803) 242-3550. Gordon W. Blackwell, C S, So. Bapt., 2,034.

Gannon College, Erie, PA 16501, Tel. (814) 456-7523. Wilfrid J. Nash, C MS, Cath., 3,869.

Geneva College, Beaver Falls, PA 15010, Tel. (412) 846-5100. Edwin C. Clarke, C MS, Ref. Presb., 1,636.

George Fox College, Newberg, OR 97132, Tel. (503) 538-2101. David C. Le Shana, C NW, Friends, 471.

Georgetown College, Georgetown, KY 40324, Tel. (502) 863-8311. Robert L. Mills, C S, So. Bapt., 1,425.

Georgetown University, Washington, DC 20007, Tel. (202) 625-0100. Robert J. Henle, C MS, Cath., 8,074.

Georgian Court College, Lakewood, NJ 08701,

Tel. (201) 363-5380. Sr. M. Stephanie Sloyan, W MS, Cath., 727.

Gettysburg College, Gettysburg, PA 17325, Tel. (717) 334-3131. C. Arnold Hanson, C MS, Luth. in Am., 1,916.

Gonzaga University, Spokane, WA 99202, Tel. (509) 328-4220. Richard E. Twohy, C NW, Cath., 2,668.

Good Counsel College, White Plains, NY 10603, Tel. (914) 949-9494. Charles E. Ford, W MS, Cath., 433.

Gordon College, Wenham, MA 01984, Tel. (617) 927-2300. Harold J. Ockenga, C NE, interdenom, 724.

Goshen College, Goshen, IN 46526, Tel. (219) 533-3161. J. Lawrence Burkholder, C NC, Menn., 1,284.

Graceland College, Lamoni, IA 50140, Tel. (515) 784-3311. William T. Higdon, C NC, Reorg. L.D.S., 1,295.

Grand Canyon College, Phoenix, AZ 85017, Tel. (602) 939-9421. Arthur K. Tyson, C NC, So. Bapt., 851.

Greensboro College, Greensboro, NC 27420, Tel. (919) 272-7102. David G. Mobberley, C. S, Un. Meth., 590.

Greenville College, Greenville, IL 62246, Tel. (618) 664-1840. Orley R. Herron, Jr., C NC, Free Meth., 819.

Grinnell College, Grinnell, IA 50112, Tel. (515) 236-6181. Glenn H. Leggett, C NC, U. Ch. of Christ, 1,261.

Grove City College, Grove City, PA 16127, Tel. (412) 458-6600. Charles S. Mackenzie, C MS, Presb. U.S.A., 2,090.

Guilford College, Greensboro, NC 27410, Tel. (919) 292-5511. Grimsley T. Hobbs, C S, Friends, 1,757.

Gustavus Adolphus College, St. Peter, MN 56082, Tel. (507) 931-4300. Frank R. Barth, C NC, Luth. in Am., 1,909.

Gwynedd-Mercy College, Gwynedd Valley, PA 19437, Tel. (215) 646-7300. Sr. Isabelle Keiss, W MS, Cath., 1,057.

Hamline University, St. Paul, MN 55101, Tel. (612) 641-2800. Richard P. Bailey, C NC, Un. Meth., 1,249.

Hampden-Sydney College, Hampden-Sydney, VA 23943, Tel. (703) 223-4381. W. Taylor Reveley, M S, Presb. U.S. 682.

Hanover College, Hanover, IN 47243, Tel. (812) 866-2151. John E. Horner, C NC, U. Presb. U.S.A., 1,003.

Hardin-Simmons University, Abilene, TX 79601, Tel. (915) 677-7281. Elwin L. Skiles, C S, So. Bapt., 1,741.

Harding College, Searcy, AR 72143, Tel. (501) 268-6161. Clifton L. Ganus, Jr., C NC, Ch. of Christ, 1,916.

Hartwick College, Oneonta, NY 13820, Tel. (607) 432-4200. Adolph G. Anderson, C MS, Luth. in Am., 1,682.

Hastings College, Hastings, NB 68901, Tel. (402) 463-2402. Arthur L. Langvardt, C NC, U. Presb. U.S.A., 863.

Haverford College, Haverford, PA 19041, Tel.

(215) 649-9600. John R. Coleman, M MS, Friends, 726.

Hawaii Loa College, Honolulu, HI 96813. Tel. (808) 521-3881. Chandler W. Rowe, C WS, Interdenom., 103.

Hebrew College, Brookline, MA 02146. Tel. (617) 232-8710. Eli Grad, C NE, Jewish, 133.

Hebrew Union College, Cincinnati, OH 45220, Tel. (513) 221-1875. Alfred Gottschalk, C NC, Jewish 255.

Heidelberg College, Tiffin, OH 44883, Tel. (419) 447-2310. Leslie H. Fishel, Jr., C NC, U. Ch. of Christ, 1,258.

Hendrix College, Conway, AR 72032, Tel. (501) 329-6811. Roy B. Schilling, Jr., C NC, Un. Meth., 979.

High Point College, High Point, NC 27262, Tel. (919) 885-5101. Wendell M. Patton, Jr., C S, Un. Meth., 1,090.

Hillsdale College, Hillsdale, MI 49242, Tel. (517) 437-7341. George C. Roche, III, C NC, Am. Bapt., 1,119.

Hiram College, Hiram, OH 44234, Tel. (216) 569-3211. Elmer Jagow, C NC, Christian Church (Disc.), 1,191.

Hobart and William Smith Colleges, Geneva, NY 14456, Tel. (315) 789-5500. Allan A. Kuusisto, Co. Ord., MS, Epis., 1,597.

Holy Family College, Philadelphia, PA 19114, Tel. (215) 637-7700. Sr. M. Aloysius, W MS, Cath., 800.

Holy Family College, Manitowoc, WI 54220, Tel. (414) 684-6691. Sr. Anne Kennedy, C NC, Cath., 615.

Hood College, Frederick, MD 21701, Tel. (301) 663-3131. A. Randle Elliott, W MS, U. Ch. of Christ, 627.

Hope College, Holland, MI 49423, Tel. (616) 392-5111. William Vander Lugt, C NC, Ref. Am., 2,071.

Houghton College, Houghton, NY 14744, Tel. (716) 567-2211. Stephen W. Paine, C MS, Wes. Meth., 1,181.

Houston Baptist College, Houston, Tx 77036, Tel. (713) 774-7661. William H. Hinton, C S, So. Bapt., 1,142.

Howard Payne College, Brownwood, TX 76801, Tel. (915) 646-2502. Guy D. Newman, C S, So. Bapt., 1,387.

Huntingdon College, Montgomery, AL 36106, Tel. (205) 263-1611. Allen Keith Jackson, C S, Un. Meth., 780.

Huntington College, Huntington, IN 46750, Tel. (219) 356-6000. E. De Witt Baker, C NC, U. Breth., 575.

Huron College, Huron, SD 57350, Tel. (605) 352-8721. Richard H. Timmins, C NC, U. Presb. U.S.A., 729.

Huston-Tillotson College, Austin, TX 78702, Tel. (512) 476-7421. John T. King, C S, Un. Meth. and U. Ch. of Christ, 664.

Illinois College, Jacksonville, IL 62650, Tel. (217) 245-7126. L. Vernon Caine, C NC, U. Presb. U.S.A. and U. Ch. of Christ, 888.

Illinois Benedictine College, Lisle, IL 60532. Tel. (312) 968-7270, Thomas J. Havlik, C NC, Cath., 966.

Illinois Wesleyan University, Bloomington, IL 61701, Tel. (309) 829-1041. Robert S. Eckley, C NC, Un. Meth., 1,693.

Immaculata College, Immaculata, PA 19345, Tel. (215) 647-4400. Sr. Mary of Lourdes, W MS, Cath., 1,506.

Immaculate Conception Seminary, Conception, MO 64433, Tel. (816) 944-2211. Kevin McGonigle, M NC, Cath., 176.

Immaculate Heart College, Los Angeles, CA 90027, Tel. (213) 462-1301. Sr. Helen Kelley, C West, Cath., 624.

Incarnate Word College, San Antonio, TX 78209, Tel. (512) 828-1261. Earl Jones, C S, Cath., 1,321.

Indiana Central College, Indianapolis, IN 46227, Tel. (317) 787-6301. Gene E. Sease, C NC, Un. Meth., 2,445.

Iona College, New Rochelle, NY 10801, Tel. (914) 636-2100. John G. Driscoll, C MS, Cath., 3,780.

Iowa Wesleyan College, Mt. Pleasant, IA 52641, Tel. (319) 385-2211. Louis A. Haselmayer, C NC, Un. Meth., 896.

Jamestown College, Jamestown, ND 58401, Tel. (701) 252-4331. Roy Joe Stuckey, C NC, U. Presb. U.S.A., 645.

Jarvis Christian College, Hawkins, TX 75765, Tel. (214) 769-2841. J. P. Jones, C S, Christian Ch. (Disc.), 707.

John Carroll University, Cleveland, OH 44118, Tel. (216) 491-4911. Henry F. Birkenhauer, C NC, Cath., 4,146.

Johnson C. Smith University, Charlotte, NC 28216, Tel. (704) 372-2370. Lionel H. Newsom, C S, U. Presb. U.S.A., 1,136.

Judaism, University of, Los Angeles, CA 90028, Tel. (213) 463-1161. David L. Lieber, C West, Jewish, 310.

Judson College, Marion, AL 36756, Tel. (205) 683-2011. Norman H. McCrummen, W S, So. Bapt., 408.

Juniata College, Huntingdon, PA 16652, Tel. (814) 643-4310. John N. Stauffer, C MS, Ch. Breth., 1,212.

Kalamazoo College, Kalamazoo, MI 49001, Tel. (616) 343-1551. Weimer K. Hicks, C NC, Am. Bapt., 1,365.

Kansas Wesleyan University, Salina, KS 67401, Tel. (913) 827-5541. Paul W. Renich, C NC, Un. Meth., 643.

Kentucky Wesleyan College, Owensboro, KY 42301, Tel. (502) 684-5261. William E. James, C S, Un. Meth., 1,042.

Kenyon College, Gambier, OH 43022, Tel. (614) 427-2244. William G. Caples, Co. Ord. NC, Epis., 1,159.

Keuka College, Keuka Park, NY 14478, Tel. (315) 536-4411. G. Wayne Glick, W MS, Am. Bapt., 857.

King College, Bristol, TN 37620, Tel. (615) 968-1187. Powell A. Fraser, C S, Presb. US., 337.

King's College, Wilkes-Barre, PA 18702, Tel. (717) 824-9931. Lane D. Kilburn, C MS, Cath., 2,381.

Knoxville College, Knoxville, TN 37921, Tel. (615) 546-0751. Hardy L. Liston, Jr. C S, U. Presb. U.S.A., 1,301.

Ladycliff College, Highland Falls, NY 10928, Tel. (914) 446-4747. Francis J. Breidenbach, C MS, Cath., 502.

Lafayette College, Easton, PA 18042, Tel. (215) 253-6281. K. Roald Bergethon, C MS, U. Presb. U.S.A., 2,161.

LaGrange College, LaGrange, GA 30240, Tel. (404) 882-2911. Waights G. Henry, Jr., C S, Un. Meth., 558

Lake Forest College, Lake Forest, IL 60045, Tel. (312) 234-3100. Eugene Hotchkiss, III. C NC, U. Presb. U.S.A., 1,365.

Lakeland College, Sheboygan, WI 53081, Tel. (414) 565-2011. John B. Morland, C NC, U. Ch. of Christ, 594.

Lambuth College, Jackson, TN 38301, Tel. (901) 427-6743. James S. Wilder, Jr., C S, Un. Meth., 834.

Lane College, Jackson, TN 38301, Tel. (901) 424-4600 Herman Stone, Jr., C S, Chr. M. E., 924.

LaSalle College, Philadelphia, PA 19141, Tel. (215) 848-8300. Br. Daniel Burke, C MS, Cath., 6,975.

La Verne College, La Verne, CA 91750, Tel. (714) 593-3511. Leland B. Newcomer, C. West, Ch. of Breth., 1,158.

Lawrence University, Appleton, WI 54911, Tel. (414) 739-3681. Thomas S. Smith, C NC, Un. Meth., 1,409.

Lebanon Valley College, Annville, PA 17003, Tel. (717) 867-3561. Frederick P. Sample, C MS, Un. Meth., 1,346.

Lee College, Cleveland, TN 37311, Tel. (615) 472-2111. Charles W. Conn, C S, Ch. of God, 1,110.

LeMoyne College, Syracuse, NY 13214, Tel. (315) 446-2882. William L. Reilly, C MS, Cath., 1,818.

LeMoyne Owen College, Memphis, TN 38126, Tel. (901) 948-6626. Odell Horton, C S, U. Ch. of Christ, 687.

Lenoir-Rhyne College, Hickory, NC 28601, Tel. (704) 328-1741. Raymond M. Bost, C S, Luth. in Am., 1,341.

Lewis College, Lockport, IL 60441, Tel. (815) 838-0500. Lester Carr, C NC, Cath., 2,400.

Lewis & Clark College, Portland, OR 97219, Tel. (503) 246-8251. John R. Howard, C NW, U. Presb. U.S.A., 2,188.

Lindenwood Colleges, The, St. Charles, MO 63301, Tel. (314) 723-7152. John Anthony Brown, Jr., Co. Ord. NC, U. Presb. U.S.A., 693.

Linfield College, McMinnville, OR 97128, Tel. (503) 472-4121. Gordon C. Bjork, C NW, Amer. Bapt., 1,058.

Livingstone College, Salisbury, NC 28144, Tel. (704) 633-7960 F. George Shipman, C S, A.M.E. Zion, 720.

Loma Linda University, Loma Linda, CA 92354, Tel. (714) 796-7311. David J. Bieber, C West, S.D.A., 3,246.

Lone Mountain College, San Francisco, CA 94118, Tel. (415) 752-7000. Sr. Gertrude K. Patch, C West, Cath., 632.

Loras College, Dubuque, IA 52001, Tel. (319) 588-7100. Burton R. McQuillan actg. C NC, Cath., 1,586.

Loretto Heights College, Denver, CO 80236, Tel. (303) 922-4011. Sr. Patricia J. Manion, C NC, Cath., 912.

Louisiana College, Pineville, LA 71360, Tel. (318) 487-7401. G. Earl Guinn, C S, So. Bapt., 904

Loyola College, Baltimore, MD 21210, Tel. (301) 435-2500. Joseph A. Sellinger, C MS, Cath., 3,029.

Loyola University, Chicago, IL 60611, Tel. (312) 944-0800. Raymond C. Baumhart, C NC, Cath., 17,271.

Loyola University, New Orleans, LA 70118, Tel. (504) 866-5471. Michael F. Kennelly, C S, Cath., 4,997.

Loyola University of Los Angeles, Los Angeles, CA 90045, Tel. (213) 776-0400. Donald P. Merrifield, M West, Cath., 3,664.

Luther College, Decorah, IA 52101, Tel. (319) 382-3621. Elwin D. Farwell, C NC, Am. Luth., 2,083.

Lycoming College, Williamsport, PA 17701, Tel. (717) 326-1951. Harold H. Hutson, C MS, Un. Meth., 1,597.

Lynchburg College, Lynchburg, VA 24504, Tel. (703) 845-9071. Carey Brewer, C S, Christian Church (Disc.), 1,915.

Macalester College, St. Paul, MN 55101, Tel. (612) 647-6207. James A. Robinson, C NC, U. Presb. U.S.A., 2,093.

MacMurray College, Jacksonville, IL 62650, Tel. (217) 245-6151. John J. Wittich, C NC, Un. Meth., 986.

Madonna College, Livonia, MI 48150, Tel. (313) 425-8000. Sr. Mary Danatha, W NC, Cath., 611.

Malone College, Canton, OH 44709, Tel. (216) 454-3011. Everett L. Cattell, C NC, Friends, 860.

Manchester College, North Manchester, IN 46962, Tel. (219) 982-2141. A. Blair Helman, C NC, Ch. Breth., 1,510.

Manhattan College, Bronx, NY 10471, Tel. (212) 548-1400. Br. Gregory Nugent, M MS, Cath., 4,940.

Manhattanville College, Purchase, NY 10577, Tel. (914) 946-9600. Mo. Elizabeth J. McCormack, C MS, Cath., 1,444.

Marian College, Indianapolis, IN 46222, Tel. (317) 924-3291. Louis Gatto, C NC, Cath., 1,008.

Marian College of Fond du Lac, Fond du Lac, WI 54935, Tel. (414) 921-3900. James M. Hanlon, C NC, Cath., 453.

Marillac College, St. Louis, MO 63121, Tel. (314) 382-2800. Thomas Fischer, W NC, Cath., 278.

UNITED STATES COLLEGES AND UNIVERSITIES

Marion College, Marion, IN 46952, Tel. (317) 674-6901. Woodrow I. Goodman, C NC, Wes. Meth., 869.

Marist College, Poughkeepsie, NY 12601, Tel. (914) 471-3240. Linus R. Foy, C MS, Cath., 1,773.

Marquette University, Milwaukee, WI 53233, Tel. (414) 244-7700. John P. Raynor, C NC, Cath., 10,678.

Mars Hill College, Mars Hill, NC 28754, Tel. (704) 689-1151. Fred B. Bentley, C S, So. Bapt., 1,494.

Mary Baldwin College, Staunton, VA 24401, Tel. (703) 885-0811. William W. Kelly, W S, Presb. U.S., 729.

Mary College, Bismarck, ND., 58501, Tel. (701) 255-4681. Harold J. Miller, C NC, Cath., 518.

Mary Hardin-Baylor College, Belton, TX 76513, Tel. (817) 939-5811. Bobby E. Parker, C S, So. Bapt., 867.

Mary Immaculate Seminary and College, Northampton, PA 18067, Tel. (215) 262-7866. Robert P. Maloney, M MS, Cath., 48.

Mary Manse College, Toledo, OH 43620, Tel. (419) 243-9241. Sr. Rose Margaret Dostal, C NC, Cath., 647.

Marycrest College, Davenport, IA 52804, Tel. (319) 326-9512. Louis Vaccard, C NC, Cath., 1,061.

Marygrove College, Detroit, MI 48221, Tel. (313) 862-8000, Arthur W. Brown, C NC, Cath., 822.

Marylhurst College, Marylhurst, OR 97036, Tel. (503) 636-8141. Robert H. Krupp, W NW, Cath., 599.

Marymount College, Los Angeles, CA 90045, Tel. (213) 670-6551. Sr. M. Raymunce McKay, Co. Ord. West, Cath., 899.

Marymount College, Salina, KS 67401, Tel. (913) 823-6317. Emerald Dechant, C NC, Cath., 568.

Marymount College, Tarrytown, NY 10591, Tel. (914) 631-3200. John J. Meng, W MS, Cath., 1,044.

Marymount Manhattan College, New York, NY 10021, Tel. (212) 861-4200. Sr. Colette Mahoney, W MS, Cath., 1,085.

Maryville College, Maryville, TN 37801, Tel. (615) 982-6912. Joseph J. Copeland, C S, U. Presb. U.S.A., 768.

Maryville College of the Sacred Heart, St., Louis, MO 63141, Tel. (314) 434-4100. Sr. Harriet K. Switzer, C NC, Cath., 576.

Marywood College, Scranton, PA 18509, Tel. (717) 343-6521. Sr. M. Coleman Nee, C MS, Cath., 1,968.

McKendree College, Lebanon, IL 62254, Tel. (618) 537-4481. Eric N. Rackham, C NC, Un. Meth., 481.

McMurry College, Abilene, TX 79605, Tel. (915) 692-4130. Thomas K. Kim, C S, Un. Meth., 1,546.

McPherson College, McPherson, KS 67460, Tel. (316) 241-0731. J. J. Melhorn, C NC, Ch. Breth., 640.

Medaille College, Buffalo, NY 14214, Tel. (716) 883-9057. Sr. Alice Huber, C MS, Cath., 462.

Mercer University, Macon, GA 31207, Tel. (912) 743-1511. Rufus C. Harris, C S, So. Bapt., 1,714.

Mercy College, Dobbs Ferry, NY 10522, Tel. (914) 693-4500, Helen W. Coogan, C MS, Cath., 1,192.

Mercy College of Detroit, Detroit, MI 48219, Tel. (313) 531-7820. Sr. Agnes Mary Mansour, C NC, Cath., 1,605.

Mercyhurst College, Erie, PA 16501, Tel. (814) 864-0681. Sr. M. Carolyn Herrmann, C MS, Cath., 675.

Meredith College, Raleigh, NC 27611, Tel. (919) 833-6461. E. Bruce Heilman, W S, So. Bapt., 1,109.

Merrimak College, North Andover, MA 01845, Tel. (617) 683-7111. John R. Aherne, C NE, Cath., 2,833.

Messiah College, Grantham, PA 17027, Tel. (717) 766-2511. D. Ray Hostetter, C MS, Breth. in Christ, 661.

Methodist College, Fayetteville, NC 28301, Tel. (919) 488-7110. L. S. Weaver, C S, Un. Meth., 810.

Midland Lutheran College, Fremont, NB 68025, Tel. (402) 721-5480. L. D. Lund, C NC, Luth. in Am., 927.

Miles College, Birmingham, AL 35208, Tel. (205) 786-5281. W. C. Williams C S, CME, 1,139.

Milligan College, Milligan College, TN 37682, Tel. (615) 928-1165. Jess W. Johnson, C S, CC/CC, 832.

Millikin University, Decatur, IL 62522, Tel. (217) 423-3661. J. Roger Miller, C NC, U. Presb. U.S.A., 1,883.

Millsaps College, Jackson, MS 39210, Tel. (601) 354-5201. Edward M. Collins, Jr., C S. Un. Meth., 952.

Mississippi College, Clinton, MS 39056, Tel. (601) 924-5131. Lewis Nobles, C S, So. Bapt. 2,371.

Missouri Valley College, Marshall, MO 65340, Tel. (816) 886-7491. W. L. Tompkins, C NC, U. Presb. U.S.A., 912.

Mobile College, Mobile, AL 36613, Tel. (205) 457-4544. William K. Weaver, Jr., C S, So. Bapt., 424.

Molloy Catholic College, Rockville Centre, NY 11750, Tel. (516) 678-5000. Mo. Celeste Beck, W MS, Cath., 1,128.

Monmouth College, Monmouth, IL 61462, Tel. (309) 457-2311 Richard D. Stine, C NC, U. Presb. U.S.A., 1,300.

Moravian College, Bethlehem, PA 18018, Tel. (215) 865-0741. Herman E. Collier, Jr., C MS, Morav., 1,718.

Morehouse College, Atlanta, GA 30314, Tel. (404) 688-4223. Hugh M. Gloster, M S, Am. Bapt., 1,009.

Morningside College, Sioux City, IA 51106, Tel. (712) 277-5100. Thomas S. Thompson, C NC, Un. Meth., 1,645.

Morris Brown College, Atlanta, GA 30314, Tel. (404) 525-7831. John A. Middleton, C S, A. M.E., 1,454.

Mt. Angel College, Mount Angel, OR 97362, Tel. (503) 845-2234. Christian Mondor, C NW, Cath., 323.

Mt. Marty College, Yankton, SD 57078, Tel. (605) 668-1011. Sr. M. Evangeline Anderson, C NC, Cath., 465.

Mt. Mary College, Milwaukee, WI 53222, Tel. (414) 258-4810. Sr. Mary Nora Barber W NC, Cath., 860.

Mt. Mercy College, Cedar Rapids, IA 52402, Tel. (319) 363-8213. Sr. Mary Agnes Hennessey, C NC, Cath., 560.

Mt. St. Mary College, Newburgh, NY 12550, Tel. (914) 561-0800. Vacant, C MS, Cath., 696.

Mt. St. Mary College, Hooksett, NH 03106, Tel. (603) 485-9536. Sr. Mary Vianney Fulham, W. NE, Cath., 288.

Mt. St. Mary's College, Emmitsburg, MD 21727, Tel. (301) 447-6122. John J. Dillon, C MS, Cath., 1,111.

Mt. St. Mary's College, Los Angeles, CA 90049, Tel. (213) 272-8791. Sr. Cecelia L. Moore, W West, Cath., 1,176.

Mount Union College, Alliance, OH 44601, Tel. (216) 821-5320. Roland G. Weber, C NC, Un. Meth., 1,268.

Muhlenberg College, Allentown, PA 18104, Tel. (215) 433-3191 John H. Morey, C MS, Luth. in Am., 1,843.

Mundelein College, Chicago, IL 60626, Tel. (312) 262-8100. Sr. Ann Ida Gannon, W NC, Cath., 1,311.

Muskingum College, New Concord, OH 43762, Tel. (614) 826-7621. William P. Miller, C NC, U. Presb. U.S.A., 1,373.

Nazareth College, Kalamazoo, MI 49074, Tel. (616) 349-7783. Sr. Mary L. Bader, C NC, Cath., 400.

Nazareth College of Rochester, Rochester, NY 14610, Tel. (716) 586-2525. Sr. Helen Malone, Co-Ord. MS, Cath., 1,462.

Nebraska Wesleyan University, Lincoln, NB 68504, Tel. (402) 466-2371. Vance D. Rogers, C NC, Un. Meth., 1,224.

Newberry College, Newberry, SC 29108, Tel. (803) 276-5010. Fredric B. Irvin, C S, Luth. in Am., 805.

Newton College of the Sacred Heart, Newton, MA 02159, Tel. (617) 332-6700. James J. Whalen, W NE, Cath., 862.

Niagara University, Niagara University, NY 14109, Tel. (716) 285-1212. Kenneth Slattery, C MS, Cath., 3,158.

North Carolina Wesleyan College, Rocky Mount, NC 27801, Tel. (919) 442-7121. Thomas A. Collins, C S, Un. Meth., 631.

North Central College, Naperville, IL 60540, Tel. (312) 355-5500. Arlo L. Schilling, C NC, Un. Meth., 869.

North Park College, Chicago, IL 60625, Tel. (312) 583-2700. Lloyd H. Ahlens, C NC, Evan. Cov. Ch. of Amer., 1,422.

Northland College, Ashland, WI 54806, Tel. (715) 682-4531. Malcolm McClean, C NC, U. Ch. of Christ, 641.

Northwest Christian College, Eugene, OR 97401, Tel. (503) 343-1641. Barton A. Dowdy, C NW, Christian Church (Disc.), 342.

Northwest Nazarene College, Nampa, ID 83651, Tel. (208) 467-8011. John E. Riley, C NW, Nazarene, 1,118.

Northwestern College, Orange City, IA 51041, Tel. (712) 737-4821. Lars I. Granberg, C NC, Ref. Am., 769.

Northwestern University, Evanston, IL 60201, Tel. (312) 492-3741. James Roscoe Miller, C NC, Un. Meth. 15,571.

Notre Dame College, St. Louis, MO 63125, Tel. (314) 544-0455. Sr. M. Francis B. Stauder, W NC, Cath., 334.

Notre Dame College, Manchester, NH 03104, Tel. (603) 669-4298. Sr. Jeannette Vezean, W NE, Cath., 426.

Norte Dame College, Cleveland, OH 44121, Tel. (216) 381-1680. Sr. Mary Luke Arntz, W NC, Cath., 602.

Notre Dame Seminary, New Orleans, LA 70118, Tel. (504) 866-7426. Alexander D. Sigur, M S, Cath., 184.

Notre Dame, University of, Notre Dame, IN 46556, Tel. (219) 284-6011. Theodore M. Hesburgh, M NC, Cath., 7,967.

Nyack Missionary College, Nyack, NY 10960, Tel. (914) 358-1710. Harold W. Boon, C MS, Chr. and Miss. All., 580.

Oakwood College, Huntsville, AL 35806, Tel. (205) 837-1630 Calvin B. Rock, C S, S.D.A., 569.

Oblate College, Washington, DC 20017, Tel. (202) 529-5244. Richard J. Murphy, M MS, Cath., 98.

Occidental College, Los Angeles, CA 90041, Tel. (213) 255-5151. Richard C. Gilman, C West, U. Presb. U.S.A., 1,868.

Ohio Dominican College, Columbus, OH 43219, Tel. (614) 253-2741. Sr. M. Suzanne Uhrhane, C NC, Cath., 940.

Ohio Northern University, Ada, OH 45810, Tel. (419) 634-3015. Samuel L. Meyer, C NC, Un. Meth., 2,201.

Ohio Wesleyan University, Delaware, OH 43015, Tel. (614) 363-1261. Thomas E. Wenslau, C NC, Un. Meth., 2,597.

Oklahoma Baptist University, Shawnee, OK 74801, Tel. (405) 275-2850. William G. Tanner, C NC, So. Bapt., 1,653.

Oklahoma City University, Oklahoma City, OK 73106, Tel. (405) 525-5461. Dolfus Whitten, Jr. C NC, Un. Meth., 1,946.

Olivet College, Olivet, MI 49076, Tel. (616) 749-2111. Ray B. Loeschner, C NC, U. Ch. of Christ, 906.

Olivet Nazarene College, Kankakee, IL 60901, Tel. (815) 939-5011. Harold W. Reed, C NC, Nazarene, 1,843.

Oral Roberts University, Tulsa, OK 74105, Tel. (918) 743-6161. G. Oral Roberts, C NC, interdenom., 1,020.

Ottawa University, Ottawa, KS 66067, Tel. (913) 242-5200. Peter H. Armacost, C NC, Amer. Bapt., 823.

Otterbein College, Westerville, OH 43081, Tel. (614) 882-3601. Thomas J. Kerr, IV, C NC, Un. Meth., 1,413.

Ouachita Baptist University, Arkadelphia, AR 71923, Tel. (501) 246-4531. Daniel R. Grant, C NC, So. Bapt., 1,393.

Our Lady of the Lake College, San Antonio, TX 78285, Tel. (512) 434-6711. John L. McMahon, C S, Cath., 1,869.

Ozarks, School of the, Point Lookout, MO 65726, Tel. (417) 334-3101. M. Graham Clark, C NC, Presby. U.S., 1,004.

Pacific Christian College, Long Beach, CA 90804, Tel. (213) 434-9991. Medford H. Jones, C West, Ch. of Christ, 234.

Pacific College, Fresno, CA 93702, Tel. (209) 251-7194. Arthur J. Wiebe, C West, Menn. Ch., 520.

Pacific Lutheran University, Tacoma, WA 98447, Tel. (206) 531-6900. Eugene W. Wiegman, C NW, Am. Luth., 2,999.

Pacific Union College, Angwin, CA 94508, Tel. (707) 965-6211. F. O. Rittenhouse, C West, S. D.A., 1,934.

Pacific, University of the, Stockton, CA 95204, Tel. (209) 946-2011. Alistair W. McCrone, actg., C West, Un. Meth., 5,080.

Pacific University, Forest Grove, OR 97116, Tel. (503) 357-6151. James W. Miller, C NW, U. Ch. of Christ, 1,249.

Paine College, Augusta, GA 30901, Tel. (404) 722-4471. Lucius H. Pitts, C S, Un. Meth. and C.M.E., 691.

Park College, Kansas City, MO 64152, Tel. (816) 741-2000. Donald M. Mackenzie, C NC, U. Presb. U.S.A., 676.

Pasadena College, Pasadena, CA 91104, Tel. (213) 798-0541. W. Shelburne Brown, C West, Nazarene, 1,260.

Pfeiffer College, Misenheimer, NC 28109, Tel. (704) 463-3111. Douglas R. Sasser, C S, Un. Meth., 882.

Philander Smith College, Little Rock, AR 72203, Tel. (501) 375-9845. Walter R. Hazzard, C NC, Un. Meth. 639.

Phillips University, Enid, OK 73701, Tel. (405) 237-4433. Hallie G. Gantz, C NC, Christian Church (Disc.), 1,392.

Pikeville College, Pikeville, KY 41501, Tel. (606) 432-3161. Robert S. Cope, C S, U. Presb. U.S.A., 739.

Portland, University of, Portland, OR 97203, Tel. (503) 289-5541. Paul E. Waldschmidt, C NW, Cath., 1,959.

Presbyterian College, Clinton, SC 29325, Tel. (803) 833-2820. Marc C. Weersing, C S, Presb. U.S., 777.

Providence College, Providence, RI 02918, Tel. (401) 861-1000. Thomas R. Peterson C NE, Cath., 2,969.

Puget Sound, University of, Tacoma, WA 98416, Tel. (206) 759-3521. R. Franklin Thompson, C NW, Un. Meth., 3,665.

Queens College, Charlotte, NC 28207, Tel. (704) 332-7121. John E. Smylie, W S, Presb. U.S., 657.

Quincy College, Quincy, IL 62301, Tel. (217) 222-8020. Titus Ludes, C NC, Cath., 2,166.

Randolph-Macon College, Ashland, VA 23005, Tel. (703) 798-8372. Luther W. White, III, C S, Un. Meth., 800.

Randolph-Macon Woman's College, Lynchburg, VA 24504, Tel. (703) 846-7392. W. F. Quillian, Jr., W S, Un. Meth., 778.

Redlands, University of, Redlands, CA 92373, Tel. (714) 793-2121. Eugene E. Dawson, C West, Am. Bapt., 1,970.

Regis College, Denver, CO 80221, Tel. (303) 433-8471. Thomas J. Casey, C NC, Cath., 1,424.

Regis College, Weston, MA 02193, Tel. (617) 893-1820. Sr. Jeanne d'Arc O'Hare, W NE, Cath., 898.

Richmond, University of, Richmond, VA 23173, Tel. (703) 285-6000. G. M. Modlin, C S, So. Bapt., 4,789.

Ricker College, Houlton, ME 04730, Tel. (207) 532-2223. Robert E. Matson, C NE, Amer. Bapt., 621.

Ripon College, Ripon, WI 54971, Tel. (414) 748-8118. Bernard S. Adams, C NC, U. Ch. of Christ, 1,067.

Rivier College, Nashua, NH 03060, Tel. (603) 888-1311. Sr. Gloria A. Lemieux, W NE, Cath., 734.

Roanoke College, Salem, VA 24153, Tel. (703) 389-2351. Perry F. Kendig, C S, Luth. in Am., 1,399.

Roberts Wesleyan College, Rochester, NY 14624, Tel. (716) 594-9471. Lawrence R. Schoenhals, C MS, Free Meth., 736.

Rockhurst College, Kansas City, MO 64110, Tel. (816) 363-4010. Maurice E. Van Ackeren, C NC, Cath., 2,469.

Rocky Mountain College, Billings, MT 59102, Tel. (406) 245-6151. Lawrence F. Small, C NW, Un. Meth., U. Ch. of Christ, U. Presb. U.S.A., 560.

Rogers College, Maryknoll, NY 10545, Tel. (914) 941-7575. Sr. Ruth Greble, C MS, Cath., 101.

Rosary College, River Forest, IL 60305, Tel. (312) 369-6320. Sr. M. Candida Lund, C NC, Cath., 1,195.

Rosary Hill College, Buffalo, NY 14226, Tel. (716) 839-3600. Sr. M. Angela Canavan, C MS, Cath., 1,262.

Rosemont College, Rosemont, PA 19010, Tel. (215) 527-0200. Sr. Ann Marie Durst. W MS, Cath., 670.

Russell College, Burlingame, CA 94010, Tel. (415) 342-8346. Raymond N. Doyle, W West, Cath., 121.

Sacred Heart College, Wichita, KS 67213, Tel. (316) 942-4291 Roman Galiarci, C NC, Cath., 652.

Sacred Heart College, Belmont, NC 28012. Tel. (704) 825-8468. Sr. Mary Stephen, W S, Cath., 350.

Sacred Heart Seminary, Detroit, MI 48206, Tel. (313) 868-2700. Thaddeus J. Ozog, M NC, Cath. 158.

Sacred Heart University, Bridgeport, CT 06604, Tel. (203) 374-9441. William H. Conley, C NE, Cath. 2,074.

St. Albert's College, Oakland, CA 94618, Tel. (415) 654-5725. Janko Zagar, M West., Cath., 97.

St. Alphonsus College, Suffield, CT 06078, Tel. (203) 668-7393. Joseph T. Hurley, M NE, Cath., 63.

St. Ambrose College, Davenport, IA 52803, Tel. (319) 324-1681. Sebastian G. Menke, C NC, Cath., 1,410.

St. Andrews Presbyterian College, Laurinburg, NC 28352, Tel. (919) 276-3652. Donald J. Hart, C S, Presb. U.S., 840.

St. Anselm's College, Manchester, NH 03102, Tel. (603) 669-1030. Placidus H. Riley, M NE, Cath., 1,615.

St. Augustine's College, Raleigh, NC 27611, Tel. (919) 828-4451. Prezell K. Robinson, C S, Epis. 1,118.

St. Bernard College, St. Bernard, AL 35138, Tel. (205) 734-4110. Gregory J. Roettger, C S, Cath., 615.

St. Bonaventure University, St. Bonaventure, NY 14778, Tel. (716) 372-0300. Reginald A. Redlon, C MS, Cath., 2,621.

St. Edward's University, Austin TX 78704, Tel. (512) 444-2621. Edgar L. Roy, Jr., C S, Cath., 1,052.

St. Fidelis College, Herman, PA 16039, Tel. (412) 287-4794. Edmund W. Quinn, M MS, Cath., 63.

St. Francis College, Biddeford, ME 04005, Tel. (207) 282-1515. Ernest R. Therrien, C NE, Cath., 1,075.

St. Francis College, Brooklyn, NY 11021, Tel. (212) 522-2300. Bro. Donald Sullivan, C MS, Cath., 2,505.

St. Francis College, Fort Wayne, IN 46808, Tel. (219) 432-3551. Sr. Joellen Scheetz, C NC, Cath., 2,226.

St. Francis College, Loretto, PA 15940, Tel. (814) 472-7000. Vincent Negherbon, C MS, Cath., 1,641.

St. Francis de Sales College. Milwaukee, WI 53207. Tel. (414) 744-5450. John E. Twomey, M NC, Cath., 168.

St. Hyacinth College, Granby, MA 01033, Tel. (413) 467-4422. Adam Zajdel, M NE, Cath., 53.

St. John College of Cleveland, Cleveland, OH 44114, Tel. (216) 771-2388. Lawrence P. Cahill, C NC, Cath., 855.

St. John Fisher College, Rochester, NY 14618, Tel. (716) 586-4140. Charles J. Lavery, C MS, Cath., 1,347.

St. John's College, Camarillo, CA 93010, Tel. (805) 482-2755. W. Theodore Weisner, M West., Cath., 178.

St. John's University, Collegeville, MN 56321, Tel. (612) 363-7761. Michael J. Bleckner, M NC, Cath., 1,581.

St. John's University, Jamaica, NY 11432, Tel. (212) 969-8000. Joseph T. Cahill, C MS, Cath., 13,619.

St. Joseph College, W. Hartford, CT 06117, Tel. (203) 523-4283. Sr. Mary Consolata O'Connor, W NE, Cath., 895.

St. Joseph College, Emmitsburg, MD 21727, Tel. (301) 447-6111. Sr. Margaret Dougherty, W MS, Cath., 518.

St. Joseph's College, Rensselaer, IN 47978, Tel. (219) 866-7111. Charles H. Banet, C NC, Cath., 1,366.

St. Joseph's College, North Windham, ME 04062, Tel. (207) 892-6766. Bernard Currier, C NE, Cath., 316.

St. Joseph's College, Philadelphia, PA 19131, Tel. (215) 879-1000. Terrence Toland, C MS, Cath., 6,938.

St. Joseph's College, Brooklyn, NY 11205 Tel. (212) 622-4696. Sr. George A. O'Connor, C MS, Cath., 560.

St. Joseph's Seminary and College, Yonkers, NY 10704, Tel. (914) 968-6200. Edward J. Montano, M MS, Cath., 91.

St. Joseph Seminary and College, Saint Benedict, LA 70457 Tel. (504) 892-1900. Marian E. Larmann, C S, Cath., 105.

St. Leo College, St. Leo, FL 33574, Tel. (904) 588-4101. Thomas B. Southard C S, Cath., 1,172.

St. Louis University, St. Louis, MO 63103, Tel. (314) 535-3300. Paul C. Reinert, C NC, Cath., 9,383.

St. Martin's College, Olympia, WA 98501, Tel. (206) 491-4700. Matthew Naumes, C NW, Cath., 644.

St. Mary College, Xavier, KS 66098, Tel. (913) 682-5151. Sr. Mary Janet McGilley, W NC, Cath., 671.

St. Mary of the Plains College, Dodge City, KS 67801. Tel. (316) 225-4171. William V. Tucker, C NC, Cath., 620.

St. Mary-of-the-Woods College, St. Mary-of-the-Woods, IN 47876, Tel. (812) 533-2181. Sr. Jeanne Knoerle, W NC, Cath., 411.

St. Mary's College, Notre Dame, IN 46556, Tel. (219) 232-3031. Sr. M Alma Peter, Co. Ord. NC, Cath., 1,719.

St. Mary's College, Winona, MN 55987, Tel. (507) 452-4430. Br. George Pahl, C NC, Cath., 995.

St. Mary's College of California, Moraga, CA 94575, Tel. (415) 376-4411. Br. Mel Anderson, C West, Cath., 1,155.

St. Mary's Dominican College, New Orleans, LA 70118, Tel. (504) 865-7761. Sr. Mary Ursula Cooper, W S, Cath., 780.

St. Mary's Seminary and College, Perryville, MO 63775, Tel. (314) 547-6533. Carl G Schulte, M NC, Cath., 73.

St. Mary's Seminary and University, Baltimore, MD 21210, Tel. (301) 323-3200. John F. Dede, M MS, Cath., 681.

St. Mary's University, San Antonio, TX 78228, Tel. (512) 433-2311. Louis J. Blume, C S, Cath., 4,211.

St. Meinrad College, St. Meinrad, IN 47577, Tel. (812) 357-6611. Hilary Ottensmeyer, M NC, Cath., 283.

St. Michael's College, Winooski, VT 05404, Tel. (802) 655-2000. Bernard L. Boütin, C NE, Cath., 1,435.

St. Norbert College, West De Pere, WI 54178, Tel. (414) 336-3181. Robert E. Christin, C NC, Cath., 1,673.

St. Olaf College, Northfield, MN 55057, Tel. (507) 645-9311. Sidney A. Rand, C NC, Am. Luth., 2,569.

St. Patrick's College, Mountain View, CA 94040, Tel. (415) 967-9501. R. Louis Stasker, M West, Cath., 110

St. Paul's College, Lawrenceville, VA 23868, Tel. (703) 848-2636. James A. Russell, Jr. C S, Epis., 449.

St. Paul's College, Washington, DC 20017, Tel. (202) 832-6262. Wilfred Dewan, M MS, Cath., 111.

St. Peter's College, Jersey City, NJ 07306, Tel. (201) 333-4400. Victor R. Yanitelli, C MS, Cath., 4,744.

St. Thomas Seminary, Denver, CO 80210, Tel. (303) 722-4687. Frances H. Agnew, M NC, Cath., 177.

St. Thomas, University of, Houston, TX 77006, Tel. (713) 522-7911. Patrick O. Braden, C S, Cath., 1,250.

St. Vincent College, Latrobe, PA 15650, Tel. (412) 537-3371. Cecil G. Diethrich, M MS, Cath., 952.

St. Xavier College, Chicago, IL 60655, Tel. (312) 779-3300. Harry A. Marmion, C NC, Cath., 985.

Salem College, Salem, WV 26426, Tel. (304) 782-2500. K. Duane Hurley, C NC, 7th Day Bapt., 1,360.

Salem College, Winston-Salem, NC 27108, Tel. (919) 723-7961. Dale H. Gramley, W S, Morav., 526.

Salve Regina College, Newport, RI 02840, Tel. (401) 847-6650. Sr. M. Christopher O'Rourke, W NE, Cath., 1,220.

Samford University, Birmingham, AL 35209, Tel. (205) 870-2011. Leslie S. Wright, C S, So. Bapt., 2,663.

San Diego, University of, Coordinate Colleges. Alcola Park, CA 92110, Tel. (714) 291-6480. Author E. Hughes Co. Ord. West Cath., 1,451.

San Francisco, University of, San Francisco, CA 94117, Tel. (415) 752-1000. Albert R. Jonsen, C West, Cath., 6,830.

Santa Clara, University of, Santa Clara, CA 95053, Tel. (408) 984-4242. Thomas D. Terry, C West, Cath., 5,983.

Scarritt College, Nashville, TN 37203, Tel. (615) 327-1311. Gerald H. Anderson, C S, Un. Meth., 141.

Scranton, University of, Scranton, PA 18510, Tel. (717) 347-3321. Dexter L. Hanley, C MS, Cath., 2,942.

Seattle Pacific College, Seattle, WA 98119, Tel. (206) 284-7700. David L. McKenna, C NW, Free Meth., 2,014.

Seattle University, Seattle WA 98122, Tel. (206) 626-6200. Louis Goffney, C NW, Cath., 3,368.

Seminary of Our Lady of Providence, Warwick, RI 02889, Tel. (401) 739-6850. Robert J. Randell, M NE, Cath., 116.

Seminary of St. Pius X, Erlanger, KY 41018, Tel. (606) 371-4448. Elmer J. Grosser, M S, Cath., 40.

Seton Hall University, South Orange, NJ 07079, Tel. (201) 762-9000. Thomas G. Fahy, actg., C MS, Cath., 9,499.

Seton Hill College, Greensburg, PA 15601, Tel. (412) 834-2200. Sr. Mary Schmidt, W MS, Cath., 791.

Shaw University, Raleigh, NC 27602, Tel. (919) 833-3812. James A. Hargroves, C S, Am. Bapt., 1,154.

Shimer College, Mt. Carroll, IL 61053, Tel. (815) 244-2811. Robert S. Long, C NC, Epis., 280.

Shorter College, Rome, GA 30161, Tel. (404) 232-2463. Randall H. Minor, C S, So. Bapt., 568.

Siena College, Memphis, TN 38117, Tel. (901) 683-2469. Sr. Marina Gibbons, C S, Cath., 239.

Siena College, Loudonville, NY 12211, Tel. (518) 785-8511. Matthew T. Conlin, C MS, Cath., 1,853.

Siena Heights College, Adrian, MI 49221, Tel. (313) 263-0731. Hugh Thompson actg., C NC, Cath., 695.

Simpson College, San Francisco, CA 94134. Tel. (415) 334-7400. Mark W. Lee, C West, S.D.A., 263.

Simpson College, Indianola, IA 50125, Tel. (515) 961-6251. Ralph C. John, C NC, Un. Meth., 1,001.

Sioux Falls College, Sioux Falls, SD 57101, Tel. (605) 336-2850. Ronald V. Wells, C NC, Am. Bapt., 979.

South, University of the, Sewanee, TN 37375, Tel. (615) 598-5720. Jefferson Bennett, C S, Epis., 993.

Southern California College, Costa Mesa, CA 92626, Tel. (714) 545-1178. Emil A. Balliet, C West, Assem, of God., 516.

Southern Methodist University, Dallas, TX 75222, Tel. (214) 363-5611. Willis M. Tate, C S, Un. Meth., 10,136.

Southern Missionary College, Collegedale, TN 37315, Tel. (615) 396-2111. Frank A. Knittel C S, S.D.A., 1,332.

Southwest Baptist College, Bolivar, MO 65613, Tel. (417) 326-5281. James L. Sells, C NC, So. Bapt., 1,219.

Southwestern at Memphis, Memphis, TN 38112, Tel. (901) 274-1800. William L. Bowden, C S, Presb. U.S. 1,051.

Southwestern College, Winfield, KS 67156, Tel. (316) 221-4150. C. Orville Strohl, C NC, Un. Meth., 675.

Southwestern University, Georgetown, TX 78626, Tel. (512) 863-2531. Durwood Fleming, C S, Un. Meth., 860.

Spelman College, Atlanta, GA 30314, Tel. (404)

688-2148. Albert E. Manley, W S, Am. Bapt., 967.

Spertus College Judaica, Chicago, IL 60605. Tel. (312) 922-9012. David Weinstein, C NC, Jewish, 406.

Spring Arbor College, Spring Arbor, MI 49283, Tel. (517) 787-1200. Ellwood A. Voller, C NC, Free Meth., 730.

Spring Hill College, Mobile, AL 36608, Tel. (205) 460-2121. William J. Rimes, C S, Cath., 970.

Stephens College, Columbia, MO 65201, Tel. (314) 442-2211. Seymour A. Smith, W NC, Am. Bapt., 2,140.

Sterling College, Sterling, KS 67579, Tel. (316) 278-2173. William M. McCreery, C NC, U. Presb. U.S.A., 569.

Stetson University, De Land, FL 32720, Tel. (904) 734-4121. John E. Johns, C S, So. Bapt., 2,586.

Stillman College, Tuscaloosa, AL 35401, Tel. (205) 752-2548. Harold N. Stinson, C S, Presb. U.S., 658.

Stonehill College, North Easton, MA 02356, Tel. (617) 238-2052. Ernest J. Bartell, C NE, Cath., 1,658.

Sulpician Seminary of the Northwest, Kenmore, WA 98028, Tel. (206) 827-5611. Edward J. Hogan, M NW, Cath., 89.

Susquehanna University, Selinsgrove, PA 17870, Tel. (717) 374-2345. Gustave W. Weber, C MS, Luth. in Am., 1,309.

Swarthmore College, Swarthmore, PA 19081, Tel. (215) 544-7900. Robert D. Cross, C MS, Friends, 1,164.

Syracuse University, Syracuse, NY 13210, Tel. (315) 476-5541. Melvin A. Eggers, C MS, Un. Meth., 18,563.

Tabor College, Hillsboro, KS 67063, Tel. (316) 947-3121. Roy Just, C NC, Menn. Breth., 406.

Talladega College, Talladega, AL 35160, Tel. (205) 362-2752. Herman H. Long, C S, U. Ch. of Christ, 533.

Tarkio College, Tarkio, MO 64491, Tel. (816) 736-4131. Eldon E. Breazier, C NC, U. Presb. U.S.A., 544.

Temple Buell College, Denver, CO 80220, Tel. (303) 394-6012. Dumont F. Kenny, W NC, Am. Bapt., 813.

Tennessee Wesleyan College, Athens, TN 37303, Tel. (615) 745-0250. Charles C. Turner, Jr., C S, Un. Meth., 761.

Texas Christian University, Fort Worth, TX 76129, Tel. (817) 926-2461. James M. Moudy, C S, Christian Church (Disc.), 6,433.

Texas College, Tyler, TX 75701, Tel. (214) 597-3200. Allen C. Hancock, C S, Chr. Meth. Epis, 534.

Texas Lutheran College, Seguin, TX 78155, Tel. (512) 379-4161. Joe K. Menn, C S, Am. Luth., 984.

Texas Wesleyan College, Fort Worth, TX 76105, Tel. (817) 534-0251. William M. Pearce, C S, Un. Meth., 1,760.

Thiel College, Greenville, PA 16125, Tel. (412)

588-7700. Chauncey G. Bly, C MS, Luth. in Am., 1,401.

Thomas More College, Fort Mitchell, KY 41017, Tel. (606) 341-5800. Richard A. DeGraff, C S, Cath., 2,227.

Tift College, Forsyth, GA 31029, Tel. (912) 994-2515. Robert W. Jackson, W S, So. Bapt., 642.

Tolentine College, Olympia Fields, IL 60461, Tel. (312) 748-9500. Donald W. Harkabus, C NC, Cath., 98.

Tougaloo College, Tougaloo, MS 39174, Tel. (601) 956-4941. George A. Owens, C S, U. Ch. of Christ and Christian Church (Disc.), 736.

Transylvania University, Lexington, KY 40508, Tel. (606) 255-6861. Irvin E. Lunger, C S, Christian Church (Disc.), 859.

Trevecca Nazarene College, Nashville, TN 37210. Tel. (615) 244-6000. Mark R. Moore, C S, Nazarene, 730.

Trinity College, Hartford, CT 06106, Tel. (203) 527-3151. Theodore D. Lockwood, C NE, Epis., 1,968.

Trinity College, Washington, DC 20017. Tel. (202) 269-2000. Sr. Margaret Claydon, W MS, Cath., 857.

Trinity College, Deerfield, IL 60015, Tel. (312) 945-6700. Harry L. Evans, C NC, Evan. Free Ch. of Am., 785.

Trinity College, Burlington, VT 05401, Tel. (802) 864-4891. Sr. Elizabeth A. Candon, W NE, Cath., 449.

Trinity University, San Antonio, TX 78212, Tel. (512) 736-4141. G. Duncan Wimpress, C S, U Presb. U.S.A., 2,894.

Tusculum College, Greeneville, TN 37743, Tel. (615) 639-2661. Andrew N. Cothran, C S, U. Presb. U.S.A., 677.

Union College, Barbourville, KY 40906, Tel. (606) 546-4151. Mahlon A. Miller, C S, Un. Meth., 926.

Union College, Lincoln, NB 68506, Tel. (402) 488-2331. Robert H. Brown, C NC, S.D.A., 893.

Union University, Jackson, TN 38301, Tel. (901) 422-2576. Robert E. Craig, C S, So. Bapt., 806.

United States International University, San Diego, CA 92101, Tel. (714) 239-0391. William C. Rust, C West, Un. Meth., 4,108.

Upsala College, E. Orange, NJ 07019, Tel. (201) 266-7000. Carl G. Fjellman, C MS, Luth. in Am., 1,843.

Ursinus College, Collegeville, PA 19426, Tel. (215) 489-4111. William S. Pettit, C MS, U. Ch. of Christ, 2,031.

Ursuline College, Cleveland, OH 44124, Tel. (216) 449-4200. Sr. Mary Kenan Dulzer, W NC, Cath., 502.

Valparaiso University, Valparaiso, IN 46383, Tel. (219) 462-5111. Albert G. Huegli, C NC, Luth. (Mo.), 4,950.

Villa Maria College, Erie, PA 16505, Tel. (814) 838-1966. Sr. M. Lawrence Antoun, W MS, Cath., 617.

Villanova University, Villanova, PA 19085, Tel. (215) 527-2100. Robert J. Welsh, C MS, Cath., 9,378.

Virginia Union University, Richmond, VA 23220, Tel. (703) 355-9331. Allix B. James, C S, Am. Bapt., 1,313.

Virginia Wesleyan College, Norfolk, VA 23502, Tel. (703) 464-6291. Lambuth M. Clarke, C S, Un. Meth., 634.

Viterbo College, La Crosse, WI 54601, Tel. (608) 784-8413. J. Thomas Finucan, C NC, Cath., 443.

Voorhees College, Denmark, SC 29042, Tel. (803) 793-3346. Harry P. Graham, C S, Epis., 624.

Wagner College, Staten Island, NY 10301, Tel. (212) 390-3000. Arthur O. Davidson, C MS, Luth. in Am., 3,225.

Wake Forest University, Winston-Salem, NC 27109, Tel. (919) 725-9711. James R. Scales, C S, So. Bapt., 3,326.

Walla Walla College, College Place, WA 99324, Tel. (509) 525-7560. Robert L. Reynolds, C NW, S.D.A., 1,245.

Walsh College, Canton, OH 44720, Tel. (216) 499-7090. Robert A. Francoeur, C NC, Cath., 1,000.

Warner Pacific College, Portland, OR 97215, Tel. (503) 775-4368. E. Joe Gilliam, C NW, Ch. of God, 441.

Warren Wilson College, Swannanoa, NC 28778, Tel. (704) 298-3325. Reuben A. Holden, C S, U. Presb. U.S.A., 373.

Wartburg College, Waverly, IA 50677, Tel. (319) 352-1200. John W. Bachman, C NC, Am. Luth., 1,404.

Wayland Baptist College, Plainview, TX 79072, Tel. (806) 296-5521. Roy C. McClung, C S, So. Bapt., 689.

Waynesburg College, Waynesburg, PA 15370, Tel. (412) 627-8191. Bennett M. Rich, C MS, U. Presb. U.S.A., 1,113.

Wesleyan College, Macon, GA 31201, Tel. (912) 477-1110, W. Earl Strickland, W S, Un. Meth., 461.

West Virginia Wesleyan College, Buckhannon, WV 26201, Tel. (304) 473-8181. Stanley H. Martin, C NC, Un. Meth., 1,771.

Western Maryland College, Westminster, MD 21157, Tel. (301) 848-7000. Lowell S. Ensor, C MS, Un. Meth., 1,936.

Westmar College, La Mars, IA 51031, Tel. (712) 546-7081. Laurence C. Smith, C NC, Un. Meth., 1,074.

Westminster College, Fulton, MO 65251, Tel. (314) 642-3361. Robert L. D. Davidson, M NC, U. Presb. U.S.A., Presb. U.S., 703.

Westminster College, New Wilmington, PA 16142, Tel. (412) 946-6710. Earland I. Carlson, C MS, U. Presb. U.S.A., 1,944.

Westminster College, Salt Lake City, UT 84105, Tel. (801) 484-7651. Manfred A. Shaw, C NW, Interdenom., 835.

Wheaton College, Wheaton, IL 60187. Tel. (312) 682-5000. Hudson Armerdino, C NC, Interdenom., 1,950.

Wheeling College, Wheeling, WV 26003, Tel. (304) 243-2000. Frank R. Haig, C NC, Cath., 744.

Whittier College, Whittier, CA 90608, Tel. (213) 693-0771. Frederick M. Binder, C West, Friends, 2,367.

Whitworth College, Spokane, WA 99218, Tel. (509) 489-3550. Edward B. Lindaman, C NW, U. Presb. U.S.A., 1,517.

Wilberforce University, Wilberforce, OH 45384, Tel. (513) 376-2911. Rembert E. Stokes, C NC, A.M.E., 1,182.

Wiley College, Marshall, TX 75670. Tel. (214) 935-9361. Robert E. Hayes, C S, Un. Meth., 502.

Williamette University, Salem, OR 97301, Tel. (503) 370-6300. Roger J. Fritz, C NW, Un. Meth., 1,713.

William Carey College, Hattiesburg, MS 39401, Tel. (601) 582-5051. J. Ralph Noonkester, C S, So. Bapt., 797.

William Jewell College, Liberty, MO 64068, Tel. (816) 781-3806. Thomas S. Field, C NC, Am. Bapt. and So. Bapt., 849.

William Penn College, Oskaloosa, IA 52577, Tel. (515) 673-8311. Duane Moon, C NC, Friends, 879.

William Woods College, Fulton, MO 65251, Tel. (314) 642-2251. R. B. Cutlip, W NC, Christian Church (Disc.), 866.

Wilmington College, Wilmington, OH 45177, Tel. (513) 382-0951. Robert E. Hinshaw C NC, Friends, 945.

Wilson College, Chambersburg, PA 17201, Tel. (717) 264-4141. Charles C. Cole, W MS, U. Presb. U.S.A., 481.

Wittenberg University, Springfield, OH 45501, Tel. (513) 327-6231. G. Kenneth Andeen, C NC, Luth. in Am., 3,289.

Wofford College, Spartanburg, SC 29301, Tel. (803) 585-4821. Paul Hardin, III, M S, Un. Meth., 989.

Woodstock College, New York, NY 10027, Tel. (212) 866-8500. Christopher F. Mooney, M MS, Cath., 129.

Xavier University, Cincinnati, OH 45207, Tel. (513) 853-3000. Paul L. O'Connor, C NC, Cath., 6,134.

Xavier University of Louisiana, New Orleans, LA 70125, Tel. (504) 486-7411. Norman C. Francis, C S, Cath., 1,422.

Yankton College, Yankton, SD 57078, Tel. (605) 665-3661. Fred S. Honkala, C NC, U Ch. of Christ, 557.

Yeshiva University, New York, NY 10033, Tel. (212) 568-8400. Samuel Belkin, Co. Ord. MS, Jewish, 3,750.

11. RELIGIOUS PERIODICALS IN THE UNITED STATES

This list has been compiled for those who may wish to utilize a relatively large, representative group of religious periodicals. Many additional titles appear in the directories of religious bodies presented in this book. Probably the most inclusive list of religious periodicals published in the United States can be found in the 1972 *Ayer Directory of Publications* (Ayer Press, West Washington Sq., Philadelphia, PA 19106).

Each entry lists, in this order: Title of periodical, frequency of publication, religious affiliation, editor's name, address, and telephone number.

A.D. (m), U. Ch. of Christ and U. Presb. Ch. USA, Robert J. Cadigan at Witherspoon Bldg., Philadelphia, PA 19107, Tel. (215) 546-2880, and J. Martin Bailey at 297 Park Ave. S., New York, NY 10010, Tel. (212) 475-2121.

Advent Review and Sabbath Herald (w and m), Seventh-day Adv., K. H. Wood, Takoma Park, Washington, DC 20012. Tel. (202) 723-3700.

Alliance Witness, The (bi-w), The Christian & Missionary Alliance, H. Robert Cowles, 260 W. 44th St., New York, NY 10036. Tel. (212) 524-9282.

America (w), Cath., Donald R. Campion, 106 W. 56th St., New York, NY 10019. Tel. (212) 581-4640.

American Baptist, The (m, except August), Am. Bapt., Norman R. De Puy, American Baptist Convention, Valley Forge, PA 19481. Tel. (215) 768-2216.

American Bible Society Record (10 issues a year), undenom., Amer. Bible Society, Benjamin A. Bankson, 1865 Broadway, New York, NY 10023. Tel. (212) 581-7400.

American Church News (m, except July and Aug.), Epis., Albert J. du Bois, 60 Rockledge Dr., Pelham Manor, NY 10803. Tel. (914) 738-2973.

American Ecclesiastical Review, The (10 issues a year), Cath., The Catholic Univ. of America, Bro. James P. Clifton, Washington, DC 20017. Tel. (202) 635-5844.

Arkansas Methodist, The (w), U. Meth., Alfred A. Knox, P.O. Box 3547, Little Rock, AR 72203. Tel. (501) 374-4831.

Banner, The (w), Chr. Ref., Lester DeKoster, 2850 Kalamazoo Ave., S.E., Grand Rapids, MI 49508. Tel. (616) 241-1691.

Baptist and Reflector (w), S. Bapt., James A. Lester, P. O. Box 647, Brentwood, TN 37027. Tel. (615) 833-4220.

Baptist Bulletin (m), Gen. Assoc. Reg. Bapt. Ch.'s, Merle R. Hull, 1800 Oakton Blvd., Des Plaines, IL 60018. Tel. (312) 827-7105.

Baptist Courier (w), S. Bapt., John E. Roberts, P.O. Box 2168, Greenville, SC 29602. Tel. (803) 232-8736.

Baptist Herald (m), N. A. Bapt. Gen. Conf., Reinhold J. Kerstan, 7308 Madison St., Forest Park, IL 60130.

Baptist Leader (m), Am. Bapt., Vincie Alessi, American Baptist Board of Education and Publication, Valley Forge, PA 19481. Tel. (215) 768-2158.

Baptist Messenger (w), S. Bapt., Jack L. Gritz, 1141 N. Robinson, Oklahoma City, OK 73103. Tel. (405) 236-4341.

Baptist Record (w), S. Bapt., Joe T. Odle, Box 530, Jackson, MS 39205. Tel. (601) 354-3704.

Baptist Standard (w), S. Bapt., John J. Hurt, 2222 San Jacinto, P.O. Box 688, Dallas, TX 75221. Tel. (214) 748-9066.

Biblical Recorder (w), S. Bapt., J. Marse Grant, P. O. Box 25053, Raleigh, NC 27611. Tel. (919) 832-4019.

B'nai B'rith Messenger (w), Jewish, Joseph Jonah Cummins, 2510 W. 7th St., Los Angeles, CA 90057.

Brethren Journal, The (m), Unity of Brethren, Jesse E. Skrivanek, 5905 Carleen Dr., Austin, TX 78731.

Catholic Chronicle (w), Cath., F. I. Nally, 1933 Spielbusch, Toledo, OH 43624. Tel. (419) 243-4178.

Catholic Digest (m), Cath., Kenneth Ryan, P. O. Box 3090, St. Paul, MN 55165. Tel. (612) 647-5296.

Catholic Herald Citizen (w), Cath., Thomas R. Leahy, 2170 N. Prospect Ave., Milwaukee, WI 53202. Tel. (414) 271-4784.

Catholic Light (w), Cath., Joseph P. Gilgallon, The Chancery Bldg., 300 Wyoming Ave., Scranton, PA 18503.

Catholic Mind (m), Cath., Donald R. Campion, 106 W. 56th St., New York, NY 10019. Tel. (212) 581-4640.

Catholic News (w), Cath., Michael G. Murphy, 68 W. Broad St., Mt. Vernon, NY 10552.

Catholic Observer (w), Cath., J. M. Hammond, 410 North Ave., Pittsburgh, PA 15209.

Catholic Review (w), Cath., Robert J. Sievers, 320 Cathedral St., Baltimore, MD 21203. Tel. (301) 727-7777.

Catholic Standard and Times (w), Cath., John P. Foley, 222 N. 17th St., Philadelphia, PA 19103. Tel. (215) 587-3660.

Catholic Transcript, The (w), Cath., John S. Kennedy, 785 Asylum Ave., Hartford, CT 06105. Tel. (203) 527-1175.

Catholic Universe Bulletin (w), Cath., Edgar V. Barmann, 1027 Superior Ave., N.E., Cleveland, OH 44114. Tel. (216) 696-6525.

Catholic Worker (m), Cath., Dorothy Day, 36 E. First St., New York, NY 10003. Tel. (212) 254-1640.

CCAR Journal (q), Jewish, Joseph R. Narot, Temple Israel of Greater Miami, 137 N.E. 19th St., Miami, FL 33132.

Chaplain, The (bi-m), interdenom., A. Ray Appelquist, 122 Maryland Ave., N. E., Washington, DC 20002. Tel. (202) 547-8310.

Christian, The (w), Disc. of Christ, Howard

E. Short, Box 179, St. Louis, MO 63166. Tel. (314) 371-6900.

Christian Advocate (bi-w), U. Meth., William C. Henzlik, Box 423, 1661 N. Northwest Hwy., Park Ridge, IL 60068. Tel. (312) 299-4411.

Christian Bookseller Magazine (m), undenom., Robert Hill, Gundersen Dr. and Schmale Rd., Wheaton, IL 60187. Tel. (312) 653-4200.

Christian Century, The (w), ecumen., James M. Wall, Man. Ed., 407 S. Dearborn St., Chicago IL 60605. Tel. (312) 427-5380.

Christian Community, The (m, except August and January), Council of Community Churches, Sterling McHarg, Box 1257, Joplin, MO 64801. Tel. (417) 781-1800.

Christian Endeavor World, The (6 times a a year), interdenom., Phyllis I. Rike, 1221 E. Broad St., Columbus, OH 43216. Tel. (614) 253-8541.

Christian Herald (m), undenom., Kenneth L. Wilson, 27 E. 39th St., New York, NY 10016. Tel. (212) 686-0712.

Christian Home, The (m), U. Meth., Florence A. Lund, 201 Eighth Ave., S., Nashville, TN 37202.

Christian Index, The (w), S. Bapt., Jack U. Harwell, 291 Peachtree St., N.E., Atlanta, GA 30303. Tel. (404) 523-6082.

Christian Index, The (bi-w), Chr. Meth. Epis., John M. Exum, P. O. Box 665, Memphis, TN 38101. Tel. (901) 947-6297.

Christian Life Magazine (m), undenom., Robert Walker, Gundersen Dr. and Schmale Rd., Wheaton, IL 60187. Tel. (312) 653-4200.

Christian Ministry, The (formerly **The Pulpit**) (6 times a year), Robert G. Kemper, 407 S. Dearborn St., Chicago, IL 60605. Tel. (312) 427-5380.

Christian Observer (w), Presb. US, Marys A. Converse, 412 S. 3rd St., Louisville, KY 40202.

Christian Science Journal, The (m), Chr. Sc., Carl J. Welz, One Norway St., Boston, MA 02115. Tel. (617) 262-2300.

Christian Science Sentinel (w), Chr. Sc., Carl J. Welz, One Norway St., Boston, MA 02115. Tel. (617) 262-2300.

Christian Standard (w), Christian Churches/ Churches of Christ, Edwin V. Hayden, 8121 Hamilton Ave., Cincinnati, OH 45231.

Christianity and Crisis (bi-w), undenom., Wayne H. Cowan, 537 W. 121st St., New York, NY 10027. Tel. (212) 662-5907.

Christianity Today (fortnightly), undenom., Harold Lindsell, 1014 Washington Bldg., Washington, DC 20005. Tel. (202) 347-1753.

Church and Crusade, The (m), Ch.'s of God in N. A., J. A. Parthemore, Jr., Box 2103. Harrisburg, PA 17105. Tel. (717) 234-2496.

Church and Society (bi-m), U. Presb. Ch. USA Presb. US, Dean H. Lewis, Witherspoon Bldg., Philadelphia, PA 19107. Tel. (215) 735-6722.

Church Herald, The (w), Ref. Ch. in Am., Louis H. Benes, 630 Myrtle St., N.W., Grand

Rapids, MI 49504. Tel. (616) 458-5156.

Church History (q), undenom., Robert M. Grant, Martin E. Marty, and Jerald C. Brauer, Swift Hall, The Univ. of Chicago, Chicago, IL 60637. Tel. (312) 753-4026.

Church Management: The Clergy Journal (m), undenom., Norman M. Hersey, 115 N. Main St., Mt. Holly, NC 28120. Tel. (704) 827-9296.

Churchman, The (m), interdenom., Edna Ruth Johnson, 1074 23rd Ave., N., St. Petersburg, FL 33704. Tel. (813) 894-0097.

Church Woman, The (m, except July and Aug.), ecumen., Church Women United, Ruth Weber, 475 Riverside Dr., New York, NY 10027. Tel. (212) 870-2354.

Clarion Herald (w), Cath., Elmo L. Romagosa, 523 Natchez St., P. O. Box 53247, New Orleans, LA 70153 Tel. (504) 523-7731.

Columban Mission (10 times a year), Cath., Peter McPartland, St. Columbans, NB 68056.

Columbia (m), Cath., Elmer Von Feldt, P. O. Drawer 1670, New Haven, CT 06507.

Columbian, The (w), Cath., John R. Hughes, 188 W. Randolph St., Chicago, IL 60601. Tel. (312) 372-2060.

Commonweal (w), Cath., James O'Gara, 232 Madison Ave., New York, NY 10016. Tel. (212) 683-2042.

Concern (m), U. Presb. Ch. USA, U. Presb. Women, Sarah Cunningham, 475 Riverside Dr., Rm. 401, New York, NY 10027. Tel. (212) 870-2661.

Congregationalist, The (m, except July and Aug.), Congr. Chr., Natl. Assn. of, Richard P. Buchman, 7330 N. Santa Monica Blvd., Milwaukee, WI 53217.

Conservative Judaism (q), Jewish, Mordecai Waxman, 3080 Broadway, New York, NY 10027. Tel. (212) 749-8000.

Criterion, The (w), Cath., Raymond T. Bosler, 124 W. Georgia St., P. O. Box 174, Indianapolis, IN 46206. Tel. (317) 635-4531.

Cross and Crown (q), Cath., John J. McDonald, 6851 S. Bennett Ave., Chicago, IL 60649. Tel. (312) 363-1500.

Cross Currents (q), Cath., Joseph E. Cunneen, 103 Van Houten Fields, West Nyack, NY 10994. Tel. (914) 358-4898.

Cumberland Presbyterian, The (bi-w), Cumb. Presb., C. Ray Dobbins, 1978 Union Ave., Box 4149, Memphis, TN 38104. Tel. (901) 276-9032.

Diakonia (q), Cath., George A. Maloney, Fordham Univ., Bronx, NY 10458.

Ecumenical Courier (q), U.S. Conference for the World Council of Churches, Elsa Kruuse, Rm. 439, 475 Riverside Dr., New York, NY 10027. Tel. (212) 870-2391.

Ecumenical Review, The (q), interdenom., Philip A. Potter, World Council of Churches, 150 Route de Ferney, CH-1211 Geneva 20, Switzerland.

Emphasis (bi-w), Missionary Ch., W. O. Klopfenstein, 3901 South Wayne, Fort Wayne, IN 46807.

Engage (m), U. Meth., Allan R. Brockway, 100 Maryland Ave., N. E., Washington, DC 20002. Tel. (202) 546-7137.

Episcopal Recorder (m), Ref. Epis., Howard D. Higgins, 25 South 43rd St., Philadelphia, PA 19104. Tel. (215) 222-5158.

Episcopalian, The (m), Epis., Henry L. McCorkle, 1930 Chestnut St., Philadelphia, PA 19103. Tel. (215) 564-2010.

Eternity (m), interdenom., Russell T. Hitt, 1716 Spruce St., Philadelphia, PA 19103. Tel. (215) 546-3696.

Evangelist, The (w), Cath., William F. Jillisky, 39 Philip St., Albany, NY 12207. Tel. (518) 434-0107.

Extension (m), Cath., George Lundy, 1307 S. Wabash Ave., Chicago, IL 60605. Tel. (312) 939-5338.

Face to Face (formerly **Builders** and **Classmate**) (m), U. Meth., Sharilyn Adair, 201 Eighth Ave., S., Nashville, TN 37202.

Faith at Work (6 copies a year), interdenom., Walden Howard, 1000 Century Plaza, Suite 210, Columbia, MD 21044.

Firm Foundation (w), Ch.'s of Christ, Reuel Lemmons, Box 610, Austin, TX 78767.

Franciscan Herald (m), Cath., Mark Hegener, 1434 W. 51st. St., Chicago, IL 60609. Tel. (312) 254-4455.

Free Will Baptist, The (w), Free Will Bapt., Tommy Manning, Free Will Baptist Press, P. O. Box 158, Ayden, NC 28513. Tel. (919) 746-6128.

Friends Journal (s-m), Friends (Quakers), James D. Lenhart, 152-A N. 15th St., Philadelphia, PA 19102. Tel. (215) 563-7669.

Gospel Advocate (w), Ch.'s. of Christ, B. C. Goodpasture, 1006 Elm Hill Pike, Nashville, TN 37210. Tel. (615) 254-8781.

Gospel Herald (w), Menn., John M. Drescher, Scottdale, PA 15683. Tel. (412) 887-8500.

Grapevine (10 times a year), Joint Strategy and Action Committee, Ms. Sheila Collins, 475 Riverside Dr., Rm. 1700-A, New York, NY 10027. Tel. (212) 870-3105.

Herald of Holiness (bi-w), Nazarene, W. T. Purkiser, 6401 The Paseo, Kansas City, MO 64131. Tel. (816) 333-7000.

Historical Magazine of the Protestant Episcopal Church (q), Epis., Lawrence L. Brown, Box 2247, Austin, TX 78767.

Home Missions (m), S. Bapt., Walker L. Knight, 1350 Spring St., N.W., Atlanta, GA 30309. Tel. (404) 873-4041.

Homiletic and Pastoral Review (m), Cath., Kenneth Baker, 86 Riverside Dr., New York, NY 10024. Tel. (212) 799-2600.

IDOC-International, North American Edition (m), 637 W. 125th St., New York, NY 10027. Tel. (212) 749-5700.

International Review of Mission (q), Commission on World Mission and Evangelism, World Council of Churches, Philip Potter, 150 Route de Ferney, CH-1211 Geneva 20, Switzerland.

Interpretation (q), Presb. US, James L. Mays,

3401 Brook Rd., Richmond, VA 23227. Tel. (703) 355-0673.

Interpreter, The (m), U. Meth., Darrell R. Shamblin, 601 W. Riverview Dr., Dayton, OH 45406. Tel. (513) 222-2531.

Jewish Digest, The (m), Jewish, Bernard Postal, P. O. Box 57, Heathcote Sta., Scarsdale, NY 10583.

Jewish Life (q), Jewish, Saul Bernstein, 84 Fifth Ave., New York, NY 10011. Tel. (212) 255-4100.

Journal of Pastoral Care (q), Nondenom., Edward Thornton, 475 Riverside Dr., Suite 450, New York, NY 10027. Tel. (212) 870-2558.

Journal of Presbyterian History (q), U. Presb. Ch. USA, James H. Smylie, 425 Lombard St., Philadelphia, PA 19147. Tel. (215) 735-4433.

Journal of Religion (q), undenom., Nathan A. Scott, Jr., B. A. Gerrish, and David Tracy, Swift Hall. The Univ. of Chicago, Chicago, IL 60637. Tel. (312) 643-0800.

Journal of the American Academy of Religion (q), undenom., Ray L. Hart, University of Montana, Missoula, MT 59801. Tel. (406) 243-5482.

Journal of the American Scientific Affiliation (q), interdenom., Richard H. Bube, Dept. of Materials Science, Stanford Univ., Stanford, CA 94305. Tel. (415) 321-5796.

Judaism (4 times a year), Jewish, Robert Gordis, 15 E. 84th St., New York, NY 10028. Tel. (212) 879-4500.

Lamp, The, a Christian Unity Magazine (m), Cath., Charles Angell, Graymoor, Garrison, NY 10524.

Liguorian (m), Cath., Louis G. Miller, Liguori, MO 63057. Tel. (314) 892-1232.

Link, The (m), interdenom., (for armed forces personnel), Edward I. Swanson, 122 Maryland Ave., N.E., Washington, DC 20002.

Living Church, The (w), Epis., Carroll E. Simcox, 407 E. Michigan St., Milwaukee, WI 53202. Tel. (414) 276-5420.

Long Island Catholic, The (50 times per year), Cath., Paul E. McKeever, 53 N. Park Ave., P. O. Box 335, Rockville Centre, NY 11571. Tel. (516) 766-4760.

Lookout, The (w), Disc. of Christ, Jay Sheffield, 8121 Hamilton Ave., Cincinnati, OH 45231. Tel. (513) 931-4050.

Louisiana Methodist, The (w), U. Meth., Alfred A. Knox, P. O. Box 3547, Little Rock, AR 72203. Tel. (501) 374-4831.

Lutheran, The (s-m), Luth. Ch. in America, Albert P. Stauderman, 2900 Queen Lane, Philadelphia, PA 19129. Tel. (215) 848-6800.

Lutheran Forum (m), Luth., Richard E. Koenig, 155 W. 22nd St., New York, NY 10010. Tel. (212) 254-4640.

Lutheran Quarterly (q), Luth., Daniel F. Martensen, Hamma School of Theology, Springfield, OH 45501. Tel. (513) 323-4377.

Lutheran Standard (s-m), Am. Luth., George H. Muedeking, 426 S. 5th St., Minneapolis, MN 55415. Tel. (612) 332-4561.

Lutheran Witness (triweekly), and **Lutheran Witness Reporter** (five times a year), Luth., Mo. Synod, Martin W. Mueller, 3558 S. Jefferson Ave., St. Louis, MO 63118. Tel. (314) 664-7000.

Maryknoll (m), Cath., Donald J. Casey, Maryknoll Fathers, Maryknoll, NY 10545. Tel. (914) 941-7590.

Message Magazine (bi-m), Seventh-day Adv., William R. Robinson, P. O. Box 59, Nashville, TN 37202.

Messenger (bi-m), Ch. Breth., Howard E. Royer, Ch. Breth., 1451 Dundee Ave., Elgin, IL 60120. Tel. (312) 742-5100.

Messenger, The (formerly **New-Church Messenger**) (m), Swedenborgian, Robert H. Kirven, 48 Sargent St., Newton, MA 02158. Tel. (617) 244-0504.

Methodist Christian Advocate, The (w), U. Meth., Herschel T. Hamner, 1801 6th Ave., N., Birmingham, AL 35203. Tel. (205) 251-5508.

Methodist Churchman, The, (continuing **Zion's Herald**) (m), U. Meth., John L. Bryan, 581 Boylston St., Boston, MA 02116. Tel. (617) 536-5160.

Mission Herald (bi-m), Natl. Bapt., Wm. J. Harvey 3rd, 701 S. 19th St., Philadelphia, PA 19146.

Missionary Seer, The (m), A.M.E. Zion, Harold A. L. Clement, 475 Riverside Dr., Rm. 1910, New York, NY 10027. Tel. (212) 870-2916.

Mississippi Methodist Advocate (w), U. Meth., G. Roy Lawrence, P. O. Box 1093, Jackson, MS 39205. Tel. (601) 354-0515.

Monitor (w), Cath., Francis A. Quinn, 441 Church St., San Francisco, CA 94114. Tel. (415) 626-7200.

Moody Monthly (m), interdenom., George Sweeting, 820 N. LaSalle St., Chicago, IL 60610. Tel. (312) 329-4373.

Muslim World (q), undenom., Willem A. Bijlefeld, Hartford Seminary Foundation, 55 Elizabeth St., Hartford, CT 06105. Tel. (203) 232-4451.

National Catholic Register, The (formerly the **National Register**), Cath., Dale Francis, Box 1348, Schick Bldg., Sixth and Throcktmorton, Fort Worth, TX 76101. Tel. (817) 335-6823.

National Catholic Reporter (bi-w, May-Sept; w, Oct.-Apr.), Cath., Donald J. Thorman, P. O. Box 281, Kansas City, MO 64141. Tel. (816) 931-6170.

New Catholic World (bi-m), Cath., Robert J. Heyer, 1865 Broadway, New York, NY 10023. Tel. (212) 265-8181.

New World (w), Cath., Floyd Andersen, 109 N. Dearborn St., Chicago, IL 60602.

New World Outlook (m), U. Meth., U. Presb. USA, Arthur J. Moore, Jr., 475 Riverside Dr., New York, NY 10027. Tel. (212) 749-0700.

North American Moravian, The (m), Morav., Bernard E. Michel, 5 W. Market St., Bethlehem, PA 18018. Tel. (215) 867-0593.

North Carolina Christian Advocate (bi-w), U. Meth., James C. Stokes, P. O. Box 508, Greensboro, NC 27402. Tel. (919) 272-1196.

Orthodox Observer, The (bi-w), Greek Orth., P. J. Gazouleas, 8 E. 79th St., New York, NY 10021. Tel. (212) 628-2500.

Our Sunday Visitor (w), Cath., Albert J. Nevins, Noll Plaza, Huntington, IN 46750. Tel. (219) 356-8400.

Pan-Anglican: Review of the World-Wide Episcopal Church, (occas), Epis., Walter H. Gray, 100 Westerly Terr., Hartford, CT 06105.

Pastoral Life (m), Cath., Victor L. Viberti, Canfield, OH 44406. Tel. (216) 533-5503.

Pentecostal Evangel (w), Assem. of God, Robert C. Cunningham, 1445 Boonville Ave., Springfield, MO 65802. Tel. (417) 862-2781.

Pilot (w), Cath. J. J. Grant, 49 Franklin St., Boston, MA 02110. Tel. (617) 482-4316.

Presbyterian Journal, The (w), Presb. US, G. Aiken Taylor, Box 3108, Asheville, NC 28802. Tel. (704) 254-4015.

Presbyterian Outlook (w), Presb. US and U. Presb. Ch. USA, Aubrey N. Brown, Jr., 512 E. Main St., Richmond, VA 23219. Tel. (804) 649-1371.

Presbyterian Survey (m) Presb. US, John Allen Templeton, 341 Ponce de Leon Ave., N.E., Atlanta, GA 30308.

Providence Visitor (w), Cath., John F. Ferry, 184 Broad St., Providence, RI 02903. Tel. (401) 272-1010.

Pulpit Digest (m, except July and Aug.), undenom., Charles Wheeler Scott, 400 Community Dr., Manhasset, NY 11030. Tel. (516) 627-9400.

Quaker Life (m), Friends United Mtg., Frederick E. Wood, 101 Quaker Hill Dr., Richmond, IN 47374. Tel. (317) 962-7573.

Ramparts (m), undenom., Patricia Shell, 2054 University Ave., Berkeley, CA 94704.

Reform Judaism (8 times a year), Ref. Jewish, Ruth A. Buchbinder, 838 Fifth Ave., New York, NY 10021. Tel. (212) 249-0100.

Religion in Life (q), interdenom., Emory Stevens Bucke, 201 8th Ave., S., Nashville, TN 37202.

Religious Broadcasting (q), National Religious Broadcasters, Ben Armstrong, Box 308, Madison, NJ 07940. Tel. (201) 377-4400.

Religious Education (bi-m), undenom., Randolph C. Miller, 409 Prospect St., New Haven, CT 06510. Tel. (203) 436-0842.

Renewal (m, except July and Aug.), interdenom., Leon Watts, 110 E. 125th St., New York, NY 10035. Tel. (212) 862-9628.

Resources for Youth Ministry (q), Luth., Mo. Synod, Martin W. Steyer, 210 N. Broadway, St. Louis, MO 63102. Tel. (314) 231-6969.

Response (m), U. Meth., Carol Marie Herb, 475 Riverside Dr., Rm. 1304, New York, NY 10027. Tel. (212) 749-0700.

Restoration Herald (m), Ch. of Christ, James W. Greenwood, 5664 Cheviot Rd., Cincinnati, OH 45239. Tel. (513) 521-0461.

Review for Religious (bi-m), Cath., Richard

F. Smith, 539 North Grand Blvd., Rm. 612, St. Louis, MO 63103.

Review of Religious Research (3 times a year), The Religious Research Assoc., Richard D. Knudten, Dept., of Soc. & Anth., Marquette Univ., Milwaukee, WI 53233. Tel. (414) 224-6846.

Risk (q), World Council of Churches, Rex Davis, 150 Route de Ferney, CH-1211 Geneva 20, Switzerland.

Rola Boza (God's Field) (bi-w), Pol. Natl. Cath., Anthony M. Rysz, 529 East Locust St., Scranton, PA 18505.

Russian American Orthodox Messenger, The (m), Orthodox Church in America, Cyril Fotiev, 59 E. 2nd St., New York, NY 10003.

Sabbath Recorder (w), Seventh Day Bapt., Leon M. Maltby, 510 Watchung Ave., Plainfield, NJ 07061. Tel. (201) 756-8403.

Saint Anthony Messenger (m), Cath., Jeremy Harrington, 1615 Republic St., Cincinnati, OH 45210. Tel. (513) 241-5616.

Saints' Herald (m), Reorg. Ch. of Jesus Christ, L.D.S., Paul A. Wellington, Box 1019, Independence, MO 64051.

Sign, The (m), Cath., Augustine P. Hennessy, Monastery Pl., Union City, NJ 07087. Tel. (201) 867-6400.

Signs of the Times (m), Seventh-day Adv., Lawrence Maxwell, Pacific Press Pub. Assn., 1350 Villa, Mountain View, CA 94040. Tel. (415) 961-2323.

Social Action (9 issues a year), U. Ch. of Christ, Council for Christian Social Action, Huber F. Klemme, 289 Park Ave., S., New York, NY 10010. Tel. (212) 475-2121.

Social Action News Letter (m, except July and Aug.), Disc. of Christ, Ian J. McCrae, 222 S. Downey Ave., Box 1986, Indianapolis, IN 46206. Tel. (317) 353-1491.

Social Questions Bulletin (m, Oct.-May and one summer issue), Methodist Fed. for Social Action (unofficial), Lee H. Ball, 11 Forest Blvd., Ardsley, NY 10502. Tel. (914) 693-2472.

South Carolina United Methodist Advocate (w), U. Meth., M. Eugene Mullikin, 1420 Lady St., P. O. Box 11589, Columbia, SC 29211. Tel. (803) 253-9446.

Southwestern News (m, except Aug.), S. Bapt., John Earl Seelig, Southwestern Bapt. Theol. Sem., Box 22,000-3E, Fort Worth, TX 76122.

Spectrum (q), interdenom., National Council of Churches, Eli Wismer, 475 Riverside Dr., New York, NY 10027. Tel. (212) 870-2276.

Standard, The (bi-w), Bapt. Gen. Conf., Donald E. Anderson, 1233 Central St., Evanston, IL 60201.

Star of Zion (w), A.M.E. Zion, M. B. Robinson, P. O. Box 1047, Charlotte, NC 28201. Tel. (704) 377-4329.

Tablet, The (w), Cath., Don Zirkel, 1 Hanson Pl., Brooklyn, NY 11243. Tel. (212) 789-1500.

Tempo Newsletter (m), National Council of Churches, Fletcher Coates, 475 Riverside Dr., New York, NY 10027. Tel. (212) 870-2254.

Texas Methodist, The (w), U. Meth., Spurgeon

M. Dunnam, III, P. O. Box 1076, Dallas, TX 75221. Tel. (214) 748-6491.

Theological Education (q), undenom., Jesse H. Ziegler, American Association of Theological Schools, 534 Third National Bldg., Dayton, OH 45402. Tel. (513) 228-1109.

Theology Digest (q), Cath., Gerald Van Ackeren, 3701 Lindell Blvd., St. Louis, MO 63108. Tel. (314) 535-3155.

Theology Today (q), undenom., Hugh T. Kerr, P. O. Box 29, Princeton, NJ 08540.

These Times (m), Seventh-day Adv., K. J. Holland, P. O. Box 59, Nashville, TN 37202.

Thought (q), Cath., Joseph E. O'Neill, Fordham Univ., Bronx, NY 10458. Tel. (212) 933-2233.

Tidings, The (w), Cath., Patrick J. Roche, 1530 W. Ninth St., Los Angeles, CA 90015. Tel. (213) 385-3101.

Together (11 issues a year), U. Meth., Curtis A. Chambers, 1661 N. Northwest Hwy., Park Ridge, IL 60068. Tel. (312) 299-4411.

Tradition (4 issues a year), Jewish (Rabbinical Council of America), W. S. Wurzburger, 220 Park Ave. S., New York, NY 10003. Tel. (212) 260-0700.

Unitarian Universalist World (bi-w), Doris L. Pullen, 25 Beacon St., Boston, MA 02108.

United Evangelical, The (bi-w), Evang. Congreg. Ch., William S. Sailer, Church Center Press, 100 W. Park Ave., Myerstown, PA 17067. Tel. (717) 866-2181.

United Evangelical Action (q), interdenom., Jim O. Jones, 350 S. Main Pl., P. O. Box 28, Wheaton, IL 60187. Tel. (312) 665-0500.

U.S. Catholic (m), Cath., Robert J. Leuver, 221 W. Madison St., Chicago, IL 60606. Tel. (312) 236-7782.

Virginia Advocate (w), U. Meth., W. Hewlett Stith, 4016 Broad St., Rm. 208, Richmond, VA 23230. Tel. (703) 358-6045.

Vital Christianity (bi-w), Ch. of God (Anderson, Ind.), Harold L. Phillips, Box 2499, Anderson, IN 46011. Tel. (317) 644-7721.

Voice of Missions (m, except July and Aug.), Afr. Meth. Epis., John W. P. Collier, Jr., 475 Riverside Dr., Rm. 1926, New York, NY 10027. Tel. (212) 864-2471.

War Cry, The (w), Salv. Army, Maj. Robert E. Thomson, 860 N. Dearborn St., Chicago, IL 60610. Tel. (312) 787-1430.

Washington Religious News (w), nondenom., Robert Tate Allan, P. O. Box 7545, B. F. Station, Washington, DC 20044.

Wesleyan Christian Advocate (w), U. Meth., William M. Holt, 501 Methodist Center, 159 Forrest Ave., N.E., Atlanta, GA 30303. Tel. (404) 659-7620.

Western Recorder (w), S. Bapt., C. R. Daley, 10701 Shelbyville Rd., Middletown, KY 40243.

White Wing Messenger, The (w), Ch. of God of Prophecy, M. A. Tomlinson, Bible Pl., Cleveland, TN 37311.

Woman's Pulpit, The (q), undenom., (International Assoc. of Women Ministers), Marietta Mansfield, P. O. Box 6, Glendale, KY 42740.

Word and Work (m), undenom., Gordon R. Linscott, 2518 Portland Ave., Louisville, KY 40212.

World Call (m, except July-Aug. in one issue), Christian Church (Disc. of Christ), James L. Merrell, P. O. Box 1986, Indianapolis, IN 46206 Tel. (317) 353-1491.

World Vision Magazine (m), undenom., Frank E. Farrell, 919 W. Huntington Dr., Monrovia, CA 91016. Tel. (213) 357-1111.

Worldview (m), Council on Religion and International Affairs, James Finn, 170 E. 64th St., New York, NY 10021. Tel. (212) 838-4120.

Worship (10 issues a year), Cath., Aelred Tegels, St. John's Abbey, Collegeville, MN 56321. Tel. (612) 363-7761.

Your Church (bi-m), undenom., William S. Clark, Box 397, Valley Forge, PA 19481.

Youth (m), U. Ch. of Christ, Epis. Ch., Anglican Ch. of Canada, U. Presb. Ch. USA, Amer. Luth. Ch., Moravian Ch., Herman C. Ahrens, Jr., 1505 Race St., Philadelphia, PA 19102. Tel. (215) 568-3950.

YWCA Magazine, The (m, except July-Sept.), undenom., Ida Sloan Snyder, 600 Lexington Ave., New York, NY 10022. Tel. (212) 753-4700.

12. RELIGIOUS PERIODICALS IN CANADA

The religious periodicals below constitute a basic core of important newspapers and periodicals circulated in Canada. For additional publications treating religion in Canada, the reader should check the denominational directories in this **Yearbook** in the section entitled "Religious Bodies in Canada." Details on other religious periodicals circulating in Canada can also be found in the section "Religious Periodicals in the United States" in this **Yearbook**.

Each entry lists, in order: Title of periodical, frequency of publication, religious affiliation, editor's name, address, and telephone number.

Advance (bi-m), Associated Gospel Churches, Alex B. Stein, 84 Merrick St., Hamilton 11, Ontario. Tel. (416) 527-4802.

Atlantic Baptist (m), Un. Bapt. Conv. of the Atlantic Provinces, George E. Simpson, Box 756, Kentville, Nova Scotia.

B. C. Regular Baptist (m), Conv. of Reg. Bapt. Churches of B. C., G. R. Dawe, 3358 S. E. Marine Dr., Vancouver, British Columbia.

Calvinist-Contact (w), Chr. Ref., D. Farenhorst, Box 312, Sta. B, Hamilton, Ontario. Tel. (416) 547-1488.

Canadian Baptist, The (semi-m), Bapt. Conv. of Ontario and Quebec and Bapt. Un. of West. Canada, Harold U. Trinier, 217 St. George St., Toronto 180, Ontario.

Canadian Churchman, The (m), Ang. Ch. of Canada, Hugh McCullum, 600 Jarvis St., Toronto 5, Ontario. Tel (416) 924-9192.

Canadian Free Methodist Herald, The (11 times a year), Free Methodist, R. Barcay Warren, 55 Quebec St., Kingston, Ontario K7K 1T8. Tel. (613) 548-8687.

Canadian Reformed Magazine, The (bi-w), Can. Ref. Churches, W. W. J. Van Oene, Box 6277, Sta. F., Hamilton, Ontario.

Catholic Register, The (incorporating **Canadian Register**), Cath., Robert G. Vezina, 67 Bond St., Toronto 205, Ontario. Tel. (416) 362-6705.

Credo (French m), Un. Ch. of Canada, 3480, Boulevard Décarie, Montreal 260, Quebec. Tel. (514) 486-9213.

Evangelical Baptist (m), Fellowship of Evan. Bapt. Churches in Canada, J. R. Armstrong, 74 Sheppard Ave., W., Willowdale, Ontario. Tel. (416) 223-8696.

Evangelical Recorder (q), nondenom., Douglas C. Percy, 16 Spadina Rd., Toronto 179, Ontario. Tel. (416) 924-7167.

Gospel Witness, The (bi-w), Bapt., H. C. Slade, 130 Gerrard St., E., Toronto, Ontario. Tel. (416) 925-3261.

Maintenant (French m), Cath., Vincent Harvey, 2765 Chemine Côte Ste-Catherine, Montreal, Quebec. Tel. (514) 739-2758.

Mennonite, The (w), Gen. Conf. Menn., Larry Kehler, 600 Shaftesbury Blvd., Winnipeg, Manitoba R3P OM4.

Mennonite Brethren Herald (bi-w), Menn. Br., Harold Jantz, 159 Henderson Hwy., Winnipeg 5, Manitoba. Tel. (214) 667-3560.

Mennonite Reporter (bi-w), Menn., Frank H. Epp, Waterloo, Ontario. Tel. (519) 884-3810.

Message de Verité (bi-m), Brethren, Jean-Paul Berney, 230 rue Lupien, Cap de la Madeleine, Quebec. Tel. (819) 374-8530.

News of Quebec (q), Brethren, Arnold Reynolds, 230 rue Lupien, Cap de la Madeleine, Quebec. Tel. (819) 374-8530.

Pentecostal Testimony, The (m), Pent. Assen., of Canada, Earl N. O. Kulbeck, 10 Overlea Blvd. Toronto 17, Ontario. Tel. (416) 425-1010.

Le Phare, Fellowship of Evan. Bapt. Churches in Canada, W. H. Frey, Case postale 72, Verdun Montreal 203, Quebec. Tel. (514) 769-5547.

Prairie Overcomer (m), nondenom., T. S. Rendall, Prairie Bible Institute, Three Hills, Alberta TOM 2AO. Tel. (403) 443-5511.

Presbyterian Record (m), Presb. Ch. in Canada, DeCourcy H. Rayner, 50 Wynford Dr., Don Mills, Ontario. Tel. (416) 429-0110.

Studies in Religion (q), nondenom., William Nicholls, Dept. of Religious Studies, University of British Columbia, Vancouver 8, British Columbia. Tel. 604) 228-2970.

Thurst (q), Evan. Fellowship of Canada, Earl N. O. Kulbeck, actg., Box 878, Term. A, Toronto, Ontario. Tel. (416) 425-1010.

United Church Observer (m), Un. Ch. of Canada, A. C. Forrest, 85 St. Clair Ave., E., Toronto 7, Ontario. Tel. (416) 925-5931.

United Churchman (11 times a year), Maritime Conf., Un. Ch. of Canada, J. Heber Kean, P.O. Box 720, Sackville, New Brunswick. Tel. (506) 536-1704.

La Vie Chrétienne (French m), Presby. Ch. in Canada, André Poulain, 6316, 30e Ave., Montreal 409, Quebec. Tel. (514) 722-1405.

War Cry (w), Salvation Army in Canada, Lt. Col. Eric Coward, 20 Albert St., Toronto 2, Ontario.

Western Catholic Reporter (w), Cath., Douglas J. Roche, 9537-76 Ave., Edmonton, Alberta. Tel. (403) 433-6466.

13. UNITED STATES SERVICE AGENCIES: SOCIAL, CIVIC, RELIGIOUS

The **Yearbook of American and Canadian Churches** offers the following selected list of Service Agencies for two purposes. The first purpose is to direct attention to a number of major agencies which can provide resources of information and service to the churches. No attempt is made to produce a complete listing of such agencies. The second purpose is to illustrate the types of resources that are available. There are many agencies providing services which can be of assistance to local, regional or national church groups. It is suggested that a valuable tool in locating such service agencies is *The Encyclopedia of Associations*, Vol. I, National Organizations of the United States. The organizations are cross-referenced and the volume is in most libraries. It is published by Gale Research Co., Book Tower, Detroit, Michigan 48226.

Accrediting Association of Bible Colleges: Box 543, Wheaton, IL 60187. Tel. (312) 653-5811. Exec. Dir., John Mostert.

Adult Education Association of the U.S.A.; 810-18th St., N.W., Washington, DC 20006. Tel. (202) 347-9574. Pres., Alfred Storey; Exec. Dir., vacant.

Periodicals: Adult Education (4 issues yearly); Adult Leadership (m, except July and Aug.).

American Academy of Political and Social Science, The: 3937 Chestnut St., Philadelphia, PA 19104. Tel. (215) 386-4594. Pres., Marvin E. Wolfgang.

Periodical: The Annals of the American Academy of Political and Social Science (bi-m).

American Association of Christian Schools of Higher Learning, The: Box 35139. Greenville, SC 29614. Pres., W.O.H. Garman; Sec.-Treas., Marshall P. Neal.

American Association of Retired Persons: 1225 Connecticut Ave., N. W., Washington, DC 20036. Tel. (202) 872-4700. Pres., Foster J. Pratt; Exec. Dir., Bernard E. Nash.

Periodicals: AARP Newsletter (m); Modern Maturity (bi-m); Dynamic Maturity (bi-m).

American Association of Theological Schools: 534 Third National Bldg., Dayton, OH 45402. Tel. (513) 228-1109. Pres., Joseph D. Quillian, Jr., Perkins School of Theology, Southern Methodist Univ., Dallas, TX 75222. Exec. Dir., Jesse H. Ziegler; Asso. Dirs., David S. Schuller, and Marvin J. Taylor.

American Civil Liberties Union: 22 East 40th St., New York, NY 10016. Tel. (212) 725-1222. Chmn. of Bd., Edward Ennis; Exec. Dir., Aryeh Neier.

Periodical: Civil Liberties (m).

American Council on Alcohol Problems: 119 Constitution Ave., N.E., Washington, DC 20002. Tel. (202) 543-2441.

American Farm Bureau Federation: 225 Touhy Ave., Park Ridge, IL 60068. Washington office, 425 13th St., N.W., Washington, DC 20004. Pres., William J. Kuhfuss; Sec.-Treas. and Dir. Washington office, Roger Fleming.

Periodicals: The American Farmer (m); AFBF News Letter (w).

American Federation of Labor and Congress of Industrial Organizations, Department of Education: AFL-CIO Bldg., 815 16th St., N. W., Washington, DC 20006; Dir., Walter G. Davis.

American Foundation of Religion and Psychiatry, Inc.: 3 W. 29th St., New York, NY 10001. Tel. (212) 685-6138. Dir., Donald E. Smith.

American Friends Service Committee, Inc.: 160 N. 15th St., Philadelphia, PA 19102. Tel. (215) 563-9372. Chmn., Henry Beerits; Exec. Sec., Bronson P. Clark.

Periodical: Bulletin (4 issues a year).

American Library Association: 50 E. Huron St., Chicago, IL 60611. Tel. (312) 944-6780. Exec. Dir., Robert Wedgeworth.

Periodicals: American Libraries (m); Booklist and Subscription Books Bulletin (semi-m); Choice (m); College and Research Libraries (bi-m); AHIL Quarterly (q); Library Resources & Technical Services (q); R. Q. (q); School Libraries (q); Top of the News (q); Journal of Library Automation (q).

American Medical Association: 535 N. Dearborn St., Chicago, IL 60610. Tel. (312) 527-1500. Pres., C. A. Hoffman, M.D.; Exec. Vice-Pres., Ernest B. Howard, M.D.

Periodicals: The Journal of the American Medical Association (w); Today's Health (m); American Medical News (w); Specialty Scientific Journals (m).

American National Red Cross, The: 17th & D Sts., N. W., Washington, DC 20006. (Area offices: Alexandria, Atlanta, St. Louis, San Francisco) Chmn., E. Roland Harriman; Pres., George M. Elsey.

Periodical: The Good Neighbor (m).

American Protestant Hospital Association: 840 N. Lake Shore Dr., Chicago, IL 60611. Tel. (312) 944-2814. Exec. Dir., John C. Eller.

Periodicals: Bulletin (3 times a year); AP HA News (bi-m).

American Public Health Association: 1015 18th St., N.W., Washington, DC 20036. Exec. Dir., James R. Kimmey, M.D.

Periodical: American Journal of Public Health (m).

American Public Welfare Association: 1313 E. 60th St., Chicago, IL 60637. Tel. (312) 324-3400. Dir., Guy R. Justis.

Periodicals: Public Welfare (q); Washington Report (5 to 8 issues a year).

Americans United for Separation of Church and State: 8120 Fenton St., Silver Spring, MD 20910. Exec. Dir., Glenn LeRoy Archer; Ed., C. Stanley Lowell.

Periodical: Church & State (m).

Association for Clinical Pastoral Education: 475 Riverside Dr., Suite 450, New York, NY 10027. Tel. (212) 870-2558. Exec. Dir., Charles E. Hall, Jr.

Periodical: Journal of Pastoral Care (q).

Association of Jewish Chaplains of the Armed Forces: 15 E. 26th St., New York, NY 10010. Tel. (212) 532-4949. Pres., Judah Nadich.

B'nai B'rith: B'nai B'rith Bldg., 1640 Rhode Island Ave., N. W., Washington, DC 20036. Tel. (202) 393-5284. Pres., David M. Blumberg; Exec. Vice-Pres., Benjamin M. Kahn.

Periodicals: The National Jewish Monthly; Jewish Heritage (q).

Boy Scouts of America: North Brunswick, NJ 08902. Pres., Norton Clapp; Chief Scout Exec., A. G. Barber.

Periodicals: Scouting Magazine (7 issues a year); Boys' Life (m); Scouting Bulletin of the Catholic Committee on Scouting (q); Ner Tamid News Bulletin (a).

Boys' Clubs of America: 771 First Ave., New York, NY 10017. Tel. (212) 684-4400. Hon. Chmn., Pres. Richard M. Nixon; Chmn. of Bd., Albert L. Cole; Pres., John L. Burns; Nat'l. Dir., A. Boyd Hinds.

Periodicals: The Boys' Club Bulletin (m); The Journal: Boys' Clubs of America (q).

Camp Fire Girls, Inc.: 1740 Broadway, New York, NY 10019. Tel. (212) 581-0500. Nat. Exec. Dir., Dr. Hester Turner.

Periodical: The Camp Fire Girl (bi-m). Today's Girl (10 issues a year).

CARE (Cooperative for American Relief Everywhere, Inc.): 660 First Ave., New York, NY 10016, Tel. (212) 686-3110. Exec. Dir., Frank L. Goffio.

Carnegie Endowment for International Peace: United Nations Plaza at 46th St., New York, NY 10017. Tel. (212) 697-3131. European Centre, 58 Rue de Moillebeau, Geneva, Switzerland. Washington Office, 1717 Massachusetts Ave., N.W., Washington, DC 20036. Pres., Thomas L. Hughes; Sec., Lee B. Harris; Counsellor, Charles G. Bolté.

Center for Applied Research in the Apostolate (CARA): 1234 Massachusetts Ave., N. W., Washington, DC 20005. Tel. (202) 783-1350. Exec. Dir., Louis J. Luzbetak.

Committee of Southern Churchmen, The: P. O. Box 12044, Nashville, TN 37212. Pres., Gideon Fryer; Dir., Will D. Campbell.

Conference Board, The: 845 Third Ave., New York, NY 10022. Tel. (212) 759-0900. Pres., A. B. Trowbridge; Sec., Herbert S. Briggs.

Cooperative League of the U.S.A.: Pres., Stanley Dreyer, 1828 L St., N.W., Washington DC 20036. Tel. (202) 872-0550. Dir. Information/Education, Gene Clifford.

Periodical: Co-op Report (bi-m); Washington /A Cooperative Slant and CLUSAgram (bi-weekly newsletters).

Council of the Southern Mountains, Inc.: Drawer N. Clintwood, VA 24228. Tel. (703) 926-4495.

Periodical: Mountain Life and Work (m).

Council on Religion and International Affairs: 170 E. 64th St., New York, NY 10021. Tel. (212) 838-4120. Chmn., Charles M. Judd; Pres., A. William Loos.

Periodicals: Worldview (m); Ethics and Foreign Policy.

Credit Union National Association: P. O. Box 431, 1617 Sherman Ave., Filene House, Madison, WI 53701. Tel. (608) 241-1211.

Periodicals: The Credit Union Magazine (m); Everybody's Money (q); Credit Union Executive (q); Yearbook (a).

Fellowship of Reconciliation, The: Box 271, Nyack, NY 10960. Tel. (914) 358-4601. Chmn., Kay Johnson; Exec. Sec., Alfred Hassler.

Periodicals: Fellowship (m); Action News Letter (occ.).

Foreign Policy Association: 345 E. 46th St., New York, NY 10017. Tel. (212) 697-2432. Pres., Samuel P. Hayes.

Periodicals: Headline Series (5 times a year), Great Decisions Booklet (a).

Friends Committee on National Legislation: 245 Second St., N.E., Washington, DC 20002. Tel. (202) 547-4343. Chmn. of Gen. Comm., Stephen L. Angell, Jr.; Exec. Sec., Edward F. Snyder.

Periodical: FCNL Washington Newsletter (m).

General Federation of Women's Clubs: 1734 N St., N.W., Washington, DC 20036. Tel. (202) 347-3168. Pres., Mrs. Kermit V. Haugan.

Periodical: General Federation Clubwoman (m).

Girl Scouts of the U.S.A.: 830 Third Ave., New York, NY 10022. Tel. (212) PL 1-6900. Pres., Mrs. William McLeod Ittmann; Nat'l. Exec. Dir., Cecily C. Selby.

Periodicals: American Girl (m); Girl Scout Leader (7 issues a year); Brownie Reader (m).

Goodwill Industries of America, Inc.: 9200 Wisconsin Ave., Washington, DC 20014. Tel. (301) 530-6500. Nat'l Exec. Dir., Robert E. Watkins.

Periodicals: Newsletter (w); Profile (m); AIM (q); Int. Bridge (q).

Hazen Foundation: 400 Prospect St., New Haven, CT 06511. Pres., William L. Bradley.

Institute of International Education: 809 United Nations Plaza, New York, NY 10017. Tel. (212) 867-0400. Pres., Kenneth Holland.

Interreligious Foundation for Community Organization: 475 Riverside Dr., New York, NY 10027. Tel. (212) 870-3151. Exec. Dir., Lucius Walker, Jr.

Periodical: IFCO Newsletter (bi-m); Report of IFCO Concerns (a).

Japan International Christian University Foundation, Inc., The: 475 Riverside Dr., Rm. 1220. New York, NY 10027. Tel. (212) 749-6734. Pres., Andrew W. Cordier; Chmn., Exec. Comm., Paul R. Gregory; Exec. Dir., Ruth L. Miller.

John Milton Society for the Blind: A Worldwide Ministry, 366 Fifth Ave., New York, NY 10001. Tel. (212) 736-4162. Gen. Sec., Francis Thom.

Periodicals (in Braille); John Milton Magazine, for Adults (m); Discovery, for Boys and Girls (m); John Milton Sunday School Quarterly (q).

Periodicals (recorded): John Milton Talking Book Magazine (q); John Milton Recorded Sunday School Lessons (q); Memorial Talking Book Edition of New English Bible-New Testament: Paul—An Ambassador for Christ.

Periodicals (in large type): John Milton Magazine-Large Type Edition (m).

All publications free on request to persons who cannot see to read ordinary printed matter.

LAOS, Inc.: 4920 Piney Branch Rd., N.W., Washington, DC 20011. Chmn. Francis B. Stevens; Dir., Tom Boone.

Periodicals: Conversations, Concerns and Challenges (4 times a year).

League of Women Voters of the U.S.: 1730 M St., N.W., Washington, DC 20036. Tel. (202) 296-1770. Pres., Lucy Wilson.

Periodical: The National Voter (6 issues a year).

Lutheran Resources Commission—Washington: Dupont Circle Bldg., Suite 725, 1346 Connecticut Ave., N.W., Washington, DC 20036. Tel. (202) 659-9864. Chmn., Carl E. Thomas, Luth. Ch. in Am.; Sec., Leslie F. Weber, Luth. Ch.—Mo. Synod; Treas., Emil Weltz, Luth. Ch. in Am.; Exec. Dir., Henry Endress, Washington, DC.

(Representing Boards and Divisions of the Lutheran Church in America and The Lutheran Church—Missouri Synod in the interests of social progress.)

National Association of Church Business Administrators, Inc.: Box 57, Bellevue, NB 68005. Tel. (402) 292-3435. Exec. Dir., Maurice Saucedo; Pres., Clayton G. Spranger, FCBA, Ascension Lutheran Church, 1236 S. Layton Blvd., Milwaukee, WI 53215.

National Association of Council Broadcast Executives: 2230 Euclid Ave., Cleveland, OH 44115. Tel. (216) 621-5925. Pres., Don Stockford.

Periodical: Newsletter (occ).

National Association of Human Rights Workers (NAHRW): P.O. Box 916, Nashville, TN 37202. Tel. (615) 747-4385. Pres., Fred Cloud.

National Association of Social Workers, Inc.: Southern Bldg., 1425 H St., N.W., Washington, DC 20005. Pres., Mitchell I. Ginsberg; Exec. Dir., Chauncey A. Alexander.

National Association for Mental Health, The: 1800 N. Kent St., Rosslyn, VA 22209. Exec. Dir., Brian O'Connell.

Periodical: Mental Hygiene (q).

National Association for the Advancement of Colored People: 1790 Broadway, New York, NY 10019. Tel. (212) 245-2100. Pres., Kivie

Kaplan; Exec. Dir., Roy Wilkins.

Periodical: Crisis (10 issues a year).

National Catholic Educational Association: One Dupont Circle, N.W., Washington, DC 20036. Tel. (202) 293-5945. Pres., C. Albert Koob.

Periodical: Momentum

National Committee of Black Churchmen: 110 E. 125th St., New York, NY 10035. Tel. (212) 862-9628. Exec. Dir., Mance Jackson.

National Conference of Christians and Jews: 43 W. 57th St., New York, NY 10019. Tel. 212 688-7530. Pres., Sterling W. Brown.

National Congress of Parents and Teachers: 700 N. Rush St., Chicago, IL 60611. Tel. (312) 787-0977. Pres., Mrs. John M. Mallory, Box 718, Union Sta., Endicott, NY 13760.

Periodical: The PTA Magazine (m, except July, Aug.).

National Consumers League: 1029 Vermont Ave., N.W., Washington, DC 20005. Tel. (202) 347-3853. Pres., Margaret J. Ackroyd; Exec. Dir., Alice Shabecoff.

Publications: Bulletin (bi-m) and periodic information on social legislation.

National Council of Community Churches, The Ecumenical Center of Ohio: 89 East Wilson Bridge Rd., Worthington, OH 43085. Tel. (614) 888-4501. Pres., Ralph E. Marsden; Sec., Mrs. Robert Henley; Exec. Dir., Joe V. Hotchkiss.

Periodical: The Christian Community (m).

National Council on Alcoholism: 2 Park Ave., New York, NY 10016. Exec. Dir., William W. Moore, Jr.; Founder-Consultant, Mrs. Marty Mann.

Periodical: Newsletter (m).

National Council on Crime and Delinquency: NCCD Center, Paramus, NJ 07652. Pres., Carl M. Loeb, Jr.; Dir., Milton G. Rector.

Periodicals: Crime and Delinquency (q); NCCD News (bi-m); Journal of Research in Crime and Delinquency (semi-a); Crime and Delinquency Literature (q).

National Education Association: 1201 16th St., N.W., Washington, DC 20036. Pres., Mrs. Catharine Barrett; Exec. Sec., Sam M. Lambert.

Periodical: Today's Education (m, except June, July, Aug.).

National Farmers Union: 12025 E. 45th Ave., Denver, CO 80201. Tel. (303) 344-1760. Pres., Tony T. Dechant.

Periodical: Washington Newsletter (w).

National Federation of Business and Professional Women's Clubs, Inc.: 2012 Massachusetts Ave., N.W., Washington, DC 20036. (202) 293-1100. Dir., Mrs. Lucille H. Shriver.

Periodical: National Business Woman (m).

National Grange: 1616 H Street. N.W., Washington, DC 20006. Tel. (202) 628-3507. Master, John W. Scott.

National Housing Conference: 1250 Connecticut Ave., N.W., Washington, DC 20036. Tel. (202) 223-8444. Exec. Vice-Pres., Miss Laurine A. Winlack.

National Planning Association: 1606 New Hampshire Ave., N.W., Washington, DC 20009. Tel. (202) 265-7685. Actg. Chmn., Charles J. Symington; Asst. Chmn. and Pres., John Miller.

Periodicals: Looking Ahead (m); Projection Highlights.

National Religious Broadcasters, Inc.: Box 308, Madison, NJ 07940. Tel. (201) 377-4400. Exec. Sec., Ben Armstrong.

National Retired Teachers Association: 1225 Connecticut Ave., N.W., Washington, DC 20036. Tel. (202) 872-4700. Pres., Joseph A. Fitzgerald; Exec. Dir., Bernard E. Nash.

Periodicals: NRTA News Bulletin (m); NRTA Journal (bi-m).

National Safety Council: 425 N. Michigan Ave., Chicago, IL 60611. Tel. (312) 527-4800. Pres., Howard Pyle.

Periodicals: National Safety News (m) Traffic Safety (m); Church and Safety (q); Family Safety (q), Accident Facts (a).

National Urban League, Inc.: 55 E. 52nd St., New York, NY 10022. Tel. (212) 751-0300 Pres., James A. Linen; Exec. Dir., Vernon E. Jordan.

Planned Parenthood—World Population (Planned Parenthood Federation of America, Inc.): 810 Seventh Ave., New York, NY 10019. Tel. (212) 541-7800. Chmn., Alan Sweezy; Pres., Alan F. Guttmacher, M.D.

Periodicals: Planned Parenthood Report (6 issues a year); Family Planning Perspectives (q).

Protestant Health and Welfare Assembly: 840 N. Lake Shore Dr., Chicago, IL 60611. Tel. (312) 944-2814. Exec. Dir., John C. Eller.

Protestant Radio and TV Center: 1727 Clifton Rd., N.E., Atlanta, GA 30329. Tel. (404) 634-3324. Pres., Ernest J. Arnold; Exec. Vice-Pres., William Horlock.

Public Affairs Committee: 381 Park Ave., So., New York, NY 10016. Tel. (212) 683-4331. Chmn., Telford Taylor; Sec., Maxwell S. Stewart.

Publications: Public Affairs Pamphlets.

Religious Education Association, The: 545 W. 111th St., New York, NY 10025. Tel. (212) 865-7408. Pres., Oswald P. Bronson; Gen. Sec., Boardman W. Kathan; Chmn. of Bd., Philip Scharper.

Periodical: Religious Education (bi-m).

Religious News Service: 43 W. 57th St., New York, NY 10019. Tel. (212) 688-7094. Man. Ed., Lillian R. Block.

Religious Research Association, Inc.: P. O. Box 228, Cathedral Station, New York, NY 10025; Pres., Thomas M. Gannon; Vice-Pres., Everett L. Perry; Treas., Charles Thorne; Sec., William Silverman.

Periodical: Review of Religious Research (3 times a year).

Society for Religion in Higher Education: 409 Prospect St., New Haven, CT 06510. Exec. Dir., Harry E. Smith.

Southern Christian Leadership Conference: 334 Auburn Ave., N.E., Atlanta, GA 30303. Pres. Ralph D. Abernathy.

Southern Regional Council: 2nd Floor, 52 Fairlie St., N.W., Atlanta, GA 30303. Tel. (404) 522-8764. Pres., Raymond H. Wheeler; Exec. Dir., George H. Esser, Jr.

Periodical: New South (q).

United Ministries in Higher Education: 825 Witherspoon Bldg., Philadelphia, PA 19107. Tel. (215) 735-6722. Adm. Sec., A. Myrvin DeLapp.

United Nations Association of the U.S.A.: 833 United Nations Plaza, New York, NY 10017. Tel. (212) 697-3232. Chapters, Council of Organizations, UNA-USA Communication Center for exhibits, seminars, briefings, catering facilities. Chmn. of the Bd., Chief Justice Earl Warren, retired; Chmn. Bd. of Governors, Robert S. Benjamin; Pres.; Porter McKeever.

Periodicals: Vista (bi-m); UNAKIT for Leadership Information (bi-m); Policy Study Reports.

United Service Organizations, Inc.: 237 E. 52nd St., New York, NY 10022. Tel. (212) 751-3020. Pres., Francis L. Sampson; Exec. Dir., Samuel G. Anderson.

United Way of America.: 801 North Fairfax St., Alexandria, VA 22314. Tel. (703) 836-7100. Natl. Exec., William Aramony.

Periodical: Community (bi-m).

Vellore Christian Medical College Board Inc.: 475 Riverside Dr., Rm. 404, New York, NY 10027. Tel. (212) 870-2642; Pres., Dr. Irene Jones; Exec. Dir., Mrs. John Carman.

Woman's Christian Temperance Union (National): 1730 Chicago Ave., Evanston, IL 60201. Tel. (312) 864-1396. Pres., Mrs. Fred J. Tooze.

Periodicals: The Union Signal (m); The Young Crusader (m).

Women's International League for Peace and Freedom: 1213 Race St., Philadelphia, PA 19107. Tel. (215) 563-7110. Pres., Ms. Marli Hasegawa.

Periodical: Peace and Freedom.

World Education, Inc.: 667 Madison Ave., New York, NY 10021. Tel. (212) 838-5255. Pres., Thomas B. Keehn; Chmn., Bd. of Trustees, Louise L. Wright; Exec. Asst., Doris R. Ward.

Periodicals: World Education Newsletter (q); World Education Reports.

World Peace Foundation: 40 Mt. Vernon St., Boston, MA 02108. Tel. (617) 227-7990. Dir., Alfred O. Hero, Jr.

Periodical: International Organization (q).

14. CANADIAN SERVICE AGENCIES: SOCIAL, CIVIC, RELIGIOUS

The following list of Canadian service agencies is offered for purposes of directing the reader's attention to a number of major Canadian agencies that can provide resources of information and service to the churches. No attempt is made to produce a complete listing of such agencies, and the reader is referred to the *Canadian Almanac and Directory* and *Directory and Almanac of Canada* for comprehensive listings of Canadian organizations.

Listings are alphabetical by name of institution and generally have the following order: Name of institution, address, telephone number, principal officers, periodical.

Alcohol and Drug Concerns: Rm. 603, 15 Gervais Dr., Don Mills, Ontario. Exec. Dir., David E. Reeve.

Alcoholics Anonymous, Toronto: c/o 2 Gerrard St., W., Toronto 101, Ontario (there are approx. 1,700 A.A. Groups in Canada). Correspondence to: The Secretary.

Association for the Advancement of Christian Scholarship, The: 229 College St., Toronto 2B, Ontario. Tel. (416) 923-3921. Exec. Dir., John A. Olthuis.

Periodical: Perspective Newsletter (bi-m).

Association of Universities and Colleges of Canada: 151 Slater, Ottawa, Ontario K1P 5N1. Tel. (613) 237-3330. Exec. Dir., Colin B. Mackay.

Periodicals: University Affairs (10 times a year); Universities and Colleges of Canada (a).

Better Business Bureaux (Association of Canadian Better Business Bureaus, Inc.): 219 Queen St., Ottawa, Ontario K1P 5E2. Exec. Sec.-Treas., H. W. deRoche.

Billy Graham Evangelistic Assn. of Canada: Box 841, Winnipeg, Manitoba R3C 2R3. Tel. (204) 943-7975.

Periodical: Decision Magazine (m).

B'nai B'rith: 164 Eglinton Ave., Toronto, Ontario. Exec. Vice-Pres., Herbert S. Levy.

Boy Scouts of Canada, National Council: P.O. Box 5151, Sta. F., Ottawa 5, Ontario. Tel. (613) 224-5131. Exec. Dir., J. Percy Ross.

Periodicals: The Canadian Leader (m); Scouting in the Church (semi-a).

Boy's Brigade in Canada, The: P.O. Box 151, Montreal 304, Quebec. Natl. Pres., J. H. Richardson; Natl. Sec., Norman R. Loiseau.

Periodical: Forward (q).

Boys' Clubs of Canada: 35 York St., Montreal 215, Quebec. Tel. (514) 481-0108. Natl Dir., Vernon F. McAdam.

Canada Council, The: 140 Wellington St., Ottawa, Ontario. Dir., Peter M. Dwyer.

Canadian Association for Adult Education: 238 St. George St., Toronto 5, Ontario. Exec. Dir., Gordon A. Hodge.

Canadian Association for the Mentally Retarded, The: Kinsmen National Institute Bldg., York Univ. Campus, 4700 Keele St., Downsview, Ontario. Tel. (416) 661-9611. Man. Dir., W. A. Gamble.

Periodicals: Deficience Mental/Mental Retardation (DM/MR) (q): Transcan—Camar Newletter.

Canadian Association of Schools of Social Work: 151 Slater St., Rm. 203, Ottawa, Ontario K1P 5H3. Exec. Dir., Marguerite Mathieu.

Canadian Association of Social Workers: 55 Parkdale Ave., Ste. 400, Ottawa, Ontario, K1Y 1E5. Tel. (613) 728-3563. Exec. Dir., Anthony J. Gray.

Periodicals: The Social Worker (4 times a year); Newsletter Information (m).

Canadian Book Publishers' Council: 45 Charles St. E., Toronto 285, Ontario. Tel. (416) 964-7231. Exec. Dir., Toivo Roht.

Periodical: CBPC Directory (a).

Canadian Catholic Organization for Development and Peace: 1452 Drummond St., Montreal, Quebec.

Canadian Chamber of Commerce, The: 1080 Beaver Hall Hill, Montreal 128, Quebec.

Canadian Civil Liberties Association: 1554 Yonge St., Toronto, Ontario. Tel. (416) 929-5775. Gen. Counsel., A. Alan Borovoy.

Canadian Coalition for Development: 4824 ch., Côte-des-Neiges Rd., Montreal 247, Quebec. Tel. (514) 735-4561. Exec. Dir., Mme Therese Demers.

Canadian Committee on the Status of Women: 53 Thorncliffe Park Dr., Apt. 708, Toronto 17, Ontario. Chmn., Miss M. E. MacLellan.

Canadian Council of Christians and Jews: 229 Yonge St., Toronto, Ontario. Tel. (416) 368-8026. Pres., Richard Ditzel Jones.

Periodical: Scope/Envergure (q).

Canadian Council on Social Development, The: 55 Parkdale Ave., Ottawa, Ontario K1Y 1E5. Tel. (613) 728-1865. Exec. Dir., Reuben C. Baetz.

Periodicals: Canadian Welfare (6 issues a year); Bien-être social canadien (5 issues a year).

Canadian Education Association: 252 Bloor St. W., Toronto 5, Ontario. Exec. Sec., F. K. Stewart.

Canadian Institute of International Affairs: 31 Wellesley St. E., Toronto 284, Ontario. Tel. (416) 923-7369. Exec. Dir., Robert W. Reford.

Periodicals: International Journal (q); Behind the Headlines (q); International Canada (m).

Canadian Institute on Public Affairs: P.O. Box 952, Sta. Q, Toronto 7, Ontario. Tel. (416) 964-2197. Pres., Michael Hind-Smith.

Canadian Labour Congress: 2845 Riverside Dr.,

Ottawa, Ontario, K1V 8N4. Tel. (613) 232-4293. Pres., Donald MacDonald.

Periodical: Canadian Labour (m).

Canadian Manufacturers' Association: 67 Yonge St., Toronto 1, Ontario. Tel. (416) 363-7261. Exec. Vice-Pres., W. D. H. Frechette.

Canadian Medical Association, The: 1867 Alta Vista Dr., Ottawa, Ontario K1G OG8. Gen. Sec., J. Douglas Wallace.

Canadian Mental Health Association: 52 St. Clair Ave. E., Toronto 7, Ontario. Tel. (416) 9207-621. Gen Dir., George Rohn.

Canadian Prisoner's Aid Societies:
-The Ontario Council of Elizabeth Fry Societies, 215 Wellesley St. E., Toronto 282, Ontario. Tel. (416) 924-3708. Exec. Dir., Miss Phyllis Haslam.

Periodical: Newsletter (6 times a year).
-John Howard Societies, 357 Bay St., Rm. 806, Toronto 1, Ontario.
-The St. Leonard's Society of Canada, 1787 Walker Rd., Rm. 9, Windsor 20, Ontario. Tel. (519) 254-9430. Exec. Dir., T. N. Libby.

Periodical: News & Views (q).

Canadian Red Cross Society: 95 Wellesley St. E., Toronto 5, Ontario. Tel. (416) 923-6692. Natl. Commissioner, A. E. Wrinch.

Periodical: Despatch (q).

Canadian Society for the Abolition of Death Penalty, The: 133 Richmond St. W., Ste. 602, Toronto 1, Ontario. Sec., M. Pelt.

Canadian Society of Biblical Studies and Society of Biblical Literature, Canadian Section: McGill Univ., Montreal 110, Quebec. Tel. (514) 392-4829. Pres., John C. Hurd, Trinity College, Toronto; Sec.-Treas., Robert C. Culley.

Periodical: The Bulletin of the Canadian Society of Biblical Studies (a).

Canadian Society of Church History: c/o E. J. Furcha, Vancouver School of Theology, Vancouver 8, British Columbia. Tel. (604) 228-9031.

Canadian Urban Training Project for Christian Service: 875 Queen St. E., Toronto, Ontario. Tel. (416) 465-9177. Exec. Dir., Edgar File.

Canadian UNICEF Committee: 737 Church St., Toronto 5, Ontario. Tel. (416) 924-0774. Exec. Dir., Paul Ignatieff.

Periodicals: Action (q); UNICEF News (5 times a year).

Canadian Unitarian Council, 175 St. Clair Ave., W., Toronto 195, Ontario. Pres., Mrs. J. B. MacDonald; Admin. Sec., Miss Barbara C. Arnott.

Canadian University Service Overseas: 151 Slater St., Ottawa, Ontario K1P 5H5. Tel. (613) 237-0390. Exec. Dir., John Gordon.

Canadian Woman's Christian Temperance Union: 30 Gloucester St., Village Gate Apartments, Apt. 302, Toronto 285, Ontario. Tel. (416) 922-0757. Natl. Pres., Mrs. James Nelson.

Periodical: Canadian White Ribbon Tidings (5 times a year).

Canadian Youth for Christ, Inc.: 605 Sheppard Ave. E., Willowdale, Ontario. Tel. (416) 223-1225. Pres., John L. Teibe.

Cansave (Canadian Save the Children Fund, The): 70 Hayter St., Toronto 101, Ontario. Tel. (416) 364-8224. Natl. Dir., Kenric R. Marshall.

Catholic Women's League of Canada, The: 890 St. James St., Winnipeg, Manitoba R3G 3J7. Exec. Sec., Miss Valerie J. Fall.

Christian Camping International (Canada): 745 Mount Pleasant Rd., Toronto 298, Ontario. Tel. (416) 487-3431. Pres., Vincent Craven. Periodical: Journal of Christian Camping (bim).

Christian Service Brigade: 1254 Plains Rd. E., Burlington, Ontario. Tel. (416) 634-1841. Gen. Dir., Tom Swan.

Christian Writers of Canada: 132 Spadina Rd. E., Kitchener, Ontario. Tel. (519) 576-4675. Pres., Barrie Doyle; Sec., Ms. Lilian M. Churchhill.

Consumers' Association of Canada: 100 Gloucester St., Ottawa, Ontario K2P OA3. Exec. Sec., Mrs. Frances Balls.

Co-operative Union of Canada, The: 111 Spark St., Ottawa, Ontario K1P 5B5. Tel. (613) 232-9657. Gen. Sec., J. T. Phalen.

Evangelical Theological Society: 10 Shrewsbury Sq., Agincourt, Ontario. Pres., J. Berkeley Reynolds.

Federated Women's Institutes of Canada, Inc.: 28 Elgin St., Ottawa, Ontario. Sec., Mrs. T. L. Jasper.

Frontiers Foundation (Operation Beaver): 2328 Danforth Ave., Toronto 13, Ontario. Tel. (416) 422-1888. Exec. Dir., Charles R. Catto.

Periodical: Beaver News (a).

Gideons International in Canada: 90 Thorncliffe Park Dr., Toronto 17, Ontario. Tel. (416) 421-4774. Exec. Dir., D. M. MacLeod.

Periodical: Canadian Gideon Magazine (6 times a year).

Girl Guides of Canada—Guides du Canada: 50 Merton St., Toronto 295, Ontario. Exec. Dir., Miss M. Ruth Warburton.

Health League of Canada, The: 76 Avenue Rd., Toronto 180, Ontario. Gen Dir., Dr. Gordon Bates.

Indian-Eskimo Association of Canada: 277 Victoria St., Toronto 2, Ontario. Tel. (416) 362-5937. Exec. Dir., John Gasson.

Periodical: Indian-Eskimo Association of Canada Bulletin (bi-m).

Interfaith Committee on Chaplaincy in the Canadian Penitentiary Service: 40 St. Clair Ave. E., Toronto 290, Ontario. Sec.-Treas., M. R. Wilkinson.

Liberal Party of Canada: 102 Bank St., Ottawa, Ontario K1P 5N4. Natl. Dir., Torrance J. Wylie.

National Association of Canadian Credit Unions: Box 800, Sta. U., Toronto 550, Ontario. Tel. (416) 621-6220. Gen. Man., Robert J. Ingram.

CANADIAN SERVICE AGENCIES

Periodicals: World Reporter (bi-m); International Yearbook (a).

National Committee on the Church and Industrial Society: 40 St. Clair Ave. E., Toronto 290, Ontario. Sec., M. P. Wilkinson.

National Inter-Faith Immigration Committee: 67 Bond St., Toronto 205, Ontario. Tel (416) 362-2481. Chmn., Claude J. Mulvihill.

New Democratic Party: 301 Metcalfe St., Ottawa, Ontario K2P 1R9. Sec., Clifford A. Scotton.

Oxfam of Canada, 97 Eglinton Ave. E., Toronto, Ontario. Tel. (416) 481-6821.

Pioneer Girls of Canada: 2320 Fairview St., Burlington, Ontario.

Progressive Conservative Party: National Headquarters, 178 Queen St., Ottawa 4, Ontario. Natl. Dir., Liam S. O'Brian.

Religion-Labor Committee: 40 St. Clair Ave. E., Toronto 290, Ontario. Sec., M. P. Wilkinson.

Scripture Union: 2100 Lawrence Ave. E., Scarborough, Ontario.

Shantymen's Christian Association of North America: 3251 Sheppard Ave. E., Agincourt, Ontario. Tel. (416) 491-1081. Pres., N. J. Notley.

Periodical: The Shantyman (m).

Social Credit Association: Box 2722, Vancouver 3, British Columbia. Natl. Pres., H. J. Bruch.

Social Science Research Council of Canada and

Humanities Research Council of Canada: 151 Slater St., Ste. 405, Ottawa, Ontario K1P 5H3. Exec. Sec., J. Banks.

Town Planning Institute of Canada: 46 Elgin St., Ste. 49, Ottawa, Ontario K1P 5K6. Exec. Dir., Mrs. K. E. Davies.

Unitarian Service Committee of Canada: 56 Sparks St., Ottawa, Ontario K1P 5B1. Tel. (613) 234-6827. Exec. Dir., Lotta Hitschmanova.

United Nations Association in Canada: 63 Sparks St., Ottawa, Ontario K1P 5A6. Pres., Mrs. B. Bazar.

Vanier Institute of the Family, The—L'institut Vanier de la Famille: 151 Slater St., Ste. 207, Ottawa, Ontario K1P 5H3. Tel. (613) 232-7115. Exec. Dir., William A. Dyson.

Periodical: Transition (bi-m).

Voice of Women/La Voix des Femmes: 1554 Yonge St., Rm. 4, Toronto 195, Ontario. Tel. (416) 925-0912.

Periodical: National Newsletter (q).

World University Service of Canada: 27 Goulburn Ave., Ottawa, Ontario K1N 8C7. Tel. (613) 237-7422. Gen. Sec., R. Roy.

World Vision International of Canada: 410 Consumers Rd., Willowdale 425, Ontario. Tel. (416) 491-2183. Dir. of Admin., James Brown.

Periodical: World Vision Heartline (bi-m).

Y.M.-Y.W. Hebrew Association: 4588 Bathurst St., Willowdale, Ontario. Pres., Bert D. Fine.

III
STATISTICAL AND HISTORICAL SECTION

This section of the **Yearbook** provides various types of statistical data and information on depositories of church history material for the U.S. and Canada. It is hoped that these materials will be useful in describing some major dimensions of religious life.

Much of the data presented here are unique, at least in form of presentation, and can be used judiciously to interpret developments in the religious life in the U.S. and Canada. Whenever necessary, qualifying statements have been made to warn the user of some of the pitfalls in the data.

Information in this section of the **Yearbook,** when compared with that of previous editions, suggests a number of interesting subjects for students, journalists, and church researchers to analyze and interpret. For the most part, generalizations on trends reflected in the data are left up to the reader.

The following information is contained in this Statistical and Historical Section.

1. **Current and Non-Current Statistical Data.** This section contains seven tables, numbered 1A-G, as follows: 1-A, United States Current and Non-Current Statistics, arranged alphabetically for 223 United States religious bodies. Included is information on Number of Churches, Inclusive Membership, Full, Communicant or Confirmed Members (current data only), Number of Pastors Having Charges, Total Number of Clergy, Number of Sunday or Sabbath Schools (current data only), and Total Enrollment (current data only). Table 1-B, Summary of United States Current and Non-Current Statistics, provides totals for the 223 bodies in the above categories and compares these totals with those in the previous **Yearbook** for 1972. Table 1-C, Some Comparative United States Church Statistics, compares data mainly for 1972 with those mainly for 1971 with regard to Church Membership as a Percent of U.S. Population, Membership Gain and Percentage of Gain over Previous Year. Table 1-D, Current and Non-Current Canadian Statistics, is more comprehensive than in previous years. It provides the same data for Canadian bodies as those described above for Table 1-A. Table 1-E, Summary of Canadian Current and Non-Current Statistics, is presented for the first time in the **Yearbook.** Table 1-F, Number of United States Churches and of Members, by Religious Groups, is continued from the previous year with all the necessary qualifications. Table 1-G, Constituency of the National Council of the Churches of Christ in the U.S.A., concludes the section.

2. **Church Financial Statistics and Related Data.** Complete data on contributions of members of 63 United States and Canadian religious bodies are supplied in the following categories: Total Contributions, Total Congregational Finances, and Benevolences. Per capita contributions based on both Inclusive and Full or Confirmed Membership are supplemented by Related Data consisting of several charts and tables reflecting relevant background trends relating to income and expenditures in the U.S. and Canada.

3. **Some Trends and Developments.** This part of the Statistical and Historical Section presents information on public and nonpublic elementary and secondary schools in the U.S., detailed 1972 statistical data for the Roman Catholic Church in the U.S., and an analysis of enrollments in seminaries related to the American Association of Theological Schools in the United States and Canada.

4. Surveys of Religion in American Life. Two surveys are presented in this part. The first is a Gallup survey on church attendance and the second a U.S. Department of Commerce survey relating to the value of new construction of religious buildings.

5. Main Depositories of Church History Material and Sources. This is a listing, by denomination, of various major depositories of historical and archival materials in the United States and Canada, including a bibliographical guide to information on church archives.

1. CURRENT AND NON-CURRENT STATISTICAL DATA

Tables 1 A-G in this section, containing current and non-current data, have been compiled from questionnaires returned to the **Yearbook of American and Canadian Churches** by statisticians and other officials of religious bodies. These statistics have been checked carefully, but in no case have they been "adjusted" by the editor in anyway for any purpose. What is reported here are official reports.

In Table 1-A, the religious bodies in the U.S. are listed alphabetically and current data appear in **bold face** type. Non-current data appear in the light face type. Current data are those compiled and reported in 1972 or 1971. Non-current data are those for 1970 or earlier. Table 1-A contains 128 current reports and 95 non-current, making a total of 223. Current reports, comprising 57 percent of all reports, account for slightly more than 87 percent of reported membership.

Statistics appearing in Table 1-G, Constituency of the National Council of Churches of Christ in the U.S.A., do not show the distinction between current and non-current data, although the date of the last statistical report received is noted for each religious body. This year Table 1-D, Canadian Current and Non-Current Statistics, contains statistical reports from 53 Canadian bodies as compared with 31 in the previous edition of the **Yearbook.**

Caution should be exercised in interpreting Table 1-B, Summary of United States Current and Non-Current Statistics, which indicates the general trends that are shown by the data in the 1973 and 1972 **Yearbooks.** Since current and non-current statistics are combined for this comparison, the dangers of elaborate generalizations are obvious. The same is true for Table 1-C, Some Comparative United States Church Statistics.

Users of church statistics are referred to "A Guide for the User of Church Statistics," found at the front of this **Yearbook.** It is essential reading for all who intend to work with, and interpret, statistics contained in this volume. The Guide is placed in this prominent position to highlight its importance, and its chief function is to state candidly the many qualifications which must be taken into account when using church statistics.

TABLE 1-A: UNITED STATES CURRENT AND NON-CURRENT STATISTICS

The following table provides current and non-current statistics for United States religious bodies listed alphabetically. Current statistics are defined as those gathered and reported for 1972 and 1971. Those bodies having current statistics, and the statistics themselves, are shown in **bold face** type. Non-current statistics are those for 1970 or earlier. They appear in light face type. No statistics for "Full, Communicant, or Confirmed Members," "Number of Sunday or Sabbath Schools," and "Total Enrollment" are reported for bodies having non-current statistics.

Religious Body	Year Reported	No. of Churches	Inclusive Membership	Full, Communicant, or Confirmed Members	No. of Pastors Having Charges	Total No. of Clergy	No. of Sunday or Sabbath Schools	Total Enrollment
Advent Christian Church	1970	392	30,713		296	493		
African Methodist Episcopal Church	1951	5,878	1,166,301		5,878	7,089		
African Methodist Episcopal Zion Church	1970	4,500	940,000		5,000	5,500		
African Orthodox Church	1957	24	6,000		24	50		
Albanian Orthodox Archdiocese in America	1971	13	62,000	46,000	18	23	13	1,375
Albanian Orthodox Diocese of America	1972	10	5,100	400	2	4	2	108
Amana Church Society	1970	7	735		None	None		
American Baptist Association	1972	3,321	869,000	869,000	3,300	3,368	3,336	450,000
American Baptist Churches in the U. S. A.	1971	6,035	1,562,636	1,562,636	4,700	8,222	N.R.	N.R.
The American Carpatho-Russian Orthodox Greek Catholic Church	1971	70	108,000	108,000	60	67	56	5,098
The American Catholic Church, Archdiocese of New York	1972	16	3,435	3,435	N.R.	N.R.	16	450
The American Catholic Church (Syro-Antiochian)	1971	5	1,090	1,031	7	9	1	37
The American Lutheran Church	1971	4,823	2,521,930	1,775,774	4,039	6,169	4,556	731,219
American Rescue Workers	1971	46	5,410	5,410	50	53	36	9,226
The Anglican Orthodox Church	1971	38	2,500	2,000	16	19	35	N.R.
Antiochian Orthodox Archdiocese of Toledo, Ohio and Dependencies in North America	1971	16	30,000	30,000	N.R.	26	12	N.R.
The Antiochian Orthodox Christian Archdiocese of New York and all North America	1970	92	100,000		96	110		
Apostolic Christian Church (Nazarean)	1971	43	4,000	2,400	138	N.R.	39	1,575
Apostolic Christian Churches of America	1971	77	9,160	9,160	N.R.	273	77	8,950
The Apostolic Faith	1971	44	4,020	4,020	75	75	44	6,380
Apostolic Lutheran Church of America	1961	58	6,994		24	28		
Apostolic Overcoming Holy Church of God	1956	300	75,000		300	350		
Armenian Apostolic Church of America	1972	29	125,000	125,000	23	34	29	2,550

TABLE 1-A: UNITED STATES CURRENT AND NON-CURRENT STATISTICS (Continued)

Religious Body	Year Reported	No. of Churches	Inclusive Membership	Full, Communicant, or Confirmed Members	No. of Pastors Having Charges	Total No. of Clergy	No. of Sunday or Sabbath Schools	Total Enrollment
Armenian Church of America, Diocese of the (including Diocese of California)	1971	62	300,000	300,000	N.R.	71	90	8,000
Assemblies of God	1972	8,799	1,078,332	679,813	8,237	12,037	9,200	1,078,332
Associate Reformed Presbyterian Church (General Synod)	1971	147	28,443	28,443	95	144	141	17,109
Baptist General Conference	1971	681	108,474	108,474	768	1,032	681	119,192
Baptist Missionary Association of America	1971	1,404	193,439	193,439	1,500	1,800	1,408	107,406
Beachy Amish Mennonite Church	1971	62	4,069	4,069	138	163	None	None
Berean Fundamental Church	1971	50	2,419	2,419	48	49	50	4,466
Bethel Ministerial Association, Inc.	1971	25	4,000	4,000	40	90	25	5,500
Bible Protestant Church	1968	42	2,254		33	59		
Bible Way Church of Our Lord Jesus Christ, World Wide, Inc.	1970	350	30,000		350	360		
Brethren Church (Ashland, Ohio)	1971	119	16,357	N.R.	N.R.	130	119	12,377
Brethren Churches, National Fellowship of	1971	226	33,392	33,392	273	418	226	40,326
Brethren in Christ Church	1971	151	9,550	9,550	160	235	155	17,729
Buddhist Churches of America	1970	60	100,000		74	101		
Bulgarian Eastern Orthodox Church (Diocese of N. & S. America and Australia)	1971	13	86,000	86,000	N.R.	11	N.R.	N.R.
Christ Catholic Church (Diocese of Boston)	1971	4	441	387	4	5	2	75
Christ Catholic Exarchate of Americas and Eastern Hemisphere	1968	16	5,513		14	17		
Christadelphians	1964	850	15,800		None	None		
The Christian and Missionary Alliance	1971	1,129	127,353	73,547	870	1,227	1,085	141,924
Christian Catholic Church	1970	6	3,000		9	15		
Christian Church (Disciples of Christ)	1971	4,868	1,386,374	884,929	4,184	6,886	4,868	623,012
Christian Church of North America, General Council	1972	110	8,500	8,500	134	136	N.R.	7,000
Christian Churches and Churches of Christ	1972	5,901	1,036,288	1,036,288	5,235	7,314	6,012	1,243,445
The Christian Congregation, Inc.	1971	263	51,310	51,310	261	267	252	33,355
Christian Methodist Episcopal Church	1965	2,598	466,718		2,214	2,259		
Christian Nation Church U.S.A.	1971	16	2,000	2,000	21	29	11	2,000
Christian Reformed Church	1971	718	286,094	155,547	601	999	601	69,240
Christian Union	1970	113	6,006	6,006	66	97	108	10,055
Christian Unity Baptist Association	1970	5	345		9	9		
Christ's Sanctified Holy Church	1957	30	600		19	30		
Church of Christ	1972	32	2,400	2,400	169	188	N.R.	N.R.

TABLE 1-A: UNITED STATES CURRENT AND NON-CURRENT STATISTICS (Continued)

Religious Body	Year Reported	No. of Churches	Inclusive Membership	Full, Communicant, or Confirmed Members	No. of Pastors Having Charges	Total No. of Clergy	No. of Sunday or Sabbath Schools	Total Enrollment
Church of Christ (Holiness) U.S.A.	1965	159	9,289		76	76		
Church of Daniel's Band	1951	4	200		4	10		
The Church of God	1971	2,025	75,890	75,890	1,910	2,737	2,025	96,500
Church of God General Conference (Oregon, Ill.)	1971	127	7,200	7,200	102	112	N.R.	8,400
Church of God (Anderson, Ind.)	1971	2,271	152,787	152,787	1,991	3,352	2,000	238,692
Church of God (Cleveland, Tenn.)	1971	4,095	287,099	287,099	6,799	7,504	5,266	478,984
The Church of God of the Mountain Assembly, Inc.	1970	100	3,500		80	121		
The Church of God (Seventh Day)	1960	7	2,000		7	9		
The Church of God (Seventh Day), Denver, Colorado	1964	56	5,500		48	76		
Church of God and Saints of Christ	1959	217	38,217		N.R.	N.R.		
Church of God by Faith	1970	135	5,000		135	155		
The Church of God in Christ	1965	4,500	425,000		4,000	6,000		
Church of God in Christ, International	1971	1,041	501,000	501,000	N.R.	1,502	984	N.R.
Church of God in Christ (Mennonite)	1971	38	6,204	6,204	80	86	N.R.	N.R.
The Church of God of Prophecy	1970	1,561	51,527		N.R.	N.R.		
The Church of Illumination	1963	14	9,000		60	60		
The Church of Jesus Christ (Bickertonites)	1970	42	2,353		80	215		
The Church of Jesus Christ of Latter-day Saints	1971	4,995	2,133,072	2,076,247	14,985	17,272	4,729	2,000,000
Church of Our Lord Jesus Christ of the Apostolic Faith, Inc.	1954	155	45,000		150	165		
The Church of Revelation, Inc.	1971	5	750	750	33	38	None	None
Church of the Brethren	1971	1,036	181,183	181,183	705	2,011	1,034	82,079
Church of the East (Assyrians)	1967	12	5,000		39	39		
Church of the Living God	1964	276	45,320		332	376		
Church of the Lutheran Brethren of America	1971	90	8,960	5,195	95	114	90	8,625
Church of the Nazarene	1971	4,654	394,197	394,197	3,950	6,774	4,806	868,911
Churches of Christ	1968	18,000	2,400,000		N.R.	6,200		
Churches of Christ in Christian Union	1971	244	8,741	8,741	147	223	231	16,623
Churches of God in North America (General Eldership)	1967	352	36,042		210	353		

Religious Body	Year Reported	No. of Churches	Inclusive Membership	Full, Communicant, or Confirmed Members	No. of Pastors Having Charges	Total No. of Clergy	No. of Sunday or Sabbath Schools	Total Enrollment
Congregational Christian Churches, National Association of	1971	336	85,000	85,000	262	391	326	30,000
Congregational Holiness Church	1966	147	4,859		146	302		
Conservative Baptist Association of America	1970	1,127	300,000		N.R.	N.R.		
Conservative Congregational Christian Conference	1971	120	19,416	19,416	154	225	117	14,169
Cumberland Presbyterian Church	1971	854	90,368	86,340	523	633	880	57,726
Duck River (and Kindred) Association of Baptists	1968	81	8,492		128	128		112
Eastern Orthodox Catholic Church in America	1971	3	293	293	6	6	1	N.R.
Elim Fellowship	1972	70	5,000	5,000	70	128	70	N.R.
The Episcopal Church	1971	7,116	3,217,365	2,143,557	7,009	11,108	6,451	685,596
Ethical Culture Movement	1972	25	5,000	4,000	30	37	20	1,325
Evangelical Church of North America	1971	115	9,451	9,451	110	160	115	13,418
Evangelical Congregational Church	1972	160	29,682	29,682	124	173	159	28,311
The Evangelical Covenant Church of America	1971	526	68,428	68,428	426	671	500	66,194
The Evangelical Free Church of America	1971	562	70,490	70,490	N.R.	N.R.	N.R.	N.R.
Evangelical Friends Alliance	1971	254	23,683	23,683	N.R.	N.R.	N.R.	N.R.
Evangelical Lutheran Church in America (Eielsen Synod)	1957	9	2,500		3	3		
Evangelical Lutheran Synod	1971	89	16,202	11,427	50	63	79	4,381
Evangelical Mennonite Brethren Conference	1971	33	3,753	3,753	35	37	33	4,854
Evangelical Mennonite Church, Inc.	1968	20	3,285		21	67		
Evangelical Methodist Church	1965	150	9,311		140	239		
The Fire-Baptized Holiness Church (Wesleyan)	1958	53	998		N.R.	N.R.		
Free Christian Zion Church of Christ	1956	742	22,260		321	340		
Free Methodist Church of North America	1971	1,264	65,040	65,040	N.R.	1,749	1,264	118,276
Free Will Baptists	1972	2,250	210,000	210,000	3,610	3,374	2,200	181,000
Friends General Conference	1971	233	26,671	26,671	N.R.	N.R.	N.R.	N.R.
Friends United Meeting	1971	512	68,773	54,522	332	554	412	36,299
Fundamental Methodist Church, Inc.	1971	14	722	722	14	16	14	684
General Association of Regular Baptist Churches	1972	1,426	204,357	204,357	N.R.	N.R.	N.R.	N.R.
General Baptists (General Association of)	1971	845	65,000	65,000	1,000	1,115	854	80,500

TABLE 1-A: UNITED STATES CURRENT AND NON-CURRENT STATISTICS (Continued)

Religious Body	Year Reported	No. of Churches	Inclusive Membership	Full, Communicant, or Confirmed Members	No. of Pastors Having Charges	Total No. of Clergy	No. of Sunday or Sabbath Schools	Total Enrollment
General Church of the New Jerusalem	1971	33	2,143	2,143	17	31	8	168
General Conference of the Evangelical Baptist Church, Inc.	1952	31	2,200		22	37		
General Conference of Mennonite Brethren Churches	1965	81	13,171		111	173		
General Convention, The Swedenborgian Church	1967	56	4,450		34	49		
General Six Principle Baptists	1970	8	308		6	8		
The Gospel Mission Corps	1972	7	175	175	4	7	5	N.R.
Greek Orthodox Archdiocese of North and South America	1972	502	1,950,000	1,950,000	545	675	639	75,191
The Holiness Church of God, Inc.	1968	28	927		26	36		
Holy Orthodox Church in America (Eastern Catholic and Apostolic)	1965	4	260		4	10		
Holy Ukrainian Autocephalic Church in Exile	1965	15	4,800		15	24		
House of God, Which is the Church of the Living God, the Pillar and Ground of the Truth, Inc.	1956	107	2,350		80	170		
Hungarian Reformed Church in America	1969	27	11,250		24	34		
Hutterian Brethren	1968	29	3,405		20	20		
Independent Assemblies of God, International	1962	136	N.R.		136	367		
Independent Fundamental Churches of America	1971	904	139,932	139,932	697	1,231	904	203,812
International Church of the Foursquare Gospel	1963	741	89,215		741	2,690		
International General Assembly of Spiritualists	1956	209	164,072		221	N.R.		
International Pentecostal Assemblies	1971	55	10,000	10,000	80	201	55	12,330
Jehovah's Witnesses	1971	5,676	416,789	416,789	N.R.	N.R.	N.R.	N.R.
Jewish Congregations	1971	5,000	5,870,000	N.R.	5,100	6,400	N.R.	N.R.
Kodesh Church of Immanuel	1936	9	582		N.R.	N.R.		
Liberal Catholic Church (California)	1956	8	4,000		8	33		
The Liberal Catholic Church (World Headquarters, London, England)	1972	18	1,500	N.R.	N.R.	84	N.R.	N.R.
Lutheran Church in America	1971	5,797	3,069,679	2,175,378	4,761	7,377	5,596	889,212

TABLE 1-A: UNITED STATES CURRENT AND NON-CURRENT STATISTICS (Continued)

Religious Body	Year Reported	No. of Churches	Inclusive Membership	Full, Communicant, or Confirmed Members	No. of Pastors Having Charges	Total No. of Clergy	No. of Sunday or Sabbath Schools	Total Enrollment
The Lutheran Church—Missouri Synod	1971	5,724	2,788,110	1,945,889	4,712	7,041	5,552	815,522
Mennonite Church	1971	1,041	88,947	88,947	2,090	2,335	967	110,475
Mennonite Church, the General Conference	1971	192	36,314	36,314	175	314	192	31,809
The Metropolitan Church Association	1958	15	443		13	62		
The Missionary Church	1971	365	22,071	22,071	420	573	365	45,301
The Moravian Church in America, Northern Province	1971	100	34,555	26,101	80	159	98	10,069
The Moravian Church in America, Southern Province	1971	49	22,784	16,963	47	58	49	10,771
National Baptist Convention of America	1956	11,398	2,668,799		7,598	28,574		
National Baptist Convention, U.S.A., Inc.	1958	26,000	5,500,000		26,000	27,500		
National Baptist Evangelical Life and Soul Saving Assembly of U.S.A.	1951	264	57,674		128	137		
The National Primitive Baptist Convention, Inc.	1971	2,198	1,645,000	1,645,000	601	601	2,150	32,200
The National Spiritual Alliance of the U.S.A.	1971	34	3,230	3,230	56	N.R.	N.R.	N.R.
National Spiritualist Association of Churches	1970	204	N.R.		163	N.R.		
Netherlands Reformed Congregations	1971	22	7,319	3,255	N.R.	N.R.	N.R.	N.R.
New Apostolic Church of North America	1971	262	20,195	20,195	327	383	262	7,186
North American Baptist General Conference	1972	341	54,441	54,441	331	423	332	55,815
North American Old Roman Catholic Church	1972	121	60,098	58,774	83	112	15	8,022
North American Old Roman Catholic Church	1965	30	18,500		30	45		
Old German Baptist Brethren	1965	54	4,225		46	130		
Old Order Amish Church	1972	368	14,720	14,720	1,472	1,497	N.R.	N.R.
Old Order (Wisler) Mennonite Church	1972	38	8,000	8,000	60	101	None	None
The Old Roman Catholic Church (English Rite)	1972	186	65,128	65,128	186	201	N.R.	N.R.

TABLE 1-A: UNITED STATES CURRENT AND NON-CURRENT STATISTICS (Continued)

Religious Body	Year Reported	No. of Churches	Inclusive Membership	Full, Communicant, or Confirmed Members	No. of Pastors Having Charges	Total No. of Clergy	No. of Sunday or Sabbath Schools	Total Enrollment
Open Bible Standard Churches	1971	275	25,000	25,000	420	725	275	24,000
The (Original) Church of God	1971	70	20,000	20,000	50	124	40	129
The Orthodox Church in America	1971	387	1,000,000	1,000,000	400	448	N.R.	N.R.
The Orthodox Presbyterian Church	1970	116	14,300		N.R.	190		
Pentecostal Assemblies of the World, Inc.	1960	550	45,000		450	600		
Pentecostal Church of Christ	1971	43	1,209	1,209	41	45	40	3,171
Pentecostal Church of God of America, Inc.	1967	975	115,000		975	1,325		
Pentecostal Fire-Baptized Holiness Church	1967	41	545		80	80		
Pentecostal Free-Will Baptist Church, Inc.	1970	150	13,500		150	192		
Pentecostal Holiness Church, Inc.	1971	1,341	72,696	72,696	2,422	2,422	N.R.	155,843
Pillar of Fire	1949	61	5,100		N.R.	N.R.		
Plymouth Brethren	1971	740	37,500	37,500	None	None	700	33,000
Polish National Catholic Church of America	1960	162	282,411		151	144		
Presbyterian Church in the United States	1971	4,230	949,857	949,857	2,949	4,858	N.R.	509,602
Primitive Advent Christian Church	1970	10	600		15	15		
Primitive Baptists	1950	1,000	72,000		N.R.	N.R.		
Primitive Methodist Church, U.S.A.	1965	86	11,946		71	60		
Progressive National Baptist Convention, Inc.	1967	655	521,692		N.R.	863		
The Protestant Conference (Lutheran)	1971	7	2,600	1,600	8	15	7	600
Reformed Church in America	1971	921	369,951	220,775	823	1,277	905	127,359
Reformed Church in the United States	1971	25	4,038	3,043	18	25	24	807
Reformed Episcopal Church	1966	75	7,085		51	90		
Reformed Mennonite Church	1970	12	500		18	21		
Reformed Methodist Union Episcopal Church	1970	20	5,000		18	21		
Reformed Presbyterian Church, Evangelical Synod	1971	129	17,798	14,027	234	320	129	10,426
Reformed Presbyterian Church of North America	1970	69	5,704		52	100		
Reformed Zion Union Apostolic Church	1965	50	16,000		23	N.R.		
Religious Society of Friends (Conservative)	1971	26	1,835	1,835	None	None	N.R.	N.R.
Religious Society of Friends (Unaffiliated Meet.)	1971	72	2,896	2,896	N.R.	N.R.	N.R.	N.R.
Reorganized Church of Jesus Christ of Latter Day Saints	1971	1,027	154,481	154,481	14,634	14,634	N.R.	N.R.
The Roman Catholic Church	1971	23,796	48,390,990	N.R.	N.R.	57,778	11,792	10,104,507
The Romanian Orthodox Episcopate of America	1971	45	50,000	50,000	42	50	39	1,693
Russian Orthodox Church in the U.S.A., Patriarchal Parishes of the	1965	67	152,973		61	98		
The Russian Orthodox Church Outside Russia	1955	81	55,000		92	168		
The Salvation Army	1971	1,104	335,684	335,684	3,759	5,180	1,112	108,910

Religious Body	Year Reported	No. of Churches	Inclusive Membership	Full, Communicant, or Confirmed Members	No. of Pastors Having Charges	Total No. of Clergy	No. of Sunday or Sabbath Schools	Total Enrollment
The Schwenkfelder Church	1967	5	2,250		6	9		
Second Cumberland Presbyterian Church in U.S.	1959	121	30,000		121	125		
Separate Baptists in Christ	1962	84	7,496		65	106		
Serbian Eastern Orthodox Church for the U.S.A. and Canada	1967	52	65,000		56	64		
Seventh-day Adventists	1971	3,235	433,906	433,906	1,482	3,365	3,315	375,031
Seventh Day Baptist General Conference	1971	66	5,376	5,376	47	81	47	2,837
Social Brethren Church	1971	31	1,672	1,672	24	42	30	N.R.
Southern Baptist Convention	1971	34,420	11,824,676	11,824,676	31,000	N.R.	33,435	7,138,741
Syrian Orthodox Church of Antioch (Archdiocese of the U.S.A. and Canada)	1971	150	9,917	9,917	55	63	150	9,630
Triumph the Church and Kingdom of God in Christ	1971	8	35,000	10,000	10	10	8	2,050
Ukrainian Orthodox Church in America	1972	495	54,307	44,460	860	1,375	495	51,777
Ukrainian Orthodox Church in America	1966	107	87,475		107	131		
Ukrainian Orthodox Church in America (Ecumenical Patriarchate)	1970	24	45,000		22	26		
Unitarian-Universalist Association	1969	1,076	265,408		538	868		
United Brethren in Christ	1971	296	26,643	24,544	N.R.	N.R.	N.R.	30,618
United Christian Church	1972	12	400	400	11	13	11	866
United Church of Christ	1971	6,688	1,928,674	1,928,674	5,136	9,378	N.R.	711,757
United Free Will Baptist Church	1952	836	100,000		915	784		
United Holy Church of America	1960	470	28,980		379	400		
The United Methodist Church	1971	40,054	10,509,198	10,509,198	20,550	34,822	37,803	5,634,662
United Pentecostal Church	1972	2,500	250,000	250,000	N.R.	N.R.	N.R.	N.R.
The United Presbyterian Church in the United States of America	1971	8,760	3,013,808	3,013,808	7,296	13,451	8,760	1,203,488
United Seventh Day Brethren	1968	4	N.R.		N.R.	N.R.		
The United Wesleyan Methodist Church of America	1972	6	400	400	8	8	N.R.	N.R.
United Zion Church	1972	17	875	875	20	24	5	1,327
Unity of the Brethren	1964	32	6,142		13	13	13	N.R.
Vedanta Society of New York	1971	13	1,000	1,000	19	N.R.		
Volunteers of America	1967	219	32,760		364	432	N.R.	
The Wesleyan Church	1970	1,898	84,499		1,918	2,925		
Wesleyan Holiness Association of Churches	1972	67	2,000	2,000	67	112	67	
Wisconsin Evangelical Lutheran Synod	1971	987	383,263	275,500	757	967	920	57,569

TABLE 1-B: SUMMARY OF UNITED STATES CURRENT AND NON-CURRENT STATISTICS

"Current" statistics are those reported for the years 1972 and 1971. "Non-Current" statistics are for the years 1970 and earlier. Only current data are provided in the following categories: Full, Communicant, or Confirmed Members; Number of Sunday or Sabbath Schools; Total Enrollment.

	Bodies Reported	No. of Churches	Inclusive Membership	Full, Communicant, or Confirmed Members	No. of Pastors Having Charges	Total No. of Clergy	Total Sunday or Sabbath Schools, No. of	Total Enrollment
1973 Yearbook								
Current	128	237,870	114,369,013	55,020,752	194,704	295,154	185,149	38,487,453
Non-Current	95	91,802	17,020,629	N.R.	62,523	101,450	N.R.	N.R.
Totals	223	329,672	131,389,642		257,227	396,604		
1972 Yearbook								
Current	140	245,109	115,442,829	52,374,772	178,702	298,988	155,054	40,501,517
Non-Current	96	83,548	15,603,124	N.R.	56,487	94,838	N.R.	N.R.
Totals	236	328,657	131,045,953		235,189	393,826		

TABLE 1-C: SOME COMPARATIVE UNITED STATES CHURCH STATISTICS

	1971	1972
Church Membership as a Percent of U.S. Population	63.2	62.4
Membership Gain over Previous Year	2,540,869	343,689
Percentage of Gain over Previous Year	1.97	.26

TABLE 1-D: CANADIAN CURRENT AND NON-CURRENT STATISTICS

The following table provides current and non-current statistics for Canadian denominations listed alphabetically. Current statistics, defined as those gathered and reported for 1972 and 1971, are shown in **bold face** type. Non-current statistics are those for 1970 and appear in light face.

Religious Body	Year Reported	No. of Churches	Inclusive Membership	Full, Communicant, or Confirmed Members	No. of Pastors Having Charges	Total No. of Clergy	No. of Sunday or Sabbath Schools	Total Enrollment
The Anglican Church of Canada	1970	1,736	1,126,570		1,690	2,658	N.R.	N.R.
The Antiochian Orthodox Christian Archdiocese of New York and All North America	1971	4	25,000	N.R.	3	3	N.R.	N.R.
The Armenian Church of North America, Diocese of Canada	1971	3	15,000	N.R.	4	4	N.R.	700
Associated Gospel Churches	1971	104	10,000	7,000	80	167	101	N.R.
Baptist Federation of Canada	1971	1,110	132,003	128,774	587	860	973	54,899
Baptist General Conference	1971	110	12,432	12,432	N.R.	N.R.	111	15,768
Bible Holiness Movement	1972	7	112	103	4	5	N.R.	N.R.
Brethren in Christ Church, Canadian Conference	1971	27	1,466	1,466	26	47	27	2,806
Buddhist Churches of Canada	1971	17	5,000	2,500	10	11	14	1,387
The Canadian Baptist Conference	1971	25	1,688	1,688	22	23	25	2,633
Canadian Jewish Congress	1970	N.R.	280,000		N.R.	N.R.	N.R.	
The Canadian Yearly Meeting of the Religious Society of Friends	1971	24	972	972	None	None	N.R.	N.R.
Christian and Missionary Alliance in Canada	1971	188	21,355	10,937	N.R.	200	178	25,951
Christian Church (Disciples of Christ)	1971	41	4,836	2,916	39	47	41	2,554
Christian Churches & Churches of Christ in Canada	1971	77	5,036	5,036	N.R.	56	77	3,265
Christian Reformed Churches in Canada, Council of	1971	152	70,747	31,690	138	138	N.R.	15,406
The Church of God of Prophecy in Canada	1972	24	1,150	650	26	42	29	1,287
The Church of Jesus Christ of Latter-day Saints in Canada	1971	214	58,683	57,294	642	1,239	214	29,400
Church of the Nazarene	1971	143	7,394	7,394	129	171	130	16,594
The Evangelical Church in Canada	1971	50	3,736	3,736	40	62	50	5,226
The Evangelical Covenant Church of Canada	1971	23	1,060	1,060	11	11	21	1,704
The Evangelical Lutheran Church in Canada	1971	318	83,274	52,768	168	242	285	23,746
Evangelical Mennonite Brethren Conference	1971	10	1,643	1,643	N.R.	N.R.	N.R.	N.R.
Evangelical Mennonite Conference	1971	25	4,000	4,000	N.R.	N.R.	N.R.	N.R.
Evangelical Mennonite Mission Conference	1971	12	1,800	1,800	N.R.	N.R.	N.R.	N.R.
The Free Methodist Church in Canada	1970	175	9,000		N.R.	N.R.	N.R.	N.R.
Greek Orthodox Archdiocese of North and South America, Ninth Archdiocesan District	1971	29	210,000	N.R.	27	28	N.R.	10,500
Independent Assemblies of God—Canada	1971	45	5,500	2,500	125	165	50	N.R.
Independent Holiness Church	1971	12	N.R.	N.R.	12	13	N.R.	N.R.
The Italian Pentecostal Church of Canada	1972	14	2,000	1,300	8	12	10	1,402
Jehovah's Witnesses	1971	790	49,204	49,204	N.R.	N.R.	N.R.	N.R.

TABLE 1-D: CANADIAN CURRENT AND NON-CURRENT STATISTICS (Continued)

Religious Body	Year Reported	No. of Churches	Inclusive Membership	Full, Communicant, or Confirmed Members	No. of Pastors Having Charges	Total No. of Clergy	No. of Sunday or Sabbath Schools	Total Enrollment
Lutheran Church—Canada	1971	370	98,097	65,459	223	287	337	29,037
Lutheran Church in America—Canada Section	1971	332	121,212	81,945	215	314	300	28,906
Mennonite Brethren Churches of North America, Canadian Conference of	1971	125	17,982	17,982	125	252	130	18,293
Mennonite Church (Canada)	1971	68	8,577	8,577	63	81	67	10,004
The Missionary Church—Canada	1970	77	4,121		79	91		
Moravian Church in America, Northern Province, Canadian District of the	1971	9	1,583	1,005	6	10	9	670
North American Baptist General Conference	1972	97	12,647	12,647	78	102	92	12,570
The Pentecostal Assemblies of Canada	1972	749	160,000	160,000	N.R.	886	831	120,000
Polish National Catholic Church of Canada	1971	11	6,000	4,000	8	8	10	N.R.
The Presbyterian Church in Canada	1971	1,069	182,559	182,559	572	866	N.R.	67,531
Primitive Baptist Conference of New Brunswick	1971	20	2,000	2,000	8	10	15	900
Reformed Church in America—Ontario Classis	1971	18	5,595	2,542	15	21	18	1,588
Reorganized Church of Jesus Christ of Latter Day Saints	1971	88	11,178	11,178	244	244	N.R.	N.R.
The Roman Catholic Church in Canada	1970	6,063	8,759,625		N.R.	14,353		
The Romanian Orthodox Church in America (Canadian Parishes)	1971	18	15,000	15,000	12	12	8	373
The Romanian Orthodox Episcopate of America	1971	14	10,000	10,000	7	9	10	530
Russian Orthodox Church in Canada, Patriarchal Parishes of the	1971	23	4,500	4,500	19	19	23	N.R.
Seventh-day Adventist Church in Canada	1971	188	20,190	20,190	74	137	219	19,451
Ukrainian Greek Orthodox Church of Canada	1970	288	140,000		N.R.	95		
Union of Spiritual Communities of Christ (Orthodox Doukhobors in Canada)	1971	25	16,000	5,000	None	None	8	632
Unitarian-Universalist Association	1971	55	6,035	6,035	23	23	N.R.	3,392
United Church of Canada	1971	4,442	1,016,706	1,016,706	2,079	3,578	3,800	329,857

Note: Table 1-D is incomplete in many ways but will, it is hoped, become more adequate each year. It suffers primarily because of the lack of current data from the Anglican Church of Canada, the Jewish community, and the Roman Catholic Church. If these three bodies had reported current totals, the data for full, communicant, or confirmed members and the Sunday or sabbath school information would be considerably altered. Another significant problem with this table is that the Roman Catholic data are derived from the Canadian Census of Population, which records religious identification, whereas the data for most Protestant groups are membership totals actually derived from parish records. There is a big difference between membership on the one hand and identification on the other. Therefore, the Roman Catholic data are overstated as to membership and the Protestant data understated, since, in many cases, children under 13 years of age are not counted as members. The reader is referred to "A Guide for the User of Church Statistics," at the front of the **Yearbook** for a more detailed discussion of this problem.

236

TABLE 1-E: SUMMARY OF CANADIAN CURRENT AND NON-CURRENT STATISTICS

"Current" statistics are those reported for the years 1972 or 1971. "Non-Current" statistics are for the years 1970 and earlier. Only current totals are provided in the following categories: Full, Communicant, or Confirmed Members; Number of Sunday or Sabbath Schools; Total Enrollment.

	Bodies Reported	No. of Churches	Inclusive Membership	Full, Communicant, or Confirmed Members	No. of Pastors Having Charges	Total Clergy	No. of Sunday or Sabbath Schools	Total Enrollment
1973 Yearbook								
Current	47	11,320	2,450,952	2,016,188	5,872	10,405	8,213	858,962
Non-Current	6	8,339	10,319,316	N.R.	1,769	17,197	N.R.	N.R.
Totals	53	19,659	12,770,268		7,641	27,602		

Table 1-E presents totals for Table 1-D, the note to which should be read for a clearer understanding of these totals.

TABLE 1-F: NUMBER OF UNITED STATES CHURCHES, AND OF MEMBERS, BY RELIGIOUS GROUPS

The 223 U.S. religious bodies reporting in this edition of the **Yearbook** may be classified, somewhat arbitrarily into seven major categories.

It should be reiterated that comparisons of statistics of the various religious groups tabulated below are not meaningful because definitions of membership vary greatly from one religious body to another. For example, Roman Catholics count all baptized individuals, including infant members, as do many Protestant bodies. Some Protestant bodies, however, count as members those who have been received into the church at baptism, which usually takes place at around age 13, thereby leaving out of official counts of membership many millions of children. Jewish statistics are estimates of the number of Jews living in communities where there are synagogues.

The definition of membership in each case is of necessity left up to the religious body itself, and the statistics reported by various religious bodies are not adjusted by the editor of the **Yearbook.**

Religious Group	Number of Bodies Reporting	Number of Churches	Number of Members
Buddhists	1	60	100,000
Eastern Churches	20	1,545	3,847,901
Jewish Congregations*	1	5,000	5,870,000
Old Catholic, Polish National Catholic, Armenian Churches	12	657	867,116
Protestants**	180	297,032	71,865,190
Roman Catholics	1	23,796	48,390,990
Miscellaneous***	8	1,582	448,445
Totals	223	329,672	131,389,642

*Including Orthodox, Conservative, and Reformed branches.
**Some bodies included here are, strictly speaking, not "Protestant" in the usual sense, such as various Latter-Day Saints groups and Jehovah's Witnesses.
***This is a grouping of bodies officially non-Christian, including those such as Spiritualists, Ethical Culture Movement, and Unitarian-Universalists.

TABLE 1-G: CONSTITUENCY OF THE NATIONAL COUNCIL OF THE CHURCHES OF CHRIST IN THE U.S.A.

A separate tabulation has been made of the constituent bodies of the National Council of Churches of Christ in the U.S.A., and is given below:

Religious Body	Year	Number of Churches	Inclusive Membership	Pastors with Charges
African Methodist Episcopal Church	1951	5,878	1,166,301	5,878
African Methodist Episcopal Zion Church	1970	4,500	940,000	5,000
American Baptist Churches in the U.S.A.	1971	6,035	1,562,636	4,700
The Antiochian Orthodox Archdiocese of Toledo, Ohio, and Dependencies in North America	1971	16	30,000	19
The Antiochian Orthodox Christian Archdiocese of New York and All North America	1970	92	100,000	96
Armenian Church of America, Diocese of the (including Diocese of California)	1971	62	300,000	62
Christian Church (Disciples of Christ)	1971	4,868	1,386,374	4,184
Christian Methodist Episcopal Church	1965	2,598	466,718	2,214
Church of the Brethren	1971	1,036	181,183	705
The Episcopal Church	1971	7,116	3,217,365	7,009
Friends United Meeting	1971	512	68,773	332
General Convention, the Swedenborgian Church	1967	56	4,450	34

Religious Body	Year	Number of Churches	Inclusive Membership	Pastors with Charges
Greek Orthodox Archdiocese of North and South America	1972	502	1,950,000	545
Hungarian Reformed Church in America	1969	27	11,250	24
Lutheran Church in America	1971	5,797	3,069,679	4,761
Moravian Church in America				
Northern Province	1971	100	34,555	80
Southern Province	1971	49	22,784	47
National Baptist Convention of America	1956	11,398	2,668,799	7,598
National Baptist Convention, U.S.A., Inc.	1958	26,000	5,500,000	26,000
Orthodox Church in America	1971	387	1,000,000	400
Philadelphia Yearly Meeting of the Religious Society of Friends	1967	202	(1965) 16,965	(1965) 23
Polish National Catholic Church of America	1960	162	282,411	151
The Presbyterian Church in the United States	1971	4,230	949,857	2,949
Progressive National Baptist Convention, Inc.	1967	655	521,692	N.R.
Reformed Church in America	1971	921	369,951	823
Russian Orthodox Church in the U.S.A., Patriarchal Parishes of the	1965	67	152,973	61
Serbian Eastern Orthodox Church for the U.S.A. and Canada	1967	52	65,000	56
Seventh Day Baptist General Conference	1971	66	5,376	47
Syrian Orthodox Church of Antioch	1971	8	35,000	10
Ukrainian Orthodox Church in America	1966	107	87,475	107
United Church of Christ	1971	6,688	1,928,674	5,136
The United Methodist Church	1971	40,054	10,509,1^8	20,550
The United Presbyterian Church in the United States of America	1971	8,760	3,013,808	7,296
Total (32) bodies		**139,001**	**41,619,247**	**106,897**

I've "rendered unto Caesar" so much on credit that I have to borrow from God's renderings to pay for it...

2. CHURCH FINANCIAL STATISTICS AND RELATED DATA

For this edition of the **Yearbook of American and Canadian Churches,** complete financial data were supplied by 42 United States communions. The results are presented in the table entitled "Some Statistics of Church Finances—United States Churches." The data are complete for each communion in the three major categories of reporting. It will be noted that Total Contributions are the sum total of Total Congregational Finances and Total Benevolences.

Similarly, data were supplied by 21 Canadian church bodies, an addition of 13 from the previous year. The information is included in the table "Some Statistics of Church Finances—Canadian Churches." Both the U.S. and Canadian data are current, and incomplete information submitted by denominations has been excluded from the tables.

A third table, "Summary Statistics of Church Finances," provides totals for the U.S. and Canadian bodies. The 42 U.S. bodies report total contributions of $4,386,-682,020 and the 21 Canadian groups, $175,394,781. It must be remembered, however, that many of the Canadian groups are not wholly Canadian denominations but, rather, sections of denominations existing and headquartered in the U.S. Only 9 of the 21 bodies listed in the table "Some Statistics of Church Finances—Canadian Churches" are strictly Canadian churches. Per capita contributions for inclusive membership of U.S. communions amounted to $93.35 and for the Canadian bodies, $62.02. Benevolences as a percentage of total contributions amounted to 19.3 percent for the U.S. bodies and 23.8 percent for the Canadian.

Readers of the tables should be aware of the fact that the Canadian and U.S. financial data appearing in this section are only a significant part of total contributions from members of all communions. Not all bodies in the U.S. and Canada gather church financial data centrally, and some have information but do not reveal it publicly. Additionally, little is known about other major segments of church financial income such as earned income, interest from investments, and bequests.

Comparisons between this year's aggregate financial data and those in previous editions of the **Yearbook** should not be made, since the same bodies do not report financial data each year. However, for an individual denomination, or groups of denominations, reporting annually over time, comparisons can be made.

Comparative data for nine major Protestant denominations in the U.S. among the 42 listed in this section show a total 1971 membership of 25,583,882, or 266,750 less than the same churches' total for 1970. Yet these fewer members contributed $2,282,628,529 in 1971, an increase of $63,433,445 over the 1970 giving for the same churches. However, with a rough inflationary increase of 5 percent calculated in these figures, what appears to be a gain of $63 million would be a decrease of $47 million. For Canada, comparative figures for eight communions indicate a decrease in membership of 22,011 to a total of 1,356,406 but an increase in giving of $1,496,010 to a total of $111,904,747. Assuming a similar inflation rate in Canada of 5 percent for 1971, the total contributions of these eight churches would represent a loss of $4,098,827.

The other statistical charts and tables as well as the textual and bibliographical materials in the section present useful background information for interpreting church finances. The data are completely new and come from both Canadian and U.S. sources.

SOME STATISTICS OF CHURCH FINANCES

COMMUNION	Year	Full or* Confirmed Membership	Inclusive** Membership	TOTAL CONTRIBUTIONS		
				Total Contributions	Per Capita Full or Confirmed Membership	Per Capita Inclusive Membership
American Baptist Convention†	1971	1,562,636	1,562,636	$133,552,574	$ 85.45	$ 85.45
The American Lutheran Church	1971	1,775,774	2,521,930	174,646,200	98.35	69.25
Assemblies of God	1972	679,813	1,078,332	163,155,120	240.00	151.30
Berean Fundamental Church	1971	2,419	2,419	1,038,216	429.19	429.19
Brethren in Christ Church	1971	9,550	9,550	3,209,511	336.07	336.07
Christian Church (Disciples of Christ)	1971	884,929	1,386,374	111,862,661	126.41	80.69
Church of God (Anderson, Indiana)	1971	152,787	152,787	33,405,886	218.64	218.64
Church of God General Conference (Oregon, Illinois)	1971	7,200	7,200	980,000	136.11	136.11
Church of the Brethren	1971	181,183	181,183	19,720,042	108.84	108.84
Church of the Nazarene	1971	394,197	394,197	93,002,530	235.93	235.93
Conservative Congregational Christian Conference	1971	19,416	19,416	2,841,437	146.35	146.35
The Cumberland Presbyterian Church	1971	57,147	92,025	7,987,595	139.77	86.80
The Episcopal Church	1970	2,208,773	3,285,826	248,702,969	112.60	75.69
The Evangelical Church of North America	1971	9,451	9,451	2,652,726	280.68	280.68
Evangelical Congregational Church	1972	29,682	29,682	4,305,804	145.06	145.06
The Evangelical Covenant Church of America	1971	68,428	68,428	18,699,077	273.27	273.27
Evangelical Free Church of America	1971	70,490	70,490	22,235,188	315.44	315.44
Evangelical Lutheran Synod	1971	11,427	16,202	1,343,472	117.57	82.92
Evangelical Mennonite Brethren	1970	3,753	3,753	868,733	231.47	231.47
Free Methodist Church of North America	1971	65,040	65,040	19,956,104	306.83	306.83
Free Will Baptists	1972	210,000	210,000	13,597,644	64.75	64.75
Friends United Meeting	1971	54,522	68,773	5,096,126	93.47	74.10
Independent Fundamental Churches of America	1971	139,932	139,932	32,674,874	233.51	233.51
Lutheran Church in America	1971	2,175,378	3,069,679	223,170,380	102.59	72.70
The Lutheran Church—Missouri Synod	1971	1,945,889	2,788,110	252,511,172	129.77	90.57
Mennonite Church	1971	88,522	88,522	15,207,066	171.79	171.79
Mennonite Church, General Conference	1971	36,314	36,314	6,201,591	170.78	170.78
The Missionary Church	1970	22,071	22,071	7,506,226	340.09	340.09
Moravian Church in America, Northern Province	1971	26,101	34,555	3,035,619	116.30	87.85
Moravian Church in America, Southern Province	1971	16,963	22,784	1,731,352	102.07	75.99
North American Baptist General Conference	1972	54,441	54,441	9,772,716	179.51	179.51
Pentecostal Holiness Church, Inc.	1971	72,696	72,696	13,698,767	188.44	188.44
Presbyterian Church in the U.S.	1971	949,857	949,857	145,972,874	153.68	153.68
Reformed Church in America	1971	223,317	375,546	42,221,910	189.07	112.43
Reformed Church in the United States	1971	3,043	4,038	264,240	86.84	65.44
Seventh-day Adventists	1971	433,906	433,906	169,121,922	389.77	389.77
Seventh Day Baptist General Conference	1971	5,376	5,376	630,001	117.19	117.19
Southern Baptist Convention	1971	11,824,676	11,824,676	974,917,401	82.44	82.44
United Church of Christ	1971	1,928,674	1,928,674	185,334,477	96.09	96.09
The United Methodist Church	1970	10,509,198	10,509,198	819,945,000	78.02	78.02
The United Presbyterian Church in the United States of America	1971	3,013,808	3,013,808	368,057,481	122.12	122.12
Wisconsin Evangelical Lutheran Synod	1971	275,500	383,263	31,847,336	115.60	83.10

† American Baptist Churches in the U.S.A. as of January 1, 1973.
* Full or Confirmed Membership refers to those with full, communicant, or confirmed status.
**Inclusive Membership refers to those who are full, communicant, or confirmed members, plus other members listed as baptized,, nonconfirmed, or noncommunicant.

UNITED STATES CHURCHES

	CONGREGATIONAL FINANCES		BENEVOLENCES			
Total Congregational Contributions	Per Capita Full or Confirmed Membership	Per Capita Inclusive Membership	Total Benevolences	Per Capita Full or Confirmed Membership	Per Capita Inclusive Membership	Benevolences as a Percentage of Total Contributions
$114,673,805	$ 73.38	$ 73.38	$ 18,878,769	$ 12.08	$ 12.08	14.1%
146,324,460	82.40	58.02	28,321,740	15.95	11.23	16.2
142,579,529	209.73	132.22	20,575,591	30.27	19.08	12.6
723,400	299.05	299.05	314,816	130.14	130.14	30.3
2,357,786	246.89	246.89	851,725	89.18	89.18	26.5
94,091,862	106.33	67.87	17,770,799	20.08	12.82	15.9
28,343,604	185.51	185.51	5,062,282	33.13	33.13	15.2
860,000	119.44	119.44	120,000	16.67	16.67	12.2
14,535,274	80.22	80.22	5,184,768	28.62	28.62	26.3
74,616,405	189.29	189.29	18,386,125	46.64	46.64	19.8
1,903,865	98.06	98.06	937,572	48.29	48.29	33.0
6,848,115	119.83	74.42	1,139,480	19.94	12.38	14.3
213,305,658	96.57	64.92	35,397,311	16.03	10.77	14.2
2,055,646	217.50	217.50	597,080	63.18	63.18	22.5
3,563,512	120.06	120.06	742,292	25.00	25.00	17.2
14,857,190	217.12	217.12	3,841,887	56.15	56.15	20.5
16,310,609	231.39	231.39	5,924,579	84.05	84.05	26.6
1,028,629	90.02	63.49	314,843	27.55	19.43	23.4
504,417	134.40	134.40	364,316	97.07	97.07	41.9
13,863,601	213.16	213.16	6,092,503	93.67	93.67	30.5
11,710,644	55.76	55.76	1,887,000	8.99	8.99	13.9
3,888,064	71.31	56.53	1,208,062	22.16	17.57	23.7
23,694,661	169.33	169.33	8,980,213	64.18	64.18	27.5
179,570,467	82.55	58.50	43,599,913	20.04	14.20	19.5
203,619,804	104.64	73.03	48,891,368	25.13	17.54	19.4
8,171,316	92.31	92.31	7,035,750	79.48	79.48	46.3
3,368,100	92.75	92.75	2,833,491	78.03	78.03	45.7
5,111,714	231.60	231.60	2,394,512	108.49	108.49	31.9
2,576,172	98.70	74.55	459,447	17.60	13.30	15.1
1,375,289	81.08	60.36	356,063	20.99	15.63	20.6
7,519,558	138.12	138.12	2,253,158	41.39	41.39	23.1
11,967,031	164.62	164.62	1,731,736	23.82	23.82	12.6
114,200,673	120.23	120.23	31,772,201	33.45	33.45	21.8
32,686,822	146.37	87.04	9,535,088	42.70	25.39	22.6
198,359	65.19	49.12	65,881	21.65	16.32	24.9
49,208,043	113.41	113.41	119,913,879	276.36	276.36	70.9
473,979	88.16	88.16	156,022	29.03	29.03	24.8
814,406,626	68.87	68.87	160,510,775	13.57	13.57	16.5
158,924,956	82.40	82.40	26,409,521	13.69	13.69	14.3
682,900,000	64.98	64.98	137,045,000	13.04	13.04	16.7
306,665,134	101.75	101.75	61,392,347	20.37	20.37	16.7
24,365,692	88.44	63.58	7,481,644	27.16	19.52	23.5

SOME STATISTICS OF CHURCH FINANCES

	Year	Full or* Confirmed Membership	Inclusive** Membership	TOTAL CONTRIBUTIONS		
				Total Contributions	Per Capita Full or Confirmed Membership	Per Capita Inclusive Membership
The Anglican Church of Canada	1970	629,819	1,126,570	$ 40,687,024	$ 64.60	$ 36.12
Baptist Convention of Ontario and Quebec	1971	46,709	46,709	6,470,145	138.52	138.52
Baptist Union of Western Canada	1971	13,922	17,151	2,984,476	214.37	174.01
The Bible Holiness Movement	1972	103	112	11,367	110.36	101.49
Brethren in Christ Church, Canadian Conference	1971	1,466	1,466	453,874	309.60	309.60
Canadian Baptist Conference	1971	1,688	1,688	346,490	205.27	205.27
Christian Church (Disciples of Christ)	1971	2,916	4,836	370,389	127.02	76.59
Church of the Nazarene	1971	7,394	7,394	1,743,757	235.83	235.83
The Evangelical Church in Canada	1971	3,736	3,736	640,983	171.57	171.57
The Evangelical Covenant Church of Canada	1971	1,060	1,060	258,946	244.29	244.29
The Evangelical Lutheran Church in Canada	1971	52,768	83,274	3,878,033	73.49	46.57
The Italian Pentecostal Church of Canada	1972	1,300	2,000	153,100	117.77	76.55
Lutheran Church—Canada	1971	65,459	98,097	5,006,189	76.48	51.03
Lutheran Church in America —Canada Section	1971	81,945	121,212	5,461,918	66.65	45.06
Mennonite Church—Canada	1971	8,577	8,577	1,263,354	147.29	147.29
The Missionary Church— Canada	1970	4,121	4,121	1,191,966	289.24	289.24
North American Baptist General Conference	1972	12,647	12,647	2,404,402	190.12	190.12
The Presbyterian Church in Canada	1971	182,559	182,559	17,484,513	95.77	95.77
Seventh-day Adventist Church in Canada	1971	20,190	20,190	5,867,248	290.60	290.60
The United Baptist Convention of the Atlantic Provinces	1971	68,143	68,143	5,087,612	74.66	74.66
The United Church of Canada	1971	1,016,706	1,016,706	73,628,995	72.42	72.42

* Full or Confirmed Membership refers to those with full, communicant, or confirmed status.
** Inclusive Membership refers to those who are full, communicant, or confirmed members, plus other members listed as baptized, nonconfirmed, or noncommunicant.

SUMMARY STATISTICS

	Total Bodies	Full or* Confirmed Membership	Inclusive** Membership	TOTAL CONTRIBUTIONS		
				Total Contributions	Per Capita Full or Confirmed Membership	Per Capita Inclusive Membership
United States Communions	42	42,204,281	46,993,140	$4,386,682,020	$103.94	$93.35
Canadian Communions	21	2,223,228	2,828,248	175,394,781	78,89	62.02

* Full or Confirmed Membership refers to those with full, communicant, or confirmed status.
** Inclusive Membership refers to those who are full, communicant, or confirmed members, plus other members listed as baptized, nonconfirmed, or noncommunicant.

CONGREGATIONAL FINANCES			BENEVOLENCES			
Total Congregational Finances	Per Capita Full or Confirmed Membership	Per Capita Inclusive Membership	Total Benevolences	Per Capita Inclusive Membership	Per Capita Inclusive Membership	Benevolences as a Percentage of Total Contributions
$ 30,401,592	$ 48.27	$ 26.99	$10,285,432	$ 16.33	$ 9.13	25.3%
5,165,789	110.60	110.60	1,304,356	27.92	27.92	20.2
2,469,179	177.36	143.96	515,297	37.01	30.05	17.3
4,024	39.07	35.93	7,343	71.29	65.56	64.6
344,199	234.79	234.79	109,675	74.81	74.81	24.2
314,629	186.39	186.39	31,861	18.88	18.88	9.2
318,931	109.37	65.95	51,458	17.65	10.64	13.9
1,359,816	183.91	183.91	383,941	51.92	51.92	22.0
415,983	111.34	111.34	225,000	60.23	60.23	35.1
187,437	176.83	176.83	71,509	67.46	67.46	27.6
3,322,764	62.97	39.90	555,269	10.52	6.67	14.3
117,000	90.00	58.50	36,100	27.77	18.05	23.6
3,853,297	58.87	39.28	1,152,892	17.61	11.75	23.0
4,315,830	52.67	35.61	1,146,088	13.98	9.45	21.0
436,845	50.93	50.93	826,509	96.36	96.36	65.4
749,596	181.90	181.90	442,370	107.34	107.34	37.1
1,873,399	148.13	148.13	531,003	41.99	41.99	22.1
13,535,565	74.14	74.14	3,948,948	21.63	21.63	22.6
1,515,579	75.06	75.06	4,351,669	215.54	215.54	74.2
4,173,038	61.24	61.24	914,574	13.42	13.42	18.0
58,743,844	57.78	57.78	14,885,151	14.64	14.64	20.2

OF CHURCH FINANCES

CONGREGATIONAL FINANCES			BENEVOLENCES			
Total Congregational Finances	Per Capita Full or Confirmed Membership	Per Capita Inclusive Membership	Total Benevolences	Per Capita Full or Confirmed Membership	Per Capita Inclusive Membership	Benevolences as a Percentage of Total Contributions
$3,539,950,471	$83.88	$75.33	$846,731,549	$20.06	$18.02	19.3
133,618,336	60.10	47.25	41,776,445	18.79	14.77	23.8

TOTAL GIVING IN 1971, CONTRIBUTIONS AND DISTRIBUTIONS, AND PERCENTAGE OF INCREASE OVER 1970
(In Billions of Dollars)

Contributions		Percent of Total	Distributions			Percent of Total
Individuals	$15.10 (up 4.86%)	71.4%	Religion	$8.6	(up 3.61%)	40.7%
Bequests	3.00 (up 36.3%)	14.2	Health and			
Foundations	2.05 (up 7.9%)	9.7	Hospitals	3.4	(up 6.25%)	16.0
Corporations	1.00 (up 0%)	4.7	Education	3.3	(up 6.5%)	15.6
			Social			
			Welfare	1.55	(up 7.33%)	7.3
			Civic and			
			Cultural	1.4	(up 16.6%)	6.6
			Other	2.9		13.7

Total giving is placed at $21.15 billion in 1971. The gain in philanthropic giving in 1971 was placed at 4.4 percent according to *Giving USA* for 1971, published by the American Association of Fund-Raising Counsel, Inc., New York.

Individual contributions of $15.10 billion show an increase of 4.86 percent in 1971. Giving to "religion" was up 3.61 percent, well below the average increase for all categories of 4.4 percent and "religion" received a lower percentage of total contributions than in previous years, dropping from 44.80 percent of total contributions in 1970 to 40.7 percent in 1971. *Giving USA* notes: "Religious institutions have probably been hurt most by inflation. Giving to religion the last 3 years gained 13.5 percent and represents a net loss to inflation of at least 2.5 percent."

CANADIAN PER TAXPAYER CHARITABLE DONATIONS REPORTED, IN DOLLARS, AND AS A PERCENTAGE OF TOTAL PER CAPITA INCOME ASSESSED, BY PROVINCE, 1970

Newfoundland	$26.37	.47%
Prince Edward Island	43.65	.91%
Nova Scotia	35.55	.64%
New Brunswick	45.55	.86%
Quebec	23.11	.37%
Ontario	41.21	.61%
Manitoba	40.59	.69%
Saskatchewan	39.98	.72%
Alberta	37.88	.60%
British Columbia	29.45	.44%
Canada	34.59	.54%

Source: Taxation Statistics, 1972 Edition, Department of National Revenue, Taxation, Ottawa, Table 5, pp. 60-91.

PERCENTAGE OF INDIVIDUAL CONTRIBUTIONS
TO ADJUSTED GROSS INCOME IN THE UNITED STATES

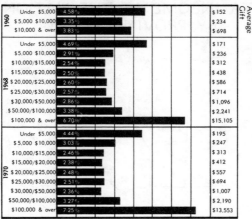

	Average Gift
1960	
Under $5,000 — 4.58%	$152
$5,000 $10,000 — 3.35%	$234
$10,000 & over — 3.83%	$698
1968	
Under $5,000 — 4.69%	$171
$5,000 $10,000 — 2.91%	$236
$10,000/$15,000 — 2.54%	$312
$15,000/$20,000 — 2.50%	$438
$20,000/$25,000 — 2.60%	$586
$25,000/$30,000 — 2.57%	$714
$30,000/$50,000 — 2.86%	$1,096
$50,000/$100,000 — 3.38%	$2,241
$100,000 & over — 6.70%	$15,105
1970	
Under $5,000 — 4.44%	$195
$5,000 $10,000 — 3.03%	$247
$10,000/$15,000 — 2.46%	$313
$15,000/$20,000 — 2.38%	$412
$20,000/$25,000 — 2.48%	$557
$25,000/$30,000 — 2.51%	$694
$30,000/$50,000 — 2.36%	$1,007
$50,000/$100,000 — 3.27%	$2,190
$100,000 & over — 7.25%	$13,553

*Breakdown for returns between $10,000 and $15,000 not available before 1966.

Source: *Giving USA* for 1971. New York, American Association of Fund-Raising Counsel, Inc., p. 13.

The above data are based on Internal Revenue Service itemized tax returns.

"Individual giving was up 4.86 percent in 1971, or $700 million to $15.10 billion. Personal income grew 6.6 percent and disposable personal income grew 7.9 percent. These smaller increases in personal income and disposable personal income are one of the main reasons for a smaller increase in individual giving" according to *Giving USA* for 1971.

TOTAL GIVING, 1961-1971
(IN BILLIONS OF DOLLARS)

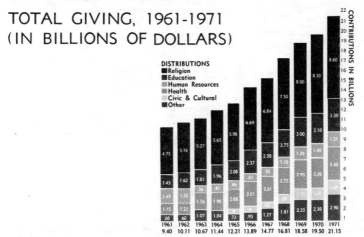

DISTRIBUTIONS
- Religion
- Education
- Human Resources
- Health
- Civic & Cultural
- Other

CONTRIBUTIONS IN BILLIONS

Year	1961	1962	1963	1964	1965	1966	1967	1968	1969	1970	1971
Religion	4.75	5.16	5.27	5.65	5.98	6.69	6.84	7.50	8.00	8.30	8.60
Education	1.45	1.62	1.81	1.96	2.08	2.37	2.50	2.75	3.00	3.10	3.30
	1.45	1.52	1.76	1.98	2.08	2.51	2.61	2.75	2.95	3.20	3.40
	1.15	1.23	1.07	1.04	.73	.95	1.27	1.81	2.23	2.30	2.90
	.60	.60									
Total	9.40	10.11	10.67	11.44	12.21	13.89	14.77	16.81	18.58	19.50	21.15

Source: *Giving USA* for 1971. New York, American Association of Fund-Raising Counsel, Inc., 1972, p. 28.

Reading from the top down on the bar graph above, the first segment is for Religion; the second, for Education; the third, for Social Welfare; the fourth, for Health; the fifth (from 1961 to 1964), for Other; the fifth (from 1965 to 1971), for Civic and Cultural; the sixth (from 1965-1971), for Other.

CANADIAN PER CAPITA PERSONAL INCOME IN DOLLARS AND AS A PERCENTAGE OF PER CAPITA INCOME AT THE NATIONAL LEVEL, BY PROVINCES, 1970.

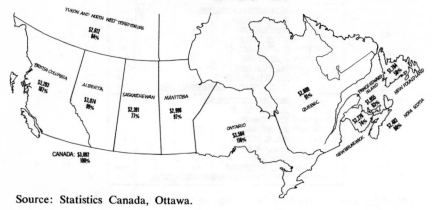

Source: Statistics Canada, Ottawa.

UNITED STATES PER CAPITA PERSONAL INCOME, 1971 BY STATES AND REGIONS

Source: U.S. Department of Commerce, Office of Business Economics, *Survey of Current Business,* April, 1972, p. 18.

"Total personal income in the nation rose 6¾ percent last year, with gains of 5¾ percent in each of the light regions and at least 4¾ percent in all but one of the States. Nationally, consumer prices rose a little more than 4 percent. The personal income gain in all regions and in the 49 States and the District of Columbia exceeded the increase in consumer prices so that the real purchasing power of consumers increased at least moderately. The one exception was the State of Washington, where income rose 4¼ percent, about the same as consumer prices."

PERSONAL INCOME, PER CAPITA, TAXES AND DISPOSABLE PERSONAL INCOME, 1949-1971 AND IN 1949 DOLLARS

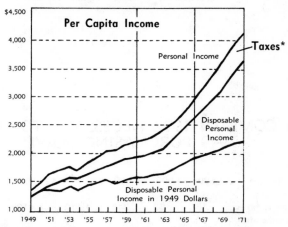

* Mainly income taxes, personal property taxes, and inheritance taxes.
Source: *Road Maps of Industry,* No. 1687, April 1, 1972. New York, The Conference Board, 1972.

"In the postwar period, taxes have absorbed increasing proportions of personal income. This trend is attributable to increases in Social Security and state and local taxes (including sales taxes), as well as in the Federal personal income tax. . . . Federal income and Social Security taxes and state and local taxes together claimed 22.3% in personal income in 1969, compared with 12.2% in 1949."

NUMBER OF FAMILIES BY FAMILY INCOME IN 1947 TO 1970 (IN CONSTANT 1970 DOLLARS)

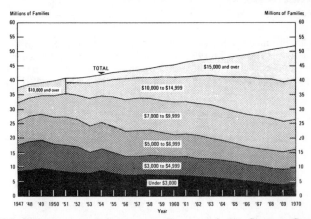

Source: U.S. Department of Commerce, Bureau of the Census, *Current Population Reports,* Series P-60, No. 80, "Income in 1970 of Families and Persons in the United States," U.S. Government Printing Office, Washington, D. C., 1971.

INCOME IN 1972 NECESSARY TO EQUAL 1949 PURCHASING POWER

1949 Gross Income	$1,500	$3,000	$5,000	$10,000	$25,000	$50,000	$100,000
Less: Income and social security taxes	15	63	344	1,112	4,410	13,076	35,438
Equals: Income after taxes	1,485	2,937	4,656	8,888	20,590	36,924	64,562
Equivalent 1971 Gross Income	2,700	5,660	9,347	18,570	46,380	96,800	187,000
Less: Income and social security taxes	134	585	1,302	3,212	10,802	32,999	75,443
Less: Lost purchasing power	1,081	2,138	3,389	6,470	14,988	26,877	46,995
Equals: Income after taxes in 1949 dollars	1,485	2,937	4,656	8,888	20,590	36,924	64,562

Source: *Road Maps of Industry,* No. 1687, April 1, 1972. New York, The Conference Board, 1972.

In order to produce an income, after taxes, equal to $8,888 in 1949 dollars, one would have to receive in 1972 a gross income of $18,570, whereas in 1949 the gross income necessary would have been only $10,000. The major reason is the lost purchasing power of the dollar during the period 1949-1972.

ANNUAL BUDGET FOR A 4-PERSON FAMILY AT THREE LEVELS OF LIVING, URBAN UNITED STATES AUTUMN, 1971

Component	Lower Level	Intermediate Level	Higher Level
Food	$ 1,964	$ 2,532	$ 3,198
Housing	1,516	2,638	3,980
Transportation	536	964	1,250
Clothing and Personal Care	848	1,196	1,740
Medical Care	609	612	638
Other Family Consumption	368	684	1,129
Personal Income Tax	629	1,366	2,614
All Other a)	744	979	1,356
Total Budget	**$ 7,214**	**$10,971**	**$15,905**

a) Including gifts and contributions, personal life insurance, occupational expenses, and social security and disability payments.

Source: U.S. Department of Labor, Bureau of Labor Statistics, Middle Atlantic Regional Office, "BLS Reports Rise in City Worker Family Budget in 1971," Press Release, April 27, 1972. Adapted from Table 6.

The above three budgets, at the lower, intermediate, and higher levels, are for a family of four consisting of husband, age 38, a wife not employed outside the home, an 8-year old girl and a 13-year old boy, in urban United States in Autumn, 1971.

Budget costs varied greatly. The lower budget totalled $7,214; the intermediate, $10,971; and the higher $15,905. The lower budget was 34 percent below the intermediate and the higher budget was 45 percent above it. These Autumn, 1971 estimates for the three budgets indicate that, as compared with Spring, 1969, the lower standard of living budget increased over the 2½ year period by 10.2 percent; the intermediate budget by 9.0 percent; and the higher by 9.1 percent.

These budget figures would vary from one urban area to another in the U.S. For example, using the Urban U.S. as whole (U.S.=100), at the intermediate budget level, some index numbers for cities are as follows: Boston (117); New York-Northeastern New Jersey (115); San Francisco-Oakland (106); Chicago-Northwest Indiana (105); Washington, D.C.-Maryland-Virginia (103); Los Angeles-Long Beach (100); Indianapolis (101); Detroit (98); Portland, Oregon (102); Denver (97); Dallas (92); Nashville (91); Atlanta (89).

AVERAGE PER CENT EXPENDITURE PER PERSON, BY PERSONAL INCOME

Sample of Persons Residing in All Canadian Communities with a
Population of 1,000 or More, After Personal Taxes.

Personal Income	All Classes	Under $3000	3000-3999	4000-4999	5000-5999	6000-6999	7000-7999	8000-8999	9000-9999	10000-10999	11000-11999	12000-14999	15000 and over
Food	21.6	28.4	26.0	25.2	23.9	23.2	22.8	22.2	21.7	20.6	20.5	19.4	17.3
Shelter	17.6	25.2	20.5	18.5	17.9	17.5	18.1	17.4	17.6	17.1	16.1	16.1	15.7
Transportation	15.1	8.7	11.9	14.6	14.3	15.6	15.5	16.1	14.9	16.2	16.4	16.2	16.0
Clothing	9.4	6.8	8.6	8.9	9.0	8.8	8.9	9.2	9.3	9.6	10.3	10.3	10.4
Security	5.0	1.1	2.1	3.0	3.9	4.6	4.8	4.9	5.3	5.3	5.4	6.0	7.1
Tobacco & Alcohol	4.4	3.8	4.6	4.5	5.0	4.8	4.5	4.5	4.6	4.3	4.6	4.3	3.9
Cigarettes & Tobacco	2.2	2.3	2.7	2.6	2.7	2.7	2.4	2.4	2.4	2.2	2.4	1.9	.1.6
Alcoholic Beverages·	2.1	1.6	1.8	1.9	2.2	2.0	2.0	2.1	2.2	2.1	2.2	2.4	2.3
Recreation	4.0	2.3	3.0	3.3	3.5	3.3	3.5	3.7	4.1	4.1	4.0	4.5	5.2
Medical & Health Care	3.9	5.5	5.1	4.4	4.3	4.1	4.0	3.8	3.8	3.7	3.6	3.5	3.3
Gifts & Contributions	3.1	3.5	3.3	3.2	3.2	3.0	2.6	2.3	2.7	2.6	2.8	3.0	4.0
Religious Orgs.	0.9	1.2	1.0	1.0	0.9	0.8	0.8	0.7	0.8	0.8	0.8	0.8	1.0
Other Orgs.	0.3	0.2	0.2	0.2	0.2	0.2	0.2	0.2	0.2	0.2	0.2	0.3	0.7
Education	1.0	0.8	0.7	0.7	0.7	0.6	0.7	0.9	1.0	1.0	1.0	1.1	1.5
Reading	0.7	0.8	0.7	0.7	0.7	0.7	0.7	0.7	0.7	0.8	0.7	0.7	0.7
Miscellaneous*	14.2	13.1	13.5	13.0	13.6	13.8	13.9	14.3	14.3	14.7	14.6	14.9	14.9

* Includes Household Operation, Furnishings and Equipment, and Personal Care.

Source: Adapted from *Family Expenditures in Canada, 1969,* Ottawa: Statistics Canada, March 1972. Table 21.

UNITED STATES PERSONAL CONSUMPTION BY TYPE OF PRODUCT 1968 and 1971
(In Billions of Dollars)

	1968	1971	% Increase
Food and Tobacco	$125.1	$148.1	18.4%
Clothing, Accessories, and Jewelry	55.5	66.9	20.5
Personal Care	9.0	10.6	17.8
Housing	77.3	99.2	28.3
Household Operation	76.2	93.6	22.8
Medical Care Expenses	37.8	51.4	36.0
Personal Business	29.5	37.1	25.8
Transportation	72.0	90.1	25.1
Recreation	33.6	42.5	26.5
Private Education and Research	8.7	11.1	27.6
Religious and Welfare Activities	7.6	9.1	19.7
Foreign Travel and Other, Net	3.8	5.2	36.8
Total	536.1	664.9	24.0

Source: U. S. Department of Commerce, Office of Business Economics, *Survey of Current Business,* July, 1972. Adapted from Table 2.5 "Personal Consumption Expenditures by Type of Product."

For 1971, the $664.9 billion in expenditures are classified as follows: Durable Commodities, $103.5 billion; Non-Durable Commodities, $278.1 billion, Services, $283.3 billion. Note that increases in expenditures for religious and welfare activities increased less than the average for the 4-year period.

THE NORTH AMERICAN INTERCHURCH STUDY: PASTORS' REPORT ON THE CONGREGATION

Douglas W. Johnson
Director, Research and Information Services
Office of Planning and Program
National Council of the Churches of Christ in the U.S.A.

The North American Interchurch Study involved 564 pastors in the United States and 98 in Canada. These pastors not only completed the same interview schedule as did the lay members included in the study, but were asked nearly 60 additional questions about their congregation. This part of the minister's interview took between 30 minutes and an hour, although, in some instances, the pastor's entire interview took upwards of two and one-half hours.

The purpose of these extended interviews was to obtain an understanding of the congregations served by these pastors. The underlying question was: "Were the laity included in the sample really representative of the membership of the church?" Attention was therefore given to asking about programs and giving. In addition, however, a series of questions to pastors probed into changes, especially in budgets, perceptions of the denomination, and ecumenical activities. All of the questions were intended to provide information for developing stewardship programs and information about the local church which would be useful in re-evaluating its stewardship programs and the use of its materials. This part of the study was an effort to provide another feedback mechanism between local churches and the denomination.

The pastors generally said that a majority of their members were "active." However, 28 percent of the U.S. and 54 percent of the Canadian pastors did say that more than one-fourth of their members were in the "inactive" category. The difference between the reports of these U.S. and Canadian pastors suggests that the membership rolls of the U.S. churches contain more members who are active than the Canadian membership rolls. This strategy of keeping only active members on the rolls is promoted by several U.S. denominations as a means of keeping assessments for denominational work which is based on the number of members reported by local churches, as realistic as possible.

Ethnicity was evident in 117 of the pastor's reports. The largest number of congregations, with 81 percent or more of a particular ethnic strand, were German in background. Blacks were reported next most frequently with a nearly even distribution of very few (1-10 percent) or very many (81 percent or more) in a congregation. Scandinavian and Spanish-speaking Americans were reported with about the same frequency.

The sex ratio was nearly 60 percent females to 40 percent males for a majority of the congregations. Canadian pastors reported slightly lower proportions of females as compared to males but the general picture indicates more females than males.

The age structure of the congregations showed more youth as members of U.S. parishes than was true in Canada. The strength of the Canadian church is in the age group of 40-64 years. Age is more evenly distributed in the United States which shows a higher percentage of persons under 40 years and a much higher percentage of members under 20 years than does Canada. These data on age structure may be one of the factors in the more positive outlook on the future of the church reported by U.S. members as opposed to Canadian members.

IS THE DENOMINATION HELPFUL?

The first phase of the study asked both clergy and laity about the denomination. Eighty percent of the respondents agreed that the denomination was important to the local church. When the pastor was asked if his congregation generally felt that the denomination was helpful, 61 percent of the U.S. and 47 percent of the Canadian pastors said yes. They explained their positive answers by saying that helpfulness came because the denomination provides leadership and organization, direct assistance, and encourages a concern for the larger mission of the church. Pastors said, on the negative side, that people did not view the denomination as helpful because they were uninformed, were too self-interested, or felt some antagonism toward the denomination.

Nearly 38 percent of the pastors in each country reported that these perceptions had changed during the past three years. The primary reason for such change was a better understanding of the denomination. Negative changes, reported by about 9 percent of the U.S. pastors indicating change, focused on dissatisfaction with the denominational machinery. Only three percent of the U.S. pastors cited social involvement of the denomination as having anything to do with changes in the perceptions of the denomination's helpfulness. This latter statistic is similar to that recorded in the earlier report where social involvement was probed as a possible reason for cutbacks in giving and support of the denomination.

The data suggest quite strongly that the pastor who is informed and has a positive attitude toward the denomination will either discover or initiate such an attitude among parishioners.

ECUMENICAL ACTIVITIES

Many ecumenical activities ranging from sharing in occasional worship services with other organizations to joint youth programs and shared staff were reported by 88 percent of the U.S. and 93 percent of the Canadian pastors. Also, about 63 percent of the U.S. and 52 percent of the Canadian pastors reported that their congregations were members of one, or more, ecumenical agencies.

In both countries, however, pastors reported that only a few persons were very active in ecumenical affairs. In fact, the pastor is the key to involvement in ecumenical activities, as reported by 46 percent of the U.S. and 27 percent of the Canadian pastors. Two-thirds of the pastors in each country reported that no one was against ecumenical activity as such, but one in five pastors did say that a conservative group of members in the congregation were against it.

The picture of ecumenical activity is projected by the involvement of the pastor, although, in some cases laity may be prime movers. Opposition to ecumenical activity appears to be concentrated in a small group of church members who play on the apathy of other church members and disinterest of the pastor.

LOCAL CHURCH BUDGET

Nearly 70 percent of the pastors in the

TABLE 1

SIZE OF TOTAL BUDGET IN U.S. CANADIAN CONGREGATIONS

	United States			Canada		
	3 yrs. ago	Now	3 yrs. from now	3 yrs. ago	Now	3 yrs. from now
No response	6.4%	0.5%	9.0%	0.7%	—	23.9%
Less than $10,000	10.4	8.5	5.7	6.1	0.8%	—
$10,000-24,999	31.6	27.6	19.8	42.2	39.5	30.7
$25,000-49,999	25.3	31.5	29.5	32.3	33.9	20.5
$50,000-99,999	18.2	20.0	20.0	14.5	20.5	21.2
$100,000-over	8.1	11.8	16.0	4.2	5.3	3.7

U.S. and 74 percent of those in Canada said that their current church budgets were less than $50,000. The data in Table 1 shows the budgets reported and projected in both countries for three time periods.

The pastors, in discussing factors which influenced the size of their local church budgets, both in the past and in the future, cited the economic situation as most important. This factor, combined with that of membership changes, applies to 56 percent of the Canadian and 44 percent of the U.S. pastors. Program was cited by 17 percent of the pastors as being critical in budget size and the internal situation of the church was important to 16 percent of the U.S. and 22 percent of the Canadian pastors.

These are rather pragmatic reasons cited by pastors for budget increases or decreases. These reasons coincide with similar ones given by laity when they were asked about the influences of the size of their gifts to the church. Perhaps the pastors over-emphasized the "internal situation" of the church, but from the point of view of the person trying to get new leadership and deal with various factions within the church, this is a very important criterion for estimating income.

As has been the case for a long time, most local churches in both countries keep most of their money to meet local expenses. Three-fourths of the pastors in each country reported that more than two-thirds of all the money collected stayed in the local church. Most of the remaining money was sent to the denomination with only a relatively small proportion (10 percent or less of the budget in 83 percent of the U.S. and 91 percent of the Canadian churches) was spent on other activities. These activities might include such things as grants to community organizations and involvement in non-church sponsored events.

Changes in proportions of giving were reported by 39 percent of the U.S. and 30 percent of the Canadian pastors. The main reasons for these changes were an increase in benevolences (35 percent of

the U.S. and 49 percent of the Canadian pastors) and building expenses (14 percent of the U.S. and 6 percent of the Canadian pastors). These changes suggest that the proportion of pastors reporting increases of money going to denominations is higher than the percentage of pastors who report less money going from the local church to the denomination.

In fact, 41 percent of the U.S. and 44 percent of the Canadian pastors reported changes during the past three years in the amounts of money going to the regional and national parts of the denomination. Of the pastors reporting changes, 70 percent of the U.S. and 86 percent of the Canadian pastors reported that these changes were increases. The pastors were asked to look to the future and predict any possible changes.

Thirty percent of the pastors predicted changes in the amounts going to the denomination in the future. Eighty-three percent of the U.S. and 78 percent of the Canadian pastors who expected changes said that these would be increases. When the predictions were for decreases, the primary reasons given were that local needs will be greater. These needs will be the results of inflation and increased costs of leadership expenses or program. On the other hand, increased interest and support were cited as the main reasons more money would be going to the denomination.

CONTRIBUTIONS TO THE LOCAL CHURCH

The percentage of persons who do not contribute to the local church is greater in Canada than in the U.S. This probably reflects, in part, the differences in activity levels between the two countries cited earlier. The membership rolls of the U.S. are probably based upon regularity of attendance and contributions to a greater degree than those in Canada. (Since the Canadian sample includes only one denomination it should not be assumed that it is different than all denominations in the U.S. However, in the composite figures, differences are apparent.)

Forty-eight percent of the U.S. and 45 percent of the Canadian pastors report that more than half of their members contribute weekly or monthly. About one-third of the pastors in each country said that between one-fourth and one-half of their members contribute occasionally. These proportions have changed in 30 percent of the U.S. and 24 percent of the Canadian churches during the past three years. Such changes were attributed to an increased attention to stewardship by 38 percent of the U.S. and 71 percent of the Canadian pastors, and to changes in the composition of the congregation such as increases or decreases in the number of members, changes in age structures, and changes in the economic level of members (50 percent of the U.S. and 17 percent of the Canadian pastors).

PLEDGE SYSTEMS

Seventy-seven percent of the U.S. pastors and 64 percent of the Canadian pastors used a pledge or commitment system in their churches and about 63 percent of the pastors reported some type of visitation for financial commitments. When asked which type of procedure for securing pledges was most effective in their church, 43 percent of the U.S. and 63 percent of the Canadian pastors said home visits. In-church commitments as a procedure was cited by 26 percent of the U.S. and 9 percent of the Canadian pastors. Also, a combination of two or more procedures was noted by 25 percent of the U.S. and 18 percent of the Canadian pastors.

The pastors gave as the reasons for their preference of procedures the effectiveness of the personal approach as a means for securing financial commitment (64 percent of the U.S. and 58 percent of the Canadian). No other single reason was given by more than a few pastors.

AVERAGE GIFT

Fifty-six percent of the Canadian pastors said that the average weekly contribution of giving units (individuals or families) in their congregations was between $1.00 and $3.00. Another 16 percent said the average was between $3.00 and $5.00. In the U.S., 23 percent of the pastors said the average gift was between $5.00 and $7.50; 26 percent said it was between $3.00 and $5.00 and 20 percent said it was between $1.00 and $3.00. These data are supportive of the statements given by lay respondents in their phase of the study.

More than half of the pastors (54 percent in each country) said that this average had increased during the past three years. On the other hand, one-third said it had remained about the same and 3 percent said it had decreased. The main reasons given for positive changes besides the economic situation were changes in membership, increased support and better stewardship programs.

WILLS AND ANNUITIES

Only 7 percent of the pastors (none in Canada) reported that they regularly observe a wills and annuities day. When asked why they did not, one-half of the U.S. and 62 percent of the Canadian pastors said that they had no motivation or had never had such an emphasis in their congregations. On the other hand, 8 percent of the U.S. pastors said that they might be interested in observing such a day.

STEWARDSHIP PROGRAM

When asked to describe their stewardship programs, 9 percent of the U.S. and 24 percent of the Canadian pastors (in addition to 6 percent not responding in each country) said they did not have one. In general, the programs reported included some type of every member enlistment (32 percent U.S.; 22 percent Canada), pastoral letters or sermons (16 percent U.S.; 23 percent Canada) or a program which extended for the entire year (16 percent U.S.; 14 percent Canada).

Denominational assistance in developing stewardship programs was reported to come in a variety of ways for 74 percent of the U.S. and 68 percent of the

Canadian pastors. Such assistance was reported as literature alone for 19 percent of the U.S. and 26 percent of the Canadian pastors. Assistance from ecumenical sources, when it came at all or was recognized, was primarily in the form of literature (20 percent in each country) although 10 percent of the U.S. pastors reported a variety of forms of assistance.

The most difficult problem faced in stewardship education was reported to be developing an understanding of the concept of stewardship by 46 percent of the U.S. and 51 percent of the Canadian pastors. (The magnitude of this problem was borne out by the definitions of stewardship given by laity in the first study. As reported then, only 41 percent of the laity were able to relate stewardship to the concept of time, talent and money generally taught by the denominations in this study.) The two other important problems cited by pastors were developing motivation (16 percent in each country) and opposition to stewardship programs among laity (9 percent in the U.S. and 12 percent in Canada).

Twenty-four percent of the U.S. and 42 percent of the Canadian pastors reported little if any relationship between the stewardship and other programs in their church. On the other hand, 42 percent of the U.S. and 32 percent of the Canadian pastors said that all of the programs in their churches including stewardship intermingled and/or integrated. The impression given by the data is that intermingled refers to a lack of conflict in major program emphases rather than having truly integrated programs with each building upon the other.

BACKGROUND MATERIALS FOR INTERPRETING CHURCH FINANCES

The following brief bibliography is supplied for those interested in developing a supportive statistical and interpretative framework for discussing trends in church finances in both the United States and Canada.

Canada Year Book, 1971. Statistics Canada, Ottawa, 1971.

Fabricant, Solomon. "Philanthropy in the American Economy," *Foundation News,* September-October, 1969.

Family Expenditure in Canada, 1969 (4 Vols.) #s. 62-535-8, Statistics Canada, Ottawa, 1972.

Financial Post Survey of Markets, 1971. Toronto, MacLean Hunter Ltd., 481 University Ave., Toronto 2, Ontario.

Giving USA, 1971. American Association of Fund-Raising Counsel, 500 Fifth Ave., New York, NY 10036.

Road Maps of Industry. The Conference Board, 845 Third Ave., New York, NY 10022; 333 River Rd., Ottawa, Ontario KIL 8B9.

Robertson, D. B. *Should Churches Be Taxed?* Philadelphia, The Westminster Press, 1968.

Statistical Abstract of the United States, 1971. 91st edition. U.S. Bureau of the Census. Washington, D. C., 1971.

Survey of Buying Power. Bill Publications, 630 Third Ave., New York, NY 10017. (Also special Canadian Section sold separately.)

Taxation Statistics, 1972 Edition. Department of National Revenue, Taxation, Ottawa.

3. SOME TRENDS AND DEVELOPMENTS

In this section trends in three areas of religious activity are reported; namely, information on Religious Components of Nonpublic Elementary and Secondary Day School Enrollment, 1972 Roman Catholic Data, and Trends in Seminary Enrollment.

The first report, dealing with the relationships between public and nonpublic elementary and secondary education in the U.S., shows that approximately one-sixth of the primary and secondary schools are private and that slightly more than one-tenth of the students and teachers are related to these schools. The great majority of nonpublic schools are Roman Catholic, but even the schools otherwise religiously connected outnumber the nonreligious schools at the elementary level. At least ten major church groupings are represented to a major degree in operating schools. Besides the Roman Catholic Church, there are, in order of rank, schools related to the Lutheran, Seventh-day Adventist, Episcopal, Jewish, Christian Reformed, Baptist, Friends, Methodist, and Presbyterian traditions.

Roman Catholic statistical data for 1972, consisting of data gathered in 1971, indicate an increase of 176,261 members over the previous year, an increase in the hierarchy of nine, and a decrease of 740 priests. There has been a marked decline in the number of schools, teachers, and students. There has also been a decline in seminaries and students.

The third report deals with trends in seminary enrollment, as reported by the American Association of Theological Schools, which reflect very little change in enrollment over the past two years. The enrollment of black students has increased by one-eighth in 1971 but still is far below the proportion of blacks in the U.S. population. The United Methodist and American Baptist groups still continue to register the largest number of black students among their student bodies.

More details follow.

RELIGIOUS COMPONENTS OF NONPUBLIC ELEMENTARY AND SECONDARY DAY SCHOOL ENROLLMENT, 1968-1969

The U.S. Office of Education in the Department of Health, Education, and Welfare has issued *Statistics of Public and Nonpublic Elementary and Secondary Day Schools,* a report prepared by Diane B. Gertler and Linda A. Barker (Washington, D.C.: U. S. Government Printing Office, 1971; Superintendent of Documents Catalog No. HE 5.220:20191).

From this report it is possible to see the nature and extent of church-related elementary and secondary day schools in relation to both nonpublic schools and public schools.

Table 1 indicates that 16.6 percent of the schools in the U.S. are nonpublic (or private) and that they enroll 11.5 percent of the pupils and employ 10.4 percent of the teachers.

TABLE 1: NUMBER AND PERCENT OF PUBLIC AND NONPUBLIC SCHOOLS, PUPILS, AND FULL-TIME EQUIVALENT TEACHERS: UNITED STATES, 1968-1969

Item	Total	Public		Nonpublic	
		Number	Percent	Number	Percent
Schools	112,096	93,544	83.4	18,522	16.6
Pupils	49,924,745	44,195,579	88.5	5,729,166	11.5
Teachers	2,162,146	1,936,918	89.6	225,228	10.4

Table 2 adapted from the report cited above, indicates the affiliation of nonpublic elementary and secondary schools in 1968-1969 in terms of enrollment, teachers, and pupil-teacher ratio.

TABLE 2: AFFILIATION OF U.S. NONPUBLIC ELEMENTARY AND SECONDARY SCHOOLS, 1968-1969 AND ENROLLMENT, TEACHERS AND PUPIL-TEACHER RATIO

	Elementary	Secondary
Schools Responding	14,452	4,100
Not religious affiliated	1,446	957
Roman Catholic	9,960	2,383
Other religious affiliated	3,046	760
Enrollment	4,376,383	1,352,783
Not religious affiliated	199,805	166,352
Roman Catholic	3,776,794	1,066,394
Other religious affiliated	399,784	120,037
Teachers	147,463	77,764
Not religious affiliated	14,978	15,589
Roman Catholic	112,774	53,454
Other religious affiliated	19,711	8,721
Pupil-Teacher Ratio	29.7	17.4
Not religious affiliated	13.3	10.7
Roman Catholic	33.5	19.9
Other religious affiliated	20.3	13.8

Table 3 provides summary information for the 18,552 nonpublic schools.

TABLE 3: PERCENTAGE DISTRIBUTION OF NONPUBLIC SCHOOLS AND ENROLLMENT, BY REGION AND AFFILIATION: UNITED STATES, 1968-1969

| Affiliation | Number Total U.S. | | As Percent of Total U.S. | | | | | | | |
| | Schools | Pupils | North Atlantic | | Great Lakes and Plains | | Southeast | | West and Southwest | |
			Schools	Pupils	Schools	Pupils	Schools	Pupils	Schools	Pupils
Total	18,552	5,729,166	35.4	42.0	33.9	34.7	13.2	9.7	17.5	13.6
Not affiliated	2,403	366,157	41.8	45.7	9.4	10.1	28.8	27.2	20.0	17.0
Affiliated	16,149	5,363,009	34.4	41.7	37.6	36.4	10.8	8.5	17.2	13.4
Baptist	133	23,671	5.3	2.5	6.8	6.0	42.1	47.7	45.9	43.8
Christian Reformed	227	45,852	6.2	5.1	69.6	71.9	4.0	2.5	20.3	20.5
Friends	59	12,169	84.7	94.2	5.1	2.4	1.7	.8	8.5	2.6
Jewish	302	66,724	83.8	89.5	7.3	5.0	3.6	2.3	5.3	3.2
Lutheran	1,394	195,690	8.0	9.1	68.6	69.8	4.8	4.8	18.6	16.4
Methodist	50	5,374	30.0	32.8	16.0	4.6	24.0	26.4	30.0	36.3
Presbyterian	38	4,732	10.5	14.7	7.9	3.8	47.4	52.9	34.2	28.6
Protestant Episcopal	319	54,122	36.1	33.9	6.3	5.9	26.3	27.5	31.3	32.7
Roman Catholic	12,343	4,843,188	38.4	43.5	36.6	36.0	10.4	8.2	14.6	12.3
Seventh-day Adventist	787	51,588	16.5	16.3	24.1	17.2	17.3	11.7	42.1	54.8
Other or unknown	497	59,899	23.3	19.7	35.8	32.3	14.7	18.8	26.2	29.1

Gertler and Barker interpret Table 3, in part, as follows: "The schools of various religious affiliations tend to be localized in one or two regions and hardly appear in others. . . . Over 80 percent of Friends schools and most of the Jewish schools (83.3 percent) were located in the North Atlantic region. In fact, 188 (62.3 percent) of the total number of Jewish schools were found in New York and 21 (35.6 percent) of the Friends schools were found in Pennsylvania. Nearly 70 percent of the Christian Reformed and Lutheran schools were located in the Great Lakes and Plains region. Almost 90 percent of the Baptist schools were divided between the Southeast region and the West and Southwest region. These same two regions together contained only 25 percent of the Roman Catholic schools."

This valuable 62-page report contains a wealth of data on public and nonpublic elementary and secondary schools. For those interested in schools affiliated with religious bodies there are tabulations, by denomination, of schools by regions and states relating to: number of schools, enrollment, percentage distribution of enrollment, teachers.

One interesting historical comparison made by the authors of this report is that "enrollment in the public schools has continued to increase since 1961-62. Combined with the decrease in the number of schools, it is evident that the trend in public education is toward fewer but larger schools. In the nonpublic sector the Roman Catholic schools have shown a percentage decrease in enrollments since 1965-66 that is slightly larger than the decrease in the number of schools. The result is fewer and smaller Roman Catholic schools. However, the nonaffiliated and the affiliated schools other than Roman Catholic have grown larger since 1965-66."

THE 1972 OFFICIAL CATHOLIC DATA

Catholics in the 50 states, including all families of the defense forces both at home and abroad, and diplomatic and other services abroad, now number 48,390,990, according to **The Official Catholic Directory** for 1972, published by P. J. Kenedy & Sons, New York. The new total represents an increase over last year of 176,261.

The Official Catholic Directory, 1972, is available only in hardcover and sells for $35.00.

Archdioceses and Dioceses

There are now 31 Archdioceses in the United States, with a Catholic population of 21,748,733, and 133 Dioceses recording a Catholic population of 26,642,257. The 31 Archdioceses reported a growth of 138,940, and the 133 Dioceses increased by 37,341. The seven Archdioceses with Catholic populations in excess of one million are Chicago, 2,496,300; Boston, 2,018,034; New York, 1,800,000; Los Angeles, 1,791,932; Newark, 1,703,356; Detroit, 1,619,081; and Philadelphia, 1,359,-012. Brooklyn continues as the largest Diocese, with a Catholic population of 1,487,360. In addition, nine Archdioceses and seven Dioceses reported Catholic populations of over one-half million.

Statistical information is available for the first time on the four new Dioceses established during 1971. They are Memphis, Tennessee; Gaylord and Kalamazoo in Michigan; and Charlotte, North Carolina.

Fifteen Dioceses reported no change in Catholic populations, and forty-eight reflected decreases. Advances were reported by 101 Sees. The largest increases have been noted in Boston, 103,684; Los Angeles, 48,768; Detroit, 31,747; El Paso, 26,331; Youngstown, 26,216.

Hierarchy and Clergy

The 1972 **Directory** lists 304 members of the hierarchy—an increase of nine over the 295 listed a year ago.

A decrease of 740 in the number of the clergy brings the total of ordained priests to 57,421; there are now 36,727, or 293 fewer, diocesan or secular priests and 20,694 religious order priests, a decrease of 447. Six bishops, three abbots, and 908 priests are listed in the Necrology. Professed religious personnel include 9,740 brothers, a decrease of 416, and 146,914 sisters, representing a decrease of 6,731.

The **Directory** reports 17,670 parishes with resident pastors and 589 parishes without resident clergy—an increase of 15—for a record total of 18,259 Catholic parishes in the 50 states. Also listed are 4,195 missions—up 74; 1,342 stations—down 1; and 11,489 chapels—down 400.

Educational Institutions

A total of 11,713 separate educational institutions—580 fewer than reported in 1971. Included are 106 diocesan seminaries; 326 religious order seminaries or novitiates and scholasticates; 260 colleges and universities; 1,086 diocesan and parish high schools; 729 private high schools; 8,877 parish elementary schools; and 329 private elementary schools. There are, in addition, 79 protective institutions, with 6,218 youths in attendance.

Teachers

Full-time teaching staffs of all educational institutions under Catholic auspices have decreased by 11,911, to a total of 188,527, comprising 8,700 priests; 625 scholastics; 4,302 brothers; 70,664 sisters; and 104,236 lay teachers. There are 1,104 fewer priests; 120 more scholastics; 612 fewer brothers; 7,707 fewer sisters; and 2,608 fewer lay teachers than a year ago.

In 1944, when first recorded, lay teachers numbered 7,633 (8.25 percent). Their number continually increased through 1971, when the total of 106,844 outnumbered religious teachers for the first time. Despite the decrease of 2,608 in 1972, lay teachers represent 55 percent of all teachers in Catholic schools (53.4 percent in 1971).

	1944	1950	1960	1970	1972
Priests	4,647	7,436	10,890	9,958	8,700
Scholastics	—	405	802	596	625
Brothers	3,233	3,411	4,778	5,297	4,302
Sisters	76,908	82,048	98,471	85,616	70,664
Total Religious	84,788	93,300	114,941	101,467	84,291
Lay Teachers	7,633	13,477	45,506	98,001	104,236
Grand Total	92,421	106,777	160,447	199,468	188,527

Schools and Enrollment

In 1945, at the start of the nation's enrollment boom, **The Official Catholic Directory** recorded 10,912 educational institutions with an enrollment of 2,590,660 students. Through 1965, the institutions increased by 3,384 (31 percent) and the students by 3,505,186 (135 percent), to totals as recorded before for 1965.

Note the complete reversal of this when 1965 is compared with 1972: 2,583 fewer institutions, a decline of 18 percent; and 1,576,617 fewer students, a decrease of 25.9 percent. (Orphanages and protective institutions are excluded.)

	1965		1972	
	Institutions	Students	Institutions	Students
Seminaries & Novitiates	596	48,992	432	22,963
Colleges & Universities	304	384,526	260	428,853
High Schools	2,465	1,095,519	1,815	961,996
Elementary Schools	10,931	4,566,809	9,206	3,105,417
Total	14,296	6,095,846	11,713	4,519,229

During 1971, there were in operation 4 fewer diocesan and 14 less religious order seminaries. The 106 diocesan seminaries report enrollments of 13,554 seminarians, a decrease of 1,433, while the 326 novitiates and scholasticates of the religious orders have 9,409 students, or 1,314 less, indicating a total of 22,963 candidates for the priesthood.

There are 260 Catholic colleges and universities, down 23 from the 283 reported in 1971. These colleges show an enrollment of 428,853, an increase of 2,648 pupils over 1970.

The number of full-time pupils in Catholic elementary and high schools decreased 361,910 during the past year. The 1,086 parish and diocesan high schools report 626,522 pupils, a decrease of 31,600 over 1971; the 729 private high schools with 335,474 show a decrease of 22,117 in one year. Pupils in 8,877 parish elementary schools now number 3,040,584, or 307,837 fewer, while students in the 329 private elementary schools now total 64,833, a decrease of 356.

Religious instruction to children under released time, in religious vacation schools and other classes, is evidenced in the 1972 reports of 1,327,331 high school pupils (up 24,299) and 4,251,729 in elementary grades (up 70,263), for a total of 5,579,060 public school children receiving religious instruction, indicating a year's increase of 94,562 pupils. There is an aggregate (including dependent children) of 10,104,507 American youths of all grades under Catholic instruction—a decrease of 269,609 over comparable figures for 1971.

Hospitals

Nineteen fewer general and sixteen fewer special institutions bring the number of Catholic hospitals to 836; bed capacity increased by 5,473 to 171,640. General hospitals number 718, with 160,895 beds, and 118 special hospitals accommodate 10,745. Patients treated increased by 722,944 to a record high of 23,240,723.

Current enrollments of 21,987 student nurses in the 201 Catholic training schools decreased by 447, in 19 fewer schools. Children in the 206 orphanages and infant asylums decreased by 571, to a total of 16,468; while 19,908 children are cared for in foster homes. The total of 36,376 dependent children reflects a decrease of 344. Homes for invalids and aged were increased by 12 and now number 432, with facilities for 43,277 guests, an increase of 1,442.

Baptisms, Converts, Marriages

The 1,054,933 baptisms recorded, a decrease of 33,530 from 1971, resumes after a one-year increase the downward trend that commenced in 1962. The number of converts was 79,012. This reflects a decrease of 5,522, and is the lowest figure recorded since the 76,705 who entered during 1940.

Marriages recorded decreased by 9,385 to 416,924; during the same period, 407,956 Catholics died in the U. S., 9,823 fewer deaths than in the previous year.

TRENDS IN SEMINARY ENROLLMENT: 1966-1971

The American Association of Theological Schools in the United States and Canada

Total fall, 1971, enrollment in AATS schools showed very little change from the preceding two years, when allowance is made for the increase in number of member schools. In 1970 a total of 179 schools reported 31,003 students, contrasted with 1971 when 187 institutions enrolled 32,750 persons. This was an actual increase in the schools reporting both years of 1.2 percent. When this total is divided into professional and graduate categories, the changes are more obvious. There was an actual increase of 2.9 percent in professional enrollments, and an 8.6 percent decrease in graduate students.

Table 1 provides an analysis of enrollment trends for the period since 1966.

TABLE 1: AUTUMN ENROLLMENT IN MEMBER SCHOOLS

	1966	1967	1968	1969	1970	1971
Number of Schools ..	140	142	156	171	179	187
Total Enrollment....	23,959	25,221	28,033	29,690	31,003	32,750
By Nation						
Canada	763	751	876	848	944	1,120
United States	23,196	24,470	27,157	28,842	30,059	31,630
By Membership Level						
Accredited	20,455	21,365	23,032	23,228	24,797	26,698
Associate	3,504	3,856	5,001	6,462	6,206	6,052
Professional Pgms ..	20,009	20,713	23,085	25,856	26,322	28,208
% of Total	(83.5%)	(82.1%)	(82.3%)	(87.1%)	(84.9%)	(86.1%)
Graduate Programs ..	3,950	4,508	4,948	3,834	4,681	4,542
% of Total	(16.5%)	(17.9%)	(17.7%)	(12.9%)	(15.1%)	(13.9%)

Adjusted Data for Schools Reporting Both in 1970 and 1971

	1970	1971	% Change
Professional	26,322	27,090	+ 2.9%
Graduate	4,681	4,277	— 8.6%
Total	31,003	31,367	+ 1.2%

Enrollment of Black Students

The AATS has been collecting Black student enrollment data for only two years, but there was a considerable increase in 1971. The total numbers rose from 808 in 1970 to 908 (+ 12.4 percent) in 1971. This remains far below the percentage of Blacks in the population, constituting only 2.8 percent of the total theological school enrollment in 1971. United Methodist and American Baptist groups of schools continue to register the largest numbers of Black students among their student bodies.

Enrollment in Doctoral Programs

Once again schools reported an increase in their doctoral program enrollments. The 8.6 percent decrease in graduate enrollment noted above was produced by a sharp reduction (16.8 percent) in S.T.M./Th.M. enrollees. Teaching-research type doctorates actually increased 18 percent at the very time when most observers are concerned about an oversupply of persons for these positions. The new Doctor of Ministry degree is also beginning to attract a substantial number of candidates, 688 being reported in 1971. Data about all doctoral enrollments for the past three years are indicated in Table 2.

TABLE 2: TRENDS IN DOCTORAL ENROLLMENT

	1969-70	1970-71		1971-72	
Degree Enrollment	Enrollment	Enrollment	Yearly Change	Enrollment	Yearly Change
D.Min./D.Rel.	346	564	+63.0%	688	+22.0%
D.R.E./Ed.D.	96	89	—7.3	103	+15.7
D.S.M./D.M.A.	36	30	—16.7	20	—33.3
Th.D./S.T.D.	590	540	—8.5	779	+44.3
Ph.D.	876	1,151	+31.4	1,217	+5.7

4. SURVEYS OF RELIGION IN AMERICAN LIFE

This section contains information on two surveys which have appeared yearly for many years. The first is the Gallup survey on church attendance and the second is that of the U. S. Department of Commerce relating to the value of new construction of religious buildings.

Generally speaking, both these reports indicate a continuing downtrend which is found in other religious indicators such as membership as a percentage of population of the U.S., membership of many large religious bodies, and percentage increase in church financial contributions in relationship to percentage increase of inflation during the period 1969-1971.

CHURCH ATTENDANCE POLLS

In 1971 the Gallup Poll made surveys of representative samples of the adult population in five weeks during the year to account for seasonal fluctuations, interviewing a total of 7,543 people, 21 or older, in more than 300 scientifically selected sampling points in the U.S., asking this question:

Did you, yourself, happen to attend church in the last seven days?

The results of this survey indicated that churchgoing in the U.S. declined in 1971, continuing a thirteen-year downtrend, since only 40 percent of adults of all faiths answered "yes" to the above question.

Following is an illustration indicating trends in churchgoing since 1955, a peak year, when 49 percent of adults of all faiths attended church in a typical week.

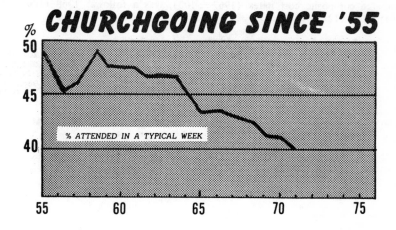

Gallup notes that "the decline in attendance in recent years has been most pronounced among Roman Catholics. In 1971, 57 percent attended in a typical week, following a steady decline since 1964 when 71 percent of Roman Catholics attended church on the average.

"Churchgoing since 1964 has remained fairly constant among both Protestants and Jews. In the 1971 audit," Gallup notes, "37 percent of Protestants and 19 percent of Jews attended houses of worship in a typical week."

Below is the 1971 record of church attendance for major groups in the population:

ATTENDED CHURCH DURING AVERAGE WEEK, 1971
(Percentage of Adults)

	%			%
National	40	Age:		
Religion:			21-29 years	28
Catholic	57		30-49 years	42
Protestant	37		50 & over	45
Jewish	19	Region:		
Sex:			East	39
Men	35		Midwest	40
Women	45		South	45
Race:			West	33
White	40			
Nonwhite	44			
Education:				
College	40			
High School	40			
Grade School	41			

VALUE OF NEW CONSTRUCTION OF RELIGIOUS BUILDINGS

Estimates of the annual value of new construction of religious buildings, 1925-1971 inclusive, indicate that there was a downward turn in 1966 from the all-time high reported in 1965. This downward trend is continuing, according to the 1971 estimates provided by the U.S. Department of Commerce.

The decline in the value of new construction in 1971, as in other recent years, is further affected by inflation in construction costs, which, using the Department of Commerce composite cost index (1967 = 100), was a follows: 1968 (106); 1969 (114); 1970 (122); 1971 (131).

Year	Value	Year	Value
1925	$165,000,000	1960	$1,016,000,000
1930	135,000,000	1965	1,207,000,000
1935	28,000,000	1967	1,093,000,000
1940	59,000,000	1968	1,079,000,000
1945	26,000,000	1969	988,000,000
1950	409,000,000	1970	931,000,000
1955	736,000,000	1971	813,000,000

Source: U.S. Department of Commerce, *Construction Review*, Vol. 18, No. 3, March 1972. Table A-2, page 14; and E-1, p. 44.

5. MAIN DEPOSITORIES OF CHURCH HISTORY MATERIAL AND SOURCES IN THE UNITED STATES

The following is condensed from an article which appeared in the March, 1939, issue of *Church History* written by W. W. Sweet, who was at that time Professor of the History of American Christianity at the Divinity School, University of Chicago. It is reprinted with permission.

This listing has been revised by various experts on church archives from time to time. It was updated and revised in August 1972 by the Rev. Aug. R. Suelflow, D.D., Director of the Concordia Historical Institute of the Lutheran Church-Missouri Synod.

Many denominations have established central archival-manuscript depositories and, in addition, are dealing with regional, diocesan, synodical or provincial subdivisions. Communions functioning through this type of structure especially are the Roman Catholic, Episcopal, Baptist, Lutheran and Methodist.

Some denominations with headquarters in the United States also have churches in Canada. Historical material on Canadian sections of these denominations will occasionally be found at the various locations cited below. The reader is also referred to the section "Main Depositories of Church History Material in Canada," which follows.

Adventists:
Adventual Library, Aurora College, Aurora, IL 60507 (Advent Christian Church)
Dr. Linden J. Carter Library, Berkshire Christian College, Lenox, MA 01240.
Andrews University, Berrien Springs, MI 49104.

Baptists:
American Baptist Historical Society (including Samuel Colgate Baptist Historical Collection), 1106 South Goodman St., Rochester, NY 14620.
Andover Newton Theological School (including Backus Historical Society), Newton Centre, MA 02159.
Bethel Seminary (Swedish Baptist material) 1480 N. Snelling Ave., St. Paul, MN 55108.
Historical Commission, Southern Baptist Convention, 127 9th Ave., N., Nashville, TN 37234.
Seventh Day Baptist Library, Seventh Day Baptist Building, Plainfield, NJ 07060.

Brethren in Christ Church:
Archives of the Brethren in Christ Church, Messiah College, Grantham, PA 17027.

Church of the Brethren:
Bethany Biblical Seminary, Butterfield and Meyers Roads, Oak Brook, IL 60521.
Historical Library, 1451 Dundee Ave., Elgin, IL 60620.
Juniata College, Huntingdon, PA 16652.

Congregationalists:
(See United Church of Christ)

Disciples:
The Disciples of Christ Historical Society, 1101 Nineteenth Ave., S., Nashville, TN 37212.
Christian Theological Seminary, Indianapolis, IN 46208.

Lexington Theological Seminary, Lexington, KY 40508.
The Disciples Divinity House, University of Chicago, Chicago, IL 60637.
The Carolina Discipliana Library, Atlantic Christian College, Wilson, NC 27893.
The Kentucky Female Orphan School, Midway, KY 40347.
Texas Christian University, Fort Worth, TX 76219.
Culver-Stockton College, Canton, MO 63435.

Episcopalians:
National Council, Protestant Episcopal Church, 815 2nd Ave., New York, NY 10017.
Library and Archives of the Church Historical Society, 606 Rathervue Pl., Austin, TX 78767.
Berkeley Divinity School at Yale, New Haven, CT 06510.
General Theological Seminary, 175 Ninth Ave., New York, NY 10011.

Evangelical United Brethren:
(see United Methodist Church)

Evangelical Congregational Church:
Historical Society of the Evangelical Congregational Church, 121 S. College St., Myerstown, PA 17067.

Friends:
Friends Meeting House, Rutherford Place, New York, NY 10003.
Friends' Historical Library, Swarthmore College, Swarthmore, PA 19081.
Historical Library, Haverford College, Haverford, PA 19041.

Jewish:
American Jewish Archives, 3101 Clifton Ave., Cincinnati, OH 45220.
Yiddish Scientific Institute—YIVO, 1048 Fifth Ave., New York, NY 10028.

STATISTICAL AND HISTORICAL SECTION

American Jewish Historical Society, 150 Fifth Ave., New York, NY 10011.

Latter Day Saints:
Historian's Office, Library-Archives, 47 East South Temple St., Salt Lake City, UT 84111.
New York Public Library, New York, NY 10036.
The Genealogical Society, 107 South Main St., Salt Lake City, UT 84111.

Lutherans:
Archives of American Lutheran Church, Wartburg Theological Seminary, 333 Wartburg Place, Dubuque, IA 52001.
Archives of the Lutheran Church in America, Lutheran School of Theology at Chicago, 1100 East 55th St., Chicago, IL 60615.
Concordia Historical Institute, 801 DeMun Ave., St. Louis, MO 63105.
Luther College, Decorah, IA 52101.
Lutheran Theological Seminary, 7301 Germantown Ave., Philadelphia, PA 19119.
Lutheran Theological Seminary, Gettysburg, PA 17325.
Concordia Theological Seminary, St. Louis, MO 63105.
Finnish-American Historical Archives, Hancock, MI 49930.
St. Olaf College (Norwegian), Northfield, MN 55057.
Archives of Cooperative Lutheranism, Library of the Lutheran Council in the U.S.A., 315 Park Ave., South, New York, NY 10010.
Lutheran Theological Southern Seminary, 4201 North Main St., Columbia, SC 29203.

Mennonites:
Bethel College, Historical Library, No. Newton, KS 67117.
The Archives of the Mennonite Church, 1700 South Main, Goshen, IN 46526.
Menno Simons Historical Library and Archives, Eastern Mennonite College, Harrisonburg, VA 22801.
Mennonite Historical Library, Bluffton College, Bluffton, OH 45817.

The United Methodist Church:
Commission on Archives and History of the United Methodist Church, Box 488, Lake Junaluska, NC 28745.
Archives of DePauw University and Indiana Methodism, Greencastle, IN 46135.
Drew Theological Seminary, Madison, NJ 07940.
Garrett Biblical Institute, Evanston, IL 60201.
Duke University, Durham, NC 27706.
United Methodist Publishing House Library, 201 Eighth Ave. S., Nashville, TN 37203.
New England Methodist Historical Society Library, Boston University, School of Theology, 745 Commonwealth Ave., Boston, MA 02215.
Emory University Library, Atlanta, GA 30322.
Perkins School of Theology, Bridwell Library, Southern Methodist University, Dallas, TX 75222.

The Upper Room Library and Museum, 1908 Grand Ave., Nashville, TN 37212.
World Methodist Council material: The World Methodist Building, Lake Junaluska, NC 28745.
Historical Society, 1810 Harvard Bldg., Dayton, OH 45406 (E.U.B.)

Moravians:
The Archives of the Moravian Church, Main St. and Elizabeth Ave., Bethlehem, PA 18018.
Moravian Archives, Southern Province of the Moravian Church, Drawer M. Salem Station, Winston-Salem, NC 27108.
Moravian Historical Society, Nazareth, PA 18064.

Pentecostals:
Oral Roberts University Library, 7777 South Lewis, Tulsa, OK 74105.

Presbyterians:
Presbyterian Historical Society and Department of History, United Presbyterian Church in the U.S.A., 425 Lombard St., Philadelphia, PA 19147.
Historical Foundation, Montreat, NC 28757.
Princeton Theological Seminary, Speer Library, Princeton, NJ 08540.
McCormack Theological Seminary, 800 West Belden Ave., Chicago, IL 60614.

Reformed:
Commission on History, Reformed Church in America, New Brunswick Theological Seminary, New Brunswick, NJ 08901.
Theological Seminary (Reformed in U. S.), Lancaster, PA 17603.

Roman Catholics:
Catholic Archives of the Archdiocese of Baltimore, 320 Cathedral St., Baltimore, MD 21201.
Department of Archives and Manuscripts, Catholic University of America, Washington, DC 20017.
University of Notre Dame Archives, Box 513, Notre Dame, IN 46556
St. Mary's Sem. & Univ., Roland Park, Baltimore, MD 21210.
Georgetown University, Washington, DC 20007.
St. Louis University, St. Louis, MO 63103.

Schwenkfelder:
Library Corporation, Pennsburg, PA 18073.

Shakers:
Western Reserve Historical Society, Cleveland, OH 44106.
Ohio Archeological and Historical Society, Columbus, OH.

Swedenborgian:
Academy of the New Church Library, Bryn Athyn, PA 19009.

Unitarians and Universalists:
Historical Library, 25 Beacon St., Boston, MA 02108.

Rhode Island Historical Society, Providence, RI.

Meadville Theological School, Chicago, IL 60637.

Universalist Historical Society, Tufts University, Medford, MA 02155.

The United Church of Christ:
Congregational Library, 14 Beacon St., Boston, MA 02108.

Chicago Theological Seminary, Chicago, IL 60637.

Divinity Library, and University Library, Yale University, New Haven, CT 06520.

Library of Hartford Theological Seminary, Hartford, CT 06105.

Harvard Divinity School Library, Cambridge, MA 02140.

Eden Archives, 475 East Lockwood Ave., Webster Groves, MO 63119. (Evangelical and Reformed)

STANDARD GUIDES TO CHURCH ARCHIVES

William Henry Allison, **Inventory of Unpublished Material for American Religious History in Protestant Church Archives and other Depositories** (Washington, D. C., Carnegie Institution of Washington, 1910, 254 pp.).

John Graves Barrow, **A Bibliography of Bibliographies in Religion** (Ann Arbor, Mich., 1955) pp. 185-198.

Edmund L. Binsfield, "Church Archives in the United States and Canada: a Bibliography," in **American Archivist,** V. 21, No. 3 (July 1958) pp. 311-332, 219 entries.

Nelson R. Burr, "Sources for the Study of American Church History in the Library of Congress," 1953. 13 pp. Reprinted from **Church History,** Vol. XXII, No. 3 (Sept. 1953).

Church Records Symposium, **American Archivist,** Vol. 24, October 1961, pp. 387-456.

Philip M. Hamer, **A Guide to Archives and Manuscripts in the United States** (New Haven: Yale University Press, 1961). Arranged by states, with complete index. Essential.

Historical Records Survey, **Guides to Depositories of Manuscript Collections in the United States** (completed for at least 18 states and 1 city. Includes depositories of church archives, continuing).

Charles Alvin Kekumano, **The Secret Archives of the Diocesan Curia; a Historical Synopsis and a Commentary** (Washington, D.C., Catholic University of America Press, 1954), 98 pp. In Catholic University of American Canon Law Studies. No. 350. Bibl., pp. 90-94. A valuable guide to the use of such records.

E. Kay Kirkham, **A Survey of American Church Records, for the Period before The Civil War, East of the Mississippi River** (Salt Lake City, 1959-60, 2 vols.). Includes the depositories and bibliographies.

Peter G. Mode, **Source Book and Bibliographical Guide for American Church History** (Menasha, Wisc., George Banta Publishing Co., 1921, 735 pp.).

Society of American Archivists. **American Archivist, 1936/37** (continuing). Has articles on church records and depositories.

Society of American Archivists, Church Records Committee. **Directory of Religious Archival and Historical Depositories in America.** 1962. (Continuing, title varies.)

Aug. R. Suelflow, **A Preliminary Guide to Church Records Repositories,** Society of American Archivists, Church Archives Committee, 1969. Lists more than 500 historical-archival depositories with denominational and religious history in America.

United States, Library of Congress, Division of Manuscripts, **Manuscripts in Public and Private Collections in the United States** (Washington, D.C., 1924).

U. S. Library of Congress, Washington, D. C.: **The National Union Catalog of Manuscript Collections,** A59—5 vols. see below. Based on reports from American repositories of manuscripts.

Vol. 1, pub. 1959—reports 1959-61.

Vol. 2, pub. 1962—2 parts, with cumulative index for 1st 2 vols.

Vol. 3, pub. 1963—1964. New index.
Vol. 4, pub. 1965—cumulative index through 1963.
Vol. 5, pub. 1966—another volume is in preparation.
Contains many entries for collections of church archives. This series is continuing. Extremely valuable collection. Researchers must consult the cumulative indexes.

Notes

The Libraries of the University of Chicago, Chicago; Union Theological Seminary, New York; and Yale Divinity School, New Haven, have large collections.

The Missionary Research Library, 3041 Broadway, New York, NY 10027, has a large collection of interdenominational material.

The Library of the American Bible Society, Broadway at 61st St., New York, NY 10023, has material on the history of transmission of the Bible text, Bible translation, etc.

Zion Research Library, Boston University, 771 Commonwealth Ave., Boston, MA 02215 has a noteworthy archival collection.

"Specialized Research Libraries in Missions" are described by Frank W. Price in **Library Trends,** Oct. 1960, V. 9, No. 2, University of Illinois Graduate School of Library Science, Urbana, IL 61801.

MAIN DEPOSITORIES OF CHURCH HISTORY MATERIAL IN CANADA

The list of depositories of church history material which follows was reviewed for this edition of the **Yearbook** by the Rev. C. Glenn Lucas, archivist-historian of the United Church of Canada, to whom the editor is grateful.

Many Canadian religious bodies have headquarters in the United States, and therefore the reader is advised to consult "Main Depositories of Church History Material and Sources in the United States," which immediately precedes this section, for possible sources of information on Canadian religious groups.

Anglican:
General Synod Archives, 600 Jarvis St., Toronto, Ontario. Archivist: Dr. T. R. Millman.

Baptists:
Baptist Historical Collection, Divinity School, McMaster University, Hamilton, Ontario, Archivist: Mrs. Gwen Bowie.
Evangelical Baptist Historical Library, 74 Sheppard Ave., Willowdale, Ontario.

Lutheran:
Lutheran Archives, Waterloo Lutheran University, Waterloo, Ontario. Archivist: Rev. Eric Schultz.

Pentecostal:
The Pentecostal Assemblies of Canada, 10 Overlea Blvd., Toronto 17, Ontario. Public Relations Officer: Rev. Earl Kulbeck.

Presbyterian:
Presbyterian Archives, Knox College, University of Toronto, Toronto, Ontario. Archivist: Rev. Fred Rennie.

Roman Catholic:
Centre for Canadian Catholic Church History, University of Ottawa, Ottawa, Ontario. (Also: Archdiocesan archives in Montreal, Quebec City, Halifax, St. John's, Kingston, Ottawa, Toronto, St. Boniface, Manitoba, and Vancouver).

United Church of Canada:
Central Archives, Victoria University, Toronto, Ontario. Archivist-Historian: Rev. C. Glenn Lucas.

A GUIDE TO CANADIAN CHURCH ARCHIVES

Edmund L. Binsfield, "Church Archives in the United States and Canada: A Bibliography," in **American Archivist,** V. 21, No. 3 (July 1958), pp. 311-332, 219 entries.

INDEX

INDEX

INDEX